Principal Gold-Producing Districts of the United States

By A. H. KOSCHMANN *and* M. H. BERGENDAHL

GEOLOGICAL SURVEY PROFESSIONAL PAPER 610

A description of the geology, mining history, and production of the major gold-mining districts in 21 States

UNITED STATES GOVERNMENT PRINTING OFFICE, WASHINGTON : 1968

UNITED STATES DEPARTMENT OF THE INTERIOR

JAMES G. WATT, *Secretary*

GEOLOGICAL SURVEY

Dallas L. Peck, *Director*

Library of Congress Catalog-card No. GS 68-341

First Printing 1968
Second Printing 1980
Third Printing 1982

For sale by the Superintendent of Documents, U.S. Government Printing Office
Washington, D.C. 20402

CONTENTS

	Page
Abstract	1
Introduction	2
Scope and objectives	3
Authorship and acknowledgments	3
Distribution of principal districts	3
Geologic relations	4
History of gold mining and trends in production	4
Alabama	6
Cleburne County	7
Tallapoosa County	8
Alaska	8
Cook Inlet-Susitna region	11
Copper River region	13
Kuskokwim region	14
Northwestern Alaska region	16
Seward Peninsula region	16
Southeastern Alaska region	19
Southwestern Alaska region	23
Yukon region	23
Prince William Sound region	31
Arizona	32
Cochise County	35
Gila County	37
Greenlee County	38
Maricopa County	39
Mohave County	40
Pima County	42
Pinal County	43
Santa Cruz County	45
Yavapai County	45
Yuma County	51
California	53
Amador County	58
Butte County	58
Calaveras County	59
Del Norte County	60
El Dorado County	60
Fresno County	61
Humboldt County	62
Imperial County	62
Inyo County	62
Kern County	64
Lassen County	66
Los Angeles County	66
Madera County	67
Mariposa County	67
Merced County	69
Modoc County	69
Mono County	69
Napa County	70
Nevada County	70
Placer County	72
Plumas County	73
Riverside County	74
Sacramento County	75
California—Continued	
San Bernardino County	75
San Diego County	76
San Joaquin County	77
Shasta County	77
Sierra County	79
Siskiyou County	80
Stanislaus County	81
Trinity County	81
Tulare County	82
Tuolumne County	82
Yuba County	84
Colorado	84
Adams County	87
Boulder County	87
Chaffee County	91
Clear Creek County	93
Custer County	97
Dolores County	98
Eagle County	98
Gilpin County	99
Gunnison County	101
Hinsdale County	102
Jefferson County	103
Lake County	103
La Plata County	105
Mineral County	106
Ouray County	107
Park County	109
Pitkin County	110
Rio Grande County	111
Routt County	112
Saguache County	112
San Juan County	113
San Miguel County	114
Summit County	116
Teller County	117
Georgia	118
Cherokee County	119
Lumpkin County	119
White County	120
Idaho	120
Ada County	120
Bingham County	121
Blaine County	121
Boise County	123
Bonneville County	126
Camas County	126
Cassia, Jerome, and Minidoka Counties	126
Clearwater County	126
Custer County	127
Elmore County	129
Gem County	130
Idaho County	130
Latah County	133
Lemhi County	134

	Page
Idaho—Continued	
Owyhee County	138
Power County	138
Shoshone County	139
Valley County	140
Michigan	141
Montana	142
Beaverhead County	144
Broadwater County	145
Cascade County	148
Deer Lodge County	148
Fergus County	149
Granite County	150
Jefferson County	152
Lewis and Clark County	154
Lincoln County	159
Madison County	160
Mineral County	164
Missoula County	164
Park County	165
Phillips County	167
Powell County	167
Ravalli County	169
Silver Bow County	169
Nevada	171
Churchill County	171
Clark County	173
Elko County	175
Esmeralda County	177
Eureka County	179
Humboldt County	180
Lander County	183
Lincoln County	185
Lyon County	186
Mineral County	188
Nye County	191
Pershing County	195
Storey County	197
Washoe County	198
White Pine County	199
New Mexico	200
Bernalillo County	202
Catron County	202
Colfax County	204
Dona Ana County	204
Grant County	205
Hidalgo County	207
Lincoln County	207
Otero County	208
Sandoval County	208
San Miguel County	209
Santa Fe County	209
Sierra County	210
Socorro County	210
North Carolina	211
Burke County	211

	Page
North Carolina—Continued	
Cabarrus County	212
Davidson County	212
Franklin County	213
Gaston and Cleveland Counties	213
Guilford County	213
Mecklenberg County	213
Montgomery County	214
Randolph County	214
Rowan County	214
Stanly County	215
Transylvania County	215
Union County	215
Oregon	216
Baker County	216
Grant County	222
Jackson County	224
Josephine County	226
Lane County	229
Malheur County	230
Pennsylvania	231
South Carolina	231
Chesterfield County	231
Lancaster County	232
McCormick County	232
South Dakota	232
Lawrence County	235
Pennington County	238
Tennessee	240
Utah	240
Beaver County	242
Iron County	243
Juab County	243
Piute County	245
Salt Lake County	246
Summit and Wasatch Counties	249
Tooele County	250
Utah County	252
Virginia	253
Fauquier County	253
Fluvanna and Goochland Counties	253
Orange County	254
Spotsylvania County	254
Washington	254
Chelan County	256
Ferry County	258
Kittitas County	259
Okanogan County	259
Snohomish County	260
Stevens County	261
Whatcom County	262
Wyoming	262
Albany County	262
Fremont County	263
Selected bibliography	263
Index of localities	277

ILLUSTRATIONS

		Page
FIGURES 1–4.	Graphs showing:	
	1. Gold production of the United States—1799 through 1965	4
	2. Gold production (to nearest 1,000 ounces) of 25 principal gold-mining districts of the United States—through 1959	5
	3. Annual gold production of Alabama, Gorgia, North Carolina, South Carolina, and Virginia, 1823–1960	7
	4. Annual gold production of Alaska, 1880–1965	9
5.	Map showing gold-mining districts of Alaska	10
6.	Graph showing annual gold production of Arizona, 1881–1965	33
7.	Map showing gold-mining districts of Arizona	34
8.	Graph showing annual gold production of California, 1848–1965	54
9.	Map showing gold-mining districts of California	56
10.	Map showing gold-mining districts of Colorado	85
11.	Graph showing annual gold production of Colorado, 1868–1965	87
12.	Map showing gold-mining districts of Idaho	122
13.	Graph showing annual gold production of Idaho, 1880–1965	124
14.	Map showing gold-mining districts of Montana	142
15.	Graph showing annual gold production of Montana, 1900–65	143
16.	Map showing gold-mining districts of Nevada	172
17.	Graph showing annual gold production of Nevada, 1880–1965	174
18.	Graph showing annual gold production of New Mexico, 1881–1965	201
19–21.	Maps showing:	
	19. Gold-mining districts of New Mexico	203
	20. Gold-mining localities of North Carolina	212
	21. Gold-mining districts of Oregon	217
22.	Graph showing annual gold production of Oregon, 1881–1965	218
23.	Map showing gold-mining districts of South Dakota	233
24.	Graph showing annual gold production of South Dakota, 1875–1965	234
25.	Map showing gold-mining districts of Utah	241
26.	Graph showing annual gold production of Utah, 1865–1965	242
27.	Graph showing annual gold production of Washington, 1881–1965	255
28.	Map showing gold-mining districts of Washington	256

PRINCIPAL GOLD-PRODUCING DISTRICTS OF THE UNITED STATES

By A. H. KOSCHMANN and M. H. BERGENDAHL

ABSTRACT

Except for small recoveries of gold by Indians and Spanish explorers, gold was first discovered and mined in the United States in North Carolina in 1799. This initial discovery was followed by others in the 1820's and 1830's in several of the other Appalachian States. These States produced significant amounts of gold until the Civil War. After the discovery of gold in California in 1848, the Western States contributed the bulk of this country's gold production. New discoveries in widely separated areas in the Western States followed in rapid succession.

From 1799 through 1965, the United States produced about 307,182,000 ounces of gold, which at the price of $35 per ounce would be valued in round numbers at $10,751 million. In an analysis of gold-production trends, the period 1932–59 is particularly informative; the effect of the increase of the price of gold in 1934 from $20.67 to $35 per ounce is clearly shown, as is the effect of a fixed selling price of gold combined with rising costs of labor and material in post-World War II years.

Districts that have produced more than 10,000 ounces are distributed in 21 States. Five States—California, Colorado, South Dakota, Alaska, and Nevada—have yielded more than 75 percent of the gold produced in this country. Of the more than 500 districts that have produced more than 10,000 ounces of gold, 45 have produced more than 1 million ounces, and four—Lead, S.D., Cripple Creek, Colo, Grass Valley, Calif., and Bingham, Utah—have produced more than 10 million ounces each. The 25 leading districts have produced about half the gold mined in the United States, and the 508 districts that are described account for roughly 90 to 95 percent.

In general, gold is derived from three types of ore: (1) ore in which gold is the principal metal of value, (2) base-metal ore which yields gold as a byproduct, and (3) placers. In the early years, most of the gold was mined from placers, but after 1873, though placers were by no means depleted and continued to contribute significantly to our annual output, production came chiefly from lode deposits. The search for gold led to the discovery and development of many silver, lead, copper, and zinc deposits from which gold was recovered as a byproduct. Since the late 1930's, byproduct gold has become a significant fraction of the annual domestic gold output.

Most of the gold deposits in the United States are closely associated with and probably genetically related to small batholiths, stocks, and satellitic intrusive bodies of quartz monzonitic composition that range in age from Jurassic to Tertiary. Some deposits, as those in the Southeastern States, may be genetically related to granitic bodies that were intruded at the close of Paleozoic time, and some deposits, as at Jerome, Ariz., are Precambrian in age.

Alaska, the fourth largest gold-producing State, yielded a total of 29,872,981 ounces from the first discovery in 1848 through 1965. More than half of this total was mined from placers in the Yukon region and the Seward Peninsula. The important lode-mining area has been in Southeastern Alaska, where mines in the Juneau and Chichagof districts produced more than 7 million ounces of gold through 1959.

Arizona ranks eighth among the gold-producing States; a total of about 13,321,000 ounces of gold was mined from 1860 through 1965. Deposits of copper and silver were known long before the Territory was acquired by the United States, but hostile Indians and lack of water discouraged any large-scale prospecting or mining. In the 1870's, after the transcontinental railroads were completed and the Indians ceased hostilities, Arizona's gold deposits received considerable attention. Mining activity increased considerably in the early 1900's, when the large porphyry copper deposits at Ajo, Bisbee, Globe-Miami, Clifton-Morenci, Ray, San Manuel, and Superior were developed. Large-scale mining of these and other copper deposits continues, and most of the gold produced after 1900 has been a byproduct of these ores.

California has produced more gold than any other State—more than 106 million ounces from 1848 through 1965. The well-known discovery in El Dorado County in 1848 sparked a series of gold rushes that indirectly led to colonization of the entire mountain West. The rich gold placers of California yielded phenomenal wealth in the early years, and as the placers were depleted, prospectors searched for and found the source of the placer gold—the high-grade gold-quartz veins of the Mother Lode and Grass Valley. Others explored the forbidding mountain ranges of southern California and found productive lodes in the Cove, Rand, and Stedman districts. Placer mining was rejuvenated in the early 1900's with the introduction of large bucket dredges. From the late 1930's onward, dredging operations were responsible for a major part of California's gold output.

Colorado ranks second among the gold-producing States; its gold output through 1965 was about 40,776,000 ounces. The first publicized discovery of gold in Colorado was in 1858. The immediate rush to the Denver area resulted in important placer finds near Idaho Springs and Central City. Prospectors ranging far up the Arkansas River valley found gold placers near Leadville as early as 1859. Many rich gold lodes were quickly discovered, and Colorado soon became a major mining area. In the 1870's, important ore discoveries were made in the San Juan Mountains, the Sawatch Mountains, and in the Leadville-Breckenridge area. Gold ore was found in the important Cripple Creek district in 1891.

Idaho, which ranks ninth among the gold-producing States, is credited with producing 8,323,000 ounces of gold from 1863 through 1965. The earliest recorded discovery in Idaho was of placer gold along the Pend Oreille River in 1852. Rich placers were found soon afterward at Pierce City, Elk

City, Orofino, Boise Basin, Florence, and Warren, and a brief period of feverish activity followed. By 1870, many of the richer placers were exhausted, and an intensive search for lode deposits resulted. Large-scale dredging rejuvenated the placers, though after 1900, most of Idaho's gold was produced from lode mines.

In Michigan the only significant gold output has come from the Ropes mine in Marquette County near Ishpeming.

Montana, which yielded a total of 17,752,000 ounces of gold from 1862 through 1965, is seventh among the gold-producing States. Gold was first discovered in 1852 in placers in Powell County, but the influx of prospectors did not begin until the discovery of rich placers in the Bannack district in 1862. Numerous placers were found in rapid succession, among them those of Alder Gulch, which were to become the most productive placers in the State. Placers, which contributed almost half of Montana's total gold, had their greatest output before 1870; nevertheless, dredging and hydraulic placer mining were conducted on a large scale until World War II. Development of lodes, hindered by lack of railroads in the early days, progressed rapidly in the 1880's and was accelerated greatly with the expansion of operations at Butte in the early 1900's.

Though Nevada is primarily a silver-mining State, it produced a total of about 27,475,000 ounces of gold from 1859 through 1965 and ranks fifth among the gold-producing States. Mining began in the early 1850's and the period 1859–79 was the boom era of the Comstock Lode and Reese River districts. After a period of decline from 1880 to 1900, the discoveries at Tonopah and Goldfield rejuvenated mining in the State until World War I. Lead, zinc, and copper mining, which yield gold as a byproduct, dominated Nevada's mining industry from the end of World War I through 1959, although for short periods large gold operations in the Potosi, Round Mountain, and Bullion districts have been significant. Discovery of the Carlin gold deposit in 1962 has revived interest in the gold potential of the State.

New Mexico produced about 2,267,000 ounces of gold from 1848 through 1965. Though gold lodes were worked on a small scale as early as 1833, prospectors showed little interest in the territory until the 1860's and 1870's. In rapid succession, lode and placer gold and rich silver and silver-lead discoveries were made, and mining flourished. By 1900, however, the oxidized ores were depleted, and interest turned to developing the primary base-metal ores from which gold is produced as a byproduct. This trend continued, in general, through 1959. The major gold districts are Elizabethtown-Baldy, Mogollon, and Lordsburg.

Oregon, the tenth most important gold-mining State, produced 5,797,000 ounces of gold from 1852 through 1965. Gold placers were worked as early as 1852, but the great rush to Oregon did not take place until 1861, after the placer discovery at Griffin Gulch in Baker County. After an initial period of high placer output, gold lodes were found and developed at a less frenzied rate. By the early 1900's, gold mining began a decline that lasted until 1934 when it was rejuvenated by the increase in the price of gold. A few districts, notably the Sumpter, were then reactivated, and gold mining was revived through the late 1930's and early 1940's until the demands of World War II diverted mining to commodities other than gold. Gold mining in Oregon in the post-World War II period has been in a steady decline.

Most of Pennsylvania's gold has been produced from the Cornwall iron mine in Lebanon County.

South Dakota, third among the gold-producing States, produced a total of about 31,208,000 ounces of gold through 1965, mostly from the Homestake mine. The gold districts are in the Black Hills in the northwestern part of the State. Most gold has been produced from lode deposits, but placers have also been mined.

In the Southeastern States, gold deposits are distributed in an area about 700 miles long and 150 miles wide east of the Appalachian Mountains. North Carolina is the largest producer; other States, in decreasing magnitude of production, are Georgia, South Carolina, Virginia, and Alabama.

Gold in Tennessee is a byproduct of the copper ores of the Ducktown district in Polk County; small amounts have been mined from placers on Coker Creek in Monroe County. Both areas are in the southeastern part of the State.

Utah, whose total gold output through 1965 was 17,765,000 ounces, ranks sixth among the gold-producing States. The first major ore discovery in the State was in 1863, when lead ore was found in Bingham Canyon. Gold placers were found nearby the following year. Silver-lead ore discoveries in the Cottonwood, Park City, and Tintic districts in the late 1860's and 1870's generated feverish activity which lasted until 1893 when the financial recession caused a sharp drop in the price of silver. In the early 1900's, large-scale mining of the low-grade copper ores of the Bingham district began. Gold has been an important byproduct of these ores. In 1965, the Bingham district, in addition to being one of the major copper producers of the world, was the second largest gold producer in the United States. The Tintic, Park City, and Camp Floyd districts also have yielded substantial amounts of gold.

Washington, whose total gold output from 1860 through 1965 was about 3,671,000 ounces, is one of the few States in which gold production has increased in recent years, mainly because of the output of the Knob Hill mine in the Republic district and the Gold King mine in the Wenatchee district. Gold was first discovered in the State in 1853 in the Yakima River valley. Placers were worked along most of the major streams of the State through the 1880's, but most of them were depleted by the early 1900's. Lode deposits were found in the 1870's and eventually supplanted placers as the chief source of gold. Of the 15 major gold districts of Washington, the most productive have been Republic, Wenatchee, and Chelan Lake.

Wyoming is a minor gold-producing State; its total output through 1965 was about 82,000 ounces. Only two districts—the Douglas Creek and the Atlantic City-South Pass—have been significant.

INTRODUCTION

Gold is probably the precious metal most prized by man. It is the universal standard of value, the common medium of exchange in world commerce, and the monetary standard of many nations. It is also widely used in the arts and industry. From 1799 through 1965 the United States, one of the leading gold-mining countries of the world, produced about 307,182,000 ounces of gold which, at the price of $35 per ounce, would be valued in round numbers at $10,751 million. After World War II the gold output of the United States declined at such a rate that after 1958 the consumption of gold in industry and the arts in the country exceeded production. An appraisal of the principal gold-producing districts indicates that the United States still has a considerable reserve of low-grade and submarginal gold ore and under favorable economic conditions could considerably increase its annual gold production.

SCOPE AND OBJECTIVES

This report is a compilation of available information on the discovery, history of development, production, and geology of more than 500 gold-producing districts in the United States. Only districts having a recorded total production to 1959 of at least 10,000 ounces are described. It is a summary of principal data of interest to geologists, mining engineers, and economists, as well as to the general public. The report should serve as a useful adjunct to the heavy metals program, a study of certain metals in short supply, including gold, begun in 1966 as a joint effort of the U.S. Geological Survey and the U.S. Bureau of Mines. It should also prove useful to the mining industry in planning prospecting or exploration programs for gold deposits.

Descriptions of the districts are necessarily brief, but they are somewhat in proportion to the importance of the individual district and to the amount of information available. A selected bibliography is given. References have been chosen to give the reader the best sources on the production, geology, and other pertinent data on the districts, and these in turn give additional references to source material.

In this professional paper the total gold production is given for each district from the time of discovery through 1959; however, production data for the years prior to 1904 are meager, widely scattered, and are based in large part on estimates. Fragmentary production figures for the years prior to 1904 are given in the reports of the Director of the Mint, but most of the early gold production data used in this report were compiled from district reports by the Geological Survey, by the Bureau of Mines, from publications of State agencies concerned with mining and geology, and from technical journals. Most of the early gold production figures cited in these reports are estimates by some of the older, well-informed residents, mining engineers, or geologists acquainted with the district or with the most important mines.

In 1904 the Geological Survey began the annual compilation of gold and silver production in the United States, and in 1924 this function was assumed by the Bureau of Mines. From 1904 through 1965, therefore, production data used in this report, unless otherwise quoted or duly credited, have been compiled from the following annual volumes: "Mineral Resources of the United States," by the U.S. Geological Survey (1904–23) and U.S. Bureau of Mines (1924–31), and "Minerals Yearbook," by the U.S. Bureau of Mines (1932–65).

The stratigraphic nomenclature used in this report is from many authors and does not necessarily follow that of the Geological Survey.

AUTHORSHIP AND ACKNOWLEDGMENTS

Both authors have actively collaborated in discussion of problems and the scope of the report and in the preparation of the introductory material. A. H. Koschmann prepared the sections on the gold deposits of Arizona, Colorado, Montana, New Mexico, South Dakota, Utah, and Wyoming. M. H. Bergendahl prepared the sections on the States east of the North American cordillera—Michigan, Pennsylvania, Tennessee, North Carolina, South Carolina, Alabama, Virginia, and Georgia, and on the Far Western States—Alaska, Washington, Oregon, California, Nevada, and Idaho. The authors gratefully acknowledge help received in the compilation of production figures by Jane Ohl, Wm. L. Emerick, and John M. Baldessari of the Geological Survey. The report was greatly improved by the thoughtful and constructive suggestions of numerous colleagues who reviewed the manuscript.

Much to the shock and deep regret of his friends and colleagues, A. H. Koschmann died suddenly in 1962. The profession lost one of its elder statesmen, a pillar of integrity, as well as a distinguished scientist. The coauthor lost a staunch friend; he has many satisfying and pleasant memories of his years with "Kosch."

DISTRIBUTION OF PRINCIPAL DISTRICTS

More than 75 percent of the gold mined in the United States has come from five Western States: California, Colorado, South Dakota, Alaska, and Nevada (fig. 1).

A total of 508 mining districts have each produced at least 10,000 ounces of gold, and many more districts have had a smaller output. Of the principal districts, 269 have produced between 10,000 and 100,000 ounces, 191 have produced between 100,000 and 1 million ounces, and 48 have produced more than 1 million ounces. Four districts, Lead, S. Dak., Cripple Creek, Colo., Grass Valley-Nevada City, Calif., and Bingham, Utah, listed according to rank, have each produced more than 10 million ounces and Lead has produced more than 20 million ounces. The 508 principal districts are distributed among the States as follows:

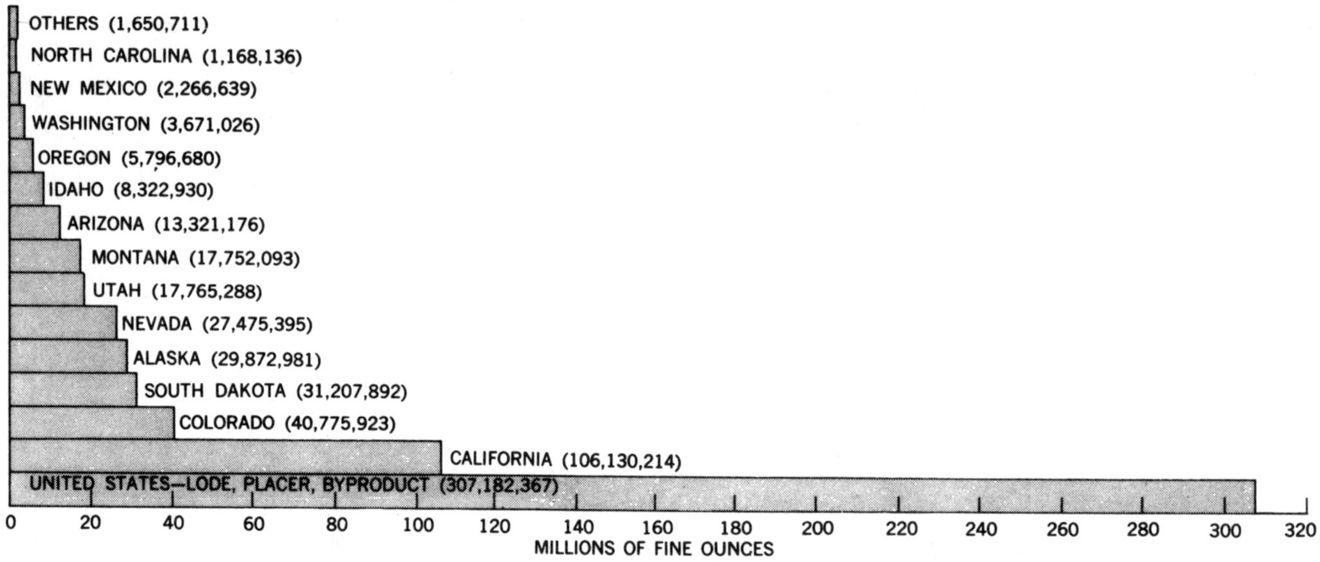

FIGURE 1.—Gold production of the United States—1799 through 1965.

Rank	*State*	*Number of Districts*
1	California	97
2	Nevada	71
3	Montana	54
4	Colorado	44
5	Alaska	43
6	Arizona	42
7	Idaho	42
8	Oregon	31
9	New Mexico	17
10	North Carolina	15
11	Washington	15
12	Utah	13
	Other States	24

About one-half of the gold mined in the United States has come from the 25 districts listed in figure 2.

GEOLOGIC RELATIONS

In general, gold is derived from three types of ore: (1) ore in which gold is the principal metal of value, (2) base-metal ore which yields gold as a byproduct, and (3) placers.

Most of the principal gold-producing districts are in the mountainous areas of the United States, where folding, faulting, and igneous intrusions have deformed the rocks. In contrast, many large base-metal deposits are found in the large relatively undeformed areas of the Central and Eastern States, but gold is not even a byproduct of these ores. Large parts of the Western States, such as the Colorado Plateau, the Columbia Plateau, and much of Wyoming, have not been subjected to violent tectonic forces and consequently contain very few gold deposits.

The occurrence of gold is erratic and many rich ore deposits have yielded relatively little or no gold. Foremost among these are the large silver-lead deposits of Coeur d'Alene, Idaho, Aspen, Colo., and Magdalena, N. Mex.; the copper deposits of Copper Mountain (Morenci), Ray, Miami, and Superior in Arizona; and the copper deposits of Santa Rita, N. Mex., and the Keweenaw Peninsula, Mich.

Most of the gold deposits in the United States are associated with and are perhaps genetically related to small batholiths, stocks, and satellitic intrusive bodies of quartz monzonitic composition that range in age from Jurassic to Tertiary. Some deposits, such as those in the Southeastern States, may be genetically related to granitic bodies that were intruded at the close of Paleozoic time, and a few deposits, as at Jerome, Ariz., are Precambrian in age.

HISTORY OF GOLD MINING AND TRENDS IN PRODUCTION

Gold in the United States was first mined in the Southeastern States about 1799, but these deposits, though rich, were relatively small. After the discovery of placer gold in California in 1848, the Western States contributed the bulk of the domestic gold production. Placer deposits offered quick and large returns with simple equipment and thus stimulated migration to the new gold fields. Many prospectors, trained in the California gold fields, spread to other parts of the new territories and many deposits were found in rapid succession in widely separated areas. The discovery of these rich placer deposits marked the beginning of active development and settlement of the West. Exploration and

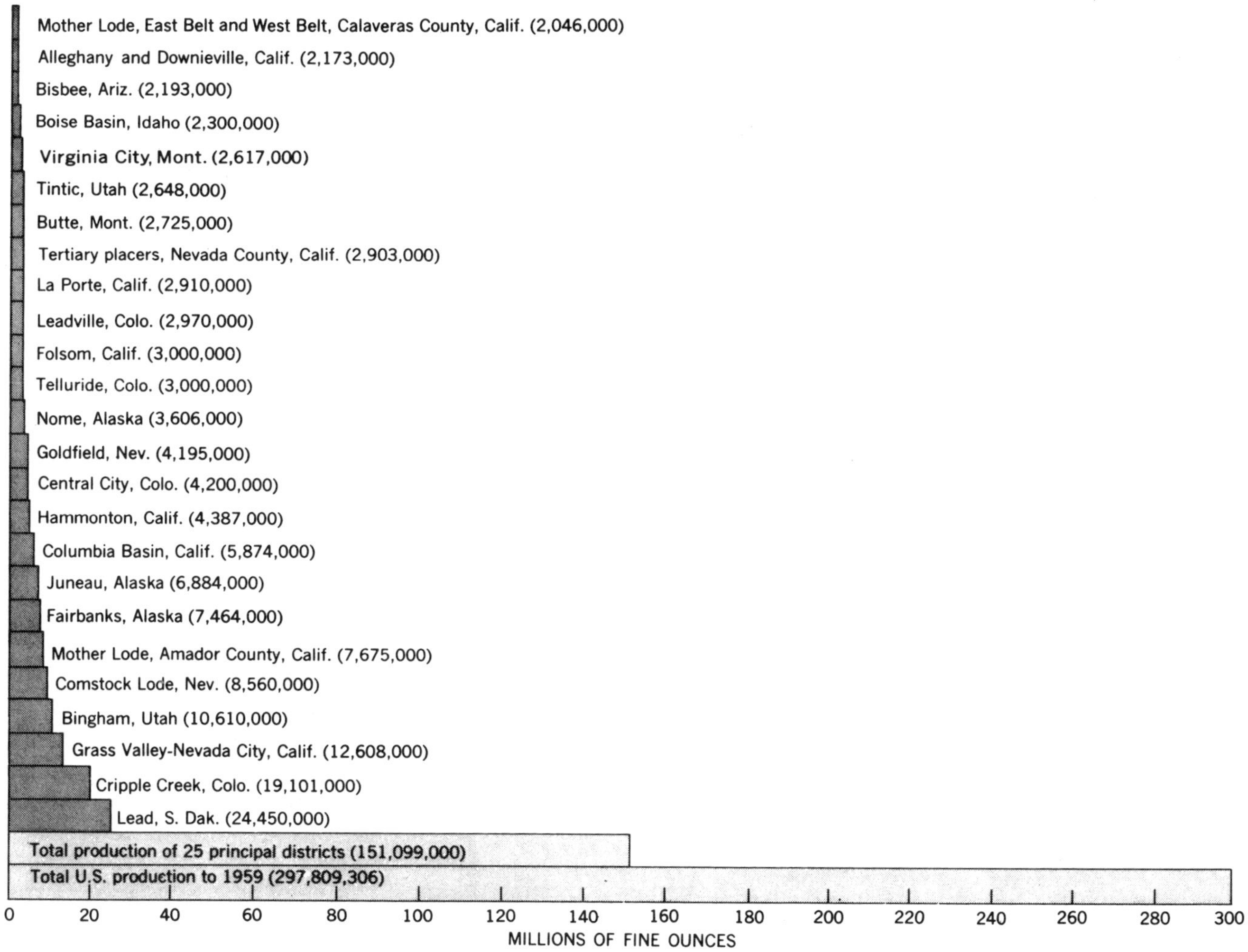

FIGURE 2.—Gold production (to nearest 1,000 ounces) of 25 principal gold-mining districts of the United States—through 1959.

mining activity boomed; gold production reached 2 million ounces in 1850 and 3 million ounces in 1853. It then declined steadily and in 1862 again dropped below the 2-million-ounce level. Placers were the chief source of our domestic output until 1873 (Loughlin and others, 1930, fig. 3), when their output was exceeded by that of lode mines, a relation that has continued through 1965. Placer activity remained at a relatively low ebb during the 1880's and early 1890's, but there were three periods in later years when placer production, though exceeded by lode production, formed a significant proportion of the domestic output—in 1896 when large dredges were introduced in California, in 1904 when large deposits of rich gravels were discovered in Alaska, and in 1934 when the price of gold was increased to $35 an ounce.

In many districts the prospectors followed gold-bearing gravél to the source of the gold in veins, and lode mining began shortly after placer mining. It was not, however, until about the middle 1860's, when the Mother Lode and Grass Valley lodes in California and the Comstock Lode in Nevada became important producers, that lode mines became significant sources of gold. Lode production increased rapidly after the discovery of gold in the Cripple Creek district, Colorado, in 1892. By 1898, production from this district together with the increased placer production in California and the accelerated output of the Homestake mine at Lead, S. Dak., had raised our annual gold production to more than 3 million ounces. Production continued to rise with the discoveries of gold at Tonopah, Nev., in 1903, the placer deposits of Alaska in 1904, and gold at Goldfield, Nev., in 1905. By 1905 gold production for the first time exceeded 4 million ounces, a level maintained until 1917. Because of a shortage of manpower during World War I, production then declined rapidly, falling almost to the 2-million-ounce level by 1920, where it remained until 1934. Many gold mines were reopened during the depression in the early 1930's. When the price of gold was raised in 1934 from $20.67 to $35 per ounce, production increased rapidly and in 1937 again passed the 4-million-ounce mark. Additional gold was obtained as a byproduct from increased output of base metals in the late 1930's, and in 1940 gold production reached an alltime high of 4,869,949 ounces. Shortly after the United States entered World War II, the gold mines were closed, and gold production in 1944 and 1945 dropped below the 1-million-ounce mark, the lowest since 1849. Production in 1965 was 1,705,190 ounces.

From 1907 until 1943 byproduct gold, obtained from base-metal ores, formed a small, though significant, fraction of the total production of this country. Only in World War II (1943–45 inclusive), when base-metal production increased and gold mines were closed, did byproduct gold contribute more than 50 percent of our annual domestic production, and since 1951 it has steadily outranked placer production. Most of the byproduct gold is recovered from porphyry copper ores. Large-scale copper mining at Bingham, Utah, has yielded sufficient gold to put this district in second place in annual gold production in recent years. The Lead district, South Dakota, has had the greatest total gold production and was also the largest producer in the United States each year from 1946 through 1965.

In an analysis of gold-production trends, the period 1932–59 is particularly informative because it reflects the most flourishing and the most adverse periods of gold mining in the United States. A long period of desultory activity ended in 1934 when the price of gold was increased from $20.67 to $35 per ounce. Mines were opened that had been closed for decades, and the gold-mining industry experienced an unprecedented interval of prosperity. This was ended in 1942 by the imposition of War Production Board Order L–208 (U.S. Bureau of Mines, 1943, p. 80–84), which resulted in most of the gold mines closing for the duration of World War II. After World War II, the gold-mining industry, plagued by constantly rising costs under a fixed selling price, failed to experience the growth and robust activity enjoyed by most industries. Thus, gold mining has been somewhat paradoxical—it reached its zenith in an economic climate unfavorable to most other industries, and it declined sharply when industrial growth was accelerating.

Of the 508 principal districts, in 1959 about 400 were either dormant or had an annual production of less than 100 ounces. Of the 25 leading districts (listed in fig. 2), 8 are dormant, 5 produce less than 100 ounces annually or have sporadic production, and only 12 of them maintain activity comparable to that of the prewar period.

ALABAMA

Gold discoveries in Georgia stimulated interest in prospecting similar-appearing crystalline rocks of Alabama and by about 1830 the first discoveries were made (Adams, 1930, p. 8). In the 1830's and 1840's, thousands of people were working the deposits at Arbacoochee and Goldville, but this boom collapsed when the California placer discoveries lured away most of the miners. Gold mining continued at a subdued pace that was broken by accelerated activity in 1874, when copper fever gripped the State, and in 1904, when cyaniding was introduced at Hog Mountain (Adams, 1930, p. 10). The increased price of gold in 1934 caused another spurt of activity, but during the late 1940's and the 1950's mines were closed once more. Gold production of Alabama from 1830 through 1959 was 49,495 ounces (fig. 3).

The belt of gold-bearing gneisses and schists extends from Georgia into east-central Alabama, where it is overlain by gently dipping unmetamorphosed sedimentary rocks of the Gulf Coastal Plain. The gneisses and schists are bordered on the northwest by the folded Paleozoic sedimentary rocks that form the southern end of the Appalachians, which become more subdued and are covered by the Coastal Plain sediments in the southwestern and western parts of the State. The gold deposits occur in the Talladega Slate, the Hillabee Chlorite Schist, the Wedowee Formation, and the Ashland Mica Schist. The ages of these rocks are not clearly defined. Butts (in Adams and others, 1926, p. 59–61) considered the age of the Talladega as ranging from Precambrian through much of the early Paleozoic. Adams (Adams and others, 1926, p. 32–33, 37) assigned a tentative Cambrian to Carboniferous age to the Wedowee Formation, and he considered the Ashland Mica Schist to be Precambrian in age. Intrusive into these metasedimentary rocks are the metaigneous Hillabee Chlorite Schist and the Pinckneyville Granite, both considered post-Carboniferous in age by Adams (1930, p. 17, 18). Most of the gold deposits are in Cleburne, Tallapoosa, Clay, and Randolph Counties, but only two districts have produced more than 10,000 ounces of gold—the Arbacoochee district in Cleburne County and the Hog Mountain district in Tallapoosa County.

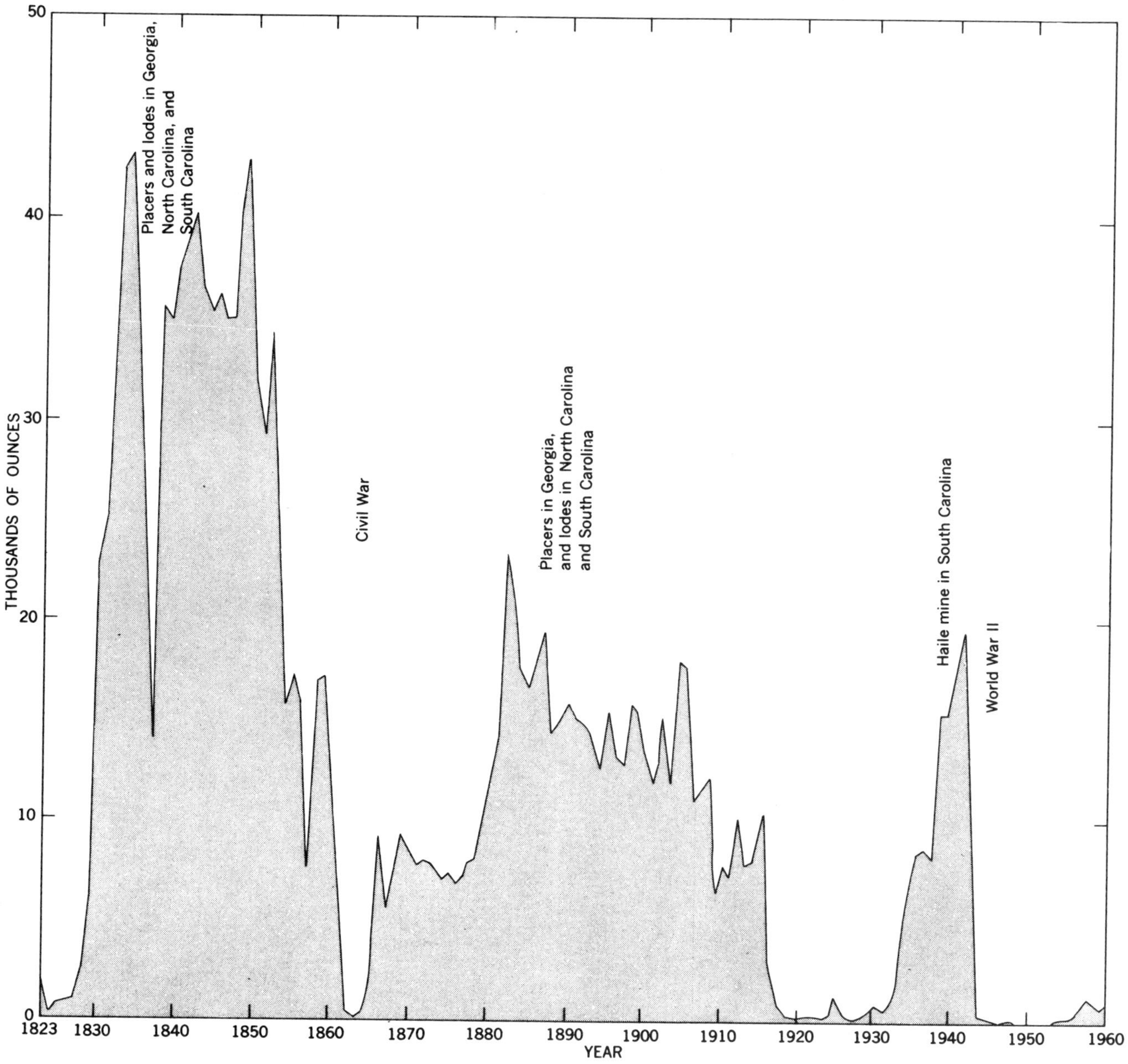

FIGURE 3.—Annual gold production of Alabama, Georgia, North Carolina, South Carolina, and Virginia, 1823–1960. Sources of data: 1823–1934 from Pardee and Park (1948), 1935–60 from U.S. Bureau of Mines (1933–66).

CLEBURNE COUNTY

The Arbacoochee district, in southern Cleburne County in Tps. 16 and 17 S., Rs. 11 and 12 E., contained the richest placers of the State; it was extremely active in the 1830's, but by 1874 only a few miners were still at work there (Adams, 1930, p. 21). Several attempts at lode mining were made in the late 1800's, but by 1900 these mines were idle (Adams, 1930, p. 22, 23).

Brewer (1896, p. 85) credited the Arbacoochee district with most of the $365,300 in gold (17,700 ounces) produced by Alabama to 1879; after 1890 this district became almost inactive and the Hog Mountain district became the State's principal producer.

Most of the gold came from residual placers in the vicinity of Gold Hill and from gravels along Clear Creek (Adams, 1930, p. 21–22). Bedrock in the southern part of the district consists of Ashland Mica Schist and in the northern part, of rocks of the Talladega Slate. These two units are separated by a band of Hillabee Chlorite Schist which was intruded along an old thrust fault plane (Adams, 1930, p. 18). Gold-bearing quartz veins with pyrite occur in the Hillabee, but they are too low grade to be economic.

TALLAPOOSA COUNTY

In Tallapoosa County the principal gold producer was the Hog Mountain district, in the north-central part of the county in T. 24 N., R. 22 E.

The only workings of any consequence in this district are those of the Hog Mountain or Hillabee mine, which opened in 1839 and operated on a small scale until 1893, when larger ore bodies were discovered and production increased. From 1893 to 1916, the mine produced $250,000 (about 12,100 ounces) in gold (Adams, 1930, p. 50). The mine was closed in 1916 because of high operating costs and was not reopened until 1933. During 1934–37 the Hog Mountain mine was the largest producer in Alabama, but it was closed in 1938 and remained inactive through 1959. Total gold production of the district through 1959 was about 24,300 ounces, about half of which was produced during 1934–37.

Bedrock in the Hog Mountain district consists of schistose rocks of the Wedowee Formation and quartz diorite (Park, 1935, p. 4–6). The schist is dark gray, graphitic, and is complexly folded and may be cut by thrust faults. The age of the Wedowee was considered by Adams (1930) to range from Cambrian to Carboniferous, but Park (1935, p. 5) thought it might even be Precambrian. The quartz diorite, which may be related to the Pinckneyville Granite of post-Carboniferous age, intruded the deformed Wedowee Formation. The larger gold veins of the district fill shear zones in the quartz diorite. Quartz is the most abundant vein mineral; pyrrhotite and small amounts of chalcopyrite, pyrite, arsenopyrite, gold, sphalerite, galena, bismuth minerals, and silver (Park, 1935, p. 12, 13) also occur.

ALASKA

Gold, the lure that drew settlers across the wide prairies and into the most remote mountain gullies in our Western States, proved also to be the dominant factor in the settlement of Alaska. This most important mineral commodity of the State was known in Alaska as early as 1848, long before the territory was acquired from Russia by the United States in 1867. P. P. Doroshin, a Russian mining engineer, made the discovery in the gravels of the Kenai River on the Kenai Peninsula, but there was no great excitement and apparently no gold was mined (Martin and others, 1915, p. 181–182). A second discovery of placer gold in 1865–66 on the Seward Peninsula by a party exploring for a telegraph route similarly failed to arouse much interest (Collier and others, 1908, p. 13–14).

Alaskan gold mining began in southeast Alaska. In 1869 miners who had been disappointed in the Cassiar gold district in British Columbia discovered gold placers at Windham Bay and Sumdum Bay southeast of Juneau. In 1870–71 the first gold produced in Alaska, reported to be worth $40,000, was extracted from these placers (Wright, 1906, p. 2). At about this time the first attempts to mine lode gold were made near Sitka (Knopf, 1912, p. 8). In the early 1870's extensive copper deposits were found on Prince of Wales Island, but because of the remoteness of the area from transportation facilities, these were not developed for many years. The major lode gold deposits of Alaska were found in 1880 at Juneau, and by 1883 Juneau was the mining center of the territory (Wright, 1906, p. 3). Encouraged by the successes at Juneau, the prospectors spread through southern Alaska and made important gold discoveries at Berners Bay and Eagle River on the mainland near Juneau, at Klag Bay on Chichagof Island, at Willow Creek near Anchorage, and even on far-off Unga Island, 1,000 miles to the west.

Numerous gold districts, the most important of which are Nome, Council, and Fairhaven, are on the Seward Peninsula. This region was prospected first by gold seekers drawn north by the great Klondike (Yukon Territory, Canada) rush of 1897–98. By 1898 the discovery of the rich Nome placers triggered a stampede to the new area and led to the rapid development of the entire peninsula. Nome, the second largest gold-producing district in Alaska, was active until 1962.

The vast Yukon drainage basin has produced more gold than any other region in Alaska, even though it was the most recent of the gold-producing regions to be exploited. With transportation virtually limited to river travel, the great distances from gold deposits to supply and population centers inhibited any large-scale mining in the early days. The first gold discoveries were made in 1878 (Mertie, 1937, p. 4); however, tales of gold had been circulated years earlier by traders and trappers who set up posts at various points along the Yukon River. Smith (1933, table facing p. 96) listed the earliest production for this region in 1883 from the Fortymile district. The important placers at Fairbanks were discovered in 1902, and by 1910 lode mines were active in this district. The Fairbanks placers proved amenable to large-scale dredging

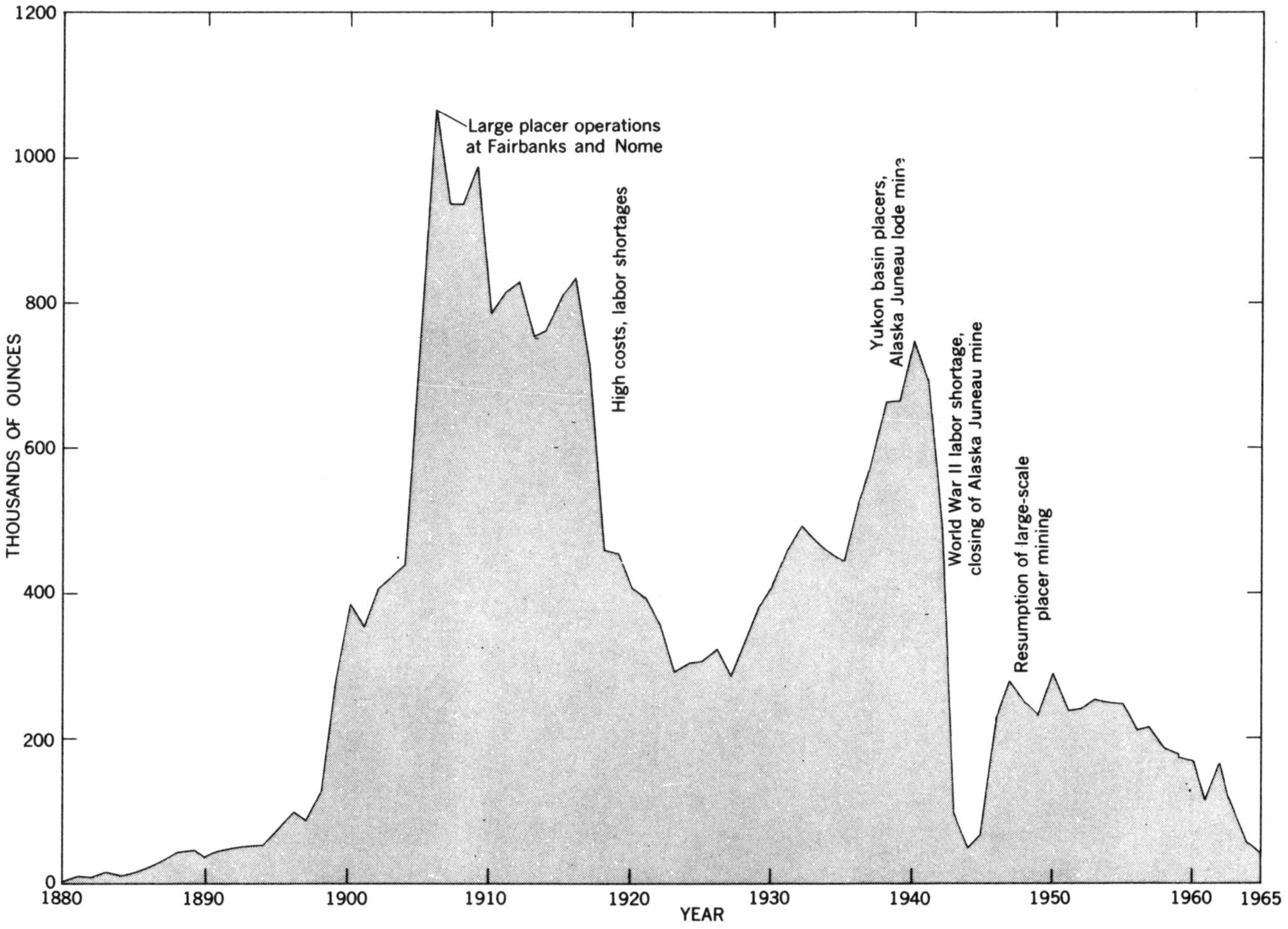

FIGURE 4.—Annual gold production of Alaska, 1880–1965. Sources of data: 1880–1900, U.S. Geological Survey (1883–1924); 1900–42, Smith (1944, p. 6); 1943–59, U.S. Bureau of Mines (1933–66). Production reported in dollar value was converted to ounces at prevailing price per ounce.

operations, which soon made this district the largest gold producer in Alaska.

As transportation facilities improved after 1900, new gold discoveries were made in the more remote areas, and previously known deposits were developed and mined. This activity extended into the 1930's, and several lode and placer districts in the Yukon basin were activated in this interval.

Gold mining in Alaska was seriously affected in 1943 by the imposition of War Production Board Order L–208 which closed nearly all of the gold mines during World War II (fig. 4). After the war the placer mines of the Fairbanks district resumed large-scale operations, and this single district accounted for more than half the total annual gold production for Alaska during 1950–65. The lode mines in Alaska were virtually inactive during 1942–65.

Of the total value of $722,122,186 of gold (28,859,718 ounces) produced in Alaska from 1880 to 1957, $504,076,577 came from placer mines (U.S. Bureau of Mines, 1957, p. 83, 85). During 1958–59 the gold production amounted to 365,353 ounces, most of which came from placers (U.S. Bureau of Mines, 1959, p. 84). Most of the lode gold has come from the Juneau district in southeast Alaska, and an unknown but probably small amount has been produced as a byproduct of copper ores in the Prince William Sound region. The gold production of Alaska before 1880 is unknown, but probably was not great.

Emmons (1937, p. 203) discussed the general relationships of gold deposits to geology. He pointed out that the chief lode deposits are associated with Mesozoic granite that have intruded rocks of Precambrian, Paleozoic, and Mesozoic ages. This belt of intrusives extends from the Seward Peninsula to the Yukon Territory. The lode deposit on Unga

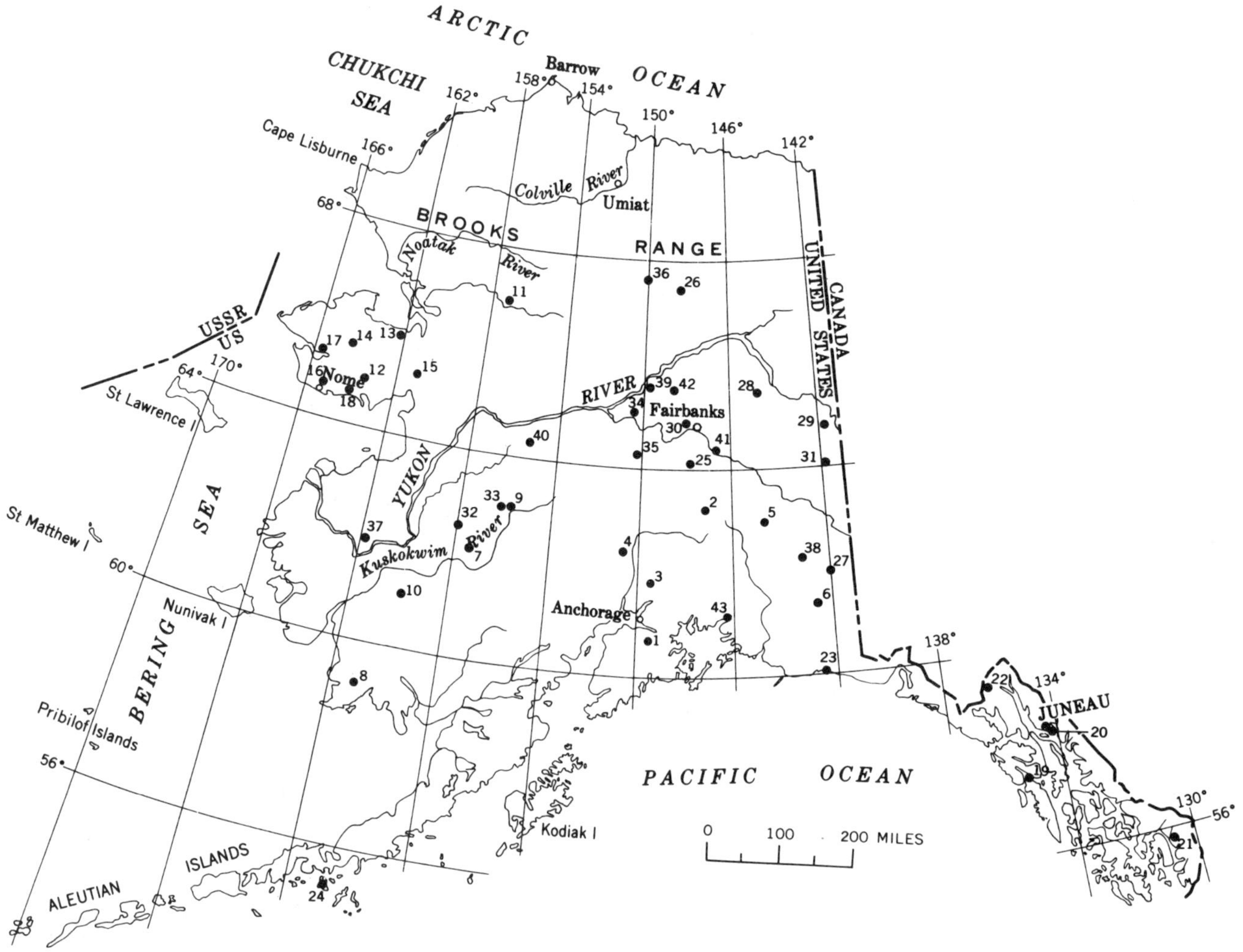

FIGURE 5.—Gold-mining districts of Alaska.

Cook Inlet-Susitna region:
1, Kenai Peninsula; 2, Valdez Creek; 3, Willow Creek; 4, Yentna-Cache Creek.
Copper River region:
5, Chistochina; 6, Nizina.
Kuskokwim region:
7, Georgetown; 8, Goodnews Bay; 9, McKinley; 10, Tuluksak-Aniak.
Northwestern Alaska region:
11, Shungnak.
Seward Peninsula region:
12, Council; 13, Fairhaven; 14, Kougarok; 15, Koyuk; 16, Nome; 17, Port Clarence; 18, Solomon-Bluff.
Southeastern Alaska region:
19, Chichagof; 20, Juneau; 21, Ketchikan-Hyder; 22, Porcupine; 23, Yakataga.
Southwestern Alaska region:
24, Unga.
Yukon region:
25, Bonnifield; 26, Chandalar; 27, Chisana; 28, Circle; 29, Eagle; 30, Fairbanks; 31, Fortymile; 32, Iditarod; 33, Innoko; 34, Hot Springs; 35, Kantishna; 36, Koyukuk; 37, Marshall; 38, Nabesna; 39, Rampart; 40, Ruby; 41, Richardson; 42, Tolovana.
Prince William Sound region:
43, Port Valdez.

Island in the Aleutian Islands is in Tertiary andesite. The placer deposits are widespread, occurring along nearly all the major rivers and their tributaries, and even in beach sands in the Nome area, on Kodiak Island, Yakataga, Lituya Bay, and Cook Inlet.

As in earlier reports of the Geological Survey (for instance, Smith, 1939), the State is subdivided into nine geographical regions: Cook Inlet-Susitna, Copper River, Kuskokwim, Northwestern, Seward Peninsula, Southeastern, Southwestern, Yukon, and Prince William Sound. The regions and the individual districts (fig. 5) within the regions are discussed in this report.

COOK INLET-SUSITNA REGION

Bounded roughly by the Aleutian or Alaska Peninsula on the southwest, the Alaska Range on the west and north, and by the Talkeetna Mountains on the east, the Cook Inlet-Susitna region includes the Kenai Peninsula, Valdez Creek, Willow Creek, and Yentna-Cache Creek mining districts.

Gold was first discovered in Alaska in 1848 in the gravels of the Kenai River. Apparently this gold was not present in minable quantities, and it was not until the 1890's that minable placers were found in the Turnagain Arm area (Martin and others, 1915, p. 181–183). The first lode deposits in the Cook Inlet-Susitna region were found in 1896 also in the Turnagain Arm area, more precisely, the Moose Pass-Hope area; however, the deposits, although rich, were of small tonnage, and there was very little lode production before 1911 (Martin and others, 1915, p. 129–131).

Placers in the Valdez Creek district, in the southern foothills of the Alaska Range, were worked from 1904 to 1924 (Ross, 1933b, p. 427–428) and desultory operations were carried on as recently as 1947 (E. H. Cobb, written commun., 1962).

In the western part of the Cook Inlet-Susitna region, placers were discovered in the Yentna-Cache Creek district in 1905 (Capps, 1913, p. 10). These deposits were moderately productive through 1957. The most productive district in the entire region is the Willow Creek district, about 20 miles north of the towns of Palmer and Wasilla, where placers were discovered in 1897. The first lode claims were located in 1906 (Capps, 1913, p. 50) and were worked fairly steadily until the early 1950's.

From 1880 through 1959, a recorded total of 919,532 ounces of gold was produced from the Cook Inlet-Susitna region. Of this, 588,361 ounces was from lode mines, 324,370 ounces from placers, and 6,801 ounces from undifferentiated sources. After the end of World War II production from both lode mines and placers declined markedly.

KENAI PENINSULA DISTRICT

The Kenai Peninsula is near the center of the southern coastline of Alaska, immediately northeast of the Alaska Peninsula.

The districts of Moose Pass-Hope, Girdwood, and Turnagain Arm—all in the central and northern part of the peninsula—have been combined in this discussion because most of their production data have been combined under "Kenai Peninsula."

Numerous small placers were discovered in the Turnagain Arm area in the early 1890's, but no significant production occurred until news of the auriferous gravels on Mills and Canyon Creeks brought several thousand prospectors to the area in 1896 (Martin and others, 1915, p. 182–183). Two years later another influx occurred. In a short time the small richer deposits were exhausted and the hand-operated rockers and sluices were supplanted by hydraulic plants that successfully mined the large reserves of low-grade gravels.

Lode mining, overshadowed by the placer operations, has been conducted chiefly in the Moose Pass-Hope camp and to a lesser degree in the Girdwood camp. The first indications of economic lode deposits were noted in 1896, but interest was diverted for a number of years to the more accessible placers. The lode deposit at the Hirshey mine, discovered in 1911, became the most consistently productive in the district (Tuck, 1933, p. 489–494). Lode mining continued sporadically until the end of World War II, when it dwindled to almost nothing.

Total recorded gold production from the Kenai Peninsula from 1895 through 1959 was 23,700 ounces from lodes, 96,500 ounces from placers, and 175 ounces from undifferentiated sources. Data from 1931 through 1945 are incomplete, so that the figures given here are minima.

The geology of the Kenai Peninsula was described by Martin and others (1915), Tuck (1933), and Park (1933). The oldest rocks on the peninsula are schists and crystalline limestones of uncertain age; however, the most widely distributed rocks are slates and graywackes that range in age from Paleozoic or Early Triassic to possible Late Cretaceous (Martin and others, 1915, p. 33–35). Granitic intrusive masses are abundant in the slaty rocks along the southern and eastern coasts. The Kenai Formation, of Eocene or younger Tertiary age, is exposed in the low country in the southwest part of the peninsula, north of Kachemak Bay, and consists of coal-bearing sand and clay. This formation is 15,000–20,000 feet thick and contains economically important oil and gas accumulations (Lian and Simonson, 1962, p. 271). Quaternary gravels—mostly till, outwash, and terrace sands and gravels—cover vast areas of lowlands in the west and northwest parts of the peninsula. The pre-Tertiary rocks that comprise most of the mountainous part of the peninsula are intricately folded whereas the Tertiary rocks, which occupy the low areas of the peninsula, are either horizontal or only gently warped into folds in which dips are generally less than 10° (Barnes and Cobb, 1959, p. 227).

The lode deposits of the Moose Pass-Hope camp consist of fissure veins. Mineralized acidic dikes are also in the district, but the gold production has been from the fissure veins that cut across the slaty cleavage of the slate and graywacke country rocks. The veins strike in all directions and have an average dip of 45° north or west (Tuck, 1933, p. 490). The ore minerals are arsenopyrite and small amounts of galena, sphalerite, pyrite, and chalcopyrite in a gangue of quartz, calcite, and ankerite (Tuck, 1933, p. 491). Free gold occurs in the quartz, commonly near accumulations of galena and sphalerite.

The placer deposits of the Kenai Peninsula, described by Martin, Johnson, and Grant (1915, p. 181–208), are most productive in the northern part of the peninsula along the various streams—Crow, Resurrection, Palmer, Bear, and Sixmile Creeks—that debouch into Turnagain Arm. Farther south, the gravels of Canyon, Mills, Falls, and Cooper Creeks, and of the Kenai River have yielded some placer gold. The deposits were formed in Quaternary time by postglacial streams reworking and resorting the debris that choked the valleys after the retreat of the glaciers. Present streams that have incised their courses in the unconsolidated material have left terraces and have further reworked the gravels. The productive glaciers are along these streams and in channel deposits in the terraces.

VALDEZ CREEK DISTRICT

The Valdez Creek district is on the southern flank of the Alaska Range at approximately lat 63°12′ N. and long 147°20′ W. The drainage area of Clearwater Creek in addition to that of Valdez Creek is usually included in the district.

Gold was first discovered in this district in 1903, in the gravels of Valdez Creek, but no production was recorded until 1908. The "Tammany Channel," a buried channel representing the course of an ancestral Valdez Creek, yielded most of the placer gold from the district. This channel, discovered in 1904, has been worked by hydraulic and underground methods (Tuck, 1938, p. 113). The chief production has been from placers. Several gold lodes were located, but none were productive to 1936 (Tuck, 1938, p. 121), and no record of any later lode production was found in 1959.

Total estimated gold production through 1936 was about 34,900 ounces, worth about $720,000 (Tuck, 1938, p. 113). The district was virtually dormant during 1937–59.

The geology of the district was described in detail by Ross (1933b, p. 428–444). Triassic(?) metasedimentary rocks—argillite, slate, and sericite and chlorite schist with limestone lenses—were intruded by a small batholith of quartz diorite in the northern part of the district and by small stocks and plugs of diorite elsewhere in the district. Structurally, the district is on the northwest flank of a large northeast-trending anticlinal fold; large normal faults trending N. 65° E. cut the metasedimentary rocks.

There are several types of veins in the district, and those showing the most promise, according to Ross (1933b, p. 456), are quartz veins associated with sheared and metamorphosed wallrocks. In their unoxidized state these veins contain pyrite, arsenopyrite, pyrrhotite, and a little chalcopyrite. Native gold occurs in the quartz. Some quartz veins contain abundant calcite (Ross, 1933b, p. 457). Ross (1933b, p. 458) believed the veins were related to hydrothermal activity that followed the intrusion of the dioritic bodies.

The placers are buried channels in which gold was concentrated next to the bedrock floor. The old gorges, eroded into bedrock, are V-shaped and probably were cut into a mature erosion surface (Ross, 1933b, p. 444–445).

WILLOW CREEK DISTRICT

The Willow Creek district, an area of about 50 square miles, is 23 miles by road northeast of Wasilla and 21 miles northwest of Palmer.

Gold-bearing veins were discovered in this district in 1906, but lack of transportation facilities hindered their development and no production was recorded until 1909 (Ray, 1954, p. 35–36). After 1909 the district developed steadily and maintained substantial annual production until 1951, after which there was only sporadic small-scale activity. Total gold production through 1959 was 652,080 ounces; nearly all production was from lode mines.

The geology and ore deposits of this district were described by Ray (1954, p. 10–54). The oldest rock is muscovite-quartz-plagioclase schist. Intruded into this is a mass of quartz diorite, the Talkeetna batholith, which underlies the major part of the district. Dikes of lamprophyre, diabase, aplite, and pegmatite cut the intrusive. The batholith is believed to be of late Mesozoic age. Sedimentary rocks, including conglomerate, arkose, shale, and sandstone of Tertiary(?) age, dip to the south, away from the quartz diorite body. Numerous faults cut the quartz diorite. Those with the larger displacements are postore in age, trend northwest, and dip northeast.

Two types of veins are in the quartz diorite: (1) an older nonproductive group, containing assemblages of chalcopyrite-molybdenite, pyrite-stibnite, or low-grade gold-quartz, and (2) minable gold-bearing quartz bodies in shear zones that occur along the southern margin of the quartz diorite. Vein minerals, in addition to quartz and gold, are pyrite, arsenopyrite, sphalerite, chalcopyrite, tetrahedrite, nagyagite, altaite, coloradoite (?), galena, stibnite(?), and sparse scheelite. Gold commonly occurs as irregular grains in and around nagyagite and as fracture fillings in pyrite, and locally occurs as blebs and stringers in quartz.

YENTNA-CACHE CREEK DISTRICT

The Yentna-Cache Creek district includes about 2,000 square miles on the southeast slope of the Alaska Range and is located roughly between lat 61°55′ and 62°45′ N. and long 150°25′ and 151°5′ W. It includes the upper drainage of the Yentna River and its tributaries, the best known of which, from the standpoint of gold mining, are Cache, Mills, Peters, and Long Creeks.

Gold was discovered in this district in 1905 in gravels in the basins of Peters and Cache Creeks. During the first few years most of the production was from these placers. In 1911 additional placers were discovered on Dollar Creek and a few years later on Thunder Creek and Upper Willow Creek (Capps, 1925, p. 54–55). The district, although not a tremendous producer, had a steady output, entirely from placers, and was active through 1957. From 1905 through 1959, about 115,200 ounces was recorded; data for 1931–46 are not available.

The geology and placer deposits were described by Capps (1913; 1925, p. 53–61). Intensely folded slates and graywackes of Mesozoic age compose most of the bedrock. Masses of granitic and dioritic rocks were intruded into the metasedimentary rocks, and Capps believed that the numerous gold-bearing quartz veins in the slates and graywackes were derived from solutions emanating from the cooling intrusives. Poorly consolidated lignitic sand and clay of Oligocene age (MacNeil and others, 1961, p. 1904) unconformably overlie the folded older rocks. The sand and clay are overlain by younger Tertiary gravels.

The placers were derived by weathering and erosion of the auriferous veins in the metasedimentary rocks, first by Tertiary streams which deposited the gold in channels in the Tertiary gravels, then by postglacial streams which reworked the glacial debris and Tertiary deposits and concentrated gold from these earlier deposits into placers in the present stream channels. Minable placers occur in the Tertiary deposits as well as in the Recent gravels.

COPPER RIVER REGION

The elliptical-shaped Copper River region, which includes a large part of the drainage basin of the Copper River, is in southern Alaska, bounded by the Alaska Range on the north, the Chugach Mountains on the southwest, and the Wrangell Mountains on the northeast. The region lies roughly between lat 61°00′ and 63°10′ N. and long 142°00′ and 146°00′ W., and it includes the major gold districts of Chistochina and Nizina.

Gold mining began in this region in 1900 in the Chistochina district, but prospectors were active in the Copper River country as early as 1898 (Schrader, 1900, p. 421). The first locations were in auriferous gravels along the Chisna, one of the main tributaries of the Chistochina River. Productive placers were discovered along the upper part of the Nizina River and its tributaries in 1902 (Mendenhall, 1905, p. 118). Minor discoveries were made elsewhere in the Copper River region about this time, and in 1914 the Nelchina placers were discovered (Chapin, 1918, p. 59)—but the bulk of the gold production came from the placers of Chistochina and Nizina. In the Copper River region, especially the Chitina district, copper deposits were worked extensively by the Kennecott Co. during 1900–38 (Moffit, 1946, p. 93), but they yielded little gold.

From 1900 to 1959 the Copper River region produced 2,400 ounces of lode gold, 295,000 ounces of placer gold, and 5,600 ounces of gold undifferentiated as to source—a total of 303,000 ounces. From World War II through 1959 only a few hundred ounces per year were produced.

The geology of the region is summarized here from a more detailed account by Moffit (1938, p. 19–107).

Throughout most of the region the low-lying areas are blanketed by glacial sands and gravels of Quaternary age. In the higher areas, a thick succession of bedded rocks range in age from early Carboniferous to Recent. The oldest rocks consist of schist and slate associated locally with altered limestone, tuff, and basalt flows, and they include the Mississippian Strelna Formation and Dadina Schist and the Carboniferous or older Klutina Series. Overlying these rocks are layers of lava flows, tuff, volcanic breccia, shale, limestone, sandstone, and conglomerate of Permian age; these are overlain by the Nikolai Greenstone, a thick sequence of basaltic lava flows of Permian and Triassic(?) age.

The post-Triassic Mesozoic rocks in the Copper River region are not fully understood because of the correlation problems imposed by variable lithology, exposures in disconnected areas, and lack of diagnostic fossils. Tuffaceous beds of Middle Jurassic age occupy a small area near the mouth of the Chitina River. Upper Jurassic rocks occur in a few places in the central part of the Copper River basin along the north tributaries of the Chitina River. Along the north side of Chitina River valley a thick series of bedded sedimentary rocks of varied lithology is Jurassic or Cretaceous in age. Black shale and sandstone, conglomerate, and sandy shale considered to be of Early Cretaceous age overlie Triassic rocks in the Nizina district. The Chugach Mountains, in the southern part of the region, are underlain by dark slate and graywacke considered to be Cretaceous or older(?). These are equivalent to the Valdez and Orca Groups of earlier reports.

The Tertiary rocks are dominantly of volcanic origin and include several thousand feet of lavas and tuffs interbedded with fresh-water conglomerate, clay, sandstone, and shale. These rocks compose the higher parts of the Wrangell Mountains.

CHISTOCHINA DISTRICT

The Chistochina district is in the northwest part of the Copper River basin near the intersection of lat 63°00′ N. and long 145°00′ W. The drainage area of the Chistochina River, including the southern foothills of the Alaska Range, roughly determines the boundaries of this district.

The initial gold discoveries of the Copper River region were made in this district along the Chisna River in 1898 by Hazelet and Meals (Moffit, 1944, p. 27). Slate Creek and Miller Gulch later became the leading gold-producing areas. Production from this district began in 1900 and continued, though at a diminishing rate in the later years, to 1942. From 1942 to 1959 the district was almost dormant, with only sporadic small-scale activity. Total production from 1900 through 1959 was about 141,000 ounces, all from placers. Production data from 1931 through 1945 are not complete.

Bedrock in the district consists of Carboniferous and Permian clastic and sedimentary rocks—predominantly shale, limestone, conglomerate and some sandstone—and subordinate volcanic tuffs and lava flows. All the foregoing rocks are cut by dikes (Moffit, 1944, p. 28). The gold placers were formed by reworking of glacial debris and occur in bench gravels as well as present stream gravels.

NIZINA DISTRICT

The Nizina district is in the eastern part of the Copper River drainage basin between lat 61°12′ and 61°37′ N. and long 142°22′ and 143°00′ W. This is a placer district along the Nizina River, a tributary of the Chitina River.

In 1898–99 prospectors were active in the Chitina River valley and some went up as far as the Nizina area. Although copper deposits were soon found and quickly developed, it was not until 1902 that placers rich enough to precipitate a rush were found on Chititu Creek (Moffit and Capps, 1911, p. 76). The rich deposits were quickly exhausted and the operators who remained developed previously known lower grade gravels on Chititu and Dan Creeks. In 1959 these gravels were still being mined, although on a smaller scale. Total production through 1959 from the Nizina district was 143,500 ounces of gold; all but about 60 ounces was from the placers.

The geology of the Nizina district was described by Moffit and Capps (1911, p. 20–75). Bedrock in the mountain areas consists for the most part of moderately folded Permian and Triassic(?) marine sediments and greenstone intruded by laccoliths, dikes, and sills of quartz diorite porphyry (E. H. Cobb, written commun., 1962). Deposits of moraine and alluvium blanket the lower slopes of the mountains and fill the river basins. The source of the gold in the placers is probably the small quartz veinlets in the black shales that may be related to porphyritic intrusives in the shales. High bench gravels, remnants of a deep alluvial valley fill, contain workable deposits, but the richest placers are in present stream gravels where the gold has been concentrated by reworking of older deposits (Moffit and Capps, 1911, p. 98–100).

KUSKOKWIM REGION

The Kuskokwim region, which includes the country drained by the Kuskokwim River, is roughly 400 miles long and 75 to 100 miles wide extending from the mouth of the Kuskokwim River, in southwest Alaska, to the northwest slopes of the Alaska Range, in south-central Alaska. Important gold-producing districts are Georgetown, Goodnews Bay, McKinley, and Tuluksak-Aniak.

The area southwest of the town of Aniak is underlain predominantly by Quaternary sands and gravels, but the more mountainous regions east and northeast of Aniak are underlain by bedded rocks that range in age from Ordovician(?) to Tertiary (Cady and others, 1955, pl. 1). Only parts of the region have been geologically studied in any detail; much of it remains to be mapped.

The Kuskokwim River, particularly its lower reaches, was penetrated first by Russians who in 1829 began exploring the area and later established trading posts along the river (Cady and others, 1955, p. 3–4). The first report of gold in this region was by Spurr (1900, p. 259–261) who, in 1898, noted that gold was present both in veins and in stream gravels at various points along the Kuskokwim. These reports were of mere occurrences rather than of bonanza deposits; thus prospectors were reluctant to enter this relatively unknown region. It was not until 1908 that the first gold was produced (Smith, 1933, table facing p. 96). Placers have been the principal producers from this region, yielding substantially even in the 1950's. Production from 1908 through 1959 totaled 640,084 ounces, of which only 41,598 ounces was from lode mines.

GEORGETOWN DISTRICT

The Georgetown district, between lat 62°00′ and 62°15′ N. and long 157°15′ and 158°15′ W., includes the upper reaches of the George River and Crooked Creek, tributaries of the Kuskokwim River.

Production data are incomplete but they indicate that the district has produced somewhat less than $300,000 in gold (about 14,500 ounces), chiefly from placers along Donlin and Julian Creeks which, respectively, are branches of Crooked Creek and the George River (Cady and others, 1955, p. 117–119). The placers were known as early as 1909, and mining began about a year later (Cady and others, 1955, p. 118). This early production either was unrecorded or was combined with some other district, as 1917 is listed as the first year of production. No gold production was reported from this district from the end of World War II through 1959. The low gold content of the deposits required that large volumes of gravel be handled—this was successfully accomplished by hydraulic methods.

The bedrock consists of interbedded graywacke and shale of the Kuskokwim Group of Cretaceous age into which sheets, dikes, and sills of albite rhyolite are intruded. Quartz veins containing small amounts of gold are at or near the contacts of the intrusives with the enclosing sedimentary rocks. These veins no doubt were the source of the gold in the placers (Cady and others, 1955, p. 116–117). Bench gravels, buried channels, and the deposits of existing streams contain concentrations of placer gold (Cady and others, 1955, p. 116).

GOODNEWS BAY DISTRICT

The Goodnews Bay district, along the southwest coast of Alaska between lat 59°00′ and 59°40′ N. and long 160°40′ and 162°00′ W., includes the area drained by the Goodnews and Arolic Rivers.

Placer gold was discovered about 1900 by prospectors from Nome (Harrington, 1921, p. 220), and for a few years thereafter placers along the Arolic River were mined on a small scale, though it is not known how much gold was produced. Several sporadic influxes of prospectors in the early 1900's were short lived because no profitable deposits were found (Harrington, 1921, p. 221). By 1911, however, production was reported annually from this district, and until 1947 the placers continued to yield small amounts of gold. From 1947 through 1959 the district was dormant. Total recorded production from 1911 through 1959 is about 29,700 ounces, all from placers. Data for 1931–46 are incomplete, so that the total given here is a minimum, though the magnitude is probably of the right order.

The placers of this district are of two types (Harrington, 1921, p. 222–225). One type occupies wide gravel-filled valleys and represents a reworking of earlier glaciofluviatile materials. The other type is found in narrow valleys and is derived from stream erosion of bedrock since glacial times. Narrow quartz veinlets in sedimentary rocks that were invaded by granitic rocks are believed to be the source of the gold in the placers. None of the auriferous veins have been of economic value (Harrington, 1921, p. 223–224).

McKINLEY DISTRICT

The McKinley district, in the eastern part of the Kuskokwim River valley, includes the placer caps of McGrath, Takotna, and Medfra and the lode deposits of the Nixon Fork country.

Placers along the Kuskokwim and its tributaries have been productive since 1908, although in recent years activity has diminished considerably. In the winter of 1919–20 production began from lode mines in the Nixon Fork area (Martin, 1922, p. 149). Production for the district from 1908 through 1959 was 40,600 ounces of lode gold and 13,900 ounces from placers, but data are incomplete for 1931–46.

In the Nixon Fork area, the oldest rocks are low-grade metamorphic rocks of pre-Ordovician age overlain by a 5,000- to 7,000-foot-thick limestone of Ordovician age and by a small patch of Permian sandstone, slate, and limestone (Brown, 1926, p. 101–127). Upper Cretaceous and Eocene(?) shale, sandstone, and graywacke cover large parts of the area and are overlain locally in the north by Tertiary andesite, basalt, and rhyolite lavas. Several small intrusive masses of diabase, quartz monzonite and granite, and porphyritic dikes and sills of variable composition cut the layered rocks.

The gold lodes in the Nixon Fork area are contact metamorphic deposits in limestone along its contact with a quartz monzonite intrusive. Native gold occurs in association with copper carbonates and sulfides in irregular masses and shoots (Brown, 1926, p. 128–134).

TULUKSAK-ANIAK DISTRICT

The Tuluksak-Aniak district comprises the drainage basins of the Tuluksak and Aniak Rivers between lat 60°30′ and 61°30′ N. and long 159°00′ to 161°00′ W.

After 1900, prospectors from Nome roamed throughout the lower Kuskokwim River valley and made placer discoveries along the Innoko and Holitna Rivers and finally, in 1907 or 1908, in the Bear Creek area of the Tuluksak watershed (Maddren, 1915, p. 299–300). About 2 years later gold was found in the gravels of the Aniak River. From 1909 through 1959 the district produced 230,555 ounces of gold; however, the data for 1931–46 are incomplete. The district was active in 1959.

Flood-plain and bench gravels have been productive. The gold probably has been derived from small quartz stringers in the country rock composed of sandstone, shale, agglomerate, and fine-grained tuffaceous rocks. A granitic stock cuts the sedimentary rocks and probably was responsible for the mineralization (Maddren, 1915, p. 327).

NORTHWESTERN ALASKA REGION

The vast, sparsely populated Northwestern Alaska region lies north of the Yukon drainage basin and the Seward Peninsula. The gold-producing districts, which are in the southern part, lie in the Kobuk and Noatak River basins.

In the late 1890's part of the horde of prospectors attracted to Alaska from the crowded Klondike fields discovered gold placers in the Kobuk River valley, and the rush that ensued culminated with about 800 men populating the valley (Smith and Mertie, 1930, p. 321). Activity declined in a few years, and these placers were never as productive as those in the neighboring Yukon basin.

The Shungnak district in the Kobuk River basin is the largest producer in the region. Small amounts of placer gold were produced from the Squirrel Creek area and the Noatak River valley. Auriferous veins are known in the Shungnak and Noatak areas, but these are little more than prospects (Smith and Mertie, 1930, p. 336–339).

Recorded gold production from the Northwestern Alaska region began in 1905. Total production through 1959 was about 23,000 ounces; presumably all production was from placers.

SHUNGNAK DISTRICT

The Shungnak district is in the Kobuk River valley between lat 66°50′ and 67°10′ N. and long 156°50′ and 157°25′ W. This was the major gold-producing district of Northwestern Alaska, having had a total production valued at approximately $200,000 (about 9,700 ounces) to 1930 (Smith and Mertie, 1930, p. 321). From 1930 through 1959 a few hundred more ounces were mined. The total production through 1959 probably was between 10,000 and 15,000 ounces.

The district was activated by the rush to the Kobuk River valley in 1898, but by 1910 it was almost deserted (Smith and Eakin, 1911, p. 271). Small amounts of gold were produced through the succeeding years to 1955.

Much of the district is underlain by metasedimentary rocks consisting of quartzose schist, crystalline limestone, and sheared conglomerate. Locally these rocks are mineralized and the gold placers are thought to be derived from such deposits (Smith and Eakin, 1911, p. 282–284).

SEWARD PENINSULA REGION

The gold placers of the Seward Peninsula, in western Alaska, rank second in production among Alaska's placer regions. The following description of its mining history has been abstracted from an excellent and detailed account by Collier, Hess, Smith, and Brooks (1908, p. 13–39).

Placer gold was discovered on Seward Peninsula in 1855–56 by Baron Otto von Bendeleben, an engineer leading a party exploring a possible route for a telegraph line. Nothing, apparently, came of this discovery, for as late as 1897 the Seward Peninsula was regarded as a wasteland. But about this time the rushes to the Klondike and the upper Yukon brought in many gold seekers who eventually prospected the lowly regarded gravels along the streams of Seward Peninsula. Discoveries were made at Council in 1897, and in 1898 the Nome district was organized. News spread slowly because of the isolation of this new district, but by 1899 the rush had begun and, swelled by new discoveries of beach placers and auriferous bench gravels, it continued through 1900.

In 1900, mining of placers began in the Fairhaven district in the northeastern part of the peninsula, and small production was made from discoveries in the Kougarok, Port Clarence, and Council districts. The Solomon-Bluff district, along the southern coast just east of Nome, also began producing placer gold in 1900, and from 1903 to 1907 lode gold was mined from the Big Hurrah mine in this district. During 1908–59 only very minor amounts of lode gold were produced from scattered localities on the peninsula.

The Koyuk district was not productive until 1918

even though for some years gold had been known in the gravels of the Koyuk River and Alameda Creek, one of its tributaries.

Through the 1950's placer mining continued to flourish on the Seward Peninsula, although at a somewhat lower rate than before World War II. The Nome district has been by far the largest producer; Council, Fairhaven, Solomon-Bluff, Kougarok, Koyuk, and Port Clarence have produced progressively lesser amounts. Total gold production of the Seward Peninsula from 1897 through 1959 was 6,060,000 ounces; all but about 10,000 ounces was from placers.

The geology of the Seward Peninsula was described by Collier (in Collier and others, 1908, p. 60–110). The peninsula is underlain chiefly by metasedimentary rocks comprising the Kigluaik and Nome Groups of early Paleozoic or older age and by unnamed slates, phyllites, and limestones some of which may be as young as Mississippian. Collectively these rocks can be considered a sequence of limestone, biotite gneiss, slate, quartzite, dark phyllite, and schist, cut locally by small bodies of greenstone and granite. Basalt of Pleistocene age covers a sizable area in the northeast part of the peninsula. Quaternary gravels blanket the low-lying coastal areas and occur in all the major stream valleys.

COUNCIL DISTRICT

The Council district, in the southern part of the Seward Peninsula, includes all the drainage area of Golovnin Bay extending eastward almost to the Tubutulik River.

Although gold had been reported in the Council area as early as 1865, there was very little excitement and no mining until after the discoveries of the rich Ophir Creek gravels in 1896–97 (Smith and Eakin, 1910, p. 343). Production began in 1900, and the district was still active in 1959. Total production through 1959 was about 588,000 ounces, all from placers. Data for 1931–46 are incomplete.

Nearly all production came from creek gravels and bench deposits in the drainage basin of the Niukluk River—including Ophir, Melsing, Goldbottom, Mystery, and Elkhorn Creeks (Collier and others, 1908, p. 238). The following summary of the geology is from Collier, Hess, Smith, and Brooks (1908, p. 234–235).

The district is underlain by rocks of the Kigluaik Group and the Nome Group, except in the southeast where part of a large granite mass forms the bedrock. Schists of the Nome Group contain numerous small veins and stringers of quartz and calcite, many of which contain gold along with sulfides. The gold of the placers is believed to have come from these veins.

FAIRHAVEN DISTRICT

The Fairhaven district, about 40 miles long and 20 miles wide immediately south of Kotzebue Sound in the northeast part of Seward Peninsula, is bounded roughly by lat 65°40′ and 66°10′ N. and long 161°40′ and 163°20′ W.

Gold was discovered in this district in 1900 on Old Glory and Hannum Creeks, and although there was no production that year, the news of the discovery spread through crowded Nome that winter and prompted a rush to the new district in the spring of 1901 (Moffit, 1905, p. 49). Rich placers, the most productive in the district, were found along Candle Creek in 1901 (Moffit, 1905, p. 49). The district produced steadily and was still active in 1957. Total recorded production through 1959 (data are incomplete for 1931–46) was 379,200 ounces, all from placers.

The predominant bedrock in the district is a series of micaceous, chloritic, and graphitic schists with intercalated thin limestones believed by Collier (in Collier and others, 1908, p. 65) to be Devonian or Silurian in age. Unaltered conglomerate, sandstone, and shale unconformably overlie the schists in a few areas. Locally coal beds are present. Small bodies of granite and quartz diorite intrude the schists, but their age relations with the unaltered sedimentary rocks are not clear (Collier and others, 1908, p. 83, 108). Large areas of the district are covered by sheets of basaltic lava, remnants of a more extensive cover. The youngest of these flows is Pleistocene; the age of the older lavas has not been satisfactorily determined (Moffit, 1905, p. 34). Low-lying coastal areas and river valleys are blanketed by unconsolidated gravels. The gold of the placers was concentrated from small amounts disseminated in quartz veinlets and stringers in the schistose country rock. These low-grade lodes have never been productive.

KOUGAROK DISTRICT

The Kougarok district is in the central part of the Seward Peninsula between lat 65°10′ and 65° 45′ N. and long 164°20′ and 165°20′ W.

The district began producing gold in 1900, after the initial discoveries the previous year sparked a rush from Nome (Brooks, in Collier and others, 1908, p. 306–307). Because of its remoteness and its paucity of bonanza-type deposits, the district developed slowly. Water shortage necessitated the construction of ditches. By 1906 several ditches were completed and sufficient water for larger scale operations was assured. Afterward, the Kougarok placers were moderately productive and were active in 1957. A total of about 150,400 ounces of gold has been produced from the district, all from placers. This is a minimum total as data for 1931–46 are incomplete.

The geology of the district was discussed by Brooks (in Collier and others, 1908, p. 297–298) and is summarized as follows. The bedrock consists of the Kigluaik and Nome Groups—the former is predominantly schist and granite; the latter is made up of a sequence of phyllite, schist, greenstone, and a consistent unit, the Port Clarence Limestone. The schistose rocks of the Nome Group contain small auriferous quartz veinlets and stringers which appear to be the source of the placer gold that has been concentrated into minable quantities in present stream gravels, bench gravels, and floodplain gravels. The lodes themselves are not of economic value.

KOYUK DISTRICT

The Koyuk district, in the southeast corner of the Seward Peninsula between lat 64°55′ and 65°40′ N. and long 160°20′ and 162°00′ W., includes the drainage area of the Koyuk River.

Although gold placers were known along Alameda and Knowles Creeks in 1900 (Smith and Eakin, 1910, p. 336–340), the area remained inactive until 1918. From 1918 to 1959, a recorded total of about 52,000 ounces of placer gold was produced, but the years 1931 through 1946 are not represented in this total because production data for these years cannot be found. The district was active in 1959.

NOME DISTRICT

The Nome district is in the south-central part of the Seward Peninsula between lat 64°25′ and 64° 57′ N. and long 165°00′ and 165°30′ W. More than half the gold mined on the peninsula has come from Nome placers. The brief summary that follows was abstracted from Brooks' (in Collier and others, 1908, p. 13–39) detailed history of mining on the Seward Peninsula.

Soon after the discoveries of placer gold at Council in 1897, placer gold was discovered on the Snake River near Nome and a short while later on Anvil Creek, Snow Gulch, Glacier Creek, and other streams. Miners streamed into the area from Golovnin Bay, and the Nome district was formed in October 1898. A great rush to the new district took place in 1899 and a still greater one in 1900. The new town was bursting, and the known placer grounds could not accommodate all those who sought gold. The unrest thus created led to claim jumping and general lawlessness which taxed the small military garrison to the utmost. With the discovery of rich beach placers in the district, this unhealthy situation was relieved somewhat in that a large new area was available for prospecting and the miners were diverted to gold mining instead of preying upon one another. After 1900, the population stabilized somewhat and with additional discoveries of deep gravels and buried beach placers, the district settled down to a long period of economic stability and orderly growth.

Production of the district from 1897 through 1959 was about 3,606,000 ounces of gold, almost all production was from placers. Data are lacking for 1931–46, so that the total given is a minimum. Cobb (1962) reported small but undisclosed production from scattered lode claims in the district. The Nome district, one of the major producers of Alaska, was active in 1959.

The Nome placers are of several varieties—residual, stream, bench, and beach. Moffit (1913, p. 74–123) discussed these in detail, and his work is the source of information in the summary presented here.

Residual placers, produced by the solution and erosion of less durable components of bedrock, have been mined profitably at a few localities, particularly at Nekula Gulch.

Stream placers are gravels that contain gold that was removed either directly from bedrock or from older gravels that contained gold. Important among the stream placers are those on Anvil Creek, Dexter Creek, and other tributaries of the Nome and Snake Rivers.

The high bench placers are remnants of deposits of an older drainage system. Present streams have eroded away most of these deposits, so that only benches remain. Such placers occur at the head of Dexter Creek and have been profitably mined.

Rich placers occur in sands of the present beaches and in older beaches that were elevated above present sea level and then buried in coastal plain deposits. Five or six ancient beaches are known and have been given local names. The second and third beaches (the present beach is the first) have been the most productive.

Structures of two ages are identifiable in the metamorphic bedrock (Hummel, 1960). The older and major set consists of large north-trending folds of Mesozoic age transected by younger east-trending folds of Tertiary age. The younger system is also characterized by three sets of faults. Some of the minor faults and joints of the younger deformation are mineralized, and these lodes are probably the source of the gold in the Nome placers.

PORT CLARENCE DISTRICT

The Port Clarence district, an area of about 2,000 square miles on the west end of the Seward Peninsula, has produced small amounts of placer gold from the Bluestone and Agiapuk River basins and from a few streams that drain into Grantley Harbor. The district was prospected as early as 1898, and by 1903 an estimated $200,000 in gold had been produced (Collier and others, 1908, p. 269). Total recorded production through 1959 is about 28,000 ounces, all from placers, but 1931–46 production is not recorded. Since World War II there has been only small-scale activity.

The district is underlain by schist, limestone, and small intrusive bodies comprising the Kigluaik and Nome Groups of early Paleozoic or older age, and by Devonian(?) slate and Carboniferous(?) limestone. Stocks and dikes of granite and greenstone intrude the metasedimentary rocks. Quaternary gravels contain gold placers which are restricted in general to areas underlain by rocks of the Nome Group. These rocks seem to contain more auriferous veinlets and stringers than the other bedrock types. The foregoing account is from Collier, Hess, Smith, and Brooks (1908, p. 268–281).

SOLOMON-BLUFF DISTRICT

The camps of Bluff and Solomon, an area enclosed by lat 64°30′ to 65°00′ N. and long 163°30′ to 164°30′ W., are combined here.

Gold was first discovered in this district in 1898 in gravels along the Casadepaga River, a tributary of the Solomon River. The following year other placers were found along the Solomon and on the beach of the mouth of Daniels Creek in the Bluff camp (Brooks, in Collier and others, 1908, p. 288). The beach placers were exhausted in about a year, but more extensive placers were found along Daniels Creek and along Hurrah and Shovel Creeks in the Solomon camp. These were worked by dredges and hydraulic methods (Smith, 1910, p. 139). The only important gold-quartz mine on the Seward Peninsula was the Big Hurrah in the Solomon camp, which was active from 1900 to 1937.

A total of 251,000 ounces of placer gold has come from the Solomon-Bluff district not including production from 1931 to 1946 for which records have not been found. Lode production was 9,375 ounces; all was presumably from the Big Hurrah mine. Total production recorded for the district is 260,375 ounces. No production was recorded from 1937 through 1959.

The district is underlain by rocks belonging to the lower part of the Nome Group of early Paleozoic or older age. These are a series of schist, slate, and limestone. The metasedimentary rocks were intruded by basic igneous rocks, were later altered to schist and greenstone, and were finally intruded by basalt (Smith, 1910, p. 49–137). Unconsolidated deposits consist of coastal plain deposits, stream gravels, and high-level gravels.

The lode deposit at the Big Hurrah mine consists of several quartz veins in a dense, hard, quartzitic, graphitic schist. There is a noticeable absence of sulfides; the minerals consist almost exclusively of native gold in quartz (Smith, 1910, p. 144).

The gold in the placers, which consist of stream and beach gravels in the Bluff area and stream and bench gravels in the Solomon area, was derived from disseminations and veinlets in rocks of the Nome Group, particularly in the schist and in the vicinity of schist-limestone contacts (Smith, 1910, p. 214–216).

SOUTHEASTERN ALASKA REGION

Southeastern Alaska, the panhandle of Alaska, is the narrow coastal strip that extends southeastward from the main peninsula and is bordered on the north, east, and southeast by Canada. Important gold-producing districts in this region are Juneau, Chichagof, Ketchikan-Hyder, and Porcupine. For the purpose of this report, the Yakataga district, which lies just to the northeast of what is usually considered to be the Southeastern Alaska region, is included in this section.

Gold was known in this region in the days of Russian ownership of Alaska, but no mining was done until 1870–71 when about $40,000 was produced from placers at Windham Bay and on nearby Powers Creek at Sumdum Bay in the Juneau district (Buddington and Chapin, 1929, p. 8). The important discoveries in the Juneau district were not made until the period 1880–85. During the 1890's and early 1900's lode gold mines began significant production in the Ketchikan and Chichagof districts, and beach placers were mined in the Yakataga district.

The Alaska Juneau mine in the Juneau district yielded the bulk of the gold produced in the Southeastern Alaska region. When this mine closed in 1944, the production of the entire region dropped accordingly to only a few hundred ounces annually.

Total gold production through 1959 for Southeastern Alaska was 7,788,514 ounces, of which

7,614,791 ounces was from lode deposits, 138,503 ounces was from placers, and 35,220 ounces was a byproduct from copper ores from the Ketchikan-Hyder district.

This is an extremely mountainous region with complex geologic structures and varied bedrock types. Dominant among the geologic features are the intrusive rocks of Late Jurassic or Early Cretaceous age that occupy much of the mainland area of this region. These rocks range in composition from gabbro to granite and are believed to be related to the great composite Coast Range batholith (Buddington and Chapin, 1929, p. 173–253). Adjacent to the intrusive rocks on the west is a belt of low-rank metasedimentary rocks comprising the Wales Group of early Paleozoic age. Other sedimentary rocks in this region represent every period from Ordovician to Cretaceous and have an aggregate thickness of about 50,000 feet. Tertiary clastic rocks and lavas accumulated in a trough between the major mountain ranges. A few sills and dikes of basalt and andesite cut the Tertiary rocks (Buddington and Chapin, 1929, p. 260–275). Quaternary deposits are of minor areal extent and consist mostly of marine gravels, delta deposits, basalt, and tuffs (Buddington and Chapin, 1929, p. 275–281).

CHICHAGOF DISTRICT

The Chichagof district comprises an area of about 4,500 square miles and includes Baranof, Chichagof, Kruzof, and Sitka Islands.

The first attempts at lode mining in Alaska, under American rule, were made near Sitka in 1871 (Knopf, 1912, p. 8). These ventures and others in the succeeding few years failed, and mining in the Sitka area lapsed into a period of dormancy until the lode discoveries were made at Klag Bay on Chichagof Island in 1905. The Chichagof mine soon became the big producer here, with a production from 1906 through 1938 of $13,784,710 in gold (Reed and Coats, 1941, p. 89). The Hirst-Chichagof mine, which went into production in 1922, produced $1,702,624 in gold through 1938 (Reed and Coats, 1941, p. 104). In succeeding years production from these mines dwindled, and the Chichagof district was operating on a very small scale in 1959. The total recorded production for the district through 1959 was 770,000 ounces, all from lode mines.

The general geology of Chichagof and Baranof Islands has been described by Knopf (1912, p. 11–21), and according to him the oldest rocks are chert and quartzite which are overlain by cherty limestone of Silurian age. Devonian limestone and tuff, Mississippian limestone, Permian or Triassic gypsiferous limestone, Mesozoic graywacke, and postglacial lavas and tuffs complete the stratified rock sequence. The central parts of the islands are composed of masses of granitoid rocks, dominantly quartz diorite of late Mesozoic age. In the Klag Bay area of Chichagof Island masses of greenstone and greenstone schist of possible Triassic age (Reed and Coats, 1941, p. 14–22) occur between the diorite and graywacke. The stratified sedimentary rocks lie on the west bank of an anticlinorium, the axial part of which in this district is occupied by the diorite. Many northwest-trending high-angle faults cut the bedded rocks (Reed and Coats, 1941, p. 64).

The ore deposits are in plunging quartz bodies along the faults. Quartz is the main constituent of these lodes, but calcite may be present. Sulfides, in conspicuously minor amounts, consist of pyrite, arsenopyrite, galena, sphalerite, and chalcopyrite. Gold is present as specks in the quartz and in the sulfides (Reed and Coats, 1941, p. 78–80).

JUNEAU DISTRICT

The Juneau district includes Douglas and Admiralty Islands, lat 57°00′ to 59°00′ N. and long 133°00′ to 135°00′ W.

Placer discoveries were made in 1869 at Windham Bay and at Sumdum Bay, about 50 miles south of Juneau, and lode gold, which has been the mainstay of the district, was discovered in 1880 by Joe Juneau and Richard Harris whose locations included the site of the Alaska Juneau mine, the largest lode gold mine in Alaska (Wright, 1906, p. 2). The discovery resulted in a rush to the area and the founding of the town of Juneau, which, by 1883, became the locus of gold mining in Alaska. Numerous lode properties were located near Juneau and on neighboring Douglas Island where the Treadwell group—including the Treadwell, Mexican, Ready Bullion, and 700 Foot mines—was quickly developed into a major producer, yielding $26,556,470 in gold through 1905. Caving, which began in the Treadwell and 700 Foot mines as early as 1913, culminated with the complete flooding of the Treadwell, 700 Foot, and Mexican mines in 1917 (Eakin, 1918a, p. 78–79). These mines were never reopened, but the Ready Bullion remained productive until 1922 (Brooks and Capps, 1924, p. 24). Other important mines in the early days of this camp were the Sumdum and Ebner. Production records for the Alaska Juneau mine began in 1893 and are complete to April 9, 1944, when the mine was closed due to manpower shortages and excessive costs (C. W. Henderson and R. V. Cushman, in U.S. Bureau of

Mines, 1945, p. 232). This mine yielded a total of 2,874,361 ounces of gold, almost as much silver, and large quantities of lead. The closing of the Alaska Juneau mine signaled the end of gold mining in Southeastern Alaska. Only a few hundred ounces of gold were produced annually from the entire region from 1944 through 1959.

Total gold production of the Juneau district from 1882 through 1959 was 6,883,556 ounces—66,279 ounces from placers, the remainder from lodes.

The eastern part of the district is underlain by the dioritic and granitic intrusives composing the Coast Range batholith of Late Jurassic or Early Cretaceous age (Buddington and Chapin, 1929, p. 173–175). This is flanked on the west by several north-trending bands of schist, slate, and greenstone (Spencer, 1906, p. 16–19) which according to Buddington and Chapin (1929, p. 73–74) may include rocks ranging in age from Ordovician to Cretaceous. Still farther west is a band of interbedded slate and graywacke with some greenstone which Buddington and Chapin (1929, p. 157) consider Jurassic or Cretaceous. The rocks have been folded into a northwest-trending synclinorium, bounded on the east by the Coast Range batholith and on the west by an anticlinorium (Buddington and Chapin, 1929, p. 289–290).

The gold deposits of the Juneau district, according to Spencer (1906, p. 22–24), are of three types: veins, impregnated deposits, and combinations of these two types, or mixed deposits. Though other rock types may be mineralized, most of the deposits are found in the slate and greenstone. The veins vary considerably in thickness, trend, and continuity. Quartz is the main constituent; however, calcite is common, and albite is abundant in some veins. Pyrite, galena, sphalerite, and arsenopyrite are the common sulfides. Gold is either associated with pyrite or arsenopyrite or is found as small flakes in the quartz (Spencer, 1906, p. 33–36). In the impregnated deposits, the country rock has been replaced by large masses of the sulfides listed above, but these deposits are relatively unimportant as a source of gold. The mixed deposits were the most important of the three types at the famous Treadwell mines (Spencer, 1906, p. 24).

KETCHIKAN-HYDER DISTRICT

The Ketchikan-Hyder district includes the southern end of the Alaska panhandle, roughly the area between lat 54°20′ and 57°00′ N. and long 130°00′ and 134°00′ W.

Most of the early mining interest in Alaska was centered in Sitka and Juneau, and Ketchikan was neglected for many years. But in the late 1890's discoveries of gold and copper were made at Ketchikan, and this together with the news of the Klondike successes encouraged many people to prospect the new area (Brooks, 1902, p. 39). By 1900 there was feverish activity in the district with several mines open and many claims located. Gold was produced from auriferous veins and from copper ores.

At Hyder, near the Canadian border, lode deposits of gold were discovered in about 1901 but were neglected until 1909, when a short-lived boom occurred (Buddington, 1929, p. 2–3). In the 1920's there were several small discoveries near Hyder that caused some mild excitement.

Production of gold from the Ketchikan-Hyder district amounts to about 62,000 ounces, of which 35,000 ounces is byproduct gold from copper ores and 27,000 ounces is from lode mines. Data for 1938–46 are incomplete. The district was still active in 1959, though only small quantities of byproduct gold were produced.

The oldest rocks in the district are limestone and phyllite of Silurian or pre-Silurian age. These are overlain by limestone, slate, and schist of probable Middle Devonian age. In the central part of the district the Devonian rocks are overlain by argillite, limestone, and sandstone of the Ketchikan Series, partly of Paleozoic and Mesozoic age. Locally, Mesozoic conglomerates overlie the Devonian rocks. A broad belt of granite (or diorite), part of the Coast Range batholith, underlies the eastern part of the district (Brooks, 1902, p. 40–41), but the most widely distributed igneous rock is the Kasaan Greenstone, which is the oldest of the intrusive rocks. Warner, Goddard, and others (1961, p. 13) imply that the greenstone is of Mesozoic age, but older than Cretaceous. In general the metasedimentary rocks throughout the district occur in northwest-trending bands (Brooks, 1902, p. 51).

The geology of the Hyder area is summarized as follows from Buddington (1929, p. 13–42). The Hazelton Group, of probable Jurassic age, is composed of greenstone, tuff, breccia, graywacke, slate, argillite, quartzite, and some limestone, and it occurs as large disconnected patches in the east and west parts of the area. The beds are tightly folded and strike predominantly to the east. A granodiorite batholith, called the Texas Creek batholith, intruded the Hazelton Group, and the Hyder Quartz Monzonite and the Boundary Granodiorite intruded both the Hazelton Group and Texas Creek batholith. The intrusive rocks are of Jurassic or Cretaceous age and are genetically related to the Coast Range batholith.

The ore deposits are somewhat varied in this district; commercial amounts of silver, copper, iron, lead, and zinc are present in addition to gold. The ore deposits are of four general types—vein deposits, breccia veins, mineralized shear zones, and contact metasomatic deposits. The veins occur in the oldest rocks of the district. They range in width from a few inches to 10 feet or more and are made up of quartz, calcite, pyrite, chalcopyrite, galena, sphalerite, and gold (Wright and Wright, 1908, p. 80–81). Breccia veins, most abundant in the limestone and schist, consist for the most part of quartz-cemented country rock. Auriferous sulfides may be in limestone fragments or in the quartz (Wright and Wright, 1908, p. 81–82). The shear zone deposits range in width from 5 to 50 feet and follow the structure of the enclosing rock—most commonly slate or greenstone. The dominant minerals are quartz and calcite in veinlets and chalcopyrite and pyrite disseminated throughout the rock. Gold occurs in the quartz-calcite veinlets (Wright and Wright, 1908, p. 82–83). The contact metamorphic deposits are in limestones near their contacts with intrusives. These deposits consist of masses of chalcopyrite, pyrrhotite, pyrite, and magnetite in a gangue of garnet, epidote, calcite, quartz, amphibole, and wollastonite. Both copper and gold are produced from these deposits (Wright and Wright, 1908, p. 83–84). On the Kasaan Peninsula, contact metasomatic deposits of magnetite, pyrite, and chalcopyrite are found in association with tactite bodies in layers and lenses of metamorphosed sedimentary rocks in the Kasaan Greenstone (Warner and others, 1961, p. 30–52).

Worthy of special mention is the Salt Chuck mine on the Kasaan Peninsula. Originally located as a copper prospect in 1905, this deposit was later found to contain platinum minerals and gold and silver in recoverable amounts (Holt and others, 1948, p. 3). The ore bodies are masses of bornite and chalcopyrite that have replaced and filled fractures in a pyroxenite country rock (Mertie, 1921, p. 124–125). According to Holt, Shepard, Thorne, Tolonen, and Fosse (1948, p. 4), a total of 326,000 tons of ore with an average gold content of 0.036 ounces per ton was produced from the beginning of mining to the spring of 1941. This amounts to 11,736 ounces of gold.

PORCUPINE DISTRICT

The Porcupine district is just north of lat 59°15′ N. at long 136°20′ W. along Porcupine Creek, a tributary of the Klehini River.

Productive gravels were discovered in 1898 along Porcupine Creek and its tributaries (Wright, 1904, p. 12). The era of greatest activity was from 1900 to 1906 when about $100,000 in gold per year was produced. Between 1915 and 1917, hydraulic equipment was installed which accounted for a brief rejuvenation of the district (Eakin, 1918b, p. 99), but from 1917 through 1959 there was only occasional small-scale production by individuals. Total production for the district through 1959 is 53,250 ounces, all from placers.

Eakin's report (1919, p. 9–21) on the Porcupine district is the source of the data on geology and placer deposits given here.

The northeast part of the district is underlain by dioritic rocks of the Coast Range batholith. Bordering this on the south is a northwest-trending belt of phyllite, slate, and limestone of Late Pennsylvanian or Early Permian age. An elongate mass of diorite cuts the metasedimentary rocks in the west and southwest part of the district. The metasedimentary rocks are also cut by numerous stringers of quartz and calcite carrying variable amounts of sulfides, and locally the rocks are impregnated with lenticular masses of sulfides.

Placers consist of creek gravels, side benches, and high benches. The gold probably was derived locally by erosion of the auriferous sulfides in the country rock.

YAKATAGA DISTRICT

The Yakataga district, an area of about 1,000 square miles, is between lat 60°00′ and 60°30′ N. and long 141°20′ and 144°40′ W., just west of the northern end of the panhandle that forms southeast Alaska.

The date of discovery of ore in the Yakataga district is unknown. According to Maddren (1913b, p. 133), gold was first found in the beach sands at Yakataga about 1897 or 1898, but Smith (1933, p. 96) listed the first production for the area in 1891. During the first years the beach sands were worked with simple rockers. Later, several attempts at larger scale mining, by using sluice boxes, were made (Maddren, 1913b, p. 133–134). Bench gravels along the White River were found to be gold bearing and these have been worked intermittently by hydraulic methods. Total recorded production for the district from 1891 through 1959 was only 15,709 ounces, all from placers. In 1959 the district was virtually inactive; less than 75 ounces was reported from 1950 through 1959.

In the northern part of the district the high St. Elias Range, which dominates the landscape, is composed of intensely contorted metamorphic and intrusive rocks. The Robinson Mountains, in the central part of the district, are composed of Tertiary and Pleistocene sedimentary rocks in northwest-trending folds. In the south, the district is covered with outwash gravel and fluvial deposits (Maddren, 1913b, p. 126–132). The gold in the beach placers was concentrated by wave action from the glaciofluvial deposits of the White River. The ultimate source of the gold was the crystalline rocks of the St. Elias Range from which the gold was removed either by glaciers or by Pleistocene streams and was redeposited at lower levels. The present stream system of the White River reworked the auriferous outwash gravel and Pleistocene fluvial deposits and concentrated the gold in channel sands which now form low benches that are being eroded (Maddren, 1913b, p. 142–143).

SOUTHWESTERN ALASKA REGION

In the Alaska Peninsula, which forms the Southwestern Alaska region, only the Unga district contains commercial gold deposits of any magnitude. There has been scattered production from the Kodiak area, where lodes and beach placers were mined on a small scale, but more than 90 percent of the total production has come from Unga. Total recorded production for Southwestern Alaska through 1959 is 112,570 ounces, of which 108,000 ounces is of lode origin and 4,570 ounces is from placers.

UNGA DISTRICT

Unga is an island, one of the Shumagin Group, between lat 55°10′ and 55°23′ N. and long 160°30′ and 160°50′ W.

Almost the entire production of this district is attributed to the Apollo Consolidated mine which began production in 1891 and by 1904 yielded between $2 and $3 million (Martin, 1905, p. 100). Production decreased markedly after 1905 and ceased after 1922. Total production through 1959 was 107,900 ounces, all of lode origin.

The country rock is andesite and dacite believed by Becker (1898, p. 83) to be Miocene or younger and by Martin (1905) to be somewhat older than Miocene. Sedimentary rocks that range in age from Oligocene to Pliocene (MacNeil and others, 1961, p. 1802) are also present on Unga Island, but their relations with the igneous rocks cannot be determined from the published literature. Becker (1898, p. 84) described the deposit as a reticulated vein—a zone of fractures that was mineralized. The wallrocks are much altered and have been replaced by chlorite and pyrite. Gangue minerals are sugary quartz with some calcite, and the ore minerals are free gold, pyrite, galena, sphalerite, chalcopyrite, and native copper (Becker, 1898, p. 83).

YUKON REGION

The vast Yukon region encompasses the entire drainage basin of the Yukon River in Alaska. It has the shape of a truncated wedge extending across central Alaska. The region is narrower (80 to 100 miles wide) along the west coast of Alaska at the mouth of the river and wider (200 to 300 miles) along Alaska's eastern border, where it includes the basins of the Yukon and one of its main tributaries, the Tanana. This has been by far the most productive of all the gold-producing regions, with a recorded total through 1959 of 12,282,250 ounces, most of it from placers.

Goodrich's detailed account (in Spurr and Goodrich, 1898, p. 103–131) of the early explorations, the discovery of gold, and the development of the first mining districts is the source of much of the material presented here.

The Yukon region had been traversed rather thoroughly after the 1840's by explorers and traders intent on establishing new posts and opening new country for the fur trade. A lively competition which developed among the Russians, the Hudson Bay Co., and the Americans was terminated by the purchase of Alaska by the United States.

In the 1860's small quantities of gold had been found at several localities in the Yukon basin, but credit for the discovery that led to intensive prospecting goes to George Holt, who made several trips to the Yukon in the 1870's and returned with glowing, if not entirely veracious, tales of gold in the interior. In 1881 a few prospectors panned some gold along the Big Salmon River, one of the tributaries of the Yukon River in the Yukon Territory, Canada. A year later, prospectors working up the Yukon from its mouth found gold in considerable quantities near what is now Rampart, in central Alaska. Discoveries in the 1880's along the boundary between Alaska and Canada in the Fortymile River area were developed rapidly, and by 1893 more than 300 men were working the gravels. Birch Creek in the Circle district next attracted attention and it soon rivaled the Fortymile district. Between 1890 and 1895 gold-bearing gravels were found along the Koyukuk River and additional discoveries were made in the Rampart area and in the adjacent Hot Springs district.

In 1902 gold was discovered in the Fairbanks district (Prindle, 1904, p. 64) which in the succeeding years developed into the leading producer in Alaska. The Fairbanks discoveries stimulated prospecting to the south in the foothills of the Alaska Range, and placers were found in the Bonnifield country in 1903 and the Kantishna district in 1906 (Prindle, 1907, p. 205).

At about the same time, commercial quantities of gold were found several hundred miles to the west in the gravels of the upper valley of the Innoko River and this led to discoveries on the adjacent Iditarod River. In about 1910 placers were found along Long Creek in the Ruby district, about 70 miles east of Koyukuk (Mertie and Harrington, 1924, p. 88, 89, 101). One of the most recently discovered placer districts in the Yukon region is the Tolavana district situated along the Tolovana River, a tributary which joins the Tanana River about 100 miles west of Fairbanks. Mining of these placers began in 1915 (Brooks, 1916, p. 201).

Most of the placer districts of the Yukon basin remained active after World War II, through 1959, though production decreased because of the constantly rising mining costs especially since 1950.

Only two districts—Fairbanks and Nabesna—have had any significant lode production, but this is dwarfed by the placer output. The Yukon basin has yielded a total of 12,282,250 ounces of gold, of which 10,776,460 ounces is from placers, 305,560 ounces is from lode deposits, and 1,200,230 ounces is undifferentiated but presumably from placers. It may seem strange that from such a large region so few commercial vein deposits have been exploited; however, several factors must be considered in an analysis of this imbalance. First, the placers are amenable to large-scale dredging methods which means that low-grade material can be mined even at present high costs. Secondly, the remoteness of the areas containing the lode deposits demands large tonnages of high-grade ores for profitable mining.

It is difficult to summarize the geology of a region as large as the Yukon drainage basin, especially in view of the fact that the region has not been completely mapped and the areas that are mapped were done at different scales at different times and by numerous individuals. The upper part of the basin, the Yukon-Tanana area, was mapped first by Spurr (in Spurr and Goodrich, 1898) and then by Mertie (1937), but that part of the basin from the junction of the Yukon and Tanana to the mouth of the Yukon has been mapped in small parcels by individuals investigating only certain districts.

In the upper part of the basin, stratified rocks ranging in age from Precambrian to Recent are exposed. Representatives of every period except Jurassic are present (Mertie, 1937, p. 44–46). Mesozoic and Tertiary granitic intrusive rocks are the most important members of the igneous family in this area, and it is believed that the metalliferous ore deposits are related to them (Mertie, 1937, p. 46).

Farther downstream, in the Ruby area, greenstones and undifferentiated metamorphic rocks of Paleozoic age and older are the predominant country rocks (Mertie and Harrington, 1924, p. 12).

In the Innoko and Iditarod districts, which may be considered the lower reaches of the Yukon, Mesozoic sedimentary rocks, chiefly Cretaceous in age, compose most of the country rock. These are interlayered locally with basic igneous rocks. Granitic intrusions make up the mountain areas, and rhyolite dikes are scattered throughout the area (Eakin, 1913, p. 295).

Throughout the Yukon basin, large areas are covered with fluvial deposits that form flats tens of miles wide. The entire region has a complex geomorphic and structural history, much of which is fairly recent in age, but not enough work has been done in the region to interpret the many anomalous features of the present drainage (Mertie, 1937, p. 237).

BONNIFIELD DISTRICT

The Bonnifield district is between lat 63°30′ and 64°50′ N. and long 145°40′ and 149°20′ W. It extends from the Tanana flats on the north to the north slope of the Alaska Range on the south, and it is bounded on the west and east by the Nenana and Delta Rivers, respectively.

The first gold was mined from the gravels of Gold King Creek in 1903. During the early years there were high hopes that the Bonnifield would become a major district, but only small amounts of gold were produced annually, and after 1949 the district was idle. Total production through 1959 was about 36,600 ounces, all from placers.

The geology, as outlined by Capps (1912, p. 17–19), is as follows. The oldest rocks in the district are metasedimentary rocks of Precambrian or early Paleozoic age—the Birch Creek Schist, consisting of quartz and mica schist, phyllite, and quartzite. Mertie (1937, p. 46) considered the Birch Creek to be Precambrian in age. The Birch Creek Schist is overlain by quartz-feldspar schists forming the Totatlanika Schist of Silurian or Devonian age. A sequence of Tertiary sediments beginning with Eocene fresh-water deposits unconformably overlies the schists. The fresh-water deposits are followed by the Nenana Gravel of middle Miocene to early Pliocene age (MacNeil and others, 1961, p.

1806) and Pleistocene and Recent glaciofluvial deposits. The schists are highly contorted, and as the Alaska Range rose in Tertiary time the Tertiary beds were subjected to considerable folding and faulting immediately after their deposition. Intrusive rocks of granitic to dioritic composition cut the schists at various localities. These bodies are older than Eocene and younger than Silurian or Devonian (Capps, 1912, p. 41–42).

The placer deposits are in the foothills between the Tanana Flats to the north and the high slopes of the Alaska Range to the south. Present streams have cut through valleys previously filled with alluvium and have reconcentrated and redeposited the detrital gold of the older alluvium.

CHANDALAR DISTRICT

The Chandalar district, between lat 67°00′ and 68°10′ N. and long 147°00′ and 150°00′ W., includes the upper drainage of the Chandalar River.

The Chandalar district, which began producing placer gold in 1906, is one of the small producers of the Yukon basin. Total placer production through 1959 was 30,708 ounces. Cobb (1962) indicated small but undisclosed lode production from the district.

Lode deposits, which have been known in the district for many years, have recently received renewed attention. In 1961 the Little Squaw Mining Co. reported blocking out an ore body worth $1,013,000 in gold (Mining World, 1961).

The geology given here is generalized from a more detailed account by Mertie (1925, p. 223–252). Schists, resembling the Birch Creek Schist, of Precambrian or early Paleozoic age are the oldest rocks in the district and are found in the southern part. Other schists and phyllites of early Paleozoic age compose the bedrock in the central part of the district, north of the area underlain by Birch Creek(?) Schist. Silurian limestone and dolomite and Devonian slate occur still farther north. In the southwest corner, Devonian or Mississippian rocks unconformably overlie the schists, and a small patch of Upper Cretaceous sandstone caps the sequence. Igneous rocks in the district consist of granite, granodiorite, and basic lavas, that range in age from Late Silurian or Early Devonian to Tertiary.

The schists contain numerous small auriferous quartz veins and stringers that no doubt were the source of the gold in the placers. Both preglacial and postglacial gravels have been productive.

CHISANA DISTRICT

The Chisana district is between lat 61°55′ and 62°20′ N. and long 141°40′ and 142°35′ W., in the drainage area of the Chisana River, a tributary of the Tanana River.

Gold lodes were known in this area before 1910, but were never developed; then in 1913 placer discoveries along Bonanza Creek started a stampede to the district (Capps, 1916, p. 89–92). The placers, however, were relatively small, and efforts to find and develop lode deposits were unsuccessful. Small amounts of placer gold were produced up to World War II, but since then the output has been insignificant. Total production from 1913 through 1959 was 44,760 ounces, all from placers.

The rocks of the district range in age from Devonian to Recent (Capps, 1916, p. 29–31). The oldest rocks are black shale, basic lava, and pyroclastic of Devonian age which are overlain by a great thickness of Carboniferous lava, tuff, breccia, agglomerate, and some limestone and shale. Shale and graywacke of Mesozoic age are faulted against the older rocks along an east-west line. Several small patches of Tertiary sediments unconformably overlie the Paleozoic rocks, and in the stream valleys considerable areas are covered with glacial debris and stream deposits interbedded with lava flows. Granitic intrusions cut the Devonian and Carboniferous rocks but the exact age of the igneous rocks is not known (Capps, 1916, p. 84–85).

Most of the placers occur in the area of Carboniferous pyroclastic rocks and the granitic intrusions. Capps (1916, p. 96–98) believed that the gold of the placers was eroded from veins in these Paleozoic rocks near their contact with the intrusives and that the present placers are a product of several previous reworkings of Tertiary auriferous gravels, first by streams, then by glaciers, then by the present streams reworking the glacial deposits.

CIRCLE DISTRICT

The Circle district is between lat 65°15′ and 66°00′ N. and long 144°00′ and 146°00′ W.

This is one of the older districts of the region, gold having been discovered along Birch Creek in 1893 (Prindle, 1906, p. 20). Production began the following year and was continuous through 1957. Hydraulic methods were used on nearly all productive streams, particularly along Mastodon Creek. Total production through 1959 was 705,660 ounces, all from placers.

The rocks, as summarized from Mertie (1932, p. 158–161), consist of schist, clastic sedimentary rock, limestone, and granitic rocks ranging in age from Precambrian to Mesozoic. Pleistocene and Recent unconsolidated deposits complete the sequence.

The Birch Creek Schist, the oldest rock, is of Precambrian or early Paleozoic age. Next youngest are lower Paleozoic metamorphic rocks—quartzite, phyllite, and slate—together with graywacke, arkose, limestone, and chert. The Crazy Mountains in the central part of the district are underlain in succession by Silurian or Devonian limestones, basic flows and sedimentary rocks of the Rampart Group of Early Mississippian age, and by a later Mississippian chert formation. Several small bodies of granite are intrusive into all the foregoing rocks, and the placer deposits are in the vicinity of the intrusive bodies. Alluvial deposits in the Circle district represent several erosional periods during Pleistocene and Recent time.

EAGLE DISTRICT

The Eagle district is between lat 64°35′ and 65° 15′ N. and long 141°00′ and 142°40′ W., along Seventymile, American, and Fourth of July Creeks, all tributaries that enter the Yukon River near Alaska's eastern boundary.

Placer gold was first found in 1895 along American Creek, and production began the following year (Mertie, 1938, p. 190). Although it attracted few miners, the Eagle district maintained a small annual production even through the difficult post-World War II years. Production data before 1906 cannot be found and was probably reported under some other district. Total recorded production for the Eagle district from 1906 through 1959 is 40,220 ounces, all from placers.

The district is underlain in the southwest by a large mass of granite of Late Jurassic age that has intruded and thrust upward a series of Precambrian and Paleozoic sedimentary rocks that are now exposed in northwestward-trending bands in the central and northern parts of the district. Lower Cretaceous marine rocks are exposed in the northern part of the district and these are succeeded by a thick series of fresh-water deposits of Late Cretaceous and Eocene age (Mertie, 1930, pl. 12). Post-Eocene uplift caused much of this covering to be removed. Unconsolidated deposits of sand and gravel of Pleistocene and Recent age are in the stream valleys. These sediments reflect a complex geomorphic cycle involving local glaciation, climatic changes, and changes in base level (Mertie, 1930, p. 147–148).

The gold placers are in present stream gravels. The gold in these deposits came originally from small veins related to the granitic mass in the southwest part of the area, but much gold also came from ancient placers in the Upper Cretaceous and Eocene clastics (Mertie, 1930, p. 161–162).

FAIRBANKS DISTRICT

The Fairbanks district, about 300 square miles between lat 64°40′ and 65°20′ N. and long 147°00′ and 148°10′ W., has produced more gold than any other district in Alaska. It is predominantly a placer district, although it also ranks high among the lode districts.

Fairbanks was slow to develop. Placer gold was known in the area as early as 1878 (Mertie, 1937, p. 4), but the active districts of Fortymile, Rampart, and Circle kept all but the most restless away from the Fairbanks area. In 1901 the town of Fairbanks was founded as a trading post, not as a consequence of gold mining (Prindle and Katz, 1913, p. 86). The following year some workable placers were found along Pedro Creek. This discovery brought a rush of miners and prospectors to the district, most of whom became discouraged and left after learning that the rich, easily accessible placers were few and that the large, lower grade deposits were buried and required processing large volumes of material with special machinery. Large investments were needed to purchase and construct hoisting machinery, large dredges, and machinery for thawing the frozen overburden. But gradually, as the obstacles were overcome, it was found that the buried gravels could be mined profitably, and the district prospered as the dredges chewed through huge reserves of auriferous gravels on Dome, Ester, Vault, Cleary, and Chatanika Creeks. Production continued at a high level even after World War II, but in 1959, activity began to diminish. The Fairbanks Daily News-Miner reported (Sept. 15, 1959) that gold dredging was gradually ceasing in this area. Two dredges were closed in 1959 and a third was transferred to the Fortymile district.

Interest in lode mining began after the placers were developed. Small-scale operations were under way in 1910 in Skoogy Gulch and upper Cleary and Fairbanks Creeks (Hill, 1933, p. 51). The peak of lode mining was reached just before World War II. The Pedro Dome and Ester Dome areas contain the most productive lode deposits.

The total gold production of the Fairbanks district through 1959 was 7,464,167 ounces—7,239,696 ounces from placers, 224,471 ounces from lodes.

The Birch Creek Schist, of Precambrian or early Paleozoic age, underlies most of the district (Hill, 1933, p. 41). This includes a variety of rock types, among which quartz schist and quartzite are dominant. Masses of crystalline limestone are present locally. Small bodies of biotite granite and quartz diorite believed to be of Mesozoic age (Hill, 1933, p. 43) intrude the Birch Creek. In the northeast corner of the district is a small patch of Tertiary sandstone and conglomerate, and in the same general area are a few small isolated areas of Tertiary basalt (Hill, 1933, p. 42–43).

The lode deposits of the Fairbanks district are fissure veins in the Birch Creek Schist in the vicinity of bodies of intrusive rock. The trends of both the veins and intrusives seem to be controlled structurally, but the trends are not consistent throughout the district (Hill, 1933, p. 63–64). All the major intrusives trend eastward; the veins in the Pedro Dome area also trend eastward, but the veins in the Ester Dome area trend more northward. The veins consist of quartz with small amounts of the sulfides arsenopyrite, pyrite, sphalerite, jamesonite, and stibnite, and free gold which is associated either with quartz or with the sulfides. Cervantite is widespread as an oxidation product of stibnite, and its yellow-green stain is a guide to high-grade gold ore in this district (Hill, 1933, p. 64–73).

The gold placers occur along stream valleys in unconsolidated gravels. The most productive layer is normally a few inches to 8 feet above the bedrock; the bedrock from 1 foot to several feet below the gravel is usually gold bearing. A thick mantle of barren material consisting of sands, clays, and muck covers the deposits (Prindle and Katz, 1913, p. 92–98).

FORTYMILE DISTRICT

The Fortymile district, between lat 64°00′ and 64°30′ N. and long 141°00′ and 142°20′ W., along the international boundary, includes the upper drainage of Fortymile River, one of the Yukon tributaries that joins the main stream in Canada. It is one of the oldest placer areas in the Yukon region and had uninterrupted output through 1959.

According to Mertie (1938, p. 157), gold was discovered in the district in 1886, but Smith (1933, p. 96) listed small production beginning in 1883. Discoveries of rich stream placers in 1893 in the Sixtymile River area, across the international boundary, drew many prospectors to the Fortymile district as well, and in a relatively short interval all the major gold-producing grounds in the Fortymile district were found. The placers of Dome, Wade, and Chicken Creeks were all discovered during the 1890's (Mertie, 1938, p. 157). Large-scale mining methods—dredge and hydraulic—have been used with success, which is probably why the district was still active in 1959.

Total recorded gold production of the Fortymile district through 1959 was about 400,000 ounces, all from placers.

The most abundant country rock of the district, according to Mertie (1938, p. 148), is the Birch Creek Schist, but locally other rocks are present. In the Chicken Creek and Franklin Creek areas granite is exposed (Mertie, 1938, p. 171, 182). Small patches of Tertiary conglomerate, shale, and sandstone are known in the Chicken Creek and Napoleon Creek areas, and some lower Paleozoic greenstone and limestone is exposed along Napoleon Creek (Mertie, 1938, p. 184). Basalt, gabbro, and diabase, younger than the granite, are found in the central part of the Chicken Creek basin.

The productive deposits are in gravels of Pleistocene to Recent age. There are also ancient placers in the Tertiary deposits, but none of these contain gold in commercial quantities. On the other hand, these Tertiary deposits, where eroded, contributed their gold to the younger deposits. Quartz veins related to the granite intrusives are the ultimate source of the gold, according to Mertie (1938, p. 154).

HOT SPRINGS DISTRICT

The Hot Springs district is between lat 65°00′ and 65°20′ N. and long 149°40′ and 151°20′ W. The drainages of Baker, Sullivan, and American Creeks are its major placer areas.

Gold-bearing gravels were discovered in 1898 on Baker and Eureka Creeks by a group of New Englanders known throughout the area as the "Boston Boys" (Mertie, 1934, p. 165–166). When the party returned in 1899 to the new settlement of Rampart, news of their discoveries leaked out and caused a rush to the Hot Springs area. The first production reported was in 1904 (Smith, 1933, table facing p. 96); a town was built a few years later (Mertie, 1934, p. 166).

The district maintained a steady output since mining began and was still active in 1959. Opencut, drifting, and hydraulic methods have been used in the mining. Total production through 1959 was 447,850 ounces, all from placers.

As the Hot Springs and Rampart districts are separated by only a narrow drainage divide, their geology can be summarized together.

Consolidated sedimentary rocks that range in age from pre-Ordovician to Tertiary and include sandstone, shale, conglomerate, chert, limestone, and coal-bearing rocks compose the bulk of the bedrock in these two districts (Mertie, 1934, p. 172–173). These are intruded locally by granite of Tertiary age.

Eakin (1915, p. 239) noted that the placers of the Hot Springs district were of several types—bench deposits, reworked bench deposits, irregular discontinuous bodies of auriferous gravel called "spots," and normal stream gravels containing pay streaks.

The gold of the placers was deposited during early and late Tertiary from lodes in and adjacent to granitic intrusives (Mertie, 1934, p. 223).

IDITAROD DISTRICT

The Iditarod district, between lat 62°10′ and 63°00′ N. and long 157°30′ and 158°30′ W., along the upper drainage of the Iditarod River and its tributaries, ranks second among the gold-producing districts in the Yukon basin.

Gold was discovered in 1908 along Otter Creek, a tributary of the Iditarod River (Maddren, 1911, p. 238). Despite its remoteness, the district developed, and in 1910 production was reported at $500,000 (Smith, 1933, table facing p. 96). Productive gravels also were found on Flat and Willow Creeks. The placers have been mined by dredges, mechanical scrapers, and hydraulic equipment (Mertie and Harrington, 1924, p. 110). Total gold production through 1959 was 1,297,500 ounces; nearly all production was from placers.

The underlying bedrock of the district, as described by Mertie and Harrington (1924, p. 12–82), consists dominantly of sandstone, shale, and conglomerate of late Cretaceous and Eocene age. In the western part of the district, west of the Iditarod River, undifferentiated metamorphic rocks of Paleozoic and Precambrian age are exposed; in the central part there are a few small stocks of quartz monzonite and basic intrusives. Unconsolidated deposits of sand, gravel, and silt of Pleistocene and Recent age are in the stream valleys.

Placers are of two types—residual and stream (Mertie and Harrington, 1924, p. 111–115). The stocks of monzonite, which are sheared and mineralized, are the source of the gold for each type.

INNOKO DISTRICT

The Innoko district, in the upper drainage area of the Innoko River between lat 62°50′ and 63°15′ N. and long 156°10′ and 156°50′ W., lies immediately northeast of the Iditarod River. The Beaver Mountains form the drainage divide between the Innoko and Iditarod Rivers.

Gold was discovered in the gravels of Ganes Creek in 1906, and despite its remoteness the new camp attracted permanent settlers (Maddren, 1911, p. 236) who began gold production in 1907 that continued uninterrupted through 1957. Most of the mining was in the Ophir, Spruce, Little, Ganes, and Yankee Creek areas (Maddren, 1911, p. 246). The Innoko is a placer district and through 1959 produced a total of 518,565 ounces of gold. Most of the placers are in the gravels of the present streams or in bench deposits.

Argillaceous beds of Late Cretaceous and Eocene age underlie most of the Innoko district, except for a small area in the northeastern part where several small bodies of quartz monzonite and basic intrusives cut the sedimentary rocks (Mertie and Harrington, 1924, p. 30, 62, 69, pl. 4).

KANTISHNA DISTRICT

The Kantishna district is an area of about 4,500 square miles, between lat 63°25′ and 65°00′ N. and long 149°00′ and 151°10′ W., that includes part of the Alaska Range foothills on the south and part of the Tanana lowlands on the north. It is bounded on the east by the Nenana River and on the west by the western tributaries of the Kantishna River.

The Tanana River valley became well populated by miners and prospectors during the early part of the Fairbanks rush, and soon the rich gravels in the Kantishna district were found. In 1904 gold was found along Toklat River and the following year a flood of hopeful gold seekers left Fairbanks for the new district (Capps, 1919, p. 75). Soon several thousand people swarmed into the area, nearly all streams were staked, and several towns were built. It soon became apparent that the deposits, though rich, were shallow and of small area, so that a dismal exodus began and the population of the district quickly dwindled to about 50 (Capps, 1919, p. 76). Those who remained were able to maintain small production from the placers, and the district was still active on that scale in 1957. In 1904–5 lode deposits of lead-silver and antimony were found, and in 1921 gold, copper, and mercury lode deposits were discovered. The antimony deposits were worked sporadically during 1936–55, but the other lode deposits never achieved any significance (Reed, 1961, p. 27–28). Total gold production from the district from 1905 through 1957 was 45,925 ounces, all from placers. No activity was reported in 1958–59.

The oldest rock in the district is the Birch Creek Schist of Precambrian age (Wells, 1933a, p. 343). This schist is succeeded by younger schists, phyllites, and gneisses, composing the Totatlanika Schist of pre-Devonian age and the Tonzona Group of Devonian or Silurian age. Pre-Tertiary greenstone, Mesozoic limestone, a sequence of Tertiary fresh-water sediments, tuffs, and flows, and Quaternary glacial, glaciofluvial, and fluvial deposits complete the sedimentary column in the district (Capps, 1919, p. 22–23). The pre-Tertiary and lower Tertiary rocks have been deformed into east-trending folds parallel to the axis of the Alaska Range to the south of the district (Capps, 1919, p. 22).

The productive placers of the district are along the streams that radiate outward from the higher parts of the Kantishna Hills. The gold was believed by Capps (1919, p. 79) to be derived from erosion of small quartz veins that cut the Birch Creek Schist.

KOYUKUK DISTRICT

The Koyukuk district, between lat 67°00′ and 68°00′ N. and long 149°00′ and 150°50′ W., drained by the north, middle, and south forks of Koyukuk River, is often considered to be one of the most northerly in the world.

Some time between 1885 and 1890 placer gold was first found in this district on the sand bars along the Koyukuk River. Maddren (1913a, p. 76) reported that by 1898 at least $4,000 in gold had been mined from them; however, Smith (1933, p. 96) did not report production from the Koyukuk district until 1900. Nearly all the upper reaches of the Koyukuk tributaries have been prospected, and the results have been rewarding. The district was still active in 1959, though only on a small scale. Total production from the district through 1959 was about 278,000 ounces, all from placers. Promising lode deposits of gold have not been found in this district.

The most abundant bedrock in the district is the ubiquitous Birch Creek Schist of Precambrian or early Paleozoic age. The schist is exposed in two belts—one in the southern part of the Endicott Mountains and the other in the Hodzana highland area, between the Yukon River and the Koyukuk valley. Numerous dikes and small intrusives of granitic composition, probably Mesozoic in age, cut the schist (Maddren, 1913a, p. 34–36). Exposed in the central and northern parts of the district are two sequences of Paleozoic rocks: one is of Devonian(?) age and consists of greenstone, slate, chert, and limestone; the other is a section of crystalline limestone and mica schist of Carboniferous(?) age. Underlying the western part of the district are Mesozoic sedimentary rocks represented by Cretaceous limestone and calcareous sandstone interbedded with basic flows and pyroclastics (Maddren, 1913a, p. 50–55).

Pleistocene gravel covers large areas in the district, including all the major stream valleys. Recent deposits include gravels along present stream courses.

The placer deposits are in present stream gravels and bench gravels; some of them are buried. Maddren (1913a, p. 83) considered that the gold in the placers was derived from the Birch Creek Schist. Auriferous pyrite occurs in carbonaceous phyllite facies and free gold is found in quartz veinlets and stringers that cut the micaceous quartz schist facies. The gold was transported by streams and glaciers and later concentrated by further stream action into the placer deposits.

MARSHALL DISTRICT

The Marshall district is between lat 61°40′ and 62°00′ N. and long 161°30′ and 162°10′ W., along the lower Yukon River.

During the early days, just after the discoveries at Nome, the port of St. Michael was the terminus and supply center for prospectors embarking on trips up the Yukon River or along the coastline of the Seward Peninsula. A portage to the upper Anvik River, one of the Yukon tributaries, greatly shortened the trip to the goldfields at Dawson and elsewhere on the upper Yukon by eliminating travel along several hundred miles of meanders on the lower Yukon River. Thus, except for a few itinerant prospectors and traders, the Marshall district was rather thinly settled and sparsely prospected.

In 1913, however, gold was discovered on Wilson Creek in the Marshall district (Harrington, 1918, p. 56). The usual rush followed. Additional placers were found on Willow Creek, and the first production was in 1914. Lode deposits were found in 1914, and a small shipment was made that same year (Harrington, 1918, p. 57). The quartz veins did not warrant extensive development; at any rate, lode production for the district is unrecorded.

After the first few years of near-bonanza placer production, activity slackened, was rejuvenated briefly in the late 1930's, then declined after World War II. In 1957 there was only small-scale activity in the Marshall district. Total recorded gold production through 1957 was 113,200 ounces, all from placers. The district was idle in 1958 and 1959.

Much of the bedrock in the Marshall district is greenstone and intercalated sedimentary rocks of Carboniferous age (Harrington, 1918, p. 22–26). These rocks are cut by several stocks and dikes of granite, quartz diorite, and dacite of possible Jurassic or Tertiary age (Harrington, 1918, p. 45–46). Cretaceous sandstone and argillite, somewhat metamorphosed, occur adjacent to the greenstone throughout much of the district. The most abundant rock type exposed in the district is the unconsolidated material deposited during Quaternary time by the debris-laden streams issuing from the huge glaciers of the interior of the Yukon River basin (Harrington, 1918, p. 36–44).

NABESNA DISTRICT

The Nabesna district is between lat 62°10′ and 62°30′ N. and long 142°40′ and 143°10′ W.

Gold had been known in this district since 1899, but there was no significant production until 1931 when the first shipments were made from the Nabesna mine, the lone producer of the district. Credit for the discovery is given to a bear who exposed the moss-covered outcrop of the principal vein while digging out a gopher. The property was developed by C. F. Whithan, who formed the Nabesna Mining Co. in 1929 and began shipping ore in 1931 (Wayland, 1943, p. 176–177). By 1939, much of the vein was worked out and in 1940 production halted. Additional exploration and development work in the district apparently was unsuccessful for there has been no further production reported. In its brief history the Nabesna district produced about 63,300 ounces of gold, all from lodes.

The rocks in the vicinity of the mine consist of the Nabesna Limestone of Late Triassic age and basaltic lavas and shale of possible Permian age (Wayland, 1943, p. 177). A few small bodies of quartz diorite cut the limestone. The thick Wrangell Lava of Tertiary and Quaternary ages unconformably overlies these rocks. Moraine and fluvial sediments of Quaternary age are found in all the stream valleys.

The ore bodies are in contact-metamorphosed limestone near the largest of the quartz diorite intrusives (Wayland, 1943, p. 183–191). Ore deposits are of three types: bodies of magnetite with pyrite, calcite, and some gold; veins and bodies of pyrrhotite with minor pyrite and gold; and gold-bearing pyrite veins in tactite or along intrusive contacts. The third type is the most important and has accounted for most of the production of the Nabesna mine.

RAMPART DISTRICT

The Rampart district, between lat 65°15′ and 65°40′ N. and long 149°40′ and 150°40′ W., joins the Hot Springs district on the north.

Gold was discovered in the gravels of Minook Creek and Hess River and their tributaries in 1882, but for the succeeding 10 years nothing was done to develop the placers. In the early 1890's more discoveries were made and finally in 1896 the first mining was done on Little Minook Creek (Hess, in Prindle and Hess, 1906, p. 26). Smith (1933, table facing p. 96), however, does not report any production until 1904. The district reached its peak of activity before 1910; after that time, production decreased, and in the 1950's only a few hundred ounces per year were mined. Total gold production through 1959 was 86,800 ounces from placers. There are no workable lode deposits in the district.

The geology of the district, as summarized by Mertie (1934, p. 172–173), is chiefly the same as that of the Hot Springs district. Consolidated sedimentary rocks—which range in age from pre-Ordovician to Tertiary and include sandstone, shale, conglomerate, chert, limestone, and coal-bearing rocks—compose the bulk of the bedrock. These are intruded locally by granite of Tertiary age. The major placers are along Minook Creek and its tributaries and along Quail Creek, one of the tributaries of Troublesome Creek.

Several prominent stream terraces containing low-grade gold deposits occur along the Minook Creek valley, but most production has come from gravels at present stream levels along Little Minook Creek (Mertie, 1934, p. 181).

RUBY DISTRICT

The Ruby district is between lat 63°40′ and 64°45′ N. and long 154°40′ and 156°20′ W.

The first discoveries of gold in this district were made in 1907 along Ruby Creek (Mertie, 1936, p. 144). These placers were soon exhausted, but other discoveries in 1910 along Long Creek and in 1912 along Poorman Creek kept the district flourishing (Mertie, 1936, p. 145, 159). Underground drifting, sluicing, and hydraulic methods have been used to mine the gravels. Although production decreased somewhat in recent years, the district was still producing substantially through 1959. Total gold production through 1959 was 389,100 ounces, all from placers.

Undifferentiated metamorphic rocks, including schist, phyllite, slate, quartzite, chert, and limestone, are mainly of Paleozoic age and are the predominant bedrock types in the Ruby district (Mertie and Harrington, 1924, p. 12). A complex of greenstone derived from basic igneous rocks, believed to be Mississippian in age (Mertie and Harrington, 1924, p. 59), is exposed throughout the district. A few granite stocks of Mesozoic(?) age intrude both the Paleozoic rock units. The generalized structure is an anticline trending northeast and plunging to the southwest.

Numerous quartz veins are in the country rocks;

some undoubtedly contain gold and could be regarded as the source of the gold in the placers. The distribution of the placers, however, does not directly coincide with areas of abundant veins, so that no clear relationship is apparent (Mertie and Harrington, 1924, p. 121). Nearly all the placer deposits are buried discontinuous bodies that occur mostly in fairly wide valleys. They were formed by streams older than those now occupying the valleys (Mertie, 1936, p. 144).

RICHARDSON DISTRICT

The Richardson (or Tenderfoot) district is between lat 64°15′ and 64°25′ N. and long 146°00′ and 146°40′ W., about 60 miles southeast of Fairbanks, along the Tanana River.

This is a little-known district, about which only a few brief accounts have been written. According to Prindle (in Prindle and Katz, 1913, p. 141) gold was discovered in the gravels of Tenderfoot Creek in 1905 and for the following 4 years the gold production was probably "$300,000 or $400,000 annually." Smith (1933, table facing p. 96), however, reported a much more conservative figure. Productive deposits also were found along Buckeye and Democrat Creeks. Activity declined after the initial boom period and in recent years the production, which is low, has been combined with that of the Fairbanks district. Total recorded production for the district through 1959 was 64,300 ounces, all from placers.

Prindle (in Prindle and Katz, 1913, p. 140–141) noted that the bedrock in the district is Birch Creek Schist of Precambrian age (Mertie, 1937, p. 46). Numerous small quartz veins, some of which carry gold and sulfides, occur in the schist. Just west of the district are some large granitic masses (Prindle, in Prindle and Katz, 1913, p. 140–141). The placers are along present streams in the area.

TOLOVANA DISTRICT

The Tolovana district is between lat 65°20′ and 65°45′ N. and long 147°50′ and 149°00′ W. in the upper drainage of the Tolovana River, a tributary of the Tanana.

Brooks (1916, p. 201) reported that placer gold had been found in this area as early as 1892 but that no interest was aroused until 1914, when placers along Livengood Creek were discovered. Mining began in 1915 and was substantially increased the following year with the development of the deposits on Livengood Creek and others on Gertrude, Ruth, Lillian, and Olive Creeks (Mertie, 1918, p. 256). The district continued to prosper and it was still productive on a small scale in 1959. Total gold production through 1959 was 375,000 ounces, all from placers.

The bedrock in the Tolovana district is distributed in several bands or belts that cross the area in a northeasterly direction. The oldest rocks in the district crop out in the southeast; the rocks become successively younger in a northwesterly direction. Briefly, the bedrock units consist of the Tatalina Group, of Cambrian or Precambrian age, Devonian and Silurian(?) sedimentary and igneous rocks, a chert unit of Devonian or Carboniferous age, and Carboniferous arenaceous and argillaceous units (Mertie, 1918, p. 230–256).

Igneous rocks, chiefly basic, occupy a considerable area in the northwestern part of the district. Small bodies of granitic intrusives are scattered throughout most of the district. In the stream valleys, unconsolidated deposits of sand and gravel were deposited during several stages in the Quaternary geomorphic cycle. The earlier of these are only remnants and are seen as benches along the valley walls (Mertie, 1918, p. 230–231).

Gold placers in the district are in bench and stream deposits (Mertie, 1918, p. 259). The bench deposits have been the more productive. The gold in the placers of Tolovana was derived from low-grade lode deposits at the heads of many of the tributary streams (Mertie, 1918, p. 274–275).

PRINCE WILLIAM SOUND REGION

The Prince William Sound region is along the southern coast of Alaska, immediately east of the Kenai Peninsula. It is a constricted area between the rugged Chugach Mountains on the north and that part of the Gulf of Alaska known as Prince William Sound. In this region copper and gold are the chief mineral commodities, and the notable mining districts are Port Wells, Port Valdez, and Ellamar. Only Port Valdez is shown on the index map (fig. 5) because it is the only district that has produced any significant quantities of gold.

The earliest record of gold production in the Prince William Sound region was in 1894, when some placers were worked on a small scale near Port Valdez (Brooks, A. H., in Grant and Higgins, 1910, p. 72). A few years later other small placers were found in the Port Wells district. Auriferous veins were found here in 1907, and in the following 6 years numerous properties were developed and small shipments were made (Johnson, 1914, p. 214–215). The Cliff mine, staked in 1906 in the Port Valdez district, became the largest gold producer in the district in the early years (Moffit, 1954, p. 228, 304).

The copper ores at Ellamar and La Touche Island carry variable amounts of gold (Grant and Higgins, 1910, p. 71), but the amount produced from this source could not be determined.

Gold production from this region reached its zenith before 1920. Thereafter, except for a slight revival in the late 1930's, output has dwindled. No production was reported for 1957–59. Total recorded gold production was 137,600 ounces, all from lode mines or as a byproduct from copper mines. Production data for individual districts have not been found. It is fairly certain that the Port Valdez district has produced most of the lode gold from this region; however, it is not known how much of the total gold production was a byproduct from copper ores of Ellamar, La Touche, or elsewhere.

Numerous fiords along the irregular coastline and glaciated islands that dot Prince William Sound give evidence of a once extensive ice covering in this region (Grant and Higgins, 1910, p. 18–19). In the northern part of the region, especially in the Port Wells district, several ice tongues still travel far enough down the valleys to meet the sea.

The rocks of this region consist of two loosely defined groups of low-rank metasedimentary rocks of Mesozoic age, distinguished from one another by minor differences in gross lithologic characteristics and by differences in metamorphism (Moffit, 1954, p. 234–250). These rocks have been complexly folded, faulted, and intruded by basaltic and granitic igneous rocks.

The Valdez Group is composed predominantly of graywacke, slate, and argillite, with subordinate siliceous and carbonaceous slate, feldspathic quartzite, and a few beds of conglomerate and impure limestone. The rocks are metamorphosed locally to schist and phyllite. The Orca Group consists dominantly of slate and graywacke, and in places greenstone and conglomerate are major components. Though the rocks of the Orca Group are intensely folded and faulted, their metamorphism seems to be related to igneous intrusions rather than regional tectonism. The distinction and separation of the Valdez and Orca Groups cannot be consistently made everywhere in the region (Moffit, 1954, p. 234–273). The ages and stratigraphic relations of these two groups have not been clearly established; however, the meager paleontological evidence suggests a Late Cretaceous age for both groups (Moffit, 1954, p. 273–275).

The gold-bearing quartz veins of the Port Valdez district are found in slates and graywackes of both the Valdez and Orca Groups. At Port Wells, gold occurs in quartz veins and stringers that occupy fissures in slate, graywacke, and conglomerate. Mineralization probably is late Mesozoic or Tertiary in age, closely associated with granitic intrusions (Moffit, 1954, p. 295). Vein minerals are pyrite, galena, sphalerite, pyrrhotite, arsenopyrite, stibnite, chalcopyrite, gold, and silver in a gangue of quartz.

The copper deposits of Prince William Sound, which have yielded moderate amounts of gold, occur as impregnations or replacement bodies usually along zones of shearing in the country rock. Chalcopyrite and pyrrhotite are ubiquitous, pyrite is common, and galena, sphalerite, bornite, chalcocite, native copper, cuprite, and malachite are present in small amounts. The nonmetallic minerals in these deposits are quartz, calcite, epidote, and chlorite (Grant and Higgins, 1910, p. 53–54).

ARIZONA

Arizona, from 1860 through 1965, produced a total of about 13,321,000 ounces of gold and in 1965 ranked eighth among the gold-producing States. As in the other Western States, the first discoveries of gold were placer deposits. Shortly afterward lode deposits were discovered in most districts, and they furnished the bulk of the early gold output of the State. From 1900 through 1965, however, most of Arizona's annual gold production came as a byproduct from the large-scale mining of porphyry copper ores (fig. 6).

Unless stated to the contrary, throughout this chapter on Arizona, production data to 1932 are from Elsing and Heineman (1936) and for 1932–65 from U.S. Bureau of Mines (1933–66).

Deposits of silver and copper in Arizona were known to the Indians and Spaniards long before the Territory was acquired by the United States (S. R. E. Heineman, in Arizona Bureau of Mines, 1938, p. 26–27). Because of the inaccessibility of the area, lack of water, and Indian raids, only a small amount of prospecting was done by Americans in the 1850's, mostly near the old Mexican settlements of Tucson and Tubac, and in the Dome (Gila City) district where rich placers were discovered in 1858 (Wilson, 1952, p. 18). Little or no lode gold was mined in these early years. During the Civil War, prospectors among the California troops in Arizona organized parties to hunt for gold. In 1862 rich placer deposits were found near the Colorado River at La Paz in western Yuma County, and from 1862 to 1870 other placer deposits were found in Yavapai County. Included among these were the Weaver-Rich Hill, Lynx Creek-Walker, Hassayampa-

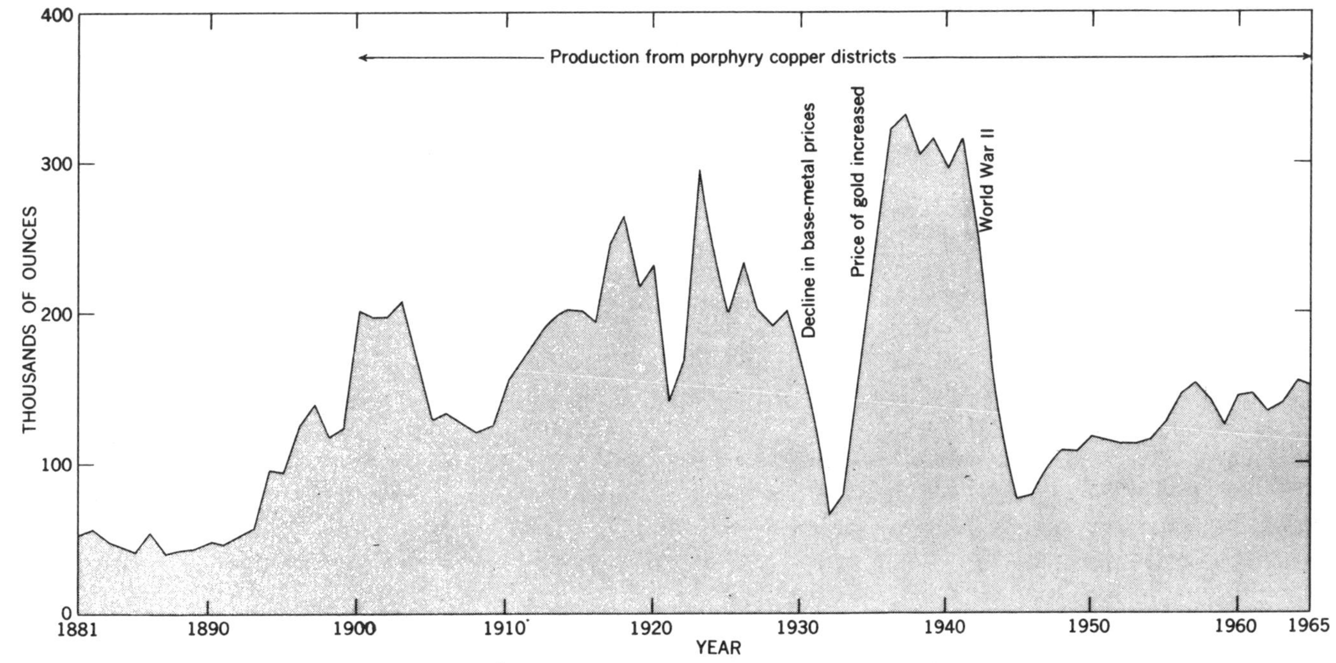

FIGURE 6.—Annual gold production of Arizona, 1881–1965. Sources of data: U.S. Geological Survey (1883–1924) and U.S. Bureau of Mines (1925-34, 1933–66). Production reported in dollar value was converted to ounces at prevailing price per ounce.

Groom Creek, Big Bug, and several smaller deposits in the Bradshaw Mountains (Wilson, 1952, p. 15, 38). In 1863 also many gold lodes were discovered in the Bradshaw Mountains in Yavapai County and in the Oatman district in Mohave County. With the end of the Civil War, troops were withdrawn from the territory, and warfare between the white settlers and the Indians prevented much mining until 1872, when a truce was declared (Tenney, 1934, p. 16).

High prices for silver and copper in the 1870's and the completion of two transcontinental railroads—the Southern Pacific and the Atchison, Topeka and Santa Fe—across Arizona in 1881 stimulated exploration which resulted in the discovery of many major deposits. In the general depression of 1884–93 and after the demonitization of silver in 1893, copper and silver mining declined but gold mining increased. By the early 1900's commodity prices again became favorable, and several companies were organized to mine the large low-grade porphyry copper deposits that have been the principal source of gold in Arizona (Tenney, 1934, p. 17).

In Arizona 42 districts in 10 counties produced in excess of 10,000 ounces of gold (fig. 7); many additional districts are credited with smaller amounts. According to Wilson, Cunningham, and Butler (1934, p. 13), nearly 80 percent of the State's lode gold production and much of the placer gold has come from deposits that occur in a northeast-trending belt called the mountain region by Ransome (1903, p. 15–16), which is about 65 miles wide and borders the southwest margin of the Colorado Plateau. Within this belt the deformed Precambrian rocks have been tilted, intensely faulted, and intruded by masses of igneous rocks. In the desert region, southwest of the mountain region, the deposits are widely scattered.

The gold deposits of Arizona are of several types. In the San Francisco and Kofa districts gold deposits occur in epithermal quartz-calcite veins of Tertiary age. The Weaver, Vulture, Harquahala, Gila City, Wallapai, and Dos Cabezas districts are representatives of mesothermal vein systems of Mesozoic or Tertiary age with sulfide-quartz veins rich in silver and gold. In the porphyry copper deposits—in the districts of Ajo, Bisbee, Clifton-Morenci, Globe-Miami, Ray, San Manuel, and Superior—the ore bodies are of late Mesozoic or Tertiary age and are in intrusive bodies of quartz monzonite and the adjacent country rocks. The porphyry copper deposit at Jerome is of Precambrian age. Replacement deposits, rich in gold, silver, and base metals, occur near granitic intrusives in the Tombstone, Big Bug, Turquoise, Banner, and Agua Fria districts.

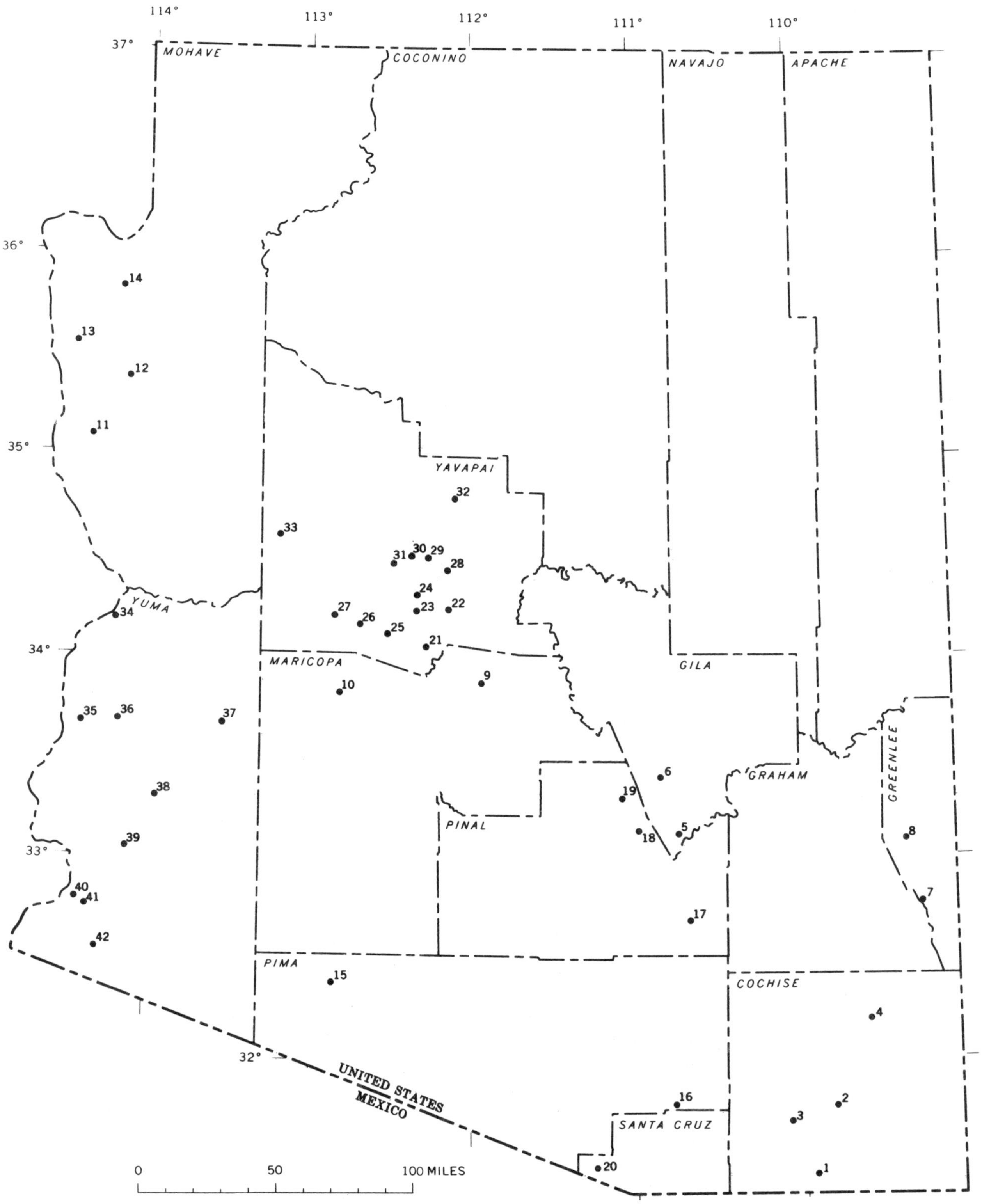

FIGURE 7.—Gold-mining districts of Arizona.

COCHISE COUNTY

Cochise County, third among the gold-producing counties of Arizona, produced approximately 2,723,000 ounces of gold from the beginning of mining in the county in about 1879 to the end of 1959. Of this amount, about $24,275,000 (1,174,408 ounces) was a byproduct of copper ores, mainly from the Bisbee district (Wilson and others, 1934, p. 117), and about 950 ounces was from placers. Other districts that have produced more than 10,000 ounces of gold are the Turquoise (Courtland, Gleeson), Dos Cabezas, and Tombstone.

BISBEE DISTRICT

The Bisbee (or Warren) district is in the southeastern Mule Mountains, in the southern part of the county, immediately north of the Mexican border. Although the Bisbee district was the largest gold producer in Arizona in 1959, most of its gold was a byproduct of copper ore.

Though lead carbonate ore was discovered in the district about 1876, there was little activity in the area until after 1880 when rail connections, generally favorable business conditions, and copper prices encouraged prospecting. The Copper Queen ore body, found in 1877, was developed in 1880. In subsequent years the Copper Queen Mining Co., under the control of Phelps, Dodge, & Co., acquired other properties in the district and became the leading producer (Ransome, 1904, p. 13–15). In 1900 the Calumet and Arizona Co., another major producer, was organized. In 1902 a custom smelter was erected at Douglas, and some of the smaller mining companies, among them the Shattuck and Denn, were started. At the end of 1931 the two largest companies, the Copper Queen and the Calumet and Arizona, were consolidated as the Phelps Dodge Corp., Copper Queen Branch (J. B. Tenney, in International Geological Congress, 1935, p. 222). In 1947 the Denn mine was sold to the Phelps Dodge Corp., and in 1949 the custom mill of the Shattuck Denn Mining Corp. was closed, leaving the Phelps Dodge Corp. as the only large producer in the district. Phelps Dodge maintained large-scale operations through 1959.

The gold production of the Bisbee district before 1895 was not ascertained. From 1895 through 1929 the district produced 1,110,058 ounces of gold (J. B. Tenney, in International Geological Congress, 1935, p. 222) and from 1930 to 1959, a total of 1,082,765 ounces was produced. Total gold production through 1959 was about 2,193,000 ounces.

The oldest rocks in the Bisbee district are the Pinal Schist and a granite of Precambrian age. These are unconformably overlain by about 5,250 feet of Paleozoic rocks which in turn are unconformably overlain by about 4,750 feet of Cretaceous sedimentary rocks. The Paleozoic rocks consist of about 430 feet of Cambrian quartzite, succeeded by about 4,800 feet of limestones of Cambrian, Devonian, and Carboniferous age. In pre-Cretaceous time, folding and faulting occurred, and in post-Cretaceous time the rocks were warped and dislocated by thrusts and normal faults of moderate throw (Ransome, 1904, p. 24–73, 106–108). Dikes, sills, and stocks of granite porphyry intrude the Paleozoic rocks, but their relation to the Cretaceous rocks is not clearly revealed (Tenney, in Ransome and others, 1932, p. 46–47; O. N. Rove, in Newhouse, 1942, p. 211–212). The main stock of granite porphyry is exposed on Sacramento Hill, the principal and most productive center of mineralization. The stock was intruded in the plane of the east-trending Dividend fault, a dominant structural feature of the district. Surrounding the intrusive mass is a zone, ranging from a few feet to 1,000 feet in thickness, of contact breccia composed of rounded and angular fragments of the intruded rocks. The border of the porphyry, the contact

---

Cochise County:
1, Bisbee; 2, Turquoise; 3, Tombstone; 4, Dos Cabezas.
Gila County:
5, Banner; 6, Globe-Miami.
Greenlee County:
7, Ash Peak; 8, Clifton-Morenci.
Maricopa County:
9, Cave Creek; 10, Vulture.
Mohave County:
11, San Francisco; 12, Wallapai; 13, Weaver; 14, Gold Basin.
Pima County:
15, Ajo; 16, Greaterville.
Pinal County:
17, Mammoth; 18, Ray; 19, Superior.
Santa Cruz County:
20, Oro Blanco.
Yavapai County:
21, Tiptop; 22, Black Canyon; 23, Pine Grove-Tiger; 24, Peck; 25, Black Rock; 26, Weaver-Rich Hill; 27, Martineez; 28, Agua Fria; 29, Big Bug; 30, Lynx Creek-Walker; 31, Hassayampa-Groom Creek; 32, Jerome; 33, Eureka.
Yuma County:
34, Cienega; 35, La Paz; 36, Plomosa; 37, Ellsworth; 38, Kofa; 39, Castle Dome; 40, Laguna; 41, Dome; 42, Fortuna.

FIGURE 7.—Continued

breccia, and the adjacent limestone are all silicified. Surrounding this silicified zone is a chloritized zone that grades outward into a marbleized zone in the limestone.

The most productive ore zone lies south of the Dividend fault and the ore bodies are arranged in a semicircle around the stock on Sacramento Hill. The copper ore occurs in irregular replacement bodies in the Paleozoic limestones, in the contact breccia, and as disseminated sulfides in the granite porphyry (Tenney, in Ransome and others, 1932, p. 56–57; C. Trischka, in Arizona Bureau of Mines, 1938, p. 38–40). A few deposits are at some distance from Sacramento Hill and are associated with small porphyry bodies (J. B. Tenney, in International Geological Congress, 1935, p. 228).

The oxidized ores consist of a blanket of copper carbonates, cuprite, copper, limonite, and local chalcocite that extends from the surface to depths of several hundred feet, and in one place to more than 2,000 feet (Tenney, in Ransome and others, 1932, p. 61). The zone of secondary sulfide enrichment contains bornite, chalcopyrite, chalcocite, and a little sphalerite and galena. The disseminated primary ore contains quartz, pyrite, chalcopyrite, and bornite. Most of the gold recovered in current mining operations is very fine grained and is probably allied with the sulfides. Ransome (1904, p. 121) reported concentrations of native gold in the Cretaceous Glance Conglomerate and Morita Formation as well as in Recent placers derived from weathering of these formations. The main ore deposit at Sacramento Hill forms an inclined blanket which is enriched toward the bottom, where the contact with the sparsely mineralized, sericitized porphyry is sharp (J. B. Tenney, in International Geological Congress, 1935, p. 228).

DOS CABEZAS DISTRICT

The Dos Cabezas district is 18 miles southeast of Wilcox in the Dos Cabezas Mountains.

Gold deposits discovered before the Civil War were worked intermittently after the 1870's and yielded about $182,000 (8,835 ounces) through 1932 (Wilson and others, 1934, p. 117). The first workings were probably in the Teviston placers on the north side of the mountains, though most of the gold came from lodes rich in copper, silver, and lead near the village of Dos Cabezas. The district was most active during 1914–20 and 1931–36. No production was reported for 1956–59. Total gold production was at least 15,000 ounces.

In the Dos Cabezas Mountains a complexly folded and faulted section of Precambrian granite and gneiss and Paleozoic and Cretaceous sedimentary rocks is cut by granitic intrusives of Late Cretaceous or Tertiary age (Cooper and others, 1959). The ore deposits occur in veins in the Precambrian granite and Cretaceous sedimentary rocks and are apparently related to rhyolite porphyry and diabase dikes of Tertiary age. Vein minerals are galena, pyrite, sphalerite, and chalcopyrite in a gangue of coarse-textured, white to grayish-white quartz. Most of the gold is in the galena.

TOMBSTONE DISTRICT

The Tombstone district, about 20 miles northwest of Bisbee in the Tombstone Hills, includes a group of low scattered mountains that extend northwestward from the Mule Mountains. Ores rich in silver were discovered in the Tombstone district in 1877, and the mines and camp developed rapidly. Tombstone produced more than $5 million worth of ore per year in 1881 and 1882, but by 1886 many of the larger ore bodies were either mined out or mined to water level and production decreased sharply, although the district was a steady producer through 1953. During 1879–86 the yield of silver, gold, and lead ore was valued at about $19 million (Butler and others, 1938, p. 38).

By 1900 many of the properties had been combined under one ownership, and an attempt was made to develop the deposits below water level, but this did not prove profitable and was abandoned in 1911 (Butler and others, 1938, p. 38–48). Production was stimulated during World War I and by the increased price of gold in 1934, but from 1948 through 1959 the district was unimportant.

Total gold production through 1959 was about 271,200 ounces, most of which was mined from 1879 through 1932 (Wilson and others, 1934, p. 122).

The oldest rocks in the district are scattered patches of Precambrian Pinal Schist and of albite granite, which are overlain by Paleozoic sedimentary rocks that include the Bolsa Quartzite and Abrigo Limestone of Cambrian age, the Martin Limestone of Devonian age, the Escabrosa and Horquilla Limestones of Mississippian and Pennsylvanian ages respectively, the Earp Formation of Pennsylvanian and Permian age, and the Colina Limestone and Epitaph Dolomite of Permian age. These rocks were folded and faulted in post-Paleozoic pre-Cretaceous time, and then the Bisbee Formation of Cretaceous age was deposited. At the end of Cretaceous time the rocks were cut by thrust faults that trend east and northwest (Gilluly, 1956, p. 128–132). The Uncle Sam Porphyry of early Tertiary age was injected along a thrust, and slightly later the Schieffelin Granodiorite of probable early or middle Tertiary age (Gilluly, 1956, p. 104) intruded the area. Patches of volcanics of Miocene age are exposed to the east of Tombstone. In Pliocene time the rocks were again faulted, this time by great normal faults that are responsible for the present major topographical features (Gilluly, 1956, p. 158–160).

The ore deposits are associated with dikes that are believed to be related to the Schieffelin Granodiorite (Butler and others, 1938, p. 26–28). Ore occurs as replacement bodies in limestones and porphyry, and as fissure fillings. The oxidized ores contain hematite, limonite, cerussite, horn silver, gold and locally abundant argentiferous galena, sphalerite, pyrite, alabandite, malachite, chrysocolla, psilomelane, and wulfenite. Most of the gold occurs as native gold in very fine particles (Wilson and others, 1934, p. 123–124).

TURQUOISE DISTRICT

The Turquoise (Courtland, Gleeson) mining district lies on the east side of the Dragoon Mountains, about 14 miles due east of Tombstone and about 18 miles north-northeast of Bisbee. During the 1880's mines near Gleeson produced oxidized ore rich in gold, silver, lead, and copper, and in 1901 mining of copper deposits near Courtland was started. Mixed oxide-sulfide ore was mined on a large scale from 1912 through 1918, but thereafter activity declined and remained at a low level through 1955. The district was idle from 1956 through 1959. Early gold production figures were not ascertained, but from 1908 through 1955 the district produced about 70,000 ounces.

The northwest-trending Dragoon Mountains are composed primarily of contorted and faulted Paleozoic sedimentary rocks and intrusive masses of monzonitic and granitic rocks of Triassic or Jurassic and Cretaceous or Tertiary age. The Paleozoic formations are the Bolsa Quartzite and Abrigo Limestone of Cambrian age, the Escabrosa Limestone of Mississippian age, the Horquilla Limestones of Pennsylvanian age, the Earp Formation of Late Pennsylvanian and Permian age, and the Colina Limestone and Epitaph Dolomite of Permian age (Gilluly, 1956, p. 14–49). In the interval between the end of the Paleozoic and the beginning of the Cretaceous the rocks were deformed and intruded by masses of Gleeson Quartz Monzonite, Copper Belle Monzonite Porphyry, and Turquoise Granite, all of Triassic or Jurassic age. The Sugarloaf Quartz Latite was probably intruded at the end of Cretaceous time. In early Tertiary time the rocks were displaced by strong northwest-trending thrust faults, and in Pliocene time normal faulting occurred which formed the major topographic features of the present (Gilluly, 1956, p. 159, 160).

The ore bodies are pyritic replacement deposits in limestone, shale, and porphyry along thrust faults. Some of the deposits are oxidized and consist of masses of iron and copper oxides containing cavities lined with chrysocolla, malachite, and azurite. The unoxidized deposits are mainly pyrite and chalcopyrite with local accumulations of bornite, sphalerite, and galena (Ransome, 1913). The gold occurs as very finely divided particles in all the ores; in the oxidized deposits some gold is contained in cerargyrite (Wilson, 1927, p. 39, 50).

GILA COUNTY

Gila County, in mountainous east-central Arizona, ranks eighth among the gold-producing counties of the State with a total of about 240,500 ounces produced through 1959. Most of the gold has been a byproduct of copper ores mined from the Globe-Miami district; a lesser amount has come from copper ores of the Banner district. Placers have yielded an insignificant amount.

BANNER DISTRICT

The Banner (Christmas) district lies in the extreme southern tip of Gila County at the southeast end of the Dripping Springs Mountains.

Many of the deposits have been known and worked intermittently since the 1870's, but little ore was shipped before 1900 (Ross, 1925, p. 29). The district is noted for its copper mines from which lead, silver, and gold were produced as byproducts. The Christmas mine, discovered in 1880 and operated intermittently through 1954, is the major mine in the district. Total gold production from 1905 through 1959 was about 26,000 ounces.

Small patches of Precambrian granite are exposed beneath a thick section of the Apache Group of late Precambrian age, Martin Limestone of Devonian age, and Tornado Limestone of Carboniferous age. The area of the Christmas mine is blanketed by sandstone, breccia, andesite, and basalt of Cretaceous age, which are overlain by patches of Tertiary bedded rocks consisting of tuff, conglomerate, basalt, and rhyolite. The Paleozoic and Cretaceous rocks throughout the district are cut by dikes and small masses of quartz-hornblende diorite and quartz-mica diorite of Cretaceous age. The rocks were slightly folded in post-Pennsylvanian time; more pronounced folding occurred in Late

Cretaceous time. This was followed by faulting which continued through much of Tertiary time (Ross, 1925, p. 6–29).

The important deposits of the district are pyritic gold deposits in shear zones and contact metamorphic deposits such as those at the Christmas and Landon-Arizona mines. The pyritic gold deposits are principally in Cretaceous volcanic rocks, whereas the contact metamorphic deposits are mostly in Paleozoic carbonate rocks. Both types are near or adjacent to bodies of quartz-mica diorite. Pyrite and local chalcopyrite, magnetite, and specularite are the principal minerals of the pyritic deposits. The contact metamorphic deposits contain a variety of minerals, including magnetite, specularite, chalcopyrite, pyrite, sphalerite, galena, fluorite, chalcedony, and lime silicate minerals. In both types the richest ore has been in the oxidized parts (Ross, 1925, p. 32–39).

GLOBE-MIAMI DISTRICT

The Globe-Miami district, in the foothills of the Pinal and Apache Mountains in the southwestern part of Gila County, is noted primarily for its copper deposits which have yielded considerable amounts of gold, silver, and lead.

The discovery of the Globe claim in 1874 marked the first activity in the area, and for a time thereafter interest centered on small silver and gold prospects. In 1882 copper deposits on the Old Dominion and Buffalo veins were mined. Development was considerably stimulated in 1898, when the first railroad reached Globe. In 1904 development was begun on the large low-grade disseminated copper deposits, which by 1911 were mined on a large scale (Ransome, 1919, p. 19–21). These operations continued with undiminished vigor through 1959 and resulted in an output of copper, lead, silver, gold, and zinc worth more than a billion dollars (Peterson, 1962, p. 81, 82). Total gold production through 1959 was 191,801 ounces.

Lower Precambrian rocks, consisting of the Pinal Schist, Madera Diorite, Ruin Granite, and an unnamed granite, are the oldest rocks exposed in the district. These are overlain by the Apache Group and Troy Quartzite, of late Precambrian age, and are intruded by dikes and sills of diabase of later Precambrian age (A. F. Shride, oral commun., 1962). The Paleozoic System is represented by the Devonian Martin Limestone, the Mississippian Escabrosa Limestone, and the Pennsylvanian Naco Limestone. Late Cretaceous and early Tertiary time was marked by igneous intrusives including the Solitude Granite, Willow Spring Granodiorite, biotite granodiorite of Gold Gulch, and Lost Gulch Quartz Monzonite. These events were followed in later Tertiary time by faulting, intrusion of porphyry dikes, and then emplacement of the Schultze Granite and of a granite porphyry. Extensive mineralization followed this granitic intrusion. The Whitetail Conglomerate of Tertiary(?) age and younger volcanic tuffs and dacite flows or welded tuffs (Peterson, 1962, p. 40–41) unconformably overlie all the older rocks. Faulting again occurred, after which the alluvial Gila Conglomerate of Tertiary and Quaternary age was deposited and later basalt flows were extruded over part of the area.

The most important ore deposits of the Globe-Miami district are disseminated copper deposits in the granite porphyry of the Schultze Granite and in the adjacent country rocks. More than 80 percent of the value of metals mined in the district has come from such deposits, of which the major examples are the Miami-Inspiration, Castle Dome, Copper Cities and Cactus deposits. In mineralized areas the rocks are shattered, and the closely spaced fractures are filled with quartz, pyrite, chalcopyrite, and molybdenite. In areas of more intense mineralization the rocks are argillized and sericitized, and much pyrite has been replaced by chalcocite. Most ore bodies are the result of supergene enrichment in which copper has been leached by ground water from an oxidized zone and redeposited as chalcocite and covellite (Peterson, 1962, p. 82–83). Very small amounts of gold are contained in these ores.

Before 1904 the important deposits of the district were copper-bearing veins of the Old Dominion vein system, in the Globe Hill area. These veins are along faults and fissures that cut Precambrian and Paleozoic sedimentary rocks, and the ore shoots are localized in intervals of favorable host rock, mainly Paleozoic limestone. The principal hypogene minerals of these deposits are quartz, pyrite, chalcopyrite, bornite, and specular hematite; sphalerite, galena, tetrahedrite, and enargite are locally present in small amounts. These ores were also enriched in copper by supergene processes. Considerable native gold was recovered from the gossan of these ores (Peterson, 1962, p. 69, 97, 98).

Deposits of copper silicates and carbonates formed by meteoric waters are important sources of copper in the district, but no gold has been reported from them.

GREENLEE COUNTY

Greenlee County is in southeastern Arizona just west of the New Mexico State boundary. It was organized from part of Graham County in 1910.

Copper is the metal of principal importance, but the county has also produced significant amounts of gold and silver. The total gold production of the county from 1882 through 1959 was about 228,000 ounces, almost all of which was a byproduct from the copper ores of the Clifton-Morenci district, one of the most productive copper camps in Arizona. A small amount of gold was derived from the silver ores in the Ash Peak district.

Placer mining was attempted several times in the Clifton-Morenci district, but the results were discouraging. The total recorded placer gold output is about 1,000 ounces.

ASH PEAK DISTRICT

The Ash Peak district is 12 miles west of Duncan. Records indicate that the deposits were exploited as early as 1907, but only silver was produced during these early operations (Elsing and Heineman, 1936, p. 93; V. C. Heikes, in U.S. Geological Survey, 1907, p. 161). Extensive development work was done in 1918 (Lines, 1940, p. 3), but the results appear to have been discouraging. Mining was resumed from 1936 through 1954, resulting in the recovery of 11,296 ounces of gold. The district was again inactive from 1954 through 1959.

The bedrock of the district consists of a series of rhyolite and andesite flows and tuffs cut by numerous dikes and volcanic plugs of diabase. The ore occurs in a vein that follows a dike intruded along a fault. The ore bodies are fairly continuous and consistent in grade and contain argentite in banded chalcedonic quartz, and varying amounts of calcite, rhodochrosite, pyrite. Lead and copper minerals occur locally. Gold, lead, and copper were produced as byproducts from the silver ores (Lines, 1940, p. 3–4, 24).

CLIFTON-MORENCI DISTRICT

The Clifton-Morenci district is in west-central Greenlee County near the towns of Clifton and Morenci.

The first ore discovery was made in 1872, but early development was hampered by lack of transportation and the activities of hostile Indians. The completion of the Southern Pacific Railroad in 1881 lowered transportation costs sufficiently to permit large-scale mining of the copper ores. The discovery in 1893 of large low-grade copper ores at Copper Mountain at Morenci assured a certain degree of stability and permanence to the future of the district (Lindgren, 1905, p. 33–34).

At first several companies were involved in development and mining, but after several mergers and consolidations, the Phelps Dodge Corp. was the major operator from 1921 through 1959. Total gold production from 1873 through 1959 was about 203,000 ounces; nearly all production was recovered as a byproduct of the copper ores.

The rocks of the district consist of Precambrian granite and schist unconformably overlain by an aggregate thickness of 1,000 feet of limestone, shale, and quartzite which ranges in age from Cambrian to Carboniferous. The Paleozoic rocks are unconformably overlain by shale and sandstone of Cretaceous age. The Cretaceous and older rocks are faulted and intruded by stocks, irregular masses, dikes, and sills of granitic, monzonitic, and dioritic porphyry. The mineral deposits are probably genetically related to these intrusions. The sedimentary rocks and intrusive porphyries are capped by a series of lavas, tuffs, and breccias of Tertiary age. Overlapping all the preceding rocks are extensive deposits of Gila Conglomerate, of Tertiary and Quaternary age.

The ore deposits are of three general types: tabular bodies in limestone or shale near contacts of stocks or dikes, fissure veins, and irregular disseminations in porphyry, quartzite, or other rocks (Lindgren, 1905, p. 97–99). The most important of these are disseminated deposits which have been oxidized and enriched by the supergene copper sulfides. These ore bodies are capped by an oxidized gossan of limonite, secondary quartz, and minor amounts of copper oxides and carbonates. The zone of secondary enrichment, below the oxidized zone, contains abundant chalcocite. The protore consists of pyrite, and small amounts of chalcopyrite and sphalerite (J. B. Tenney, in International Geological Congress, 1935, p. 218–221). Second in importance are the tabular replacement deposits in limestone and shale. Ore bodies are in the oxidized parts of the deposits and consist of masses of malachite, azurite, and cuprite and small amounts of native copper and chalcocite in a gangue of decomposed lime silicate minerals. The fissure vein deposits, which are nearly exhausted, are in fissures in Precambrian granite and Cambrian quartzite closely associated with dikes. The ore minerals are pyrite, chalcopyrite, sphalerite, molybdenite, chalcocite, cuprite, chrysocolla, brochantite, and malachite.

The ores of the district contain relatively insignificant quantities of gold, and the mode of occurrence and mineral associations of the gold are not clearly understood.

MARICOPA COUNTY

Maricopa County, in southwestern Arizona, is a region of broad desert plains and scattered mountain ranges. Most of the gold was mined in the county before 1900 from the Vulture mine in the Vulture district. The Cave Creek district has yielded a small amount of gold. Maricopa County is the fifth largest gold producer of Arizona, and from 1863 through 1959 its total production was about 428,000 ounces. Most of this was from lode mines; only about 3,000 ounces was attributed to placers.

CAVE CREEK DISTRICT

The Cave Creek district, 25 to 45 miles north of Phoenix, was active at least as early as the 1890's, when the Phoenix and Maricopa mines were the major properties and were yielding gold ore. A few copper deposits were also worked before 1900 (Wilson and others, 1934, p. 164–165). Total gold production of the district through 1959 was about 17,000 ounces, most of which was mined before 1900.

VULTURE DISTRICT

The Vulture district is on the south side of the Vulture Mountains, in northwestern Maricopa County.

Gold-bearing quartz veins were discovered in 1863. In 1866 the Vulture mine began operations that continued on a fairly large scale until it was closed in 1888. The mine was active again from 1910 to 1917, during which time it yielded $1,839,375 in ore (Wilson and others, 1934, p. 157, 160). The mine was reopened again in 1931 and remained active until 1945. Total gold production for the district through 1959 was about 366,000 ounces. About 250 ounces of this was from placers; most of the remainder was from the Vulture mine.

The Vulture Mountains are faulted andesitic and rhyolitic lavas of Tertiary age. These rocks overlie Precambrian schist and granite which are intruded by monzonite dikes of probable Mesozoic age. The ore deposits are in veins in the schist (Wilson, 1952, p. 58). The veins are chiefly coarse quartz with pyrite, galena, sphalerite, chalcopyrite, and native gold. Gold also occurs in the galena, and Hutchinson (1921) reported that clean galena concentrates assayed $600 per ton in gold.

MOHAVE COUNTY

Mohave County, in the northwestern corner of Arizona, ranks second among the gold-producing counties of the State, with a total of about 2,461,000 ounces through 1959. More than half of this total came from lode mines of the San Francisco district. Three other districts have produced more than 10,000 ounces: Wallapai, Weaver, and Gold Basin. All these districts are in the west-central part of the county, an area of mountain ranges and valleys that trend north-northwest.

GOLD BASIN DISTRICT

The Gold Basin (Salt Springs) district is in the eastern part of the White Hills west of Hualpai Wash, 40 miles north of Hackberry and 60 miles north of Kingman.

Gold-bearing veins were discovered in the early 1870's, but their development was inhibited by the remoteness of the area and scarcity of fuel and water (Schrader, 1909, p. 118–127). Before 1900, however, the district yielded gold ore worth between $50,000 and $100,000, most of which came from the Eldorado mine. Production continued to 1920 on a small scale and a period of inactivity from 1920 to 1932 followed. A few mines were reopened from 1932 to 1942, but the district was dormant from 1943 to 1959. Total minimum gold production of the district was about 15,000 ounces, most of which was from lode mines.

The ore deposits occur in veins in Precambrian granite and schist. The gold is associated with lead or copper ores that contain pyrite, chalcopyrite, galena, molybdenite, and wolframite. The oxidized parts of the veins contain limonite, malachite, cerussite, and vanadinite (Schrader, 1909, p. 119).

SAN FRANCISCO DISTRICT

The San Francisco district is near the south end of the Black Mountains about 29 miles by road southwest of Kingman. It includes both the Oatman and the Katherine camps; Gold Road and Union Pass are local names applied to parts of the district. Gold is the principal valuable metal in the ore deposits of this district.

Soldiers from Camp Mohave on the Colorado River first discovered gold in the Oatman area in 1863 or 1864, in what is now known as the Moss vein (Ransome, 1923, p. 3–8). Other veins with prominent outcrops were discovered soon afterward. Although some rich ore was taken from a pocket close to the surface in the Moss vein in the first 3 or 4 years, most of the development was discouraging and the Oatman camp was inactive for more than 30 years. The earliest locations in the Katherine area were probably made in the early 1880's (Lausen, 1931, p. 13). In 1901 good ore was found in shallow shafts on what is now known as the Tom Reed vein, and in 1902 a stampede to the district occurred when rich ore was found in the outcrops of the Gold Road vein (Ransome, 1923, p. 4; Schrader, 1909, p. 153–154). A high level of activity continued through 1924. The district was revived from 1930 through 1942, and produced a maximum of 48,000 ounces in 1936. From 1943 through 1951, activity was sporadic and was carried out on a small scale, and from 1952 through 1959 no production was reported. The total gold production of the district from 1897 through 1951 was about 2,045,400 ounces.

In general the geology of the district can be described as an uneven terrain of Precambrian rocks overlain unconformably by a thick section of Tertiary volcanic rocks including trachyte, andesite, latite, rhyolite, and basalt flows. The volcanic rocks are the predominant bedrock in the Oatman area, whereas the Precambrian granitic rocks crop out extensively in the Katherine area (Lausen, 1931, p. 22–23). Bodies of quartz monzonite porphyry, sodic granite porphyry, and rhyolite porphyry intruded Precambrian and the lower Tertiary rocks. The rocks were tilted and faulted, and mineral deposits were emplaced in the fractures in late Tertiary time. Most of the deposits are in the Oatman Andesite, although in the Katherine area important deposits are found in faults in the Precambrian granite (Lausen, 1931, p. 101–124).

The veinfilling is a typical epithermal mineral assemblage. Bands of quartz, calcite, and adularia contain clusters and stringers of native gold, hematite, limonite, manganese oxides, fluorite, and a little pyrite, chalcopyrite, and chrysocolla (Lausen, 1931, p. 58–62).

WALLAPAI DISTRICT

Located near the center of the Cerbat Mountains, which extend north-northwestward from Kingman for about 30 miles, the Wallapai district includes the mining camps of Chloride, Mineral Park, Cerbat, and Stockton.

Unlike the San Francisco district immediately to the southwest in the Black Mountains, where gold is the principal metal, in the Wallapai district lead-zinc ores are prevalent and silver and gold are chiefly byproducts. Many of the veins in the Cerbat Mountains were discovered in the early 1860's by prospectors in search of precious metals (Schrader, 1909, p. 51, 80, 91, 107). Chloride, founded in the early 1870's and named from the character of its rich silver ore, was the first settlement in this area. Ores rich in gold and silver yielded a large production in the 1870's, but activity waned when the price of silver began to decline in 1882. Base-metal ores below the oxidized zone apparently were not mined extensively until the completion of the branch railroad from Kingman to Chloride in 1899 (Nolan, in Hewett and others, 1936, p. 19). Thereafter lead-silver ores were mined, and subsequent improvement in milling methods led to exploitation of complex lead-zinc ores (R. M. Hernon, in Arizona Bur. Mines, 1938, p. 111). Zinc-lead mining reached its peak from 1915 through 1917 owing to high metal prices during World War I, declined abruptly after 1917, and thereafter exploitation was confined to veins with a relatively high gold content. Gold production began to increase in 1935 and reached its peak in 1937–38 (Dings, 1951, p. 126). After 1942, activity declined sharply, and from 1950 through 1956 gold production was less than 100 ounces annually. None was recorded for 1957–59. From 1904 through 1956 the mines of the district produced 125,063 ounces of gold. Dings (1951, p. 125) estimated the value of combined metals produced before 1904 at $5 million, but the amount of gold represented in this total is unknown.

The rocks of the district consist of granite, gneiss, and schist of Precambrian age, stocks and irregular bodies of granite and gabbro probably Mesozoic in age, and still younger dikes of lamprophyre, rhyolite, granite pegmatites, and porphyritic granite. The veins, which occur in all rock types, occupy fault fissures; a few follow dikes (Dings, 1951, p. 127–139).

The veins that yield most of the gold consist mainly of fine-grained quartz with pyrite, sphalerite, galena, and chalcopyrite. The veins locally include arsenopyrite, proustite, molybdenite, and argentite and rarely include tennantite, pearceite, and polybasite. Other gangue minerals are calcite, manganiferous siderite, and rarely rhodochrosite. Gold and silver are in the galena and sphalerite. The sulfides have been moderately oxidized to depths of about 75 to 200 feet, and partly oxidized ore has been found down to 600 feet. The principal ore minerals in the oxidized zone are cerargyrite, native silver, cerussite, and native gold, and the most common gangue minerals are limonite and limonitic quartz (Dings, 1951, p. 141–142).

WEAVER DISTRICT

The Weaver district is in the northern Black Mountains, 10 to 25 miles west and northwest of Chloride. The Mockingbird, Pyramid, and Pilgrim camps are on the eastern slope; the Virginia camp is on the western slope.

Gold was discovered in 1904 in the Pilgrim camp; however, miners had found gold as early as 1892 in the Gold Bug camp, several miles north of the Weaver district (Schrader, 1909, p. 214, 217). Incomplete production records credit the district with about 1,900 ounces of gold before 1932 (Nolan, in

Hewett and others, 1936, p. 17, 19). The period of greatest activity was 1932–42, after which the district declined to the extent that only 138 ounces of gold was reported for 1943–59. Total gold production of the district through 1959 was about 63,200 ounces.

The oldest rocks of the district are Precambrian granite, gneiss, and schist, which are exposed mainly along the eastern slope of the Black Mountains and are overlain on the west slope by Tertiary volcanic rocks intruded by porphyry dikes (Wilson and others, 1934, p. 78–79). The ore, which yields native gold and small amounts of silver, is in veins chiefly in the volcanic rocks. The gangue is quartz, adularia, calcite, and local hematite.

PIMA COUNTY

Pima County, which lies in part along the southern border of Arizona, is a region of broad desert plains and mountain ranges that trend north-northwest. Only two districts have produced more than 10,000 ounces of gold—the Ajo, where considerable amounts have been recovered as a byproduct from copper ores, and the Greaterville, where most of the gold was from placer deposits. Elsing and Heineman (1936, p. 98) credited the Papago district with a production of $250,000 in placer gold before 1933, but this probably is in error, for no other known account cites more than a very small amount. The total gold production of Pima County through 1959 was roughly 1,081,000 ounces—about 1,015,000 ounces from lodes and about 66,000 ounces from placers.

AJO DISTRICT

The Ajo district is in western Pima County, 125 miles west of Tucson.

Small-scale mining of copper deposits was done by Spaniards and Mexicans as early as 1750, and Indians used the red oxides and green carbonates from the Sierra Del Ajo to paint their bodies. Americans entered the area after the Gadsden Purchase of 1853 and located the Ajo mine. After a boundary dispute with Mexico was settled, numerous attempts at mining were made, but all ended in failure due to high freight costs and lack of water. In 1909 three companies conducted separate exploration programs, none of which was considered encouraging.

The Calumet and Arizona Copper Co. entered the district in 1911 and organized the New Cornelia Copper Co., which found a large tonnage of carbonate ore containing 1 to 2 percent of copper underlain by sulfide ore containing disseminated chalcopyrite and bornite. Drilling later revealed considerable ore on other properties. Experiments to leach and recover copper from the carbonate ore were started in 1912 and were concluded successfully in 1915. By 1917 a 5,000-ton leaching plant was built, permitting large-scale exploitation of the carbonate ores. After the exhaustion of the known reserves of carbonate ores, a 5,000-ton sulfide concentrator was put into operation in 1923, and production from the sulfide ores soon became predominant (Gilluly, 1956, p. 98–100). In 1931 the New Cornelia Copper Co. was merged with the Phelps Dodge Co. which continued to be the sole operator in the district through 1959.

Significant recovery of gold began with the production of copper from the sulfide ore of the New Cornelia mine. Prior to 1924 the district produced only 178 ounces. From 1924 through 1934 about 130,000 ounces was recovered (Gilluly, 1946, p. 101), and from 1935 through 1959 about 860,000 ounces was recovered. The total gold production of the district through 1959 was about 990,000 ounces.

The oldest formation in the vicinity of the mineralized area is the Cardigan Gneiss, of Precambrian (?) age. It is bounded on the east along north-trending Gibson fault by the Concentrator Volcanics of Cretaceous(?) age. The Cornelia Quartz Monzonite of Tertiary age is a stock that occupies much of the northern part of the district and crosscuts the older rocks. The Locomotive Fanglomerate of Tertiary age overlies parts of the eroded surface of Cornelia Quartz Monzonite. The rocks were faulted several times during Tertiary time (Gilluly, 1956, p. 57–58, 105–106). The ore body consists of chalcopyrite, bornite, and a little pyrite in veinlets and scattered grains in the quartz monzonite. Less abundant minerals are tennantite, sphalerite, molybdenite, magnetite, and specularite. The richest ore occurs where the rock is impregnated with orthoclase.

The oxidized zone ranges from 20 to 190 feet in thickness and its base terminates sharply at a horizontal plane. In this zone are abundant malachite, and small amounts of azurite, cuprite, tenorite, chrysocolla, hematite, and limonite (Gilluly, 1956, p. 2). Considerable supergene chalcocite has accumulated just below the oxidized zone.

Gold has not been seen in the sulfide ore. However, the close relationship of the ratios of recovered gold to total gold and recovered copper to total copper led Gilluly (1956, p. 87) to conclude that the gold in the ores is associated with copper sulfides rather than pyrite.

GREATERVILLE DISTRICT

The Greaterville district is in southeastern Pima County, about 34 airline miles southeast of Tucson. It is chiefly a placer district, though for many years preceding the Civil War, silver and copper lodes were worked successfully in the Patagonia and Santa Rita Mountains south of the district. In 1874 silver and lead lode deposits were discovered in Hughes Gulch in the Greaterville district, and later in the year placer gold was found which started a rush, during which most of the richer placers were mined out. By 1886 the district was practically dormant (Hill, 1910b, p. 11–12). From 1900 through 1959 there was only desultory activity and very small production. According to Hill (1910b, p. 12), the placers yielded about $7 million in gold before 1900; however, Elsing and Heineman (1936, p. 98) estimated the total production was worth $650,000. From 1903 through 1959 only 4,146 ounces of gold was mined in the district.

The placer deposits occupy a triangular area of about 8 square miles on the lower east slope of the Santa Rita Mountains. The richest gravels are those along present stream courses, although placers are also in older gravels on benches and tops of ridges. The source of the gold was probably the auriferous pyritic-quartz veins of nearby Granite Mountain or the veins in Tertiary andesite that once covered the district (Schrader, 1915, p. 161–165).

PINAL COUNTY

Pinal County, in south-central Arizona, is characterized by broad alluvial plains and scattered mountain ranges, which are composed of Precambrian schist and granite unconformably overlain by younger Precambrian and Paleozoic sedimentary rocks and by Tertiary volcanic rocks. Dikes, irregular bodies, and stocks of granitoid rocks and rhyolite of Cretaceous and Tertiary ages have intruded the Paleozoic and older rocks. Large areas are covered by sedimentary rocks of Cenozoic age.

The principal mining districts from which gold is produced are the Mammoth, Ray, and Superior. Most of the gold is a byproduct of copper ores, although a small amount has come from placers. Total gold production from 1858 through 1959 was about 893,350 ounces.

MAMMOTH DISTRICT

The Mammoth (or Old Hat) district is in southeastern Pinal County on the east flank of the Black Hills, about 50 miles northeast of Tucson.

The history of mining in the district is focused on the development of two mines—the Mammoth which produced mainly gold and, for a short time, molybdenum and the San Manuel which is in a disseminated copper deposit. The first claims were located in the district in 1879. The Mammoth mine was operating on a large scale by 1888, and continued to be active until 1901, when the workings caved. Demand for molybdenum during World War I created new interest in Mammoth because of the wulfenite content of the ores that previously had been mined for gold alone. For a few years almost the entire molybdenum output of the United States came from this area. Between the end of World War I and 1934 the district was practically dormant (Peterson, 1938, p. 25–30). The increase in the price of gold rejuvenated the district from 1934 through 1943. Production of the Mammoth mine declined after 1944, but the important development of the great San Manuel copper deposit in 1943 assured the district a prosperous future.

Total gold production of the district through 1959 was roughly 403,000 ounces, of which about 40,000 ounces was a byproduct of the San Manuel copper ores.

The Mammoth district is underlain by the Oracle Granite (quartz monzonite) of Precambrian age, which is cut by dikes and irregular bodies of monzonite porphyry, diabase, and rhyolite of late Mesozoic to Tertiary age. Much of the area is covered by the Gila Conglomerate of Tertiary and Quaternary age, which unconformably overlaps the older rocks. All the rocks are cut by strong northwest-trending faults, the most prominent of which is the San Manuel fault (Schwartz, 1953, p. 7–16). The vein deposits are along faults and brecciated zones in rhyolite and Precambrian quartz monzonite. The veinfillings consist of quartz and calcite with sphalerite, galena, and a little chalcopyrite, chalcocite, and pyrite. Wulfenite, vanadinite, chrysocolla, cerussite, malachite, smithsonite, and hematite are fairly common in the oxidized ore bodies. Native gold is associated with quartz and coats breccia fragments in the hypogene deposits (Peterson, 1938, p. 30–38).

The San Manuel ore body consists of chalcopyrite and pyrite disseminated in quartz monzonite, monzonite porphyry, and diabase. The ores have been oxidized to variable depths, and in places zones of supergene enrichment are at the base of the oxide zone (Schwartz, 1953, p. 46–55).

RAY DISTRICT

The Ray (or Mineral Creek) district is in northeastern Pinal County about 17 miles south of Miami. It lies between the Dripping Springs Range to the east and the Tortilla Range to the west. Copper is the major commodity of this district; gold is a byproduct.

The district was organized by silver prospectors, probably before 1873, and the first locations were made about 1880 (Arizona Bureau of Mines, 1938, p. 80–81). The first copper company was organized in 1883, but attempts at exploitation over the next 23 years failed, owing to the generally low grade of the ore. In 1906 some high-grade copper ore was mined. In 1907 the Ray Consolidated Copper Co. was organized, and extensive surface drilling and underground exploration revealed enormous copper ore bodies which were mined on a large scale in the spring of 1911 (Ransome, 1919, p. 17–19). Ray Consolidated soon became the largest producer in the district. The property continued to be an important source of copper, though ownership was changed to Ray Division of Kennecott Copper Corp.

The Ray district has produced a surprisingly small amount of gold, considering the large production of copper. Total gold production through 1959 was about 35,250 ounces.

The rocks exposed in the Ray district are similar to those of the Globe-Miami district. The oldest rocks are granitic intrusives and Pinal Schist of Precambrian age. Unconformably overlying them are altered sedimentary rocks of the Apache Group and the Troy Quartzite of late Precambrian age. Great sills of diabase were intruded into the Apache Group and the older rocks (A. F. Shride, oral commun., 1962). In the eastern part of the district lower Paleozoic sedimentary rocks are exposed in a few fault blocks. Dikes, sills, and irregular bodies of quartz diorite, quartz monzonite, and granite, of probable early or middle Tertiary age intrude the Precambrian and Paleozoic rocks. Conglomerate and a dacite flow of late Tertiary age and the Gila Conglomerate of Tertiary and Quaternary age discordantly overlap the older rocks (Ransome, 1919, p. 123–126). The rocks in the eastern part of the district are displaced by a mosaic of normal faults. West of Mineral Creek, which is in general parallel to the Ray fault (the major structural element in the district), Precambrian and Tertiary rocks are exposed and are considerably less faulted than the rocks east of Mineral Creek (Ransome, 1919, p. 127, 128).

The ore deposits consist of disseminated chalcocite of secondary origin associated with primary pyrite and are chiefly in the Pinal Schist and in diabase adjacent to quartz monzonite intrusives and in the intrusives themselves. The primary deposits, which underlie the chalcocite ore, contain pyrite and chalcopyrite. The chalcocite ore is generally overlain by a leached capping of variable thickness which locally is rich in chrysocolla and malachite. The ore bodies are undulate, flat-lying masses of irregular outline and thickness (Ransome, 1919, p. 12).

SUPERIOR DISTRICT

The Superior (Pioneer) district is about 15 miles southwest of Miami and 12 miles northwest of Ray. Most of its gold has been a byproduct from copper ores of the Magma property; however, some gold ore has been mined south of the main copper mines.

The first significant mineral discovery in the Superior district was of nugget silver in 1873 or 1874 at the Silver Queen mine, now known as the Magma mine, and the initial locations were made in 1875. Rich silver ore was mined in the early years and the camp was active until 1893 when a drop in the price of silver halted operations. Several unsuccessful attempts at silver mining were made in later years (Short and others, 1943, p. 59–75, 139–141). Exploration in the old Silver Queen mine by the newly organized Magma Copper Co. in 1912 revealed large bornite-chalcopyrite ore bodies which effected a rejuvenation of the district that was sustained through 1959. Gold is produced from the copper ores and also from auriferous quartz veins in the old Lake Superior and Arizona workings (Gardner, 1934, p. 1–2).

Prior to 1912 the output of gold from the district was small, probably less than 500 ounces. From 1914 through 1959 the recorded production was 397,700 ounces.

Rocks of the area range in age from Precambrian through Tertiary. The oldest is the Pinal Schist, unconformably overlain by the Apache Group and Troy Quartzite of late Precambrian age. Thick diabase sills, considered to be of Precambrian age, intrude the foregoing rocks (A. F. Shride, oral commun., 1962). An aggregate thickness of about 2,000 feet of Paleozoic strata, predominantly limestone, overlies the Precambrian rocks. The Paleozoic rocks were faulted and invaded by dikes and stocks of quartz monzonite porphyry and quartz diorite of late Mesozoic or Tertiary age. Parts of the district are covered by conglomerate and thick dacitic flows and tuffs of Tertiary age and by conglomerate of Tertiary and Quaternary age. Additional crustal movement involving tilting and faulting occurred during middle and late Tertiary time (Short and others, 1943, p. 12–15). Small plugs, flows, and dikes of basalt were intruded locally during Pliocene or Pleistocene time.

The Magma deposits are a series of disconnected ore shoots in replaced shattered country rock between two east-trending shear zones. The richest ore bodies are found along the Magma fault, where it intersects diabase. The principal ore minerals are pyrite, bornite, chalcopyrite, and enargite, with subordinate tennantite and hypogene chalcocite. In places sphalerite is the predominant sulfide; small amounts of galena accompany the sphalerite. Most of the ore bodies were enriched by supergene copper sulfides (Short and others, 1943, p. 74–78).

A considerable amount of gold ore has been mined from the Lake Superior and Arizona property and lesser amounts from similar gold lodes in the Belmont-Queen Creek area. The gold occurs in small lenticular ore bodies 10 to 20 feet above the base of the Martin Limestone (Devonian) and adjacent to faults. Gold, malachite, and chrysocolla occur in a gangue of iron and manganese oxides and quartz. Silver is associated with the copper minerals and gold (Short and others, 1943, p. 138).

SANTA CRUZ COUNTY

Santa Cruz County is in south-central Arizona along the Mexican boundary. Both lode and placer gold have been produced, but the placer output has been small. From 1900 through 1959, the county produced about 108,200 ounces of gold, mostly from the Oro Blanco district. From 1942 through 1959 gold production was very low.

ORO BLANCO DISTRICT

The Oro Blanco district is in western Santa Cruz County near Ruby, about 32 miles by road northwest of Nogales and about 70 miles by road south-southwest of Tucson. Deposits of gold and silver have attracted the most attention. Some of the gold deposits probably were worked by the Indians and early Spanish explorers. Placers and rich outcrops attracted early American prospectors who made their first locations in 1873 (Wilson and others, 1934, p. 188–189; Milton, 1913, p. 1005). The deposits were successfully exploited through the middle 1880's. Most of the mines were inactive from 1887 to 1893; thereafter mining was intermittent, and production in general was small. Production rose rapidly in 1934 but declined again in the early 1940's. From 1942 through 1959 the district was almost dormant. The gold mined in the district from 1873 through 1957 has been estimated as worth $2,626,000, which is equivalent to about 100,200 ounces (Wilson, 1962, p. 109). About $20,000 worth of placer gold was produced between 1896 and 1904. Production was not recorded for 1957–59.

Not much is known about the geology of the district. According to Wilson (Wilson and others, 1934, p. 189), metamorphosed sandstones, conglomerates, shales, and interlayered volcanic rocks of probable Cretaceous age overlie altered diorite, are intruded by dikes of basic to acid composition, and are complexly faulted.

The deposits are of three types: gold-bearing quartz veins, mineralized shear zones, and mineralized country rock. Pyrite, chalcopyrite, galena, and sphalerite are the common ore minerals, and the tellurides have been reported (Milton, 1913, p. 1006).

YAVAPAI COUNTY

Yavapai County, in the central part of Arizona, ranks first in the State in gold production through 1959.

The production by ounces is as follows:

	Lode	*Placer*
Prior to 1900 [1]	477,703	193,500
1900 to 1934 [1]	1,934,447	33,204
1935 to 1959 [2]	1,064,000	40,100
Total	3,476,150	266,804

[1] Elsing and Heineman (1936, p. 60).
[2] U.S. Bureau of Mines (1936–60). Includes 28,137 ounces for 1958 undifferentiated as to source.

The Jerome (Verde) district is the largest gold producer, having contributed about 1,565,000 ounces to the total lode production.

Though mineral deposits were known in this area long before the Civil War, the first prospectors were Union soldiers with mining experience from California (Wilson and others, 1934, p. 23). Placers at Rich Hill were discovered in 1862 and those along Hassayampa and Lynx Creeks were discovered in 1863 (Lindgren, 1926, p. 2–5). Silver ore, first discovered in the Big Bug district in 1870, was found at other localities in Yavapai County in the 1870's. Claims were located in the Jerome district in 1876.

The northern part of Yavapai County is in the plateau region, and the southern part is in the mountain region, which consists of a series of short mountain ranges of the fault-block type that trend north-northwest and are separated by broad valleys filled with fluvial and lacustrine deposits. The mountains consist chiefly of Precambrian metamorphic and igneous rocks, which are intruded locally by stocks, plugs, and dikes of granitic rocks of Late Cretaceous or early Tertiary age. Large areas are covered by volcanic rocks of Tertiary and Quaternary age.

The ore deposits, which are in the mountain region, consist of veins and replacement deposits of Precambrian age and veins of Mesozoic or early Tertiary age. Placer deposits have also been important.

AGUA FRIA DISTRICT

The Agua Fria district is southeast of Prescott along the headwaters of the Agua Fria River about 4½ miles northeast of Mayer. Both gold and silver are byproducts of copper ore.

The Stoddard mine in this district is one of the earliest locations in Arizona but no dates of discovery or location are known (Lindgren, 1926, p. 148). The district was active during World War I and into the early 1920's—probably its period of greatest production. From 1936 through 1957 the mines were operated intermittently. Total gold production through 1959 was about 12,710 ounces.

The rocks exposed in the district are chiefly schists of the Precambrian Yavapai Series, which are intruded by the Precambrian Bradshaw Granite. The Yavapai Series includes many quartz lenses and bodies of fissile quartz porphyry. The Precambrian rocks are capped locally by volcanic flows and tuffs of Tertiary age (Lindgren, 1926, p. 146–147).

The ore deposits are replacement bodies of quartz, pyrite, and chalcopyrite, and tetrahedrite in the schists.

BIG BUG DISTRICT

The Big Bug district, on the northeast slope of the Bradshaw Mountains, is about 12 miles east-southeast of Prescott. Copper, gold, silver, lead, and zinc are obtained from a variety of ore deposits in the district.

Wilson, Cunningham, and Butler (1934, p. 39) referred to activity at the Big Bug mine as early as 1866, and other properties were producing gold and silver from oxidized ores before 1870. After a period of decline, some mines were reopened in the late 1890's and maintained a small sporadic annual output through 1933. The tempo of mining increased from 1934 through 1959 mainly because of expanded operation of the Iron King mine. Gold placers were highly productive during the 1880's (Wilson, 1952, p. 48–50) and from 1933 through 1942, after which they declined in importance.

Total gold production from 1867 through 1959 was about 627,000 ounces, of which about 42,700 ounces was from placers.

The Yavapai Series, which here consists of interlayered sedimentary rocks and volcanic tuffs and breccias, was intruded by a variety of Precambrian granitic rocks—gabbro, diorite, granodiorite, and granite—and by dikes of rhyolite porphyry (Lindgren, 1926, p. 126–127; Anderson and Creasey, 1958, pl. 1). Tertiary volcanic rocks younger than the ore deposits locally form a cover.

Lindgren (1926, p. 127) recognized four classes of ore deposits in the district; however, the lead-zinc-silver veins of the Iron King mine have yielded the most gold, and the gold vein of the McCabe-Gladstone property has probably been the second largest gold producer.

The Iron King deposit is a system of 12 massive sulfide veins oriented en echelon in a mylonitized shear zone in the Spud Mountain Volcanics of the Precambrian Yavapai Series (Creasey, in Anderson and Creasey, 1958, p. 156–169). The wallrock is so intensely altered by hydrothermal introduction of quartz, sericite, and pyrite that in places the nature of the original rock cannot be determined. Two groups of veins are recognized in the deposit: well-defined massive sulfide veins, from which all but a few tons of the total ore has been mined, and poorly defined veins, chiefly of pyrite, ankerite, and quartz. The massive sulfide veins comprise thin layers of fine-grained pyrite, sphalerite, chalcopyrite, arsenopyrite, galena, and tennantite. Quartz and ankerite are the major gangue minerals. Gold is in the pyrite, and silver is probably in the tennantite.

The McCabe-Gladstone is one of several mines on the 14,000-foot-long Silver Belt-McCabe vein, a mineralized shear zone in the breccia facies of the Spud Mountain Volcanics. Ore occurs as discontinuous lenses or pods of coarsely crystalline drusy masses of sulfides, with numerous open vugs. The mineralogy of the ore is variable. Silver and lead are abundant in the ores at the north end of the vein. Toward the south end the ores are more complex and contain lead, zinc, iron, silver, copper, and gold. The McCabe-Gladstone mine, which is at the south end of the vein, is in ore composed of arsenopyrite, pyrite, chalcopyrite, and quartz. The gold and silver are in the sulfides (Creasey, in Anderson and Creasey, 1958, p. 169–171).

BLACK CANYON DISTRICT

The Black Canyon district is in southeastern Yavapai County between the eastern foothills of the Bradshaw Mountains and the Agua Fria River, at Bumblebee.

The first locations were made probably as early as 1873, but the first record of mineral production was in 1904. The district was active through 1956, with the highest output from 1934 through 1941. Total gold production from 1904 through 1959 was about 46,700 ounces.

A belt about 2 miles wide of Yavapai schist trends northward through the district and is flanked on the east by a narrow mass of diorite and Bradshaw Granite and on the west by Bradshaw Granite. These rocks, which are all of Precambrian age, are overlain in the eastern part of the district by volcanic rocks of Tertiary age (Lindgren, 1926, p. 153).

The gold ore is in Precambrian high-angle veins and in flat veins of a younger age (Lindgren, 1926, p. 156–159).

The Precambrian veins contain coarse glassy quartz and small amounts of chalcopyrite, pyrite, galena, sphalerite, and native gold. Aggregates of minute prisms of blue, brown, or colorless tourmaline are associated with the sulfides. The flat veins, which are also found in the Precambrian rocks, consist of quartz with a little pyrite, galena, chalcopyrite, and locally contain sphalerite and proustite. The gold in these veins is probably in the sulfides.

BLACK ROCK DISTRICT

The Black Rock district, about 12 to 15 miles northeast of Wickenburg, was prospected for copper and silver in the 1870's, but according to meager records the deposits were not developed until 1900 or later (Wilson and others, 1934, p. 62–65). Through about 1932 the district is credited with a gold production of $195,000 (9,438 ounces), most of which came from the Gold Bar (O'Brien) mine (Elsing and Heineman, 1936, p. 103). From 1932 through 1955 the district produced 2,754 ounces of gold, of which at least 99 ounces was placer gold. The total through 1959 was about 12,190 ounces.

The principal rocks of the region are schist and granite of Precambrian age, volcanic rocks (chiefly andesite) of Cretaceous(?) and Tertiary age, and local remnants of basalt of Quaternary age (Arizona Bureau of Mines, 1958).

The ore deposit in the Gold Bar mine is a fissure vein consisting of coarse glassy quartz with pyrite and free gold. In the oxidized zone the quartz is cellular; its cavities are filled with hematite and limonite formed from pyrite, which is common in the deeper zones. Gold occurs as fine to medium-coarse particles, both in the quartz and with the iron minerals (Wilson and others, 1934, p. 63–64).

EUREKA DISTRICT

The Eureka (Bagdad) district is in western Yavapai County, 42 miles west of Prescott. Most of the mines are near Bagdad in the southwestern part of the district.

Although the district is noted mainly for copper, its deposits were mined originally for silver, gold, and lead. The first claims were located in 1880, and mining began in 1887. Until 1917 most production was from ores rich in gold and silver, with subordinate lead and zinc, from the Hillside mine. Copper minerals were known in the district as early as 1882; however, sporadic exploration through the early 1900's failed to disclose any significant copper ore bodies until 1929 when the Bagdad mine began operations. Gold and silver production from the Hillside mine and several smaller properties continued until 1942, when the Hillside mine was closed. Meanwhile the Bagdad mine expanded due to the demand for copper during World War II. Large-scale activity continued after the war. The Hillside mine was reopened during 1948–51; open-pit mining increased the Bagdad mine production after 1947; and other properties were developed to mine tungsten and zinc. Copper output at the Bagdad mine continued to be significant through the 1950's, and in 1959 it was the largest copper producer in the county.

Total gold output of the district from 1887 through 1951 was 59,787 ounces, of which 58,748 ounces is attributed to the Hillside mine (Anderson and others, 1956, p. 46, 84). From 1952 through 1959 the district produced only 179 ounces of gold. The copper ores at the Bagdad mine yielded insignificant amounts of gold.

Most of the bedrock in the Eureka district is of Precambrian age and consists of metamorphosed volcanic and tuffaceous sedimentary rocks and intrusive masses of rhyolite, gabbro, anorthosite, quartz diorite, diabase, alaskite, granodiorite, and granite. Rhyolite tuff of Cretaceous(?) or Tertiary (?) age unconformably overlies the Precambrian rocks in the southwestern corner of the area, and small stocks, plugs, and dikes of quartz monzonite, quartz monzonite porphyry, and diorite porphyry, slightly younger than the rhyolite tuff, are scattered throughout the older terrain. A thick section of Tertiary and Quaternary clastic sedimentary rocks intercalated with basalt and rhyolite flows and tuffs caps the mesas and overlaps the older rocks (Anderson and others, 1956, p. 6–29). The Precambrian rocks show effects of folding, dynamic and thermal metamorphism, and several periods of faulting. Faulting continued during at least three periods in post-Precambrian time, when some of the major faults related to the mineral deposits were formed (Anderson and others, 1956, p. 29–39).

The gold-silver-zinc-lead deposit at the Hillside mine is a fissure vein in the Hillside fault, which trends N. 10° W. to N. 25° E. and dips steeply to the west in the mine vicinity. The mineralization was related to the quartz monzonite intrusions and occurred during Cretaceous or early Tertiary time. Postmineral faulting, resulting in gaps and overlaps of ore, is a factor to be considered in exploiting these deposits. The hypogene vein minerals are pyrite, arsenopyrite, galena, sphalerite, argentite, chalcopyrite, freibergite, and tetrahedrite in a gangue of quartz. Most of the gold is associated with pyrite and arsenopyrite. The upper part of the vein is oxidized to limonite-stained quartz and variable amounts of gold, silver, cerargyrite, cerussite, malachite, chalcanthite, and goslarite (Anderson and others, 1956, p. 77–79).

HASSAYAMPA-GROOM CREEK DISTRICT

The Hassayampa-Groom Creek district is on the western slopes of the Bradshaw Mountains, 6 miles south of Prescott.

Gold placers were discovered in 1864 along the Hassayampa River, and shortly afterward many quartz veins were found. Considerable gold and silver was extracted from the shallow oxidized parts of these veins, and after 1895 the primary sulfide ore was mined for gold, silver, copper, lead, and zinc (Wilson and others, 1934, p. 41). The placers were worked most intensively between 1885 and 1890; thereafter, operations were carried out on a small scale (Wilson, 1952, p. 52). From 1953 through 1959 the district produced only a few ounces of gold per year from lodes and placers.

Total gold production through 1959 was about 127,000 ounces—18,700 ounces from placers and 108,300 ounces from lodes. Schists of the Yavapai Series and the Bradshaw Granite, the oldest rocks of the district, were intruded by several small masses of diorite and granodiorite and dikes of rhyolite porphyry, all of Precambrian age (Lindgren, 1926, p. 114–115, pl. 2).

Most of the ore deposits are in fissure veins in the schist, a few are in the granite and diorite. The ore consists of pyrite, arsenopyrite, sphalerite, galena, chalcopyrite, and local tetrahedrite, in a gangue of quartz and a little carbonate. Gold is associated with quartz and sulfides, and in some deposits, with specularite. Some veins are of Precambrian age, others are of probable Tertiary age (Lindgren, 1926, p. 114–126).

JEROME DISTRICT

The Jerome (Verde) district is on the eastern slope of the Black Hills in northeast Yavapai County just west of the Verde River. Both gold and silver have been produced as byproducts of copper mining from the two major mines in this district—the United Verde and the United Verde Extension.

Centuries ago the copper ores at Jerome were utilized by Indians for jewelry and dyes. In 1582 and 1598 Spanish explorers visited the deposits and located claims, though they did not work them. The deposits remained unnoticed and undeveloped until their rediscovery in 1875 by U.S. Army troops. In 1876 prospectors entered the area, and by 1882 the newly organized United Verde Copper Co. began consolidating the numerous claims and later became the largest producer of the district. Oxidized ores rich in gold, silver, and copper were mined in 1883–84, but by the end of 1884 the ore was exhausted and the price of copper dropped, so that work was suspended at the United Verde property until 1888. Prospecting elsewhere in the district in the early 1900's was successful, and for a time several small mines were active. The United Verde Extension Gold, Silver, and Copper Mining Co. was organized in 1899, and under its successors it became the second largest mine of the district. In the early 1900's the United Verde Extension Co. explored extensively, first to the southwest and later east of the prospering United Verde property. Most of these efforts were fruitless; nevertheless, work continued until the company was on the verge of collapse. Finally in 1914, a rich chalcocite ore body was found on the 1,200 level, and in 1916 a much larger ore body was found. The company operated on a large scale until 1938 when the deposit was mined out and the mine was closed.

The United Verde mine continued its underground operations until 1931, after which open-pit mining was the chief activity. Depletion of reserves finally forced the mine to close in 1953 (Anderson and Creasey, 1958, p. 84–90).

The large-scale copper mining yielded a total of about 1,565,000 ounces of byproduct gold from 1883 through 1951 (Anderson and Creasey, 1958, p. 101). Total gold production from 1883 through 1959 was about 1,571,000 ounces.

Most of the central and southern parts of the Jerome district are underlain by slate, phyllite, schist, gneiss, and granulite that make up the Yavapai Series of Precambrian age. These rocks are intruded by numerous irregular bodies of quartz porphyry, gabbro, quartz diorite, and granodiorite, also of Precambrian age. Paleozoic sedimentary rocks, which cover parts of the northern half of the district, overlie the Precambrian rocks unconformably and range in age from Cambrian to Pennsylvanian or Permian. Rocks of Mesozoic age do not occur in the district; a thick section of lava flows and intercalated sedimentary rocks of Pliocene(?) age and lake deposits of late Pliocene and Pleistocene age overlap the older rocks (Anderson and Creasey, 1958, p. 8–61).

The Precambrian rocks were deformed during several periods of faulting and folding. Later faulting, accompanied by tilting, displaced the Paleozoic and Cenozoic rocks (Anderson and Creasey, 1958, p. 62–83). The important ore deposits of the district are massive sulfide deposits of Precambrian age. At the United Verde mine the main ore body was a pipelike mass of pyrite, chalcopyrite, sphalerite, quartz, and carbonates that replaced quartz porphyry and tuffaceous sedimentary rocks. The deposits of the United Verde Extension mine were buried beneath a cover of Paleozoic and Tertiary sedimentary rocks. Ore consisted of elliptical masses of chalcocite in Precambrian rocks. Massive sulfide, similar in composition to the United Verde ore body, underlies the chalcocite. In both mines the sulfide ore bodies were overlain by oxidized zones containing iron oxides, malachite, azurite, chrysocolla, gold, silver, and native copper (Anderson and Creasey, 1958, p. 103–145).

LYNX CREEK-WALKER DISTRICT

The Lynx Creek-Walker district is about 7 miles southeast of Prescott. Lynx Creek is one of the most productive placer streams in the State; moreover, lode mines in the Walker camp have yielded considerable gold, silver, copper, and lead.

The placers were discovered by a party of California miners in 1863, and as they worked upstream they found the gold-bearing veins of the Walker camp (Lindgren, 1926, p. 108–109). The richest placers were depleted in the early days, but small and intermittent placer operations continued for many years. From 1927 through 1941 large-scale dredging operations were successful, but from 1942 through 1959 the placer mining was desultory and was carried out on a small scale. In the Walker camp only oxidized ore was mined in the early years and was worked in arrastres. Deep mining into the sulfide zone presumably was begun some time before 1910. Lode production probably was never very large, and it fluctuated considerably but was almost continuous from 1905 through 1952.

According to Lindgren (1926, p. 109) the placer output through 1924 was about $1 million, most of which was extracted in the early years. Wilson (1952, p. 39, 42) reported that production before 1881 was estimated at $1 million (48,379 ounces), and from 1900 to 1949 it was about $1 million, mostly during 1933–42. Total gold output of the district through 1959 was about 140,000 ounces: 97,000 ounces from placers and 43,000 ounces from lodes.

Underlying the district are schists of the Yavapai Series and the Bradshaw Granite intruded first by a granodiorite stock and later by a number of rhyolite porphyry dikes. The ore deposits are in sulfide-bearing quartz veins that transect the granodiorite. Ore minerals are pyrite, sphalerite, chalcopyrite, galena, and tetahedrite. Gold is contained in chalcopyrite, and gold and silver seem to be associated with galena and tetrahedrite. The ores were mined mainly for gold (Lindgren, 1926, p. 111).

MARTINEZ DISTRICT

The Martinez district is in southwestern Yavapai County in the southeastern Date Creek Mountains a few miles northwest of Congress.

Gold was produced almost entirely from quartz veins and mostly from the Congress mine. The first discoveries were made in 1870, but the ore was not free milling and thus progress was impeded until a cyanide plant was built in 1895. High production was maintained until 1910 (Wilson and others, 1934, p. 69–71). Except for a span of intensive operation by lessees during 1938–42, the mine was virtually idle from 1910 through 1959. The total minimum gold production of the Congress mine from 1887 through 1959 was about 396,300 ounces.

The eastern Date Creek Mountains consist of coarse-grained granite, intruded by pegmatites, aplites, and basic dikes. The gold deposits are along low-dipping faults in veins that consist of coarse-textured quartz with pyrite and some galena (Wilson and others, 1934, p. 69). At the Congress mine the most productive veins are within the basic dikes, mostly near their footwalls. Veins in the granite are of lower grade; they carry small amounts of galena and larger amounts of silver (Staunton, 1926, p. 769). Ore has been mined to a depth of 4,000 feet.

PECK DISTRICT

The Peck district is in the drainage area of Peck Canyon and Bear Creek, about 20 miles south-southeast of Prescott.

Rich silver ore was discovered in the Peck mine in 1875, and in the following 10 years $1 to $1½ million worth of silver was mined. Other silver deposits were found in the late 1870's. By 1885 the rich ore of the Peck mine was depleted, and work in the succeeding years was mainly by lessees. In the early 1900's copper-silver properties were developed which yielded considerable byproduct gold. From 1932 through 1959 the district was for the most part inactive. Total gold production from 1890 through 1959 was about 15,550 ounces.

The area is underlain by Precambrian rocks, chiefly the Yavapai Series, which here includes quartzite and layers of amphibolite, chlorite, and sericite schist. The belt of schist, about 2 miles wide, lies between areas of Precambrian Bradshaw Granite. Porphyry dikes intruded the schist parallel to its strike (Lindgren, 1926, p. 160).

The veins, found in the quartzite and schist, are parallel to the foliation. The rich silver-bearing veins contain a gangue of siderite or ankerite, which near the surface is almost wholly oxidized to limonite. The principal ore minerals are bromyrite and subordinate native silver, but locally the veins contain chalcopyrite and silver-rich tetrahedrite. The copper-rich ore bodies found in the De Soto mine are overlapping lenses of fine-grained quartz in the chloritic schist of the Yavapai Series. They contain pyrite, chalcopyrite, some sphalerite and galena, and sparse tetrahedrite and arsenopyrite (Lindgren, 1926, p. 161–163). Gold occurs as microscopic grains in the sulfides.

PINE GROVE-TIGER DISTRICT

The Pine Grove-Tiger (Crown King) district is in the heart of the Bradshaw Mountains 40 miles by road southeast of Prescott; the Tiger camp lies immediately south of the Pine Grove camp. The ores, which were very rich in silver and gold near the surface, also contained significant amounts of copper, lead, and zinc.

A few mines in this district were worked as early as 1874, but there is little indication of any significant development until after 1890. The Crown King mine, the most important gold property of the district, was most active between 1893 and 1900 (Lindgren, 1926, p. 168). More recent productive flurries occurred during 1903–23 and 1934–51. The total gold production through 1959 was about 130,275 ounces.

Bedrock in the district consists of Precambrian Yavapai Series and Bradshaw Granite which are intruded by a stock and dikes of granodiorite of Mesozoic or Tertiary age and by younger dikes of rhyolite porphyry and granite porphyry (Lindgren, 1926, p. 21–23, 164–176).

The ore is in veins which are most abundant in the granodiorite; a few extend into the surrounding rocks. The vein minerals are pyrite, chalcopyrite, sphalerite, galena, and some tetrahedrite in a gangue of quartz with a little ankerite and calcite. In some of the sulfide ore, native gold is present. Much of the mined ore was partly oxidized and rich in gold and silver (Lindgren, 1926, p. 164–165).

TIPTOP DISTRICT

The Tiptop district is in the southern foothills of the Bradshaw Mountains in southeastern Yavapai County, about 45 miles north-northwest of Phoenix.

The history and production of the district is mainly that of the Tiptop mine (Lindgren, 1926, p. 180). This mine, located in 1875, yielded about $2 million probably all in silver and gold, before 1883, when it was closed. The mine was reopened from 1886 to 1888, but apparently it has been closed since that time. A small amount of tungsten ore was mined, probably during World War I. Since then the district has been dormant, except for minor activity during the 1930's and early 1950's. Lindgren (1926, p. 180) considered the estimated total production of $4 million somewhat high. Total gold production through 1959 was about 10,000 ounces.

The host rock is the Bradshaw Granite which intruded a north-trending belt of Yavapai Series, exposed just east of the district. The granite is cut by dikes of rhyolite porphyry and is overlain by a remnant of Tertiary lava flows at the south end of the district (Lindgren, 1926, p. 179–180).

The ore deposits are fissure veins in the granite. The principal gangue mineral is fine to coarse quartz, and some druses are coated with chalcedony. The ore minerals, in paragenetic order, are wolframite, arsenopyrite, pyrite, sphalerite, bornite, and galena. Cerargyrite and ruby silver were common in the oxidized ore; antimonial silver minerals and native silver were probably also present. Some veins rich in galena contained gold and some silver (Lindgren, 1926, p. 181–182).

WEAVER-RICH HILL DISTRICT

The Weaver-Rich Hill district is in southwestern Yavapai County along the southwestern front of the Weaver Mountains, 5 to 8 miles east of Congress. Both lodes and placers have been important sources of gold in this district.

An accidental discovery of gold nuggets on top of Rich Hill in the early 1860's kindled interest in the area and before long gold placers along Weaver and Antelope Creeks and the lode deposit at the Octave mine were found (Wilson, 1952, p. 43). By 1883 the placers had yielded $1 million in gold, but thereafter the deposits were worked sporadically and were idle from 1952 through 1959.

Little development of the Octave mine was attempted until the perfection of the cyanide process in the 1890's. Between 1900 and 1905 gold and silver ore worth $1,900,000 was mined. Activity declined after 1905, and the mine was closed in 1930. Under new ownership of the American Smelting and Refining Co., the mine was reopened in 1934 (E. D. Wilson, in Arizona Bureau of Mines, 1938, p. 131) and was worked until December 1942 (Woodward and Luff, 1943, p. 258). Lode production of the district declined sharply in 1943 and was negligible through 1959.

Placers in the district are credited through 1959 with about 104,000 ounces of gold and lodes with about 204,000 ounces, a total of 308,000 ounces. All but about 1,500 ounces of the lode gold came from the Octave mine.

The country rock of the district is mainly granite and quartz diorite with lenses and septa of schist. These rocks are cut by dikes of pegmatite, aplite, and diabase (Wilson and others, 1934, p. 66–68).

The veins in the district occur along low-angle fault zones that are chiefly in the granite, but some are in the schist. The main Octave vein, which is in granitic rocks (Nevius, 1921, p. 123), consists of coarse white quartz that carries irregular masses, disseminations, and layers of fine-grained pyrite, galena, and sparse sphalerite and chalcopyrite and a little native gold. Most of the gold is contained in the galena (Wilson and others, 1934, p. 67, 68).

YUMA COUNTY

Yuma County, in the southwest corner of Arizona, ranks fourth among the gold-producing counties of the State. The terrain includes many mountains of the fault-block type that trend north-northwest and are separated by broad desert plains. The bedrock of the mountains consists of schist, gneiss, and granite of Precambrian age, sedimentary and metamorphic rocks of Paleozoic, Mesozoic, and Tertiary age, granite of Tertiary age, and volcanic rocks of Cretaceous to Quaternary age (Wilson and others, 1934, p. 124). Nine mining districts, mainly in the central and western parts of the county, have had a total output of more than 10,000 ounces of gold each.

The mines of Yuma County produced a total of about 771,000 ounces of gold through 1959.

CASTLE DOME DISTRICT

The Castle Dome district is in south-central Yuma County in the southern Castle Dome Mountains, about 20 to 25 miles north of Wellton.

Organized in 1863, the Castle Dome district has produced about equal amounts of placer and lode gold. The first discoveries were of silver-bearing lead ore; gold placers were found in 1884, and gold-quartz veins, although known for some time, received little attention until 1912 (Wilson, 1933, p. 85, 87; 1952, p. 23). Activity in the district has been sporadic, and from 1942 through 1959 the mines were dormant. Total gold production through 1959 was between 9,500 and 10,500 ounces.

In the Castle Dome district gneiss, schist, and granite, all probably Precambrian in age, are unconformably overlain by thick-bedded shales and impure cherty limestones of Cretaceous(?) age. These rocks were intruded by numerous dikes of diorite porphyry. Broad areas of the older rocks are capped by volcanic rocks and cut by dikes of rhyolite porphyry (Wilson, 1933, p. 78–81).

The mineral deposits in the district are argentiferous galena-fluorite veins, gold-quartz veins, and some veins that carry copper, gold, and silver. The deposit of the Big Eye mine, one of the major gold producers, occurs in a sheared zone in volcanic rocks. The vein consists of brecciated yellow quartz interlaced with veinlets of calcite. The gold was probably free milling and did not continue in minable quantities below depths of 30 feet (Wilson, 1933, p. 102–103).

CIENEGA DISTRICT

The Cienega district is in northwestern Yuma County, 5 to 8 miles northeast of Parker.

Some mining was done as early as 1870 (Wilson and others, 1934, p. 126). Gold-copper lodes developed during 1909–20 had small sporadic yields. Intermittent activity continued through 1957.

Nolan (in Hewett and others, 1936, p. 31) estimated that the district produced ore worth $80,000 (chiefly in gold) before 1908, but Elsing and Heineman (1936, p. 104) credited the district with $415,000 (about 20,000 ounces), from 1870 to 1933, most of which must have been mined before 1908 because recorded production from 1908 to 1933 was only 4,271 ounces. Total gold production through 1959 was at least 10,000 ounces.

A thick section of Paleozoic metamorphosed sedimentary rocks, consisting of limestone, shale, and quartzite, is the predominant bedrock in the district. These rocks are cut by intrusive bodies of granite and are overlain locally by basalt. Gold, chrysocolla, malachite, limonite, and specularite occur in brecciated pockets of sedimentary rock along shear zones.

DOME DISTRICT

The Dome (Gila City) district is at the north end of the Gila Mountains, about 15 miles east of Yuma.

Discovered in 1858, this placer district attracted a horde of prospectors who worked the rich gravels of Monitor Gulch and other gulches and benches near the newly founded settlement of Gila City, just west of the present town of Dome (Wilson, 1952, p. 18–19). By 1865 the high-grade placers were worked out, but spasmodic activity continued to 1950. Total gold production through 1959 was about 24,765 ounces, the bulk of which was mined before 1865.

ELLSWORTH DISTRICT

The Ellsworth (Harquahala) district is in the Little Harquahala Mountains, 5 to 10 miles south of Salome.

Small placer deposits in Harquahala Gulch were worked in 1886 and 1887, and the lodes of the Bonanza and Golden Eagle mines, from which most of the gold of the district has been mined, were found in 1888. The period of greatest activity was from 1891 to 1897, after which the ore bodies were considered to be worked out (Wilson and others, 1934, p. 128). Small production by lessees continued at intervals through 1957. Total gold production of the district through 1959 was about 134,000 ounces; nearly all production was from lodes.

Granite, of probable Precambrian age, is overlain by schist, quartzite, shale, and limestone, some of which may be as young as Carboniferous (Darton, 1925, p. 221–223). Gold-bearing quartz veins are along shear zones in the sedimentary rocks and granite. The oxidized ores contain much free-milling gold; the sulfide ores, mined in more recent years, contain pyrite, galena, and local covellite (Bancroft, 1911, p. 106–114).

FORTUNA DISTRICT

The Fortuna district is on the west flank of the central part of the Gila Mountains, 21 miles southeast of Yuma.

Discovered sometime between 1892 and 1895, the Fortuna mine has been the only profitable gold-mining venture in the district. The first period of operation was between 1896 and 1904, during which 123,050 ounces of gold was produced. The mine was closed in 1904 after several fruitless attempts to locate the continuation of the vein beyond a fault (Wilson, 1933, p. 189–198). There was minor production in 1913, 1926, 1939, and 1940; but apparently no substantial segment of the vein was found. Total gold production of the district through 1959 was 125,332 ounces.

The Gila Mountains in the vicinity of the Fortuna mine are composed of schist and gneiss, of probable Precambrian age, and intrusive granite, amphibolite, and pegmatite and aplite dikes. These rocks are disrupted by a network of faults of several ages. Some of the older faults were mineralized, and the veins were then displaced by later faulting, as at the Fortuna mine. The Fortuna ore body has been described as a vein that cropped out as two branches that joined at about 500 feet below the surface and as a southwestward-plunging chimney with two branches that joined at depth. The vein consists of coarse-grained quartz with disseminated native gold in little grains or particles. The quartz is locally stained with malachite and is transected by veinlets of hematite (Wilson, 1933, p. 190–194).

KOFA DISTRICT

The Kofa district is in the central part of the county, on the southwestern flank of the Kofa Mountains.

Nearly the entire gold output of this district came from the King of Arizona and the North Star lode mines, discovered in 1896 and 1906 respectively. The King of Arizona mine was operated until 1910 and the North Star until 1911 (Wilson, 1933, p. 109–113). A brief flurry of production occurred in the late 1930's, but during most of 1942–59 the district was idle. The total gold production of the district was about 237,000 ounces.

The principal bedrock exposed in the Kofa Mountains is relatively flat-lying rhyolite and andesite lavas, tuffs, and breccias of Tertiary(?) age, capped by olivine basalt flows. The major gold deposits are in brecciated zones and veins in the andesite. The deposit at the King of Arizona mine consists of anastomosing stringers of quartz and calcite in silicified andesite breccia. The gold occurs in finely divided particles. Ore in the North Star mine is also in silicified andesite breccia, whose angular fragments are cemented by banded chalcedonic quartz containing fine-grained pyrite and adularia. Gold is present as very fine particles associated with the pyrite (Jones, 1916b, p. 154–159).

LAGUNA DISTRICT

The Laguna district is immediately north of the Gila River and east of the Colorado River, at the south end of the Laguna Mountains.

The important mineral deposits are gold-quartz veins and placers in the Las Flores area in the southeastern part of the Laguna Mountains, placers in the McPhaul area along the southern foot of the mountains, and placers in the Laguna Dam area on the west side of the mountains. Mexican and Indian placer miners were busy in the Las Flores area in the 1860's, and some activity was reported in gold-bearing veins before 1870. Efforts were made in 1884 or 1885 to dredge gravels in the Laguna Dam area, but the dredge was destroyed in a flood. In the early 1900's small amounts of gold were recovered from potholes in gulches along the Colorado River. More recent operations were desultory, and the district was inactive from 1941 through 1959. Total gold production through 1959 was roughly 10,500 ounces, mostly from placers.

The gold-quartz veins are in zones of sheared and brecciated schist of Precambrian age. Locally the quartz is brecciated. The gold occurs in ragged grains in the quartz and is associated with iron oxides; no sulfides occur in the oxidized ore from the shallow workings (Wilson, 1933, p. 214).

Many arroyos have dissected the area, and placer gold has been found on benches as well as along the arroyo bottoms. In the Laguna Dam area rather coarse gold has been found in potholes as much as 100 feet above the river.

LA PAZ DISTRICT

The La Paz (Weaver) district, in west-central Yuma County, is 9 miles west of Quartzite and 6 miles east of the Colorado River, along the west side of the Dome Mountains.

Gold has come chiefly from placers, but a small amount has been mined from quartz veins. Indians gave a few nuggets to a trapper in 1862 and guided him and his party to the rich gold-bearing gravels. News of this spread quickly, and several hundred miners rushed to the new area. By 1864, however, the higher grade placers were exhausted. The district was dormant until 1910, when plans were made to mine the gravels by hydraulic methods. These operations were thwarted when the land was included in an Indian reservation. Several later plans for large-scale mining were never carried out (Wilson, 1952, p. 25, 26). Lode deposits, probably discovered at about the same time as the placers, were worked intermittently and yielded about $100,000 worth of gold through about 1933 (Wilson and others, 1934, p. 136).

The placer gold production was estimated at about $2 million (96,800 ounces) in the first 5 years (Browne, 1868, p. 454–455). Total production from placers through 1959 was about 100,000 ounces, and total output from lodes was about 4,000 ounces.

The placers occur along gulches that drain the western slopes of the Dome Rock Mountains. These include the Goodman Arroyo and Arroyo La Paz and their tributaries, among which is Ferrar Gulch which contained the richest and most productive gravels of the district. The gold was recovered entirely by dry washing (Jones, 1916a, p. 49–52).

The rocks in the La Paz district are chiefly Precambrian schist and gneiss which were intruded by granitic rock of probable Mesozoic age (Wilson, 1952, p. 28). The gold occurs in quartz veins in the schist. Some of the veins are parallel to the foliation and others, referred to as gash veins, cut across. Those along the foliation are the larger; the gash veins are too small for exploitation (Jones, 1916a, p. 54–55).

PLOMOSA DISTRICT

The Plomosa district is near the town of Quartzite on La Posa Plain, between the Plomosa Mountains on the east and the Dome Rock Mountains on the west.

This is mainly a placer district; however, gold, copper, and lead have been produced from lode mines. In 1862, prospectors on their way west to the rich La Paz gravels found placers on the east side of the Dome Rock Mountains, at Oro Fino, La Cholla, and Middle Camp. These were worked intermittently until the 1950's, and several unsuccessful attempts were made to mine the gravels on a large scale (Jones, 1916a, p. 52). Gold, copper, and lead veins were exploited after 1900 but their yield was small (Nolan, in Hewett and others, 1936, p. 33). Total gold production of the district through 1959 was about 24,570 ounces: about 19,400 ounces from placers and about 5,000 ounces from lodes.

The northern Plomosa Mountains, in which the auriferous veins occur, are composed of metamorphosed limestone, shale of probable Cretaceous age, and intrusive granite (Wilson and others, 1934, p. 134–135). The veins are along a fault zone in the shale. Gold occurs in fine flakes with hematite.

CALIFORNIA

For many years gold was California's most valuable mineral commodity, and even today despite high mining costs and a fixed selling price, gold ranks fourth in the value of mineral commodities in the State. The total amount of gold production reported in California from 1848 through 1965 was 106,130,214 ounces: about 68,200,000 ounces placer and about 37,900,000 ounces lode and byproduct gold.

The discovery of gold in California usually is attributed to James W. Marshall, whose highly publicized placer discovery, on the American River in El Dorado County in 1848, led to the gold rush of 1849. But long before Marshall's discovery, as

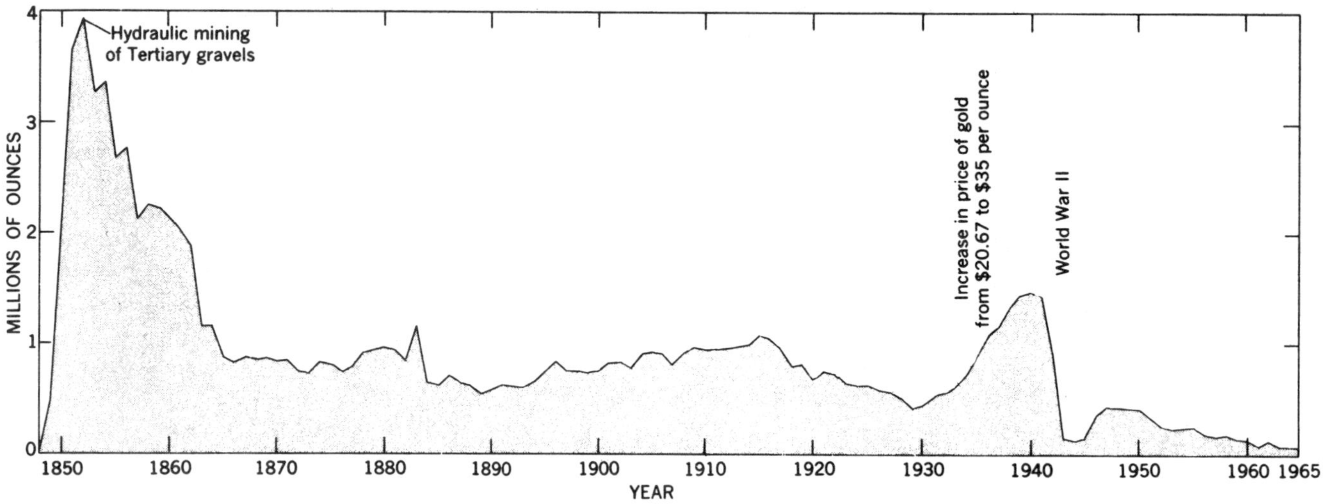

FIGURE 8.—Annual gold production of California, 1848–1965. Sources of data: 1848–1946 from Averill, King, Symons, and Davis (1948, p. 41), 1947–1965 from U.S. Bureau of Mines (1933–66).

early as 1775, Mexicans mined small amounts of placer gold from the Colorado River and lode gold from the Cargo Muchacho Mountains (Clark, 1957, p. 223), and in the 1830's gold was discovered in Los Angeles County. These early operations were in remote, sparsely settled areas under the control of Mexico and were far from any lines of communication; thus the news did not spread.

The early placer operations, 1948–49, were small scale, the deposits were quickly depleted, and attention soon was directed to the large deposits of gold-bearing gravels of Tertiary age. In 1852 large-scale hydraulic mining began on these deposits, which for many years were the main source of the State's gold production (fig. 8). These operations were so large they caused heavy silting of navigable stream channels, partial blockage of tributary streams, and ruination of agricultural lands by debris-laden streams during spring floods. This silting even caused the Golden Gate bar in San Francisco Bay to move inshore. Beginning in 1884, court actions brought against the miners to curtail this devastation culminated in the passage by Congress of the California Debris Commission Act (or Caminetti Act) in 1893. As a result, the cost of constructing required debris dams and settling basins caused many operators to abandon large-scale hydraulic mining in favor of drift mining of the buried Tertiary channel gravels.

Lode mining of gold became important in the 1860's, and between 1884 and 1918 gold-quartz veins were the major source of California's gold production. Beginning in 1898 placer mining was rejuvenated when huge bucket dredges were introduced to work the auriferous gravels of the rivers flowing westward from the Sierra Nevada. In the 1930's and continuing to 1955 these dredge operations were the principal producers of placer gold in the State (Clark, 1957, p. 223). In 1959 a major part of the State's placer production came from seven bucketline dredges in Sacramento and Yuba Counties (Davis and Ashizawa, 1960, p. 168, 192–193, 204).

The most productive gold-bearing region in the State is in the central part of the Sierra Nevada on the west slope (fig. 9). This region contains the Tertiary channel gravels, the Quaternary stream deposits, the Grass Valley-Nevada City lode district, the Alleghany and Downieville districts, and the complex vein system of the Mother Lode, East Belt, and West Belt. The Mother Lode and the placer deposits are exploited in many individual mining districts in numerous counties. The history and production of each of these districts are distinctive, but the geology is much the same. To avoid needless repetition of the geology of the Mother Lode in each of the five counties it traverses and the geology of each Tertiary placer district, this material is outlined in the following paragraphs.

The auriferous gravels of California are of two general types: buried placers of Tertiary age and normal stream placers of Quaternary age. The gold was derived from the many gold-bearing veins, including those of the Mother Lode, in the mountains that had been formed at the close of Jurassic time by the intrusion of the Sierra Nevada granitic batholith (Lindgren, 1911, p. 9–11), most of which was emplaced in Late Cretaceous time (Curtis and others, 1958, p. 10). A long period of erosion followed during Tertiary time when the mountains were nearly leveled, and gold from the eroded parts of the veins was concentrated in stream channels. Some of the resulting Tertiary placers were extremely rich. The Tertiary drainage system consisted of six main streams (Lindgren, 1911, p. 33–37). One of these, the Jura River, flowed northward in Plumas County; the others flowed westward. The names of the major westward-flowing streams, not to be confused with their present-day counterparts, are the Yuba in Yuba and Nevada Counties, the American in Placer and El Dorado Counties, the Mokelumne in Calaveras and Amador Counties, the Calaveras in Tuolumne and Calaveras Counties, and the Tuolumne in Tuolumne County. Near the end of the Tertiary Period, much of the region was covered with volcanic debris, composed chiefly of andesite. The old drainage pattern was obliterated, but a new one soon developed on the new volcanic surface as the present Sierra Nevada range was uplifted. During Quaternary time the new streams cut deep canyons through the volcanics, exposed and eroded parts of the old Tertiary channels, and reconcentrated some of the gold in the gravels of the new streams. Only scattered remnants of the Tertiary channels which are higher than the channels of the present streams are now found preserved beneath ridges of resistant volcanic rocks. Rich Quaternary placers have been mined very successfully in numerous districts along the present-day Feather, American, Yuba, Mokelumne, and Merced Rivers, and low-grade Quaternary placers have been profitably dredged in the central valley where the gradient of these rivers is nearly level and only fine-grained gold is concentrated.

Outstanding among the lode deposits of the Sierra Nevada is the Mother Lode system of gold deposits, a strip of mineralized rock 1 to 4 miles wide that extends 120 miles along the lower western flank of the Sierra Nevada. From near Georgetown in El Dorado County it extends southward to Mormon Bar, 21 miles southeast of Mariposa, in Mariposa County. The five counties it traverses—El Dorado, Amador, Calaveras, Tuolumne, and Mariposa—are often referred to as the Mother Lode counties.

The bedrock in the Mother Lode counties consists of steeply dipping, northwest-trending belts of phyllite, schist, slate, and greenstone, intruded locally by small bodies of peridotite and granodiorite (Knopf, 1929, p. 8–9). The oldest rock unit in the area, the Calaveras Formation of Carboniferous age, is composed chiefly of black phyllite with minor quartzite, limestone, and chert. Green amphibolite schists are interbedded with the Calaveras Formation and are believed to be of equivalent age (Knopf, 1929, p. 10). Overlying the Calaveras Formation is the Mariposa Slate, of Jurassic age. This unit, which is considerably less metamorphosed than the Calaveras, consists of black clay slates and graywacke with small local bodies of conglomerate, sericite schist, and limestone (Knopf, 1929, p. 12). Greenstones are intimately interlayered with the black slate. The rocks have been invaded by intrusives of several ages. The Calaveras Formation is cut by metadiorites, and both formations are intruded by lenses of serpentine, which was originally peridotite, and by dikes and masses of hornblendite, gabbro, granodiorite, and albitite porphyry. Potassium-argon age determinations on minerals of some of these granitic bodies give evidence of two separate orogenies in Mesozoic time—one in Late Jurassic and one in Late Cretaceous (Curtis and others, 1958, p. 5–10). All these rocks are overlain by patches and sinuous deposits of interbedded stream gravels and rhyolite, andesite, and basalt flows.

The Mother Lode gold deposits probably were formed during the final stages of the intrusion of the Sierra Nevada batholith (Knopf, 1929, p. 48).

The gold deposits of the Mother Lode are associated with a zone of reverse faulting that is parallel in general to the northwesterly trend of the Calaveras and Mariposa Formations but locally cuts all rock types of both formations. Ore bodies are of two general types—quartz veins and mineralized country rock (Knopf, 1929, p. 23).

The quartz veins are large tabular masses of quartz that strike northwest and dip northeast. Though they appear to be locally conformable with the country rock at the surface, the veins cut across various units of the country rock along the strike and down the dip. Individual veins, as much as 50 feet thick and a few thousand feet long, are localized in systems of parallel or subparallel lenses with blunt ends, some of which fray out into stringers. The vein mineralogy is simple. Milky quartz, the predominant veinfilling, is characteristically ribboned, different layers having been deposited at different times. A small amount of sulfides, mostly pyrite, accompanies the quartz (Knopf, 1929, p. 27). Gold occurs in the free state, commonly in steeply pitching shoots where the veins bulge or at vein junctions and in stringer lodes. The gold is interstitial with the quartz and the sulfides.

The ore bodies in country rock are of diverse types, but the mineralized greenstone, known as gray ore, and mineralized schists are the most productive. The mineralized greenstone is composed of

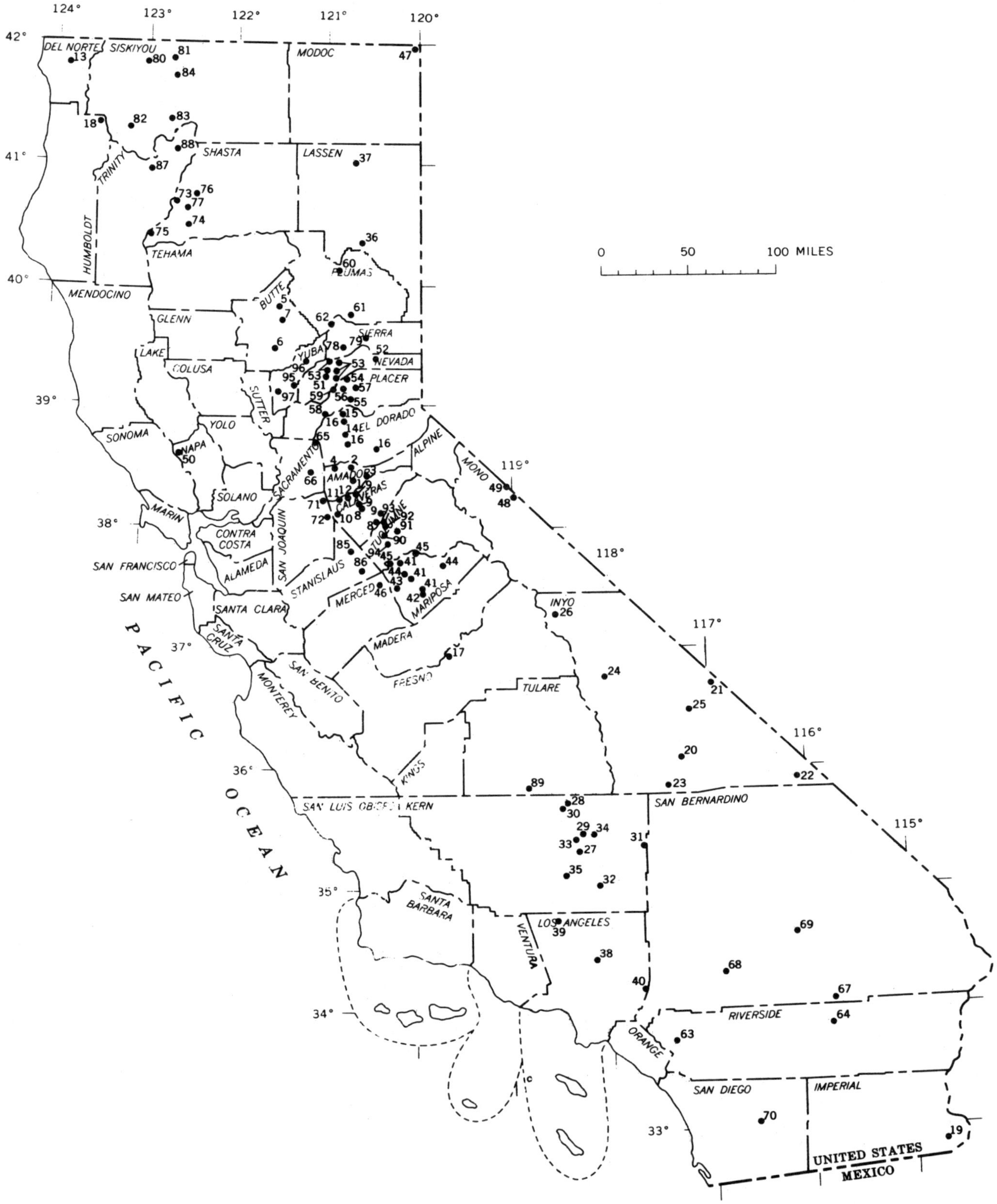

FIGURE 9.—Gold-mining districts of California.

ankerite, sericite, albite, quartz, and 3 to 4 percent pyrite and arsenopyrite (Knopf, 1929, p. 33). It is interlaced with veinlets of quartz, ankerite, and albite. Gold is intergrown with the sulfides or is interstitial with quartz. The mineralized schist ore bodies are composed chiefly of ankerite and subordinate sericite, pyrite, quartz, and albite (Knopf, 1929, p. 34). Free gold is associated with pyrite.

Flanking the main vein system of the Mother Lode on the east and west are two additional zones of mineralization known as the East Belt and West Belt. These belts are shorter and less continuous than the Mother Lode and may be separated from it by 5 to 15 miles of unmineralized country rock (Julihn and Horton, 1938, p. 4); nevertheless, they are similar to it genetically and mineralogically and many authors have considered them as part of the Mother Lode. In production reporting, however, the East Belt and West Belt have been considered as being districts separate from the Mother Lode; so to avoid confusion, this distinction is also made in this report.

Gold deposits are not confined to the Mother Lode area, for of the 58 counties in California, significant quantities of gold have been mined in 41. Production data for the counties are fairly complete since 1880, but for many individual districts they are spotty and fragmentary, even though many such

Amador County:
1, Mother Lode; 2, Fiddletown; 3, Volcano; 4, Cosumnes River placers.
Butte County:
5, Magalia; 6, Oroville; 7, Yankee Hill.
Calaveras County:
8, Mother Lode, East Belt, and West Belt; 9, Placers in Tertiary gravels; 10, Jenny Lind; 11, Camanche; 12, Campo Seco.
Del Norte County:
13, Smith River placers.
El Dorado County:
14, Mother Lode, East Belt, and West Belt; 15, Georgia Slide; 16, Placers in Tertiary gravels.
Fresno County:
17, Friant.
Humboldt County:
18, Klamath River placers.
Imperial County:
19, Cargo Muchacho.
Inyo County:
20, Ballarat; 21, Chloride Cliff; 22, Resting Springs; 23, Sherman; 24, Union; 25, Wild Rose; 26, Willshire-Bishop Creek.
Kern County:
27, Amalie; 28, Cove; 29, Green Mountain; 30, Keyes; 31, Rand; 32, Rosamond-Mojave; 33, Joe Walker mine; 34, St. John mine; 35, Pine Tree mine.
Lassen County:
36, Diamond Mountain; 37, Hayden Hill.
Los Angeles County:
38, Antelope Valley; 39, Acton; 40, San Gabriel.
Mariposa County:
41, Mother Lode, East Belt; 42, Mormon Bar; 43, Hornitos; 44, Merced River placers; 45, Placers in Tertiary gravels.
Merced County:
46, Snelling.
Modoc County:
47, High Grade.
Mono County:
48, Bodie; 49, Masonic.
Napa County:
50, Calistoga.
Nevada County:
51, Grass Valley-Nevada City; 52, Meadow Lake; 53, Tertiary placer districts.
Placer County:
54, Dutch Flat-Gold Run; 55, Foresthill; 56, Iowa Hill; 57, Michigan Bluff; 58, Ophir; 59, Rising Sun mine.
Plumas County:
60, Crescent Mills; 61, Johnsville; 62, La Porte.
Riverside County:
63, Pinacate; 64, Pinon-Dale.
Sacramento County:
65, Folsom; 66, Sloughhouse.
San Bernardino County:
67, Dale; 68, Holcomb; 69, Stedman.
San Diego County:
70, Julian.
San Joachin County:
71, Clements; 72, Bellota.
Shasta County:
73, Deadwood-French Gulch; 74, Igo; 75, Harrison Gulch; 76, West Shasta; 77, Whiskeytown.
Sierra County:
78, Alleghany and Downieville; 79, Sierra Buttes.
Siskiyou County:
80, Humbug; 81, Klamath River; 82, Salmon River; 83, Scott River; 84, Cottonwood-Fort Jones-Yreka.
Stanislaus County:
85, Oakdale-Knights Ferry; 86, Waterford.
Trinity County:
87, Trinity River; 88, Carrville.
Tulare County:
89, White River.
Tuolumne County:
90, Mother Lode; 91, East Belt; 92, Pocket Belt; 93, Columbia Basin-Jamestown-Sonora; 94, Groveland-Moccasin-Jacksonville.
Yuba County:
95, Browns Valley-Smartville; 96, Brownsville-Challenge-Dobbins; 97, Hammonton.

FIGURE 9.—Continued.

districts have had substantial production. In the publications of the U.S. Bureau of Mines (1925–34; 1933–66) and U.S. Geological Survey (1904–24) production data for several counties or districts frequently are combined or listed as unapportioned to conceal production of a specific company. Thus in this report the production totals for counties and districts are minimum figures.

AMADOR COUNTY

The initial discoveries, in 1849, of gold-quartz veins in Mariposa County at the southern end of the Mother Lode soon led to discoveries in Amador County, which became the most productive of the Mother Lode counties.

Placers were also productive after the 1850's, especially at Volcano, but also at Fiddletown and other localities along the Cosumnes River.

Early gold production is unrecorded, but from 1880 through 1959 Amador County produced 6,320,000 ounces. Between 1903 and 1958, a total of 4,173,947 ounces was produced from lode mines, and 289,835 ounces, from placers. In 1959 only 62 ounces, undifferentiated as to source, was produced. Carlson and Clark (1954, p. 164) estimated that lode mines produced a total of more than $160 million (about 7,729,000 ounces).

COSUMNES RIVER PLACERS

The Cosumnes River placers are along the Cosumnes River in the northwest part of Amador County, near Plymouth.

The U.S. Bureau of Mines (1933–66) reported that only 166 ounces of gold was produced from this district since 1932; however, Carlson and Clark (1954, p. 199) reported that in recent years intermittent dredging operations processed 2,125,000 cubic yards of gravel of the Cosumnes River, which averaged 18 cents in gold per cubic yard. This is roughly equivalent to 10,900 ounces of gold.

FIDDLETOWN DISTRICT

The Fiddletown district is in the southern part of T. 8 N., R. 11 E., in northwest Amador County. Only meager data are available on its history and production. Drift mining and dredging of the Tertiary gravels began in the 1850's and continued on a small scale until the early 1950's (Carlson and Clark, 1954, p. 199). Fragmentary records indicate that the district produced between 10,000 and 100,000 ounces of gold.

MOTHER LODE DISTRICT

The Mother Lode district, about a mile wide, crosses the west-central part of Amador County from north to south.

The lode mines began producing in the 1850's, and by 1872, 35 mills were in the district. The Old Eureka mine, 1,350 feet deep, was acknowledged as the deepest shaft in the United States (Knopf, 1929, p. 5) and was the largest producer on the entire Mother Lode in the early days. It was consolidated with the Central Eureka in 1924 after several years of inactivity. Production from these two mines to 1951 was about $36 million (Carlson and Clark, 1954, p. 174). Other important Mother Lode mines in Amador County were the Kennedy, Argonaut, and Keystone, which produced $34,280,000, $25,179,000, and $24,000,000 in gold respectively (Carlson and Clark, 1954, p. 166). Total production of the district through 1959 was about 7,675,000 ounces.

VOLCANO DISTRICT

The Volcano district is in T. 7 N., R. 12 E., in west-central Amador County. Other than brief mention by Lindgren (1911, p. 199) and Carlson and Clark (1954, p. 165), little has been published about this district.

Volcano was the center of the early hydraulic mining of the gravels of the Tertiary Mokelumne River. As production data were not found, it can only be roughly estimated that of the 289,835 ounces of gold produced from placers in Amador County since 1903, the Volcano district probably produced not more than 100,000 ounces, and this was before 1932.

BUTTE COUNTY

Butte County has held a high position among the gold-producing counties of California; nevertheless, very little has been published on the geology and production of the mining districts.

Most of the gold came from placers, which produced about 3,123,115 ounces from 1880 to 1959.

During 1903–58, Butte County produced 103,800 ounces of gold from lode mines and 2,332,960 ounces from placers. Although there is no record of gold production before 1880, undoubtedly there was intensive activity.

The major gold-producing districts in the county are Oroville (Quaternary placers), Magalia (Tertiary placers), and Yankee Hill (mostly lode, some Tertiary placers).

The western half of Butte County is covered by alluvial gravels; the eastern half is dominated by the northwest-trending Sierra Nevada composed of granitic batholith and the intruded older metavolcanics and metasediments (O'Brien, 1949, p. 417–433). These older metamorphic rocks are also intruded by serpentine and are covered locally by basalt flows of Miocene and Pliocene age.

The metavolcanics contain gold-bearing quartz veins in the area between Oroville, Cherokee City, and Oregon City. Gold-quartz veins are also present at Magalia.

MAGALIA DISTRICT

The Magalia district is in north-central Butte County near the town of Magalia.

Tertiary gravels of the Magalia channel, a minor Tertiary stream, were mined by underground methods in the early days. The Perschbaker, one of the major mines of the district, produced more than $1 million in gold to about 1910 (Lindgren, 1911, p. 92). Later production is not known, but O'Brien (1949, p. 429) noted that the mine had been idle since 1947.

The production of the entire district before 1932 cannot be determined; from 1932 through 1959 it was 15,976 ounces. Adding to this the 50,000 ounces representing the early production of the Perschbaker mine, we arrive at a minimum total of about 66,000 ounces for the district.

OROVILLE DISTRICT

The Oroville district is in southern Butte County, along the Feather River.

The Quaternary flood-plain gravels of the Feather River near Oroville yielded a total of 1,964,130 ounces of gold from 1903 to 1959 and therefore made the Oroville district the largest producer of Butte County. In 1898 the first floating bucketline dredge was successfully operated in the district (O'Brien, 1949, p. 420), and by 1905, 35 dredges were mining the Feather River gravels (Lindgren, 1911, p. 90). Production continued at a high rate until the early 1950's. From 1957 through 1959 only a few ounces per year was reported.

YANKEE HILL DISTRICT

The Yankee Hill district is in T. 21 N., Rs. 4 and 5 E., in central Butte County.

Most of the lode production of Butte County came from this district; however, published details on its history and geology were not found.

From 1929 through 1959 the district produced 34,427 ounces of gold from lode mines and 5,154 ounces from placers. Production before 1910 was about $1,520,000 (57,000 ounces), mostly from the Hearst mine (Lindgren, 1911, p. 84).

CALAVERAS COUNTY

Gold was discovered in Calaveras County in 1849 in gravels along Carson Creek, a tributary of the Stanislaus River. In 1850, rich lode deposits were found above the placer diggings on Carson Hill, where a single nugget from the outcrop was valued at more than $40,000 (Julihn and Horton, 1938, p. 12).

Many methods of placer mining have been utilized in working the Quaternary deposits in this county: hand rocking, sluicing, hydraulicking, dredging, and dragline operations. The rich auriferous channel gravels of the Tertiary Calaveras River and the Cataract or Table Mountain channel have been mined by drifts. Most of the production from 1880 through 1959 was from lode mines in the Mother Lode, East Belt, and West Belt districts.

There is no record of production before 1880, when mining of the rich placers was at its peak, but Julihn and Horton (1938, p. 21) estimated that the placers yielded a minimum of $50 million (about 2,415,000 ounces) in gold in the early years. From 1880 through 1959, a total of 580,600 ounces of gold was mined from placer deposits, and 2,045,700 ounces, from the siliceous ores of the Mother Lode, East Belt, and West Belt. Production since 1950 decreased sharply; in 1959 the county produced only 167 ounces of gold.

The Mother Lode, East Belt, and West Belt districts have produced nearly all the lode gold reported from Calaveras County. Copper ores in the Campo Seco district have yielded a relatively small amount of gold. Important placer localities are along the channel systems of the Tertiary Calaveras River and the Tertiary Table Mountain channel, and Quaternary gravels have been highly productive at Jenny Lind and Camanche.

CAMANCHE DISTRICT

The Camanche district is in northwest Calaveras County, near the Mokelumne River.

Gold was recovered, by bucket-type dredges and draglines, from late Tertiary or early Quaternary gravels, some of which are in the flood plain of the Mokelumne River. Production is not known, but 100,000 to 1 million ounces is estimated.

CAMPO SECO DISTRICT

The Campo Seco district, in Tps. 4 and 5 N., R. 10 E., in northwestern Calaveras County, has yielded gold from Quaternary gravels of the Mokelumne River and also as a byproduct of copper ores.

Most of the placer mining was before 1900, and the amount of gold produced in those early operations cannot be estimated. Most of the byproduct gold was from the Pern mine, which operated from 1899 to 1919 (Julihn and Horton, 1938, p. 112).

During that time an estimated 800,000 tons of ore was mined which contained 0.03 to 0.10 ounce of gold per ton, or a total of 40,000 to 50,000 ounces. The mine was inactive until 1937, when the workings were unwatered, and copper was recovered from the mine water. Significant amounts of gold were produced during the 1940's, but after World War II when the demand for copper ceased, the mine became dormant. Total gold production of the district was about 60,000 ounces.

The geology of the area was discussed briefly by Julihn and Horton (1938, p. 112–113). The ore bodies are massive sulfide replacement bodies in zones of amphibole schist and sericitized greenstone. The ore consists of an intimate mixture of fine-grained pyrite, chalcopyrite, and sphalerite, and smaller quantities of bornite and tetrahedrite.

JENNY LIND DISTRICT

In the Jenny Lind district, in T. 3 N., R. 10 E., along the Calaveras River, Quaternary and late Tertiary gravels have been mined on a large scale by dredges and draglines. The gold production is unknown but is probably between 100,000 and 1 million ounces.

MOTHER LODE, EAST BELT, AND WEST BELT DISTRICTS

The Mother Lode, East Belt, and West Belt districts compose a north-trending belt in the western part of Calaveras County that contains about 800 lode mines and prospects (Julihn and Horton, 1938, p. 94). These three districts are combined here because it has not been possible to assign specific production data to any one district nor to determine with any degree of accuracy which mines are in which district.

The first lodes discovered in the county were on Carson Hill, on the Mother Lode, where extremely rich gold-quartz ore was found in wallrocks adjacent to the vein outcrops. The discoveries precipitated a rush to the area which culminated in the founding of the town of Melones and the feverish exploitation of the rich ores of the now-classic Carson Hill (Julihn and Horton, 1938, p. 101–102). Elsewhere in the county, quartz mining developed more slowly. In the 1890's mines near Angels Camp boosted the output of Calaveras County above that of Amador County (Knopf, 1929, p. 6). The mines on Carson Hill have been the most productive in the county. By 1938 they had yielded a total of about $25 million in gold (Julihn and Horton, 1938, p. 107). At Angels Camp the Utica and Gold Cliff group produced gold valued at $16,400,000 (Julihn and Horton, 1938, p. 136). In the West Belt district, the Royal mine, discovered in the early 1870's, was the most important; to about 1938 its production was valued at about $3 million (Julihn and Horton, 1938, p. 117). The Sheepranch mine, the deepest and most productive in the East Belt district, had yielded about $5 million in gold by 1938 (Julihn and Horton, 1938, p. 110).

After 1950, lode mining in Calaveras County declined markedly; only a few ounces was produced in 1957–58. Total production from 1880 through 1959 was 2,045,700 ounces.

The geology of this district is discussed on pages 55–57.

PLACERS IN TERTIARY GRAVELS

The placers in Tertiary channel gravels in Calaveras County have been productive at Mokelumne Hill in T. 5 N., R. 11 E., at San Andreas in T. 4 N., R. 12 E., and near Murphys in T. 3 N., R. 14 E.

Two of the productive Tertiary channel systems —the Tertiary Calaveras River and the somewhat younger Cataract or Table Mountain channel—pass through the county (Julihn and Horton, 1938, p. 22). These deposits first were worked by both drift and hydraulic methods, but legislation curtailed hydraulicking, and drift mining was then used exclusively. Production before 1880 is unrecorded but probably was large. Records of the placer gold mined from these deposits since 1880 are incomplete because placer production from all sources was grouped in the annual reports. Incomplete records of individual drift mines total 106,000 ounces (Julihn and Horton, 1938, p. 33–75); therefore this total may be considered a minimum production from the Tertiary gravels.

DEL NORTE COUNTY

The most complete published account of the geology and ore deposits of Del Norte County is that of O'Brien (1952b, p. 266–267, 277–279).

The total gold production from 1880 through 1959 was about 44,700 ounces; about 40,000 ounces was from early placer operations along the Smith River and its tributaries. In the eastern part of the county, quartz veins and stringers containing gold, pyrite, and arsenopyrite occur in greenstone and slate near the contact with diorite and granodiorite. An undisclosed amount of gold has been recovered from copper ore in the Low Divide district in the northwestern part of the county.

EL DORADO COUNTY

The discovery of gold in El Dorado County in 1848 by James Marshall at Coloma, on the south fork of the American River 8 miles northwest of Placerville (Clark and Carlson, 1956, p. 371), was the widely publicized event that precipitated the fabulous gold rush to California in 1849. Soon thousands of gold seekers swarmed over the county, and in the 1850's it was one of the most populous areas in the State. With all the stream gravels being diligently worked, soon discoveries of vein deposits were made, and in 1851 lode mining began at Nashville (Clark and Carlson, 1956, p. 372). Since 1884, when legislation restricted hydraulic mining, lode mines have been the major source of gold in the county; however, the placers were rejuvenated briefly in the late 1930's, when large floating dragline dredges were introduced.

From 1880 through 1959, a total of 1,267,700 ounces of gold was mined in the county. From 1903, when systematic recording began, through 1958, about 190,600 ounces was mined from placers, and 534,000 ounces, from lode mines; data before 1880 have not been found.

The lode deposits are in quartz veins in the Mother Lode, in the East Belt, and in the West Belt. Lode gold also occurs in contact metamorphic and replacement deposits.

The most productive placer deposits were in the Tertiary channels near Placerville and in the Grizzly Flat-Fairplay-Indian Diggings area (Clark and Carlson, 1956, p. 431). Placer deposits are also found along the American and Cosumnes Rivers.

GEORGIA SLIDE DISTRICT

The Georgia Slide district is in T. 12 N., R. 10 E., in the northwestern part of El Dorado County.

This district, in the northern part of the Mother Lode, is characterized by its rich seams of gold that occur in narrow quartz veinlets that impregnate a zone several hundred feet wide in slate, amphibolite, and chlorite schist of the Mariposa Slate. Intersections of two vein systems, or of a large quartz vein, with a veinlet system are richest in gold. The upper parts of these veins were weathered extensively and the soluble components were removed, but the gold remained and was thus concentrated. In the 1860's and 1870's these deposits were worked by hydraulicking. After the residual mantle was removed, the unweathered deposits were mined by conventional underground methods (Clark and Carlson, 1956, p. 435).

Gold production from this district through 1955 was estimated at $6 million (Clark and Carlson, 1956, p. 436). No activity has been reported in recent years.

MOTHER LODE, EAST BELT, AND WEST BELT DISTRICTS

The Mother Lode, East Belt, and West Belt districts, composing a zone 10 to 20 miles wide extending from north to south in western El Dorado County, are combined here because their individual production cannot be determined.

Most of the lode gold produced in the county to 1959 came from mines of the Mother Lode which were developed in the early 1850's. Two of these, the Union and Church mines, produced $600,000 in gold before 1868 (Clark and Carlson, 1956, p. 427). The Union was the largest in this district, with a total gold production of $2,700,000 to $5 million (Clark and Carlson, 1956, p. 427). Other mines with $1 million or more total production are the Big Canyon, Mount Pleasant, Pyramid, Sliger, Taylor, and Zantgraf.

From 1903 through 1958 the lode mines of the district produced roughly 500,000 ounces of gold. Total production could possibly be 1 million ounces or more.

The geology of this district is covered in the description of the Mother Lode on pages 55–57.

PLACERS IN TERTIARY GRAVELS

Placer gold has been mined from Tertiary gravels in three localities in El Dorado County: Georgetown in the northern part in T. 12 N., R. 10 E., Placerville in the west-central part in T. 10 N., R. 11 E., and Grizzly Flat about 18 miles south of Placerville in T. 9 N., R. 13 E.

The most productive channels in the county were at Placerville where a total of $25 million in gold was extracted after the 1860's (Clark and Carlson, 1956, p. 433). Production from the Georgetown and Grizzly Flat areas is not known. From 1903 through 1959 the production from these three areas totaled about 190,000 ounces. Annual production has been combined with that of the Mother Lode, East Belt, and West Belt districts by U.S. Bureau of Mines (1933–1966).

FRESNO COUNTY

Most of the early production of Fresno County came from lode mines in the area now included in Madera County, which was created from part of Fresno County in 1893 (Logan and others, 1951, p. 503). The gold production of Fresno County from 1880 to 1892 (Logan and others, 1951, p. 494) is credited to Madera County on page 67 of this present report. From 1880 to 1959, the placer and lode gold production of the area remaining in Fresno county was 121,000 ounces. After 1929, most of the gold came from placers, but some was a byproduct of the sand and gravel operations at various points along the San Joaquin River between Friant and Herndon. During 1940–42, $196,977 worth of gold was recovered from sand and gravel processed for use in building Friant Dam on San Joaquin River (Logan and others, 1951, p. 503).

HUMBOLDT COUNTY

Gold is the principal mineral resource of Humboldt County. The bulk of the production has been from Quaternary placer deposits in channels and terraces along the Trinity and Klamath Rivers. There has also been some placer mining of beach sands. Averill (1941b, p. 508–516) listed six lode properties and 12 placer properties in the county. Total production through 1959 was 131,300 ounces of gold.

There are some lode deposits in quartz veins in andesite, in Precambrian schists, and in diorite, but details of the geology of the county have not been published.

IMPERIAL COUNTY

Gold deposits are scattered throughout Imperial County in the numerous desert mountain ranges, but the bulk of the production has come from the eastern third of the county, particularly the Cargo Muchacho, Picacho, and Tumco districts. Other smaller producing districts are the Chocolate Mountains and the Paymaster districts.

Data on production are incomplete, but mining was done in the Picacho district as early as 1857. From 1907 to 1941 about 81,000 ounces of gold was mined in the county (Sampson and Tucker, 1942, p. 110–111); however, Henshaw (1942, p. 152) credited the Cargo Muchacho district alone with about $4 million in gold (193,500 ounces). Minimum total production for the county is about 235,000 ounces: only a small amount was produced from placers, the rest came from lodes.

Sampson and Tucker (1942, p. 112–113) gave brief accounts of the geology of the auriferous areas. In the Cargo Muchacho Mountains, the gold deposits consist of small gold-bearing quartz veins that cut metasediments and dioritic and monzonitic intrusives. The Picacho Mountains are composed of lavas, tuffs, and conglomerates underlain by gneisses and schists that contain the auriferous veins. A few small gold-producing localities are in the Chocolate Mountains, but their production has been minor. Through 1959, only the Cargo Muchacho district had produced more than 10,000 ounces of gold.

CARGO MUCHACHO DISTRICT

The Cargo Muchacho district is in the southeast corner of Imperial County, immediately northeast of Ogilby.

Mining began here on a fairly large scale in 1879, but previously there had been desultory activity by explorers and Mexicans. From 1892 to 1938 the district produced $2,437,760 in gold (Henshaw, 1942, p. 153). Total production of the district to 1938 is conservatively estimated at about $4 million, or about 193,500 ounces (Henshaw, 1942, p. 152). From 1938 through 1959, the output was 31,200 ounces of gold, mostly from lodes, but some was from dry placers. The district was idle in 1959.

Rocks exposed in the district are predominantly quartzite, schists, and arkosite of possible Precambrian age (Henshaw, 1942, p. 149) that have been separated into the Vitrefrax and Tumco Formations. These were intruded by quartz diorite, quartz monzonite, and granite of probable Mesozoic age and andesite dikes of probable Tertiary age (Henshaw, 1942, p. 153–190). The ore deposits are tabular bodies of quartz, gold, and copper sulfides that are alined along major north-trending faults in the area. Where fractures were open, as in the metamorphic rocks and quartz diorite, economic concentrations of metals were deposited, but in the granite or quartz monzonite the fractures were rather tight and very little material was deposited. Gold occurs as fine grains disseminated through the country rock, as wire gold and grains in quartz veins, as microscopic grains in pyrite, and as placer nuggets (Henshaw, 1942, p. 184).

INYO COUNTY

Gold has been produced from numerous mines scattered throughout Inyo County, but, unfortunately, details of the geology and production of individual districts are incomplete.

From 1880 through 1959, a total of 496,000 ounces of gold was mined in the county. Most of this was lode production, but a considerable quantity was a byproduct from lead-silver, tungsten, and copper ores. Mining began as early as 1861 (Knopf, 1918, p. 105) in the Russ district in the Inyo Range, but production data for these early years are incomplete.

The lode deposits are scattered throughout numerous mountain ranges in the county. The most important gold-producing districts are the Ballarat and Wild Rose in the Panamint Range, the Chloride Cliff in the Funeral Range, the Resting Springs in the Nopah Range, the Sherman in the Argus Range, the Union in the Inyo Range, and the Willshire-Bishop Creek, an important tungsten district on the east slope of the Sierras. In the early days, gold placers were worked on a small scale in Mazourka and Marble Canyons, on the west and east slopes of the Inyo Range.

BALLARAT DISTRICT

The Ballarat (South Park) district, at about lat 36°00′ N. and long 117°10′ W., is in the Panamint Range in south-central Inyo County.

The Ratcliff mine, the chief mine in this district, was located in 1897 and in the next 6 years it produced gold valued between $300,000 and $1 million (Norman and Stewart, 1951, p. 47–48). After an indefinite period of inactivity, the mine produced $250,000 in gold from 1927 to 1942 (Norman and Stewart, 1951, p. 48). A much more conservative estimate of $500,000 as the total production from the entire district was given by Nolan (1936b, p. 39). The district was active on a small scale in 1959.

The Ratcliff ore body is in a north-trending vein in country rock that has been described variously as a biotite schist, sericite schist, metaquartzite, or conglomerate schist (Norman and Stewart, 1951, p. 48). The vein consists of quartz lenses and masses containing gold associated with pyrrhotite, pyrite, and chalcopyrite.

CHLORIDE CLIFF DISTRICT

The Chloride Cliff district, at lat 36°40′ N. and long 116°55′ W., is on the slope of the Funeral Range.

The district, discovered about 1903, had a total gold production of about 60,000 ounces through 1959, mostly from Keane Wonder mine. Most of the activity in the district occurred before 1916 (Nolan, 1936b, p. 36), and since then there has been only sporadic small production.

Only brief accounts of the geology of the district were found in the literature. Nolan (1936b, p. 36) reported that the deposits consisted of gold-bearing quartz veins in Paleozoic sedimentary rocks. Norman and Stewart (1951, p. 38) stated that lenticular quartz ore bodies are enclosed in schist at the Keane Wonder mine.

RESTING SPRINGS DISTRICT

Gold is a byproduct from lead-silver ores in the Resting Springs district, which is 5 to 10 miles east of Tecopa, in the southeast corner of Inyo County.

Discovered in 1865, the district produced very little before 1910 (Nolan, 1936b, p. 39). The period 1912–28 was one of fairly large scale activity and about $3 million in lead and silver was produced from the Shoshone group of mines (Norman and Stewart, 1951, p. 80). The amount of gold produced in this interval is not given. From 1939 to 1959 the district produced 15,005 ounces of gold.

Only brief accounts of the geology of this district appear in the published literature. Nolan (1936b, p. 39) described the deposits as lenticular bodies of oxidized lead-silver ore along fissures in Paleozoic sedimentary rocks. Norman and Stewart (1951, p. 80) stated that the country rock is Noonday Dolomite, of Early Cambrian age, and that the ore deposits are fissure fillings in a fault zone that strikes northwest and dips moderately to the northeast. The ore is localized at the intersections of the main fault zone with nearly vertical north-trending cross fractures. The predominant ore minerals are argentiferous galena in the primary ore and cerussite and anglesite in the oxidized ore.

SHERMAN DISTRICT

The Sherman district is 10 to 15 miles southwest of Ballarat, in T. 23 S., Rs. 42 and 43 E., in the Argus Range.

The chief gold producers have been the Arondo and the Ruth gold mines; other mines in the district worked for lead and silver have also yielded gold as a byproduct.

There was some activity in the district from the 1890's through World War I (Norman and Stewart, 1951, p. 38). From 1939 through 1941, the district produced 14,184 ounces of lode gold. No production was reported from 1942 to 1959 and data before 1932 have not been found.

The deposit at the Arondo mine consists of finely divided free gold in quartz fragments and stringers mixed with talcose and clay gangue, and siderite and hematite in a shear zone in granitic country rock (Norman and Stewart, 1951, p. 38, 49). At the Ruth mine, the ore consists of free gold associated with pyrite in iron-stained quartz stringers in a fissure in quartz monzonite country rock.

UNION DISTRICT

The Union (Inyo Range) district is between lat 36°35′ and 36°45′ N. and long 118°00′ and 118°10′ W., in the Inyo Range in north-central Inyo County.

Gold deposits were discovered in the 1860's by Mexicans (Knopf, 1918, p. 118). Both veins and placers were worked, but the placers were soon exhausted. Many veins in the district have been worked, but the chief producers were the Reward and Brown Monster veins which produced $200,000 in gold before 1884 (Knopf, 1918, p. 121). In more recent years operations in the district have been desultory. Total gold production for the district could not be determined, but was estimated to be between 10,000 and 50,000 ounces. The geology of the area was described by Knopf (1918, p. 121–122, pl. 2). The country rock consists of Carboniferous shale, limestone, and conglomerate, and Triassic shales, tuffs, and volcanic breccias. These rocks were intruded by masses of granite and quartz monzonite and the veins are distributed near the contacts between the intruded and intrusive rocks. The near-surface ore is highly oxidized and consists mainly of quartz and minor amounts of limonite, calamine, chrysocolla, and wulfenite. Unoxidized ore consists of quartz with small amounts of pyrite, galena, sphalerite, and chalcopyrite.

WILD ROSE DISTRICT

The Wild Rose district is at about lat 36°25′ N. and long 117°07′ W., in the Panamint Range.

Deposits were discovered in this area about 1906, and the peak production period was 1908–17, when about $1½ million, chiefly in gold, was produced from the Skidoo mine (Nolan, 1936b, p. 39). Since then various lessees have worked the property for short periods, but production is not known (Norman and Stewart, 1951, p. 51). Minimum total gold production for this district through 1959 was about 73,000 ounces.

Descriptions of the geology of this area are sketchy. Nolan (1936b, p. 39) reported that the deposits are gold-quartz veins in granitic gneiss. Norman and Stewart (1951, p. 51) stated that there are two systems of veins in a body of quartz monzonite and that both have been explored by more than a mile of underground workings.

WILLSHIRE-BISHOP CREEK DISTRICT

The Willshire-Bishop Creek district, 7 to 17 miles west of Bishop, is on the east slope of the Sierra Nevada and in the Tungsten Hills.

This is predominantly a tungsten district, but some gold has been produced as a byproduct. Activity began about 1916 and continued through 1959. The Pine Creek mine, the largest domestic tungsten producer, was the principal source of gold mined in the district, and through the 1950's was the chief source of gold in Inyo County. The Cardinal Gold Mining Co. deposit was mined for gold alone, but it has been closed since 1938 (Bateman, 1956, p. 80). The gold production of this district through 1959 was between 75,000 and 100,000 ounces.

In the mineralized parts of the district the predominant country rock consists of a complex of granitic to dioritic intrusive bodies and roof pendants and discontinuous septa of metavolcanic and metasedimentary rocks of varied lithologic types. The metamorphic rocks are of Paleozoic and Mesozoic age; the igneous intrusives are of later Mesozoic age (Bateman, 1956, p. 9). At the Pine Creek mine, a folded pendant almost 7 miles long that consists of marble, biotite-quartz, hornfels, and metavolcanic rocks is bounded by granite, quartz monzonite, and hornblende gabbro. The tungsten ore bodies are in masses of tactite in the marble along its contact with quartz monzonite. Scheelite and powellite are disseminated in pyroxene and garnet tactite. Molybdenum ore shoots are in silicified zones in tactite bodies containing the ore minerals molybdenite, chalcopyrite, and bornite. Gold is recovered from these sulfides during smelting (Bateman, 1956, p. 22–34).

The deposit at the Cardinal mine is in a shear zone in quartzite in a quartzite and schist septum bordered by quartz monzonite and granodiorite. The ore minerals, which are finely disseminated in the sheared quartzite, consist dominantly of pyrrhotite with lesser amounts of arsenopyrite, sphalerite, chalcopyrite, pyrite, and molybdenite. Most of the gold is in the sulfides, but some of it is free (Bateman, 1956, p. 80, 81).

KERN COUNTY

Gold was discovered in Kern County in 1851 in Greenhorn Gulch, near the Kern River, by a member of General Fremont's party. Mining began in 1852 at the Keyes and Mammoth mines in the Keyes district. From 1880 through 1959 about 1,777,000 ounces of gold was mined, mostly from lode deposits. The major districts are the Amalie, Cove, Green Mountain, Keyes, Rand, and Rosamond-Mojave.

AMALIE DISTRICT

The Amalie district is between the south summits of the Piute Mountains and Caliente Creek in T. 30 S., Rs. 33 and 34 E. The principal mine, the Amalie, produced $600,000 in gold through 1932 (Tucker and Sampson, 1933, p. 280–281). Total production of the district through 1959 was about 30,000 ounces; nearly all production was from lode mines.

The country rock is dominantly granitic and contains narrow belts of schist and slate. Most of the veins are found in quartz porphyry.

COVE DISTRICT

The Cove district is 45 miles northeast of Bakersfield near Kernville, in T. 25 S., R. 33 E.

In the late 1850's a few placers were worked in the Cove district by the more persistent of the prospectors drawn to the area by the original discoveries in Kern County, along the Kern River, in 1851. Gold-bearing quartz veins were found in 1860. The towns of Quartzburg and Kernville, which were founded in the boom that followed, experienced a period of orderly growth and prosperity. The Big Blue mine of Kern Mines, Inc., was discovered early in the history of the district. The mine became the major producer and was credited with $1,746,910 in gold to 1933 (Tucker and others, 1949, p. 211); most of this production was in the first few years of the mine's activity. In 1883 most of the workings were destroyed by fire, and the mine was inactive until 1907 when the first of several unsuccessful attempts was made to rehabilitate the property.

Total gold production of the district through 1959 was about 262,800 ounces; none had been reported since 1942.

The country rock consists of metasediments—phyllites, quartzites, and limestone of the Kernville Series of Carboniferous(?) age, and the Isabella Granodiorite and acidic dikes of Jurassic(?) age. The granodiorite is probably related to the main Sierra Nevada batholith (Prout, 1940, p. 385–389; Miller and Webb, 1940, p. 378).

The metamorphic rocks are intensely deformed and crumpled by the intrusive rock. Along the east edge of the Cove district is the north-trending Kern Canyon fault, the major structure in the area.

Ore deposits consist of veins which seem to be related to the closing stages of igneous activity. The veins occur in shear zones, parallel to the Kern Canyon fault, and are associated with acidic dikes that cut the granodiorite and metasediments (Prout, 1940, p. 386, 391–392). The veins are dominantly quartz with small amounts of calcite. The ore minerals are gold, which occurs in the free state, arsenopyrite, galena, and sphalerite (Prout, 1940, p. 411–412).

GREEN MOUNTAIN DISTRICT

The Green Mountain district includes the area between Piute, on the west slope of the Piute Mountains, and the edge of Kelsey Valley, on the east side of the Piute Mountains.

Gold production of this district through 1959 was about 33,100 ounces. The Bright Star mine was the major producer, with an estimated $600,000 total output (Tucker and Sampson, 1933, p. 280).

Bedrock in the area consists of metasedimentary rocks of the Kernville Series of Carboniferous(?) age and Isabella Granodiorite of Jurassic(?) age (Miller and Webb, 1940, p. 349–358). The metasedimentary rocks occur in northwest-trending bands and include marble, phyllite, mica schist, and quartzite. The gold deposits are in small, but rich, shoots in narrow quartz veins.

KEYES DISTRICT

The Keyes district, 35 miles north of Caliente in T. 26 S., Rs. 32 and 33 E., produced about 39,600 ounces of gold through 1959, all from lodes.

Detailed accounts of the history and geology of this district were not found; however, Tucker and Sampson (1933, p. 283) reported that the deposits in the district are in narrow high-grade veins in granite.

RAND DISTRICT

The Rand district is on the San Bernardino-Kern County line. Randsburg, 45 miles northeast of Mojave, is in the center of the district. Although more than half the area is in San Bernardino County, nearly all the gold mined in the district has come from the western part, in Kern County. This is the most important district in Kern County, and it contains the largest gold mine in the county, the Yellow Aster. Gold has been the chief commodity mined; silver has been a byproduct.

Placer gold was discovered in the winter of 1893–94 at Goler Wash, 9 miles northwest of Randsburg, and by 1895 the lode deposits of the Yellow Aster mine were developed (Hess, 1910, p. 31–32). Of the estimated $9 to $10 million worth of ore mined before 1910, the Yellow Aster produced $6 million (Hess, 1910, p. 32).

Tucker and Sampson (1933, p. 285–286) gave estimates of the production and a brief account of the geology. Gold production through 1959 was 836,300 ounces, all but about 1,700 ounces was from lode mines.

The country rock in the gold-producing part of the district consists of the Rand Schist and the Atolia Quartz Monzonite which intruded the schist. Numerous rhyolite pipes, dikes, and sills of late Miocene age are found locally. Gold ores occur in fissure veins and as impregnations and stockworks in both the monzonite and Rand schist. The strongest veins have been found to be in two systems—one strikes N. 80° E. and the other, northwest. The principal vein minerals are quartz, arsenopyrite, pyrite, galena, gold, scheelite, iron oxides, and calcite. Only the oxidized parts of the veins have been mined.

ROSAMOND-MOJAVE DISTRICT

The Rosamond-Mojave district is 4 miles southwest of Mojave, in Tps. 10 and 11 N., Rs. 11, 12, and 13 W. Production from this district, all from lode mines, to about 1933 was about $3½ million in gold and silver, and gold was apparently the major commodity. This includes production from the Tropico mines, which are a short distance outside the district (Tucker and Sampson, 1933, p. 280–284). Total gold production through 1959 was about 278,250 ounces.

Granite, the oldest rock in the district, is overlain by rhyolite porphyry, which is well exposed throughout the area. The rhyolite porphyry is overlain by sheets and remnants of rhyolite (Tucker and Sampson, 1933, p. 283). Gold deposits are in steeply dipping quartz veins in the rhyolite porphyry that seem to flatten at depth and then follow the porphyry-granite contact. The veinfilling consists of quartz, granite fragments, calcite, ferruginous clay, and manganese (Tucker and Sampson, 1933, p. 284). Native gold occurs in association with pyrite, chalcopyrite, and minor amounts of galena, marcasite, and sphalerite. The silver minerals are cerargyrite and argentite (Tucker and Sampson, 1933, p. 284).

OTHER LOCALITIES

Several additional gold-producing localities in Kern County were listed by Tucker and Sampson (1933, p. 280). These are the Joe Walker mine, 7 miles northwest of Piute in T. 29 S., R. 33 E., with a production valued at $600,000; the St. John mine, 16 miles south of Weldon in T. 28 S., R. 35 E., with a production worth $700,000; and the Pine Tree mine in T. 11 N., R. 15 W., which produced $250,000 worth of gold. The Pioneer district, mentioned by Tucker and Sampson (1933, p. 280) as having produced $500,000 in gold, could not be located, and no additional data on this district were found in the literature.

LASSEN COUNTY

Gold production from Lassen County has come mainly from the Diamond Mountain and Hayden Hill districts.

Production for 1880–1959 was 107,200 ounces. There probably was considerable production, especially from placers, before 1880, but no systematic records of this have been found.

DIAMOND MOUNTAIN DISTRICT

The Diamond Mountain district is 6 miles south of Susanville in T. 29 N., Rs. 11 and 12 E.

In the early days, most of the production was from placers; later it was almost entirely from lodes. The total recorded gold production through 1959 was 21,800 ounces, of which at least 9,700 ounces came from placers.

The district is underlain by intrusive rocks of Mesozoic age that are overlain by Tertiary gravels, lava, and alluvium (Averill and Erwin, 1936, p. 409–422). The intrusive rocks consist of biotite-quartz diorite, hornblende-quartz diorite, and granite. Overlying the gravels and capping some of the mountains are andesite lavas of Pliocene age.

The lode deposits are gold-quartz veins that occur in all three types of the igneous rocks, but the most productive deposits are in the biotite-quartz diorite. The Tertiary gravels are auriferous and have been mined locally.

HAYDEN HILL DISTRICT

The Hayden Hill district is in north-central Lassen County, in Tps. 36 and 37 N., Rs. 10 and 11 E.

Estimated production for 1880–1959, utilizing estimates of Hill (1915, p. 32), was about 116,000 ounces, and all may be attributed to the lode mines, because there is no record of any placer production.

Gold was discovered in this district in 1870; in 1873 it produced $40,000 in gold. The periods 1880–84 and 1904–9 were the most productive. In 1910 most of the town of Hayden Hill was destroyed by fire (Hill, 1915, p. 30–31), and the district remained almost inactive through 1959.

The geology of this district was described by Hill (1915, p. 30–38), and the following is from his report. The country rock in the Hayden Hill district is rhyolite tuff of Tertiary age. This is cut by two sets of gold-bearing quartz veins of late Tertiary age; one trends N. 68° W., the other N. 38° E. Unconsolidated fault breccia fills many of the veins. Gold, accompanied by pyrolusite, occurs with fine sandy material in the veins.

LOS ANGELES COUNTY

Gold was mined in Los Angeles County—long before James Marshall's discovery in El Dorado County in 1848—by Spaniards and Mexicans who worked placers 35 miles northwest of Los Angeles from 1834 to 1838. During the rush to California many prospectors settled in the Los Angeles area, where in 1857–58 more than 6,000 people were mining gold (Gay and Hoffman, 1954, p. 493).

Most of the production from the county was from lode deposits, although the San Gabriel district produced considerable placer gold. Gay and Hoffman (1954, p. 497) reported total county gold production at more than $2¼ million (about 109,200 ounces). From 1957 through 1959 gold mining was restricted to small yields from itinerant sand-and-gravel operations.

Gold has been mined at many places in the county. Some of the larger producers are the Acton and Neenach lode districts, the Bouquet and Texas Canyon placer districts, and lode and placer districts in the San Gabriel Mountains near Mount Baldy and in eastern San Gabriel Canyon. More than half the county production from 1880 through 1953 came from the Governor lode near Acton (Gay and Hoffman, 1954, p. 497).

ACTON DISTRICT

The Acton (Cedar and Mount Gleason) district, in north-central Los Angeles County, produced at least 50,000 ounces of gold during 1880–1959, all attributed to lode mines, the most important of which was the Governor mine.

Pyritiferous gold-bearing veins occupy faults and zones of fractures in basic intrusives and metamorphic rocks of the Pelona Schist (age unknown) and in the San Gabriel Complex of Precambrian(?) age (Gay and Hoffman, 1954, p. 494).

ANTELOPE VALLEY DISTRICT

The Antelope Valley district is in northwest Los Angeles County, south of Neenach, along the Kern County line.

Gold was discovered in this area in 1934, and a small rush immediately followed. Although many claims were staked and many pits were dug, only the group of claims controlled by the Rivera Mining Co. was successful. Most of the mining was done during the first few years, and by 1946 all properties were idle (Wiese, 1950, p. 47). Total production was about 9,700 ounces of gold.

The country rock in the vicinity of the gold deposits is quartz monzonite of Jurassic(?) age. It contains large inclusions of limestone, hornfels, and quartzite, which are remnants of a metasedimentary sequence tentatively regarded to be of Paleozoic age (Wiese, 1950, p. 18–19).

The ore deposits are in quartz veins along the contact between the quartz monzonite and metasedimentary rocks. The gold occurs free in the quartz or is associated with sulfides that are present in small amounts (Wiese, 1950, p. 47).

SAN GABRIEL DISTRICT

The San Gabriel district, in east-central Los Angeles County, has produced both placer and lode gold. The San Gabriel River area has been worked intermittently for placer gold since 1848, but no production was reported for 1957–59. Before 1874, more than $2 million worth of placer gold (about 100,000 ounces) was mined; since 1880, about 20,000 ounces was mined. The lodes are credited with 50,000 ounces of gold (Gay and Hoffman, 1954, p. 495–496), most of which was probably mined before 1880. Total production for the district was about 165,000 ounces.

The lode deposits consist of gold-quartz veins that cut metamorphosed igneous and other metamorphosed rocks of the San Gabriel complex (Gay and Hoffman, 1954, p. 495). The veins are narrow and discontinuous, and the ore shoots are irregularly distributed.

MADERA COUNTY

A variety of metals and nonmetals occurs in economic amounts in Madera County. In addition to gold, there are important tungsten deposits and occurrences of natural gas.

Madera County was formed from part of Fresno County in 1893, and included within the new county were nearly all the productive gold mines. Gold-quartz ore was found at or near the contact of the Sierra Nevada batholith with pre-Cretaceous schist and slate in an area that extends from Grub Gulch to Hildreth (Logan, 1950, p. 447). In the 1950's small amounts of gold came from dredging operations along the Fresno, Chowchilla, and San Joaquin Rivers. After 1954 gold mining virtually ceased; no production was reported in 1959. Total production for the county through 1959 was 79,281 ounces, mostly from placers. It has not been possible to delineate any mining districts that have produced as much as 10,000 ounces of gold.

MARIPOSA COUNTY

Mariposa County, the southernmost of the Mother Lode counties, has had a long and productive mining history. Most of the gold has come from lode mines on the Mother Lode and West Belt and lode and placer mines in the Hornitos district. Quaternary gravels have been productive along the Merced River and near Mormon Bar. Before 1900, unrecorded amounts of gold were mined from Tertiary placers in the Blanchard district in the Jawbone Ridge area and on the ridge between Moore and Jordan Creeks.

Gold production of Mariposa County for 1880–1959 was about 2,144,500 ounces: about 583,500 ounces came from placers and about 1,561,000 ounces came from lodes. Production before 1880 has not been determined.

Gold mining began at an early date in the county. Gravels along Agua Fria and Mariposa Creeks were worked before 1849 and were thoroughly mined out by the hordes of prospectors who overran the area during the gold rush of 1849. By July 1849 a stamp mill was processing ore from the first lode discovery in the county, the Mariposa mine on the Mother Lode (Bowen and Gray, 1957, p. 39, 43).

Lode mining in Mariposa County was inhibited by the controversial Las Mariposas land grant which gave title to 14 of the 24 miles of the Mother Lode in the county to Gen. John C. Fremont. This grant was unsurveyed and was made before gold was discovered. Long before Fremont attempted to establish his right, the grant was overrun with prospectors and miners, who understandably were reluctant to give up what they considered just claims. After years of conflict in and out of the courts, Fremont's claim to the grant was formally recognized. But by then the property was plagued by mismanagement and inefficiency and the mines never fulfilled the expectations of the authorities who evaluated them (Julihn and Horton, 1940, p. 95–96).

Another large estate, the Cook estate, which encompassed most of the mines along a 2-mile length of the Mother Lode in the Coulterville area, further complicated operations on the Mother Lode in Mariposa County (Julihn and Horton, 1940, p. 96–97).

Despite the early frustrations, lode mining in Mariposa County flourished and was especially successful in the late 1930's and early 1940's before most of the mines closed in compliance with War Production Board Order L–208 issued in October 1942. After World War II gold mining declined, and during 1950–59 the average annual gold output was less than 1,000 ounces.

The western two-thirds of the county is underlain by metasedimentary rocks and metavolcanics of Paleozoic and Late Jurassic age, and the eastern one-third is underlain chiefly by intrusives of Late Jurassic or Early Cretaceous age (Bowen and Gray, 1957, p. 45). The intrusive rocks consist of various types of granitic and peridotitic rocks, but biotite-hornblende granodiorite is predominant.

HORNITOS DISTRICT

The Hornitos district, in western Mariposa County at lat 37°30′ N. and long 120°14′ W., is noted for gold production from both placers and lodes.

In the early days the Quaternary gravels of Hornitos Creek yielded considerable gold, but these were nearly exhausted before 1900. The lode mines are all west of the Mother Lode, in the zone of veins referred to as the West Belt. Total production from the district is not known, but a minimum of 500,000 ounces seems to be a reasonable estimate.

The gold deposits of the West Belt are in veins that cut several rock types, chiefly metasedimentary rocks of the Mariposa Formation of Jurassic age. The Mariposa is intruded locally by serpentinized peridotite, pyroxenite, basic intrusives altered to hornblende schists, and acid intrusives such as granite and granodiorite (Julihn and Horton, 1940, p. 116–117). Most of the gold deposits are along contacts of igneous rocks and metasedimentary rocks.

MERCED RIVER PLACERS

Quaternary gravels along the Merced River west of Bagby were a source of placer gold in the late 1860's and 1870's (Bowen and Gray, 1957, p. 187), but little activity has been reported in recent years. Production from these deposits is not known, but probably was at least 50,000 ounces of gold.

MORMON BAR DISTRICT

The Mormon Bar district is in T. 5 S., R. 18 E., about 2½ miles south of the town of Mariposa.

In the early days of mining in Mariposa County, the headwaters of Mariposa Creek near Mormon Bar was the scene of considerable placer activity. By 1870, however, the deposits, which were only about 6 feet thick, were almost worked out, and thereafter the placer output of the entire county averaged only a few hundred ounces per year (Julihn and Horton, 1940, p. 159, 162). In the late 1930's a slight revival took place, and the gravels at Mormon Bar were worked industriously by dragline (Julihn and Horton, 1940, p. 159). Total gold production for the district is estimated at about 75,000 ounces.

MOTHER LODE AND EAST BELT DISTRICTS

The Mother Lode, which has its southern terminus in Mariposa County, is a northwest-trending zone that is 3 or 4 miles wide and extends from the town of Mormon Bar northward through Coulterville into Tuolumne County. Roughly parallel veins east of this zone are referred to as the East Belt.

Though much has been said about the production of the Mother Lode, the mines of the East Belt and

West Belt (Hornitos) districts have produced most of the lode gold in Mariposa County. Recorded production from mines on the Mother Lode to about 1939 totaled $6,300,000 (Julihn and Horton, 1940, p. 103–116). Prominent among these are the Princeton, Pine Tree and Josephine, and the Mount Ophir. The East Belt in Mariposa County is a continuation of the same belt in Tuolumne and Calaveras Counties, to the north. Incomplete production data from individual mines give a minimum total of almost $12 million in gold to about 1939 (Julihn and Horton, 1940, p. 134–158). The major mines in this area are the Original and Ferguson, Hite, and Mariposa. Total gold production of the Mother Lode and East Belt districts through 1959 was approximately 1,009,000 ounces.

The geology of the Mother Lode, East Belt, and West Belt has been discussed on pages 55–57.

PLACERS IN TERTIARY GRAVELS

Placers in Tertiary gravels at three localities were reported by Bowen and Gray (1957, p. 189) to be gold bearing: in the Blanchard district in the northwestern part of the county; along the Tuolumne County line, just south of Jawbone Ridge; and on the ridge between Moore and Jordan Creeks, 4 or 5 miles northwest of Bower Cave.

The protective cap of Tertiary lavas that preserved the gravels in counties to the north probably did not extend as far south as Mariposa County; consequently, most of the Tertiary alluvial deposits have been eroded away. The remaining deposits yielded considerable gold in the early days, but their production is unrecorded. They probably produced a maximum of about 75,000 ounces of gold.

MERCED COUNTY

Merced County, which adjoins Mariposa County on the southwest, has produced considerable gold from one general locality—the alluvial plain of the Merced River between Merced Falls and Snelling. Small quantities of gold were mined in the early days; then in 1907, the Yosemite Mining and Dredging Co. began operating the first connected bucket dredge in the country, and immediately production doubled. From 1929 to 1943 several bucket dredges operated in the Snelling area—this was the era of peak gold production for Merced County (Davis and Carlson, 1952, p. 221–222). The War Production Board Order L–208 of 1942, rising costs, and resoiling ordinances all contributed to a marked decline in large-scale dredging, and gold mining in Merced County never regained the magnitude of the 1930's.

Total production from 1880 through 1959 was about 516,346 ounces, all from placers.

MODOC COUNTY

Modoc County produced about 14,400 ounces of gold from 1880 through 1959. The High Grade district, in the northeast corner of the county, has been the only important gold-mining area.

Gold was first discovered in the district in 1870, but it was not until 1909 that any great interest was shown in prospecting the area (Hill, 1915, p. 38). Apparently the district was never developed on a large scale, and it is doubtful that the total production by 1959 exceeded 11,000 ounces of gold.

The country rock in the district consists of a series of andesite, rhyolite, and basalt lava flows that have been displaced and tilted by movement along generally north-trending normal faults. The ore deposits are in quartz veins and mineralized breccia zones in rhyolite and andesite. The vein minerals are quartz, adularia, and small amounts of pyrite and gold (Hill, 1915, p. 40–47).

MONO COUNTY

Mining began in Mono County in 1862, when silver ore was discovered at Blind Springs Hill (Sampson and Tucker, 1940, p. 117), but gold mining became commercially important some time later. The most important lode districts were Bodie and Masonic. Small amounts of placer gold have been mined near the headwaters of the Walker River, Virginia Creek, and Dog Creek, and at Bodie Digging, north of Mono Lake (Sampson and Tucker, 1940, p. 121). According to Rinehart and Ross (1956, p. 16), scattered mines in the Casa Diablo Mountains quadrangle have produced less than $1 million in gold and silver.

Total gold production for the county from 1880 through 1959 was 1,176,200 ounces, the bulk of which was lode gold. More than 90 percent of this came from the Bodie district. The following summary of the geology has been prepared from reports by Sampson and Tucker (1940, p. 118) and Rinehart and Ross (1956).

The western part of the county is underlain predominantly by granodioritic rocks of the Sierra Nevada batholith and a narrow belt of lower Paleozoic or Precambrian metasedimentary rocks. The Benton Range, in the southeastern part of the county, is also composed of these rocks. Most of the remainder of the county is underlain by bodies of granitic rocks, diorite, and gabbro, of Cretaceous (?) age, and by basalt and rhyolite flows and rhyolite tuff of Tertiary and Quaternary age. Granitic stocks of Cretaceous(?) age form the White Mountains, at the southeast boundary of the county, and Blind Springs Hill, east of Benton.

BODIE DISTRICT

The Bodie district is in northeast Mono County, in T. 4 N., R. 27 E. Mining was started in 1860, and the district was active until 1955. Total gold production was 1,456,300 ounces, most of which came from the Standard mine.

Country rock in the district consists of a "complex of igneous rocks and breccias" overlain (perhaps along a fault) by Tertiary hornblende andesite (Brown, 1908, p. 343–344). Ore bodies occur in three sets of auriferous quartz veins in the andesite (Brown, 1908, p. 345–346).

MASONIC DISTRICT

The Masonic district is in northeast Mono County, in T. 6 N., R. 26 E. Gold occurs in quartz veins in metamorphic rocks and granite. The Pittsburg-Liberty mine, with a record of $470,000 in gold (about 34,000 ounces), has been the important producer (Sampson and Tucker, 1940, p. 121). The district was active on a small scale in 1959. No detailed descriptions of the geology were found.

NAPA COUNTY

Total recorded gold production for Napa County is 23,225 ounces, all from the Calistoga district in the northwest corner of the county. The first gold production recorded was in 1875 when $93,000 in combined gold and silver was listed (Davis, 1948, p. 165). Intermittent production continued to 1941. Gold has been a byproduct from the Palisade and Silverado silver mines (Davis, 1948, p. 183). No other information on this district could be found.

Along the eastern border of the county is a 4-mile-wide belt of folded siltstones, sandstones, and a few limestones composing the Shasta Series, of Cretaceous age (Davis, 1948, p. 162). These rocks are flanked on the west by a 1½-mile-wide strip of the Jurassic Knoxville Formation, which is the lower, conglomeratic unit of the Shasta Series (Weaver, 1949, p. 21–22). The remainder of the northern half of the county is underlain by metamorphic and cherty sedimentary rocks and associated basic intrusive rocks of the Franciscan Group, of Jurassic age. In the western part of the county, the east side of the Napa Valley is covered by a thick section of Pliocene volcanic rocks, and on the west side of the valley, the Shasta Series is overlain locally by Pliocene volcanic rocks.

NEVADA COUNTY

The gold-quartz mines of the Grass Valley-Nevada City district in Nevada County have been the most productive in the State, and the Empire mine in the same district was in continuous operation from 1850 to 1940, which at that time was the longest period of operation for any gold mine in the country (Logan, 1941, p. 375). Placer production has also been significant, especially in the early days; however, no consistent records have been kept. Tertiary gravels on San Juan Ridge, North Columbia, Sailor Flat, Blue Tent, Scotts Flat, Quaker Hill, and Red Dog-You Bet still contain tremendous reserves, but these are for the most part undeveloped because of the curtailment of hydraulic mining.

The total gold production of the county from 1849 through 1959 was 17,016,000 ounces, including Lindgren's (1896, p. 26) estimate of $133,800,000 in gold. Since 1903, when placer and lode production have been reported separately by the U.S. Geological Survey (1904–24) and U.S. Bureau of Mines (1925–34, 1933–66), 286,655 ounces of placer and 7,119,353 ounces of lode gold have been mined in the county.

GRASS VALLEY-NEVADA CITY DISTRICT

Because the towns of Grass Valley and Nevada City, which form the center of the Grass Valley-Nevada City district, are only 4 miles apart and because of their similarity in geology, distribution and mineralogy of veins, and common history and development, they are discussed together.

The initial rush to this area took place in 1850 after rich gravels were discovered near the present site of Nevada City. In October of the same year, the first lode discovery was made at Gold Hill on the outskirts of Grass Valley (Johnston, 1940, p. 19). Almost immediately the towns of Grass Valley and Nevada City were founded; they grew rapidly, prospered, and became permanent communities.

By 1851 quartz mines had been developed at Nevada City, but these early ventures failed. The miners turned to working the rich Tertiary gravels on a large scale by introducing hydraulic methods (Lindgren, 1896, p. 19). The discovery at Gold Hill was followed by discoveries of veins at Ophir Hill, Rich Hill, and Massachusetts Hill, and by 1867 most of the major mines of the district had been located. Grass Valley, where 1,600 men were working and 284 stamps were crushing the ore, was then one of the leading camps in California (Johnston,

1940, p. 19). Meanwhile new discoveries of lode deposits were made at Nevada City, and quartz mining became dominant there after 1880. Some of the important mines at Nevada City are the Champion, Providence, Canada Hill, Hoge, and Nevada City. The Empire, North Star, and Idaho-Maryland mines have accounted for more than two-thirds of the production of Grass Valley and have exerted considerable influence on the economic life of the community. Indeed, in 1938 and 1939 the Idaho-Maryland had the largest gold output of any mine in the State. In recent years activity has declined in the district, and in 1957–58 most of the production was from cleanup operations at the Empire and North Star mines.

Production of the Grass Valley-Nevada City district is difficult to determine accurately because of the incompleteness of the early records. Of the estimated $113 million worth of production from 1849 to 1893, at least 60 percent was credited to the lode mines (Lindgren, 1896, p. 28). From 1903 through 1958, Nevada County produced 7,119,353 ounces of lode gold and 286,655 ounces of placer gold. Almost all of the lode gold is assumed to have come from the Grass Valley-Nevada City district. Converting Lindgren's estimate to ounces, the total production of the district through 1959 was approximately 10,408,000 ounces of lode gold and 2,200,000 ounces of placer gold.

The reports of Lindgren (1896) and Johnston (1940) have been drawn upon for the following discussion of the geology of the district.

At the Grass Valley camp, the oldest rocks are schists and slates of the Calaveras Formation, of Carboniferous age, and relatively unaltered clay slates of the Mariposa Formation, of Jurassic age. Igneous rocks in the area consist of large masses of diabase, porphyrite, and amphibolite schist of Carboniferous to Jurassic age and serpentine, gabbro, diorite, granodiorite, and quartz porphyry, of Jurassic and Cretaceous age. Andesite flows of Tertiary age cover large areas east and southeast of the town of Grass Valley. The most characteristic geological feature of the Grass Valley camp is the elongate body of Cretaceous granodiorite which is 5 miles long and ½ to 2 miles wide. The ore deposits are gold-quartz veins in the granodiorite mass and in the serpentine, porphyrite, and diabase wallrock. The veins in the granodiorite, porphyrite, and diabase, in the central and southern part of the camp, strike north or slightly northwest, parallel to the contact of the intrusive. Veins in the northern part of the camp are north of the granodiorite and are in serpentine. These strike predominantly east. Quartz is the principal vein material, and it appears in several textural types representative of successive stages of mineralization. Comb quartz, milky quartz, ribbon quartz, and brecciated quartz are the most common varieties. Ankerite and calcite are common gangue minerals but are less abundant than quartz. The principal sulfides are pyrite, galena, and sphalerite; also present, but less common, are arsenopyrite and chalcopyrite. Gold occurs along cracks and grain boundaries in the sulfides and in brecciated quartz. Commonly bounding the ore shoots in the granodiorite are vertical or steeply dipping fractures, called crossings, that strike northeast, normal to the long axis of the granodiorite body.

The Nevada City camp, about 4 miles northeast of Grass Valley, is at the south end of a large body of granodiorite that extends northward into Butte County. This mass is separate from the stock at Grass Valley but is probably of the same age. A narrow belt, 400 to 1,500 feet wide, consisting of argillites, quartzites, and mica schists of the Calaveras Formation, is in contact with the southern end of the granodiorite and crosses the Nevada City camp in a northwesterly direction. Masses of porphyrite, diabase, and amphibolite schist, of Carboniferous to Jurassic age, form irregular lenses and bands southwest of the Calaveras Formation. North of the town of Nevada City are several ridges of Tertiary gravels capped by andesite lava flows. In general, the veins of Nevada City are mineralogically similar to those at Grass Valley, the main difference being the larger amount of coarse gold in the Grass Valley veins. The Nevada City veins are concentrated in the vicinity of the granodiorite-country rock contact and they are arranged into two systems: (1) a system that trends west-northwest with steep dips to the north or south, and (2) a system that trends north with medium eastward dips and contains the most productive veins.

MEADOW LAKE DISTRICT

The Meadow Lake district, 35 miles east of Grass Valley, is a relatively minor lode district and has been inactive since 1905. Production, which began in 1863, totaled at least 10,000 ounces of gold, but records are fragmentary.

Bedrock consists of granodiorite intruded into and bordered on the east by diabase and eruptive rocks (Wisker, 1936, p. 192–194). Most of the veins are in the granodiorite, a few are in the diabase. There are two productive vein systems: the major one trends N. 25° W.; the other, composed of smaller veins, ranges from N. 45° W., to N. 85° W.

Some of the larger veins are remarkably persistent and can be traced for as much as 6,000 feet on the surface. High amounts of pyrite, arsenopyrite, and chalcopyrite are present in the veins. Quartz is not as abundant as it is in the typical California gold-quartz veins. Free gold is associated with pyrite and rarely with quartz.

TERTIARY PLACER DISTRICTS

The Tertiary placer districts include the placer deposits in the following areas: San Juan Ridge, North Columbia, Sailor Flat, Blue Tent, Scotts Flat, Quaker Hill, and Red Dog-You Bet.

Most of the placer production of Nevada County before 1900 came from hydraulic mining of the Tertiary gravels from these localities. The production of individual areas is not known, but Lindgren (1911, p. 133) estimated that their aggregate production through 1909 was at least $60 million in gold. After passage of the California Debris Commission Act of 1893, many operators closed down, even though huge reserves of auriferous gravels still remain in these areas. In recent years, production from these areas has been sporadic and small scale.

PLACER COUNTY

Placer County, noted chiefly for its placer mines, has also produced substantial lode gold particularly from the Ophir district. Gold was discovered in 1848 in Auburn Ravine. In the 1850's, bars in the American River and its tributaries were worked, and quartz mining also began. In the Foresthill Divide area, Tertiary channels were mined by drifts, and in the Dutch Flat-Gold Run, Iowa Hill, and Yankee Jim districts, gold was extracted from gravels by hydraulic methods. The Michigan Bluff placers have also been productive.

The center of lode mining in Placer County is the Ophir district. Gold-quartz mines were active in the Canada Hill district (Logan, 1936, p. 10), but production from this area could not be ascertained. Logan (1936) described the gold deposits of this county and was the chief source of information for the production and description of the districts. Total production for the county from 1880 through 1959 was about 2,014,000 ounces.

DUTCH FLAT-GOLD RUN DISTRICT

The Dutch Flat-Gold Run district is along the north boundary of Placer County on the system of Tertiary channel deposits that extends south from Nevada County.

Placer mining began in 1849, and by 1857 hydraulic and drift mines were producing on a fairly large scale. Though early records are almost nonexistent, it was estimated (Logan, 1936, p. 58, 65–70) that the district produced about 479,000 ounces of gold to 1935. In recent years, because of high costs and restrictive legislation, production has decreased to less than 1,000 ounces per year. Total production through 1959 was about 492,000 ounces.

FORESTHILL DISTRICT

The Foresthill district is in south-central Placer County. Foresthill Divide is a complex system of Tertiary channels capped by lavas. The gravels have been extensively worked by drift mines which reached their peak of productivity in the 1860's (Logan, 1936, p. 49). Before 1868 the Independence, New Jersey, and Jenny Lind mines produced $2,400,000 in gold. Estimates of production of individual mines given by Logan (1936, p. 51–80) give a minimum total for the district of about 338,000 ounces of gold. In recent years, the district has been virtually dormant. Total gold production through 1959 was about 344,000 ounces.

IOWA HILL DISTRICT

The Iowa Hill district is about 5 miles east of the town of Colfax. Thick Tertiary gravels have been worked by hydraulic and drift mines in this district (Lindgren, 1911, p. 148–149). The Morning Star mine, with a production worth $1,750,000 to 1901, was the largest of the drift mines (Logan, 1936, p. 71). Total production of this district to 1910 was about $10 million (Lindgren, 1911, p. 149). No activity has been reported in the area since before 1932, except in 1958 when about 300 ounces was produced.

MICHIGAN BLUFF DISTRICT

The Michigan Bluff district is in southern Placer County, about 5 miles east of Foresthill.

From 1853 to 1880 considerable hydraulic and drift mining was done in the Tertiary channel gravels that underlie the eastern part of Foresthill Divide at Michigan Bluff. According to Logan (1936, p. 53–70), an area of 40 acres yielded $5 million in gold. The Big Gun mine with an output of about $1 million to 1882 was the largest individual producer of the hydraulic mines, and the Hidden Treasure mine was the most productive of all the drift mines in the Tertiary gravels in the State, with a total of about $4 million in gold. Several lode mines were important gold producers—the Pioneer, with $900,000 in gold, and the Rawhide, with $300,000, were the most productive.

The total gold production of the district through 1959 was about 300,000 ounces. In recent years activity has slackened, and during 1942–59 less than 100 ounces per year was reported.

No details on geology or history could be found.

OPHIR DISTRICT

The Ophir district, near Auburn, is the most productive lode-gold district of Placer County; it also has produced significant amounts of placer gold. The first reported production from the quartz mines was in 1867, when the Green Emigrant mine yielded $100,000 (Logan, 1936, p. 28). In the 1870's many mines were developed, and although not all prospered, the district continued to be moderately active until 1921. From about 1936 to 1942 the mines were very productive, but during 1942–59 less than 100 ounces per year was produced. The chief lode mines were the Crater, Bellevue, Oro Fina, and Three Stars. Total estimated lode production of the district through 1959, including Logan's (1936, p. 29) estimate of $3 million (145,300 ounces), is about 255,500 ounces.

Placers along the American River in the Ophir district were worked as early as 1850, but these shallow gravels were exhausted by 1880 (Logan, 1936, p. 49). The production for these years is unknown. In the late 1930's, dredges started working the gravels near Loomis and in a few years recovered more than 73,000 ounces of gold.

The geology of the district was briefly described by Logan (1936, p. 8–9). Granite, which is the eastern part of a batholith, is intruded into amphibolite schist. The ore deposits are near the contact and are found in both the granite and in the schists. The gold occurs in lenticular quartz veins and is associated with small amounts of pyrite, galena, sphalerite, and copper sulfides.

RISING SUN MINE

The Rising Sun mine, 1½ miles west of Colfax, with an estimated total production of $2 million in gold (Logan, 1936, p. 34), is the leading lode-gold producer in Placer County.

Opened in 1866, the mine produced continuously until 1884. Thereafter it was in operation for several brief periods, the most recent on record was in 1932. The Rising Sun deposit is in a zone of altered diabase, serpentine, and slate of the Mariposa Formation of Jurassic age, near a large stock of gabbro. The main vein averaged 18 inches in width and contained rich pockets of free gold in quartz (Logan, 1936, p. 34).

PLUMAS COUNTY

Placer deposits in the Tertiary gravels in Plumas County were worked on a large scale by hydraulic methods in the early years. The peak production was during 1855–71, when at least $60 million (about 2,912,000 ounces) in gold was shipped from the La Porte district alone (Lindgren, 1911, p. 103). Lode mines also were developed at an early date, especially in the Johnsville district where some mines were active as early as 1851.

Recorded gold production of Plumas County from 1880 through 1959 was 1,670,000 ounces. Adding to this Lindgren's estimated $60 million from the La Porte district, the total from 1855 through 1959 was about 4,582,000 ounces.

The geology of Plumas County was described by Averill (1937, p. 82–88). In brief, the rocks consist of a series of sedimentary, metasedimentary, and metavolcanic formations that have been folded, faulted, and intruded by granodiorite of Late Jurassic and mid-Cretaceous age. Most of the western two-thirds of the county is underlain by northwest-trending bands of these folded rocks; the granodiorite occupies the eastern part.

The oldest rock in the county is metarhyolite which is overlain by quartzite and shale of the Grizzly Formation of Silurian age. The remainder of the stratified rocks, in ascending order, are the Montgomery Limestone of Silurian age, the Taylorsville Formation of Devonian age, the Calaveras Formation of Carboniferous age, the Hosselkus Limestone and Swearinger Slate of Triassic age, and seven other sedimentary formations of Early and Middle Jurassic age. Patches of Tertiary gravels mark the northward-trending course of the ancient Jura River and the northeasterly course of the Tertiary Yuba River.

Igneous rocks, in addition to those already mentioned, consist of basic flows and dikes of Carboniferous age, peridotite and pyroxenite bodies of Jurassic age, and greenstones, amphibolites, and metadiorites of Jurassic age. The northwest and large areas of the southeast and southwest parts of the county are covered by rhyolite, dacite, andesite, and basalt lava flows of Tertiary and Quaternary age.

CRESCENT MILLS DISTRICT

The Crescent Mills district, in T. 26 N., R. 9 E., has produced chiefly lode gold, but a small output has also been derived from Quaternary gravel deposits. The major mine in this district is the Green Mountain, with a production of between $1 and $2 million in gold to 1890 (Averill, 1937, p. 111). From

1933 to 1952 the district produced 32,069 ounces of lode gold and 3,255 ounces of placer gold; no production was reported during 1952–59. Total minimum production through 1959 was about 100,000 ounces.

The bedrock in the southwest part of the district consists of a northwest-trending band of metasedimentary rocks of the Calaveras Formation. This is bordered on the northeast by a parallel band of pre-Devonian metavolcanic rocks. A few small bodies of granodiorite, of Jurassic age, cut the older rocks. The ore deposits are in veins in the metavolcanic rocks near the granodiorite and in the granodiorite itself. The veins consist of quartz with free gold and small amounts of sulfides.

JOHNSVILLE DISTRICT

The Johnsville, in the east half of T. 22 N., R. 11 E., in south-central Plumas County, is primarily a lode district, but it has produced some placer gold from Tertiary and possibly also from Quaternary gravels.

The Plumas Eureka mine, the largest lode mine in the district, began operations in 1851 and had a total estimated yield of $8 million in gold to about 1925 (Averill, 1937, p. 118). In more recent years the district has been only sporadically active; during 1933–59, only 2,009 ounces of lode gold and 1,413 ounces of placer gold were reported. Its total gold production was about 393,000 ounces.

The bedrock in the district consists of a broad northwest-trending band of metasedimentary rocks which belong to the Calaveras Formation of Carboniferous age (Averill, 1937, map) and which are intruded by small bodies of andesite of Carboniferous age. The gold deposits are in the quartz veins in the metasedimentary rocks.

LA PORTE DISTRICT

The La Porte district, in T. 21 N., R. 9 E., in southwest Plumas County, was the center of hydraulic mining of gravels of the Tertiary Yuba River in the 1850's and 1860's. After the enactment of debris control laws, the gravels were worked by drift mines on a much-reduced scale. During 1932–59 the district produced 9,347 ounces of gold. Total production from 1855 through 1959 was about 2,910,000 ounces. A small amount of production was reported in 1957, but none was reported in 1958–59.

The channel near La Porte is about 500 feet wide. Gold was concentrated on the amphibolite bedrock or in the lowermost 2 feet of the gravel. The main channel has been traced a distance of 10 miles to the northeast, and it ranges from 500 to 1,500 feet in width and from 14 to 129 feet in depth. The channel is offset near La Porte by numerous faults which have an aggregate displacement of about 500 feet (Lindgren, 1911, p. 105–108).

RIVERSIDE COUNTY

Gold deposits are distributed rather widely throughout Riverside County, but not one of these has been an exceptionally large producer. Before 1893, particularly during 1876–86, there was considerable mining activity, and the aggregate production may have been as much as $1 or $2 million, mostly in lode gold; little placer mining has been done in the county. The Pinacate and Pinon-Dale districts are the major gold producers in the county, and small amounts of gold have been mined from scattered localities in the Chuckawalla Mountains and the Bendigo district. Total gold production for the county from 1893 through 1959 was 108,800 ounces.

The geology of the mining districts has not been published, but the generalization can be made that most of the gold occurs in quartz veins that occupy fissures in granitic rocks or in country rock near granodiorite bodies (Nolan, 1936b, p. 43–45).

PINACATE DISTRICT

The Pinacate district, in Tps. 4 and 5 S., R. 4 W., a few miles west and southwest of Perris, produced a total of about 104,000 ounces of gold through 1959, all from lodes. The principal mine in this district is the Good Hope mine, originally worked by Mexicans at an unknown date; the property is credited with a production of about $2 million in gold before 1896 (Tucker and Sampson, 1945, p. 133). The district declined until the mid-1930's at which time attempts were made to rehabilitate the Good Hope and several other mines, but these efforts were largely unsuccessful. During 1943–59 only 3 ounces of gold was produced from the district.

The predominant country rock in the district is granodiorite of undetermined age (Tucker and Sampson, 1945, p. 133, 135, 138–139). Quartz veins, containing free gold and minor sulfides, cut the granodiorite.

PINON-DALE DISTRICT

The Pinon-Dale district, a large area along the north boundary of Riverside County, includes Tps. 2 and 3 S., Rs. 10 to 12 E.

Although Nolan (1936b, p. 44) reported that the district has been known for a long time, published information on it is meager. Production of the district to 1943 was a minimum of 32,000 ounces of gold, and during 1943–59 only 75 ounces was reported. The major mines are the Lost Horse, with an estimated gold output of $350,000, and the New Eldorado.

The country rock of the district consists of granite, schist, and quartzite (Tucker and Sampson, 1945, p. 130–132). The gold occurs in quartz veins, most of which are in the granite.

SACRAMENTO COUNTY

Sacramento County ranks among the leading gold-producing counties in California.

Auriferous quartz veins have been mined intermittently since the gold-rush days, but lode production is insignificant compared to the amount of gold dredged from the gravels along the American River. From 1880 through 1959, production in the county was 5,005,700 ounces; only about 5,000 ounces was from quartz lodes.

The productive gravels are at the base of Pliocene and Pleistocene terraces or near the contact of the Pliocene Laguna Formation with the underlying Miocene Mehrten Formation (Carlson, 1955, p. 134). Bucketline and dragline dredges have been used extensively to mine these gravels. Folsom has been the center of this activity; other dredge operations were at Sloughhouse and at various localities along the Cosumnes River. In 1952, bucketline dredging was reactivated south of the American River, and some gold was also obtained from sand and gravel preparation plants. Production for several years before and through 1959, however, was only a few ounces annually.

Quartz veins containing gold are found in green metavolcanic rocks and in the Mariposa Slate of Jurassic age but do not occur in any of the rocks of Late Cretaceous age or younger (Carlson, 1955, p. 133).

FOLSOM DISTRICT

The Folsom district is in the southeast part of T. 10 N., R. 7 E., along the American River, in the northeast corner of Sacramento County.

Lindgren (1911, p. 222) considered this district to be the largest area of Quaternary gravels in the State. In 1899 the first bucketline dredge used in Sacramento County was installed at Folsom. Before this the gravels were mined by drift and hydraulic methods. Huge electrically powered draglines and dredges were introduced in the late 1920's and 1930's, and some of these continued operating into the 1950's (Carlson, 1955, p. 136–142). The largest dredge handled about 4 million cubic yards of gravel per year. Rising cost gradually forced curtailment of these large-scale activities, but in 1958 some dredging was resumed in the district. Before 1930 some drift mines were operating, but later the dredges accounted for most of the production. The total production of the district through 1959 was at least 3 million ounces.

SLOUGHHOUSE DISTRICT

The Sloughhouse district is in T. 7 N., R. 7 E., along the Cosumnes River.

The auriferous gravels of the Tertiary Ione Formation were mined by hydraulic methods in the early years, but most of this activity was curtailed by a court decree in 1884 aimed to prevent devastation of farmlands by debris-laden streams (Carlson, 1955, p. 143).

Large-scale dredging operations were conducted during the 1930's, 1940's, and early 1950's. In this district, as in the Folsom area, large deposits of late Tertiary and Quaternary gravels carried small quantities of gold. Total production through 1959 is not known but was probably about 1,700,000 ounces.

SAN BERNARDINO COUNTY

Gold deposits are scattered throughout San Bernardino County. They occur in the Slate Range in the northwest, the Whipple Mountains in the southeast, the San Gabriel Mountains in the southwest, and the Clark Mountain area in the northeast. The report of Wright and others (1953, p. 53–86) has been the source of information on the geology and gold deposits of this county.

As early as the 1850's, placer gold was mined at several localities, but lode mines have been the most important sources of gold. Of the many mining districts in the county, the most important are the Dale, Holcomb, and Stedman. Production from 1880 through 1959 was 517,000 ounces; nearly all production was from lode mines. Production has declined rapidly in recent years. Only 102 ounces of gold was produced in 1958, mostly as a byproduct from silver ore in the Rand district. Production for 1959 was combined with other counties.

San Bernardino County is characterized by numerous steep mountain ranges separated by arid basins, many of which are undrained. Exposed in the higher ranges are metasedimentary rocks of Archean and Algonkian age. These rocks are overlain by thick sections of Paleozoic sedimentary rocks that range in thickness from 9,000 feet in the northeastern part of the county to more than 22,000 feet in the north-central part. Mesozoic sedimentary rocks as much as 4,000 feet thick are found in the northeastern part of the county. Metavolcanic rocks of Triassic or Jurassic age are found in a few localities in the western part of the county. Numerous quartz monzonite stocks and small batholiths of late Mesozoic age intruded the sedimentary rocks, and most of the ore deposits are genetically related to mineralizing solutions that emanated from these plutons. Tertiary volcanic rocks form several mountain ranges in the northeastern, west-central, and south-central parts of the county. Numerous gold and silver deposits are associated with these rocks. Large basins were formed in Tertiary time, and in these, thick deposits of interbedded saline and alluvial sediments accumulated.

DALE DISTRICT

The Dale district, in T. 1 S., Rs. 11 and 12 E., about 15 miles southeast of the town of Twentynine Palms, began producing gold as early as 1893 from the Brooklyn mine. In the early 1900's production from the Supply and Nightingale mines made the district one of the more prosperous in the county. Production declined after World War II, and the district has been almost dormant in recent years. Total gold production through 1959 was about 63,500 ounces.

Bedrock in the district, as noted in mine descriptions by Wright, Stewart, Gay, and Hazenbush (1953, p. 70–86), consists of quartz diorite, andesite porphyry, and granodiorite. The gold deposits are in quartz veins cutting these rocks. Gold occurs in the free state with iron and manganese oxides in some mines; in others, the gold is associated with sulfides.

HOLCOMB DISTRICT

The Holcomb district is 20 to 25 miles northeast of San Bernardino, in Tps. 2 and 3 N., Rs. 1, 2, and 3 E.

Activity in this district began in the 1850's, when the Ozier mine was the major producer of gold ore (Wright and others, 1953, p. 77). In the late 1860's, when the gravels of Holcomb Valley were found to be auriferous, prospectors flocked into the area and in a few years took out about $7 million (about 340,000 ounces) in gold (Vaughn, 1922, p. 409). The large placer production seems somewhat questionable, because nowhere else in the literature is any mention made of the Holcomb Valley placers. The lode mines flourished until the early 1900's but have been virtually idle since then. Only 3 ounces of gold was reported from the district during 1950–59. Data are incomplete for the early years, although Wright, Stewart, Gay, and Hazenbush (1953, p. 70–86) estimated the output of a few of the lode mines. Total gold production, including Vaughan's estimate of the early placer output, was about 400,000 ounces, of which about 54,500 ounces was from the lode mines.

The geology of the area has been described by Vaughan (1922, p. 344–411). In the vicinity of the mines the country rock, which is primarily a sequence of Paleozoic sedimentary formations, is complexly folded, faulted, and intruded by the Cactus Granite of Jurassic age. The sedimentary rocks are the Arrastre Quartzite of Early Cambrian age, the Furnace Limestone of Late Cambrian and Ordovician age, and the Saragossa Quartzite of Silurian or Devonian age. Most of the deposits are in quartz veins along limestone-granite contacts or are associated with limestone beds transected by granitic dikes. A few deposits are in thick quartz veins in quartzite. The ore minerals are pyrite, galena, sphalerite, chalcopyrite, pyrrhotite, and free gold. Azurite and malachite are found in the oxidized zones. Considerable amounts of contact metamorphic minerals such as garnet, epidote, wollastonite, and tremolite are found locally with the ore deposits.

STEDMAN DISTRICT

The Stedman district is about 7 miles south of Ludlow, in Tps. 6 and 7 N., R. 8 E.

Total gold production, entirely from lode mines, has been in excess of $6 million (291,000 ounces), more than half the total recorded gold production of San Bernardino County (Wright and others, 1953, p. 71). The Bagdad-Chase mine, which is the principal mine, was discovered in 1903, and during 1904–10 it produced $4½ million in gold. Large quantities of copper and silver were also produced from this mine. After 1940 the mine was operated by lessees; however, no production was reported during 1950–59.

The geology of the Bagdad-Chase mine was described briefly by Wright, Stewart, Gay, and Hazenbush (1953, p. 71, 82). The ore is in a mineralized breccia zone between a body of quartz monzonite and rhyolite. The breccia is composed of fragments of both rock types cemented by silica, which carries gold and oxidized copper minerals.

SAN DIEGO COUNTY

Gold was first discovered in San Diego County in 1869 by discharged Confederate soldiers who worked small placers near Wynola. Some time later gold veins were discovered in the Julian and Banner areas which were later consolidated into the Julian district, the most important gold district in the county. Most of the data presented here are from Donnelly's (1934) report on the history, geology, and mines of the Julian district. After 1900 the Julian district had very little activity. A mild rejuvenation in the late 1930's and early 1940's produced about 1,500 ounces, but during 1950–59 the district was idle. The total gold production of San Diego County through 1959 was about 219,800 ounces, mostly from the Julian district. Only about 700 ounces of this is from placer deposits scattered throughout the county.

The Julian district is about 55 miles northeast of San Diego, near the center of the county. The oldest bedrock in the district is quartz-muscovite-biotite schist and quartzite composing the Julian Formation, of Triassic and Jurassic age. These rocks were invaded by three intrusives of Mesozoic age: the Stonewall Granodiorite, Rattlesnake Granite, and Cuyamaca Gabbro and norite of the Cuyamaca. The Stonewall Granodiorite is the oldest; the Cuyamaca basic intrusive is believed to be the youngest.

The most productive gold deposits are lenticular quartz veins in the Julian Schist. These are conformable in strike and dip with the foliation of the schist. Other deposits in the schist are in gold-bearing quartz lenses and V-shaped quartz rolls. The ore mineralogy of all three types is rather simple and uniform. Massive and banded quartz, accompanied by minor amounts of biotite, calcite, and sericite, comprises the gangue. The ore minerals are pyrrhotite, arsenopyrite, pyrite, and native gold. The gold occurs most commonly in intimate association with pyrrhotite, but the coarser gold is embedded in quartz.

SAN JOAQUIN COUNTY

Gold production in San Joaquin County, which has been sporadic, has been entirely from Quaternary placers along the Mokelumne River between Clements and Camanche and along the Calaveras River near Bellota, Linden, and Jenny Lind.

Small amounts of placer gold were mined along the Mokelumne River in the latter part of the 19th century (Clark, 1955, p. 37). From 1918 to 1920 there was a brief spurt of activity, and from the mid-1930's until 1951 several dredging companies worked the placers, especially those in the Clements district. Total production from 1885 through 1959 was 126,400 ounces.

BELLOTA DISTRICT

The Bellota district, in T. 2 N., R. 9 E., along the Calaveras River, in east-central San Joaquin County is actually the westward extension of the Jenny Lind district in Calaveras County.

Quaternary gravels have been worked by dredges; however, details on the production and mining history could not be found. In 1959 this district was inactive and had been for several years. The scale of operations in the neighboring Jenny Lind district (Julihn and Horton, 1938, p. 75) indicates that the total production of the Bellota district probably was between 20,000 and 40,000 ounces.

CLEMENTS DISTRICT

The Clements district is in the northeast corner of San Joaquin County, along the Mokelumne River.

The Quaternary gravels were worked on a small scale before 1900; after World War I, dredges were introduced and were very active during the 1930's. Activity slackened soon thereafter, and during 1951–59 the district was dormant. Total gold production is not precisely known but probably was between 50,000 and 100,000 ounces.

SHASTA COUNTY

Lode and placer gold as well as large amounts of byproduct gold from the West Shasta copper-zinc district have been mined in Shasta County. The major lode districts are the Deadwood-French Gulch, Harrison Gulch, Old Diggings, and Whiskeytown. Placer operations are centered in the Igo district and along the Roaring River.

Total gold production of Shasta County from 1880 through 1959 was 2,033,000 ounces, mostly of lode and byproduct origin. Output of placer gold from 1905 through 1959 was 375,472 ounces. Most of the foregoing production was before 1940; during 1950–59 less than 1,000 ounces per year was reported.

Precambrian rocks are exposed in the southwestern part of the county (Averill, 1939, p. 110–111). Northeastward the country rock changes successively to the Copley Greenstone of Early(?) Devonian age, then to sedimentary rocks of Devonian, Carboniferous, Permian, Triassic, and Jurassic ages. The southern part of the county is covered with sedimentary rocks of Cretaceous, Tertiary, and Quaternary ages. The east half of the county is blanketed by a series of lava flows extruded during Tertiary and Quaternary time. Lassen Peak, the only active volcano in California, is in the southeast corner of the county.

DEADWOOD-FRENCH GULCH DISTRICT

The Deadwood-French Gulch district is along the central part of the west border of Shasta County.

Gold was discovered in this general area in 1848 in the gravels of Clear Creek, and 4 years later gold-bearing veins were producing at the Washington mine (Ferguson, 1914, p. 33). Activity in the district continued at a rather moderate rate until 1941, after which only a few ounces were produced annually. Ferguson (1914, p. 55) reported a production of $1,607,764 (78,000 ounces) through 1911. Production through 1959 was about 128,900 ounces of gold, mostly from lode mines.

The western part of the area is underlain by biotite-hornblende schists of pre-Devonian age, and the eastern part is underlain by a younger rock, the Copley Greenstone, of Early (?) Devonian age, which is overlain by the Bragdon Formation of Mississippian age (Ferguson, 1914, p. 24). These rocks were invaded in Late Jurassic time by a series of granitic and porphyritic rocks. The gold deposits are in fissure veins that are most numerous in the Bragdon Formation, but some veins occur also in quartz diorite and alaskite porphyry. The vein minerals consist of pyrite, arsenopyrite, sphalerite, galena, native gold, and a minor amount of chalcopyrite in a quartz gangue.

HARRISON GULCH DISTRICT

The Harrison Gulch district is in the southwest corner of Shasta County.

The Midas mine, discovered in 1894, was the major producer in the district and had an output of $3,563,587 in gold until 1914 (Logan, 1926, p. 173–174), when a fire caused it to close. It was reopened the following year under new ownership, and operations continued until 1920. The district was inactive from 1920 through 1959. The total production for the district was about $4 million (Averill, 1939, p. 142). No placer production is recorded in this district.

At the Midas mine, gold occurs in three lenticular quartz veins in a schistose country rock (Logan, 1926, p. 174).

IGO DISTRICT

The Igo district is in T. 31 N., R. 6 W., along Clear Creek. The quaternary gravels along Clear Creek near Igo were worked in the early days, but they are only briefly mentioned in the literature (Diller, 1914a, p. 20–21), and no published account of their discovery, development, or early production was found.

The district was revived in 1933 and through 1942 produced more than 113,000 ounces of placer gold, but after 1942 operations were sharply curtailed and the district was dormant in 1959. Total recorded production from 1933 through 1959 was 115,022 ounces; all but a few hundred ounces was from placers.

WEST SHASTA COPPER-ZINC DISTRICT

The West Shasta copper-zinc district, 20 miles northwest of Redding, originally was a gold district, but it later became one of the chief copper producers in the State. Prospectors, drawn to Shasta County by the placer discoveries on Clear Creek in 1848, soon found gold placers in the area west of Redding (Kinkel and others, 1956, p. 76). Copper deposits were also noted at this time, but interest was centered on the gold. In 1879 considerable excitement was aroused by the discovery of silver in the gossan at the Iron Mountain property in the southern part of the district. Later, in the search for precious metals, large quantities of copper sulfides were found beneath the gossan. In the early 1900's copper was mined on a large scale from the Iron Mountain and Balaklala mines, and gold and silver were obtained as byproducts. Small bodies of high-grade zinc ore were mined at the Mammoth and Iron Mountain mines. After 1919, production declined, and by 1953 gold was no longer listed in the annual production data for the district. Total gold production through 1959 was about 520,000 ounces.

The oldest rocks of the West Shasta copper-zinc district are basic lava flows, breccias, and tuffs that characterize the Copley Greenstone of Early(?) Devonian age. This is overlain by the Balaklala Rhyolite of Middle Devonian age, and the Balaklala is overlain by the Kennett Formation, which is composed of black cherty shale, tuff, and limestone of Middle Devonian age. Shale, sandstone, and conglomerate of the Bragdon Formation of Mississippian age rests on the Kennett Formation. In Jurassic time the Paleozoic rocks were invaded first by the Mule Mountain albite granite stock and then by the Shasta Bally biotite-quartz diorite batholith. Deformation accompanied the intrusions, and the Paleozoic formations were folded into a broad anticlinorium. Numerous faults dislocate parts of the arch. In the southern part of the district, clastics of the Chico Formation of Late Cretaceous age and of the Red Bluff Formation of Pleistocene age unconformably overlie the Copley Greenstone (Kinkel and others, 1956, p. 8–9).

The ore deposits, which were emplaced during Late Jurassic or Early Cretaceous time, consist of massive base-metal sulfide replacement bodies in the Balaklala Rhyolite. The ore minerals are pyrite, chalcopyrite, and sphalerite, and small amounts of magnetite, galena, tetrahedrite, pyrrhotite, gold, and silver. The ore controls are believed to be a combination of the anticlinorium structure, favorable lithologic features of the Balaklala Rhyolite, and fissures, which provided access for solutions (Kinkel and others, 1956, p. 79–100).

WHISKEYTOWN DISTRICT

The Whiskeytown district is along Clear Creek about 5 miles southeast of French Gulch.

The mines are along the edge of a mass of alaskite porphyry of Jurassic or Cretaceous age that cuts the Copley Greenstone of Early(?) Devonian age and lies adjacent to a large mass of quartz diorite and granodiorite of Jurassic or Cretaceous age (Ferguson, 1914, p. 47). The Bragdon Formation, of Mississippian age, is exposed in the northern part of the district.

The Mad Mule mine, which has been the largest producer of the district, is in a diorite porphyry dike that cuts the Bragdon Formation. The ore bodies are small lenses of calcite that occur at irregularities along the contact between the dike and sedimentary rock. Gold occurs most commonly as a thin film on calcite at its junction with the enclosing slate. Gold also is found within the calcite masses along cleavage planes. Pyrite and manganese-bearing quartz stringers are minor constituents of the calcite lenses (Ferguson, 1914, p. 52–54). Other ore deposits in the district are in quartz veins with minor calcite and with pyrite as the principal sulfide. Gold occurs free in the quartz and in the pyrite.

Production through 1911 was 63,300 ounces ($1,365,000) of gold (Ferguson, 1914, p. 47–55). The district has been inactive for many years.

SIERRA COUNTY

Sierra County has two major gold-producing areas: the Alleghany and Downieville districts, and the Sierra Buttes district. The total recorded gold production from 1880 through 1959 was about 2,161,000 ounces, most of it from lode mines. If the estimated gold output before 1880 is considered, the total production would be about 3 million ounces. Large placer production has come from both Tertiary and Quaternary gravels, but the exact amount is not known.

ALLEGHANY AND DOWNIEVILLE DISTRICTS

The Alleghany and Downieville districts, about 5 miles apart in the southern part of Sierra County, are considered as one area for the purpose of this report. The lode mines have been productive since the early 1850's, and their total production through 1959 was 1,590,990 ounces. The earliest record of mining was in 1852 when the Tertiary gravels were worked at several localities by both drift and hydraulic methods. Drift mining of the rich gravels was on a large scale to 1888, after which production declined (Ferguson and Gannett, 1932, p. 25–26). About $10 million (485,000 ounces) in gold was produced from the drift mines, and between $2 million (97,000 ounces) and $4 million (194,000 ounces) was produced from the hydraulic operations.

Lode mines developed slowly because of the rich yields of the placers in the early years, but by 1898 they were the chief source of gold in the districts. The ore has been rich but spotty; therefore, except for a few mines, lode mining has had alternating periods of prosperity and inactivity (Ferguson and Gannett, 1932, p. 27). The Sixteen to One mine, the most productive in the Alleghany district, had a total output of about $9 million in gold to 1928 (Ferguson and Gannett, 1932, p. 106). Lode mining has continued to flourish in the districts. Production of more than 17,000 ounces was reported in 1958, and an undisclosed amount was produced in 1959. Total minimum production through 1959, including the estimated early production from the placers, was about 2,173,000 ounces.

The following summary has been abstracted from the detailed geology by Ferguson and Gannett (1932, p. 5–24). The oldest rocks in the area are quartzite, slate, greenschist, and conglomerate. These rocks make up five sedimentary formations that can be correlated with part of the Calaveras Formation of Carboniferous age. The rocks dip steeply and crop out as belts that trend north-northwest. They are intruded by gabbro, now partly serpentinized, and younger granitic rocks. Auriferous gravels of Eocene and Miocene age, andesite breccia of Miocene(?) age, and some Pleistocene and Recent gravels overlie the older rocks with marked unconformity. The rocks were affected by two periods of metamorphism and deformation. The first period took place between Carboniferous and early Triassic time and resulted in folding, faulting, and regional metamorphism. The second period was at the close of the Jurassic and was accompanied by intrusions of basic rocks first and then granitic rocks, by the development of a complicated fault pattern, and by mineralization.

The principal veins in the Alleghany and Downieville districts strike northwestward and dip gently eastward. They follow minor reverse faults that cross all pre-Tertiary rocks except the larger serpentine masses. Other veins have similar strikes but dip steeply to the west (Ferguson and Gannett, 1932, p. 29–31). There were four stages of mineralization: (1) chloritization and serpentinization of the wallrock, (2) deposition of quartz and minor amounts of arsenopyrite, pyrite, albite, oligoclase, and barite, (3) replacement of quartz by gold, and of wallrock by ankerite and sericite, and (4) deposition of veinlets of fine pyrite and calcite in the veins and country rock, and of drusy coatings of these minerals on the quartz (Ferguson and Gannett, 1932, p. 38–39).

SIERRA BUTTES DISTRICT

The Sierra Buttes district is 10 to 12 miles east of Downieville.

Lode mining began in the 1850's but no record could be found of any early placer mining in this district. The most important mine was the Sierra Buttes, whose total production of between $15 and $17 million in gold made it the largest single gold producer in Sierra County (Averill, 1942, p. 44). The mine was closed in 1938, and though cleanup operations were conducted in 1941, no further activity had been reported through 1959. Total gold production for the district was about 825,000 ounces; nearly all production was from the Sierra Buttes mine.

Most of the country rock in the district consists of altered quartz porphyry and rhyolite porphyry bordered on the west by bands of slate, quartzite, and limestone of the Calaveras Formation of Carboniferous age that trend north-northwest (Logan, 1929, p. 155–156). The metasediments are probably older than the porphyries. The ore deposits are gold-bearing quartz veins.

SISKIYOU COUNTY

Siskiyou County is one of the three northernmost counties of California. Most of the gold mined in this county has been from placers, the largest of which are along the Salmon, Scott, and Klamath Rivers. Considerable production also came from scattered lode deposits in the Humbug, Yreka, Fort Jones, Cherry Creek, and Cottonwood areas. Total production of individual districts could not be determined, and the production for the districts is estimated by the authors, on the basis of the sparse published data for the county. Gold production of Siskiyou County from 1880 through 1959 was 1,773,000 ounces.

The east half of the county is underlain by Quaternary volcanic rocks, Pleistocene lake beds, Recent alluvium, and scattered patches of marine sandstone of the Upper Cretaceous Chico Formation. The west half is underlain by interbedded sedimentary and volcanic rocks of Devonian and Carboniferous age. These are severely folded and faulted and are cut by bodies of granodiorite, gabbro, and peridotite of Late Jurassic or Early Cretaceous age (O'Brien, 1947, p. 415). Throughout Cretaceous time the western part of Siskiyou County was an island and is devoid of any marine sediments of Cretaceous age or later (Averill, 1935, p. 257).

COTTONWOOD-FORT JONES-YREKA DISTRICT

The Cottonwood-Fort Jones-Yreka district is a large area extending from T. 43 to T. 47 N. and from R. 6 to R. 9 W.

Much of it is covered by basal beds of the Upper Cretaceous Chico Formation which unconformably overlie the undifferentiated Paleozoic sequence of shale, slate, sandstone, and limestone. Some of the Cretaceous beds contain coal; others that are conglomeratic indicate proximity to the Cretaceous island of western Siskiyou County (Averill, 1935, p. 258). The conglomerates are auriferous, and reworking of these by recent streams such as Cottonwood and Rancheria Creeks formed placers that yielded about $4 million in gold in the 1850's (Dunn, 1894, p. 466). The gold in the conglomerate was no doubt eroded from the quartz veins that transect the Paleozoic rocks. The early lode production of this district could not be ascertained; however, the magnitude of operations is indicated by O'Brien (1947, p. 437), who stated that the Golden Eagle mine produced $1 million (about 48,500 ounces) in gold before 1931.

HUMBUG DISTRICT

The Humbug district, in T. 46 N., Rs. 10 and 11 W., has been chiefly a lode district, although placers were productive before 1900. Total production through 1959 probably was between 25,000 and 50,000 ounces.

Bedrock in this district consists of metasediments, serpentine, diorite, and diabase of Cambrian to Carboniferous age (Averill, 1935, p. 257–258). Most of these rocks are schistose, and the principal veins are concordant with the schistosity. Some ore is also found in serpentine. No additional information could be found on this district.

KLAMATH RIVER DISTRICT

The Klamath River district is a large area along the Klamath River in the northwest part of Siskiyou County.

In the early days there was considerable hydraulicking of the Quaternary gravels of the Klamath River and its tributaries, and Averill (1935, p. 259) noted that many unworked terrace deposits still remained in the district.

Gold-quartz veins have been productive at scattered localities, particularly at the Independence mine south of Happy Camp, and in recent years lode production exceeded placer production. From 1933 through 1959 the district produced 53,619 ounces of lode gold and 140,364 ounces from placers. No record could be found of earlier production.

SALMON RIVER DISTRICT

The Salmon River district, an area of about 800 square miles, includes most of the drainage of the Salmon River.

The Quaternary placers between Sawyers Bar and Forks of Salmon have produced an estimated $25 million in gold (Averill, 1935, p. 260) and therefore made this district the most productive in Siskiyou County. Lode deposits have also been developed in the district but their early production is not known. From 1932 through 1959 the district was credited with 18,868 ounces of lode gold and 15,981 ounces from placers. No information on the geology of this district could be found.

SCOTT RIVER DISTRICT

The Scott River district, a poorly defined area, is centered around the town of Callahan and extends north along the Scott River.

In the early days there was considerable placer activity near Callahan and at Scott Bar (Averill, 1935, p. 257), and lode mines were also highly productive. Although the early placer production is not known, an incomplete record of lode production was found. The Black Bear mine produced $3,100,000 (about 150,500 ounces) in gold, and the McKeen mine, $250,000 (about 12,100 ounces) (O'Brien, 1947, p. 429, 447).

The most abundant country rock in the district is an undifferentiated sequence of Paleozoic or pre-Paleozoic shales, slates, limestones, and calcareous sandstones. This sequence of rocks was intruded by masses of serpentine and then by gabbro and granodiorite, all of unknown age (Averill, 1931, p. 8–9, 18, 21–22). No details on the nature of the lodes could be found.

STANISLAUS COUNTY

All the gold mined in Stanislaus County has come from placers. The Quaternary gravels along the Stanislaus River above Oakdale (the Oakdale-Knights Ferry district) and in the channels of the Tertiary Tuolumne River near Waterford have been the most productive (Charles, 1947, p. 92). In the early 1900's large-scale dredging of Quaternary gravels began along the Tuolumne River between La Grange and Waterford, and most of the gold produced in Stanislaus County from 1932 through 1959 came from this area. In the late 1940's gold mining declined sharply, and during 1952–59 only a few ounces per year was produced as a byproduct of various sand and gravel operations. Gold production of the county from 1880 through 1959 was 364,600 ounces.

Published information on the geology and development of the individual districts could not be found; however, during 1932–59 the Oakdale-Knights Ferry district produced 28,399 ounces, and the La Grange-Waterford district produced 108,512 ounces.

TRINITY COUNTY

Substantial amounts of gold have been mined from lodes and placers in Trinity County. Mining began in the early 1850's with small-scale placer operations in the Trinity River basin. Later the terrace and channel gravels were worked by hydraulic methods, and huge dragline dredges were used near Junction City and Weaverville. Lode mining has also been successful in the Carrville district.

Total gold production of Trinity County from 1880 through 1959 was 2,036,300 ounces, mostly from placers.

The central part of the county is traversed by a northwest-trending belt of schists belonging to the Abrams Mica Schist and the Salmon Hornblende Schist, both believed to be Precambrian in age, and concordant Paleozoic metasedimentary rocks including quartzites, cherts, slates, limestones and interbedded lavas, greenstones, and amphibolite schists (Averill, 1941a, p. 10). Northeast of this sequence of metasedimentary rocks are large masses of intrusive rocks ranging in composition from granite to serpentine, of probable Late Jurassic age. Sedimentary rocks, possibly equivalent to the Franciscan Group of Jurassic(?) age, are exposed in the southwestern part of the county (Averill, 1941a, p. 10).

CARRVILLE DISTRICT

The Carrville district is about 5 miles north of Trinity Center, along the Trinity River near its junction with Coffee Creek. Almost its entire production has come from lode deposits, which produced an estimated $1 million in gold through 1910 (MacDonald, 1913, p. 20) ; however, no activity has been reported in recent years.

The country rock consists of schists, of possible Precambrian age, a complex of greenstone of pre-Carboniferous age, and slates and conglomerates that compose the Bragdon Formation of Carboniferous age (MacDonald, 1913, p. 10–14). Intrusive granodiorite masses of Late Jurassic or Early Cretaceous age cut the foregoing rocks. Large areas of the district are underlain by serpentine believed to be Jurassic in age, and the serpentine is cut by numerous lamprophyre dikes.

The most important ore bodies are replacements of basic dikes in or near granodiorite porphyry masses (MacDonald, 1913, p. 14). The ore is highly oxidized and sheared, and the gold occurs in the oxidized products of pyrite or in the country rock or in the veins in the form of tellurides. Small amounts of silver are present.

TRINITY RIVER BASIN

The Trinity River basin is a large area that includes most of the drainage of the Trinity River, and it extends from Coffee Creek southward through Trinity Center, Dedrick, Helena, Junction City, Weaverville, Lewiston, and Douglas City, and west to the Hay Fork area.

Mining began in this area in the early 1850's and was still active in 1959, though on a much-reduced scale. Placer mining was formerly done on a large scale by hydraulic operations, but large dragline dredges have supplanted the hydraulic giants. The La Grange mine near Weaverville was the largest hydraulic mine in this area (MacDonald, 1910, p. 51). Production of gold from the gravels of the Trinity River basin from 1880 through 1959 was about 1,750,000 ounces.

The gold-bearing gravels of the Trinity basin are related to two cycles of erosion of the Klamath Mountains. The older gravels are partly cemented and locally deformed, whereas the younger gravels occur along the present streams and are undisturbed (Diller, 1914a, p. 14–20). Both types contain workable placers.

TULARE COUNTY

Although more than 50 gold mines are scattered throughout Tulare County, only those in the White River district—where gold was discovered in 1853 (Goodwin, 1958, p. 339)—have had significant production.

Production of Tulare County from 1880 through 1959 was about 20,325 ounces, all from lodes. The peak year of production was 1884, when $70,000 in gold was mined. Except for a brief flurry in the early 1930's, there has been very little activity in the gold mines since 1906 (Goodwin, 1958, p. 340).

The gold in the White River district is in quartz veins in granite and in metasedimentary rocks (Goodwin, 1958, p. 340).

TUOLUMNE COUNTY

Tuolumne County, one of the Mother Lode counties, is in central California between Calaveras County on the north and Mariposa County on the south.

In the 1850's the gold-rush prospectors and adventurers overran the entire Mother Lode country. They soon found the gold placers of Tuolumne County, which became the richest in California. During 1850–70 this county was one of the leading gold producers in the State. At least $151,175,000 (about 7,338,600 ounces) of placer gold was produced before 1899, mostly from the Tertiary and Quaternary gravels in the Columbia Basin and the Table Mountain channel in the Jamestown-Sonora area (Julihn and Horton, 1940, p. 69).

After 1890, as the placers were depleted, mining of quartz veins increased, and after 1903 lodes exceeded placers in production. Total estimated production for the county through 1959 was 10,131,000 ounces: 2,580,000 ounces from lodes and 7,551,000 ounces from placers.

Nearly all the lode mines lie in a zone about 14 miles wide that crosses the county from northwest to southeast. Deposits in the Mother Lode are along the southwest side of the zone near the contact between the Calaveras and Mariposa Formations. Deposits of the East Belt are on the northeast side, parallel to the Mother Lode. Between the two is a chain of small but rich deposits known as the Pocket Belt.

COLUMBIA BASIN-JAMESTOWN-SONORA DISTRICT

The Columbia Basin-Jamestown-Sonora district is in parts of Tps. 1 and 2 N., Rs. 14 and 15 E., in northwest Tuolumne County.

From 1853, when the placers were discovered, to 1870, an area less than 2 miles in diameter—the well-known Columbia Basin—produced more than $55 million in gold (Julihn and Horton, 1940, p. 71). Other rich deposits were at Sonora, Yankee Hill, and Jamestown. More than 95 percent of the placer gold of Tuolumne County was derived from Quaternary gravels, the gold of which was reworked from eroded Tertiary gravels (Julihn and Horton, 1940, p. 70). In the Columbia Basin most of the gold was extracted by hand from natural riffles and from between pinnacles on the limestone bedrock surface at the base of the gravels. In the vicinity of Jamestown and Sonora, Tertiary channel gravels were worked by drift mines. The richest placers were exhausted fairly early and by the late 1870's placer production dropped sharply. This trend was reversed for a short time in the late 1930's, but production decreased after World War II. Total gold production from this area was about $121 million, or about 5,874,000 ounces (Julihn and Horton, 1940, p. 69).

The Tertiary gravels, which yielded gold valued at between $5 and $6 million, were worked chiefly by drift mines in the Table Mountain channel and by surface mines at Chinese Camp and Montezuma (Julihn and Horton, 1940, p. 70).

EAST BELT DISTRICT

The East Belt district includes a system of lodes parallel to the Mother Lode, about 10 miles to the east. The settlements of Pooleys Ranch, Soulsbyville, and Tuolumne are along the East Belt.

The first claims on the East Belt were located in the mid-1850's. The deposits proved to be extremely rich in gold, and before 1899 the yield of 38 East Belt mines was about $19,340,000 (about 938,800 ounces), a far greater output than that of the Mother Lode for this period (Julihn and Horton, 1940, p. 19). These veins, however, were for the most part shallow, and high production could not be maintained for any extended period. Nevertheless, the Soulsby mine has produced $6,750,000, and there are five other mines with a production of $1 million or more (Julihn and Horton, 1940, p. 52–53). Total production through 1959 of the East Belt in Tuolumne County was about 965,000 ounces.

The veins of this district are in and grouped around a stock of granodiorite that intruded the Calaveras Formation (Julihn and Horton, 1940, p. 51–52). Pegmatites cut both the granodiorite and Calaveras Formation, and the gold-bearing veins are later than the pegmatite. Most of the veins are in the granodiorite and along the granodiorite-country rock contact. The veins are narrow and they pinch and swell; nevertheless, they are remarkably persistent. Free gold is found in these veins with quartz and with sulfides which include pyrite, pyrrhotite, chalcopyrite, galena, sphalerite, and complex sulfides of lead and antimony.

GROVELAND-MOCCASIN-JACKSONVILLE AREA

The Groveland-Moccasin-Jacksonville area is in parts of T. 1 S., Rs. 14, 15 and 16 E., in southern Tuolumne County.

Before 1899, Quaternary gravels in this area yielded about $34 million in gold (Julihn and Horton, 1940, p. 69). There is no consistent record of later production, although Julihn and Horton (1940, p. 81, 82) reported dredging operations along Moccasin Creek in 1937 and 1938.

The Longfellow mine, the most productive of a group of lode mines near Groveland, produced an estimated $½ million in gold (about 24,200 ounces) before 1899. No record was found of any later lode mining in this district.

MOTHER LODE DISTRICT

The Mother Lode district is delineated by a chain of about 40 mines that crosses Tuolumne County from northwest to southeast from a point just west of Tuttletown in the north to the headwaters of Moccasin Creek in the south, where the lode enters Mariposa County.

Probably the first major property to be developed in this district was the Harvard mine, discovered in 1850 (Julihn and Horton, 1940, p. 30). In 1852 the Dutch claim was located. The claim was later consolidated with the Sweeney and App-Heslep mines, and this combination became the most productive property in the district with an output of about $9 million in gold to 1928 (Julihn and Horton, 1940, p. 20). Another important group of mines, first operated in the 1860's, was the Golden Rule (Julihn and Horton, 1940, p. 42). The Mother Lode mines developed slowly, but as they were deepened, higher grade ore was found and their production increased. Probably the most active period was between 1890 and 1920 when the Rawhide, Harvard, Dutch-App, and Eagle-Shawmut were at their peaks of activity. After World War I, there was a long period of idleness which was ended by the increased price of gold in 1934. The mines were pumped dry and retimbered, and a short period of prosperity returned to the district. During World War II the mines were closed again, and in the postwar period resumption of mining was discouraged by the low grade of the ore and the constantly increasing costs made even higher by the great depths of the mines.

The Mother Lode district in Tuolumne County is credited with $4,310,000 in gold before 1899 (Julihn and Horton, 1940, p. 18). The six largest mines produced a total of $29,750,000 in gold to 1928, and from 1933 through 1959 the Mother Lode produced

86,112 ounces of lode gold and 41,524 ounces of placer gold. The placer production is probably from Tertiary gravels near Jamestown and no doubt should have been credited to that district rather than the Mother Lode. The minimum total production for the district is about 1,550,000 ounces.

POCKET BELT DISTRICT

The Pocket Belt district, 5 to 6 miles wide, is between the Stanislaus River and the Jamestown-Sonora area.

This district is known for the extreme richness of small veins that produced minor fortunes in a very short time with small investments. Perhaps the best known of these mines was the Bonanza, located in 1851, which in a single week produced about $300,000 worth of gold. The Pocket Belt has been noted for spectacular short-term operations; thus it exerts a persistent lure, and sporadic activity will probably continue indefinitely.

Production of the district was about $5½ million (267,000 ounces) (Julihn and Horton, 1940, p. 60).

Bedrock is the Calaveras Formation, which has been fractured and laced with seams of quartz and calcite. Locally, where these seams swell, there are concentrations of coarse gold. Some of the gold is crystallized, and in some places it is accompanied by petzite, calaverite, and other tellurides. The seams or pockets are noted for their discontinuity (Julihn and Horton, 1940, p. 60).

YUBA COUNTY

Auriferous gravels have been highly productive in Yuba County. The Hammonton vicinity alone yielded $100 million in gold from the gravels along the Yuba River after dredging started in 1903 (O'Brien, 1952a, p. 148). Considerable placer gold has come from Tertiary gravels but much more has come from the Quaternary gravels.

Gold-bearing quartz veins have been mined in the Browns Valley-Smartville and Brownsville-Challenge-Dobbins districts where the veins are found in metamorphic rocks near the contact with a granodioritic body.

Total recorded production from 1880 through 1959 was 5,294,600 ounces: 4,387,100 ounces from placers and 907,500 ounces from lodes.

BROWNS VALLEY-SMARTVILLE AND BROWNSVILLE-CHALLENGE-DOBBINS DISTRICTS

These districts are discussed jointly here because of the paucity of published information regarding their individual history, geology, and production. The Browns Valley-Smartville district is in central Yuba County, in T. 16 N., R. 5 E. The Brownsville-Challenge-Dobbins district is in the northern part of the county, in Tps. 18 and 19 N., Rs. 6 and 7 E.

The gold deposits of these districts were described briefly by Lindgren and Turner (1895). In the Browns Valley-Smartville area, gold-bearing quartz veins occur in amphibolitic schists and diabase. The principal mine here was the Hibbert and Burris. In the Brownsville-Challenge-Dobbins area, gold-quartz veins are associated with masses of granodiorite.

Production from these districts is not known, but it may be assumed that it represents all the lode gold credited to Yuba County—907,500 ounces from 1880 through 1959.

Metasedimentary rocks of the Calaveras Group are exposed in two northwest-trending belts—one passes through Camptonville, the other near Challenge. A younger group of greenstones and green schists is also exposed in this area, but their stratigraphic relations are not known (O'Brien, 1952a, p. 144–145). Intrusive rocks consisting of small bodies of diabase, gabbro, and peridotite, and of large masses of granodiorite of the Sierra Nevada batholith cut the metasedimentary rocks and greenstones.

HAMMONTON DISTRICT

The Hammonton district, in parts of Tps. 15 and 16 N., Rs. 4 and 5 E., is along the Yuba River in the southern part of Yuba County.

Beginning in 1903, large-scale dredging of the Quaternary gravels produced about $2 million in gold annually, and by 1949 the district had produced about $100 million in gold (O'Brien, 1952a, p. 145). In 1952 six dredges were in operation. Total production through 1959 was about 4,387,100 ounces.

COLORADO

Colorado ranks second among the States in total gold production, with an aggregate of about 40,776,000 ounces through 1965.

Gold and other ore deposits are mostly in a northeast-trending belt, known as the Colorado mineral belt, in the mountainous western part of the State. From near Boulder on the northeast this belt extends southwest to the San Juan Mountains and beyond (fig. 10). The Cripple Creek district, the largest gold producer in Colorado, and several minor districts lie southeast of the mineral belt.

Before 1858 Colorado was explored by fur trappers and special expeditions, but apparently most of these early adventurers paid little or no attention to the mineral deposits in the area. According to C. W. Henderson (in Finch and others, 1933, p.

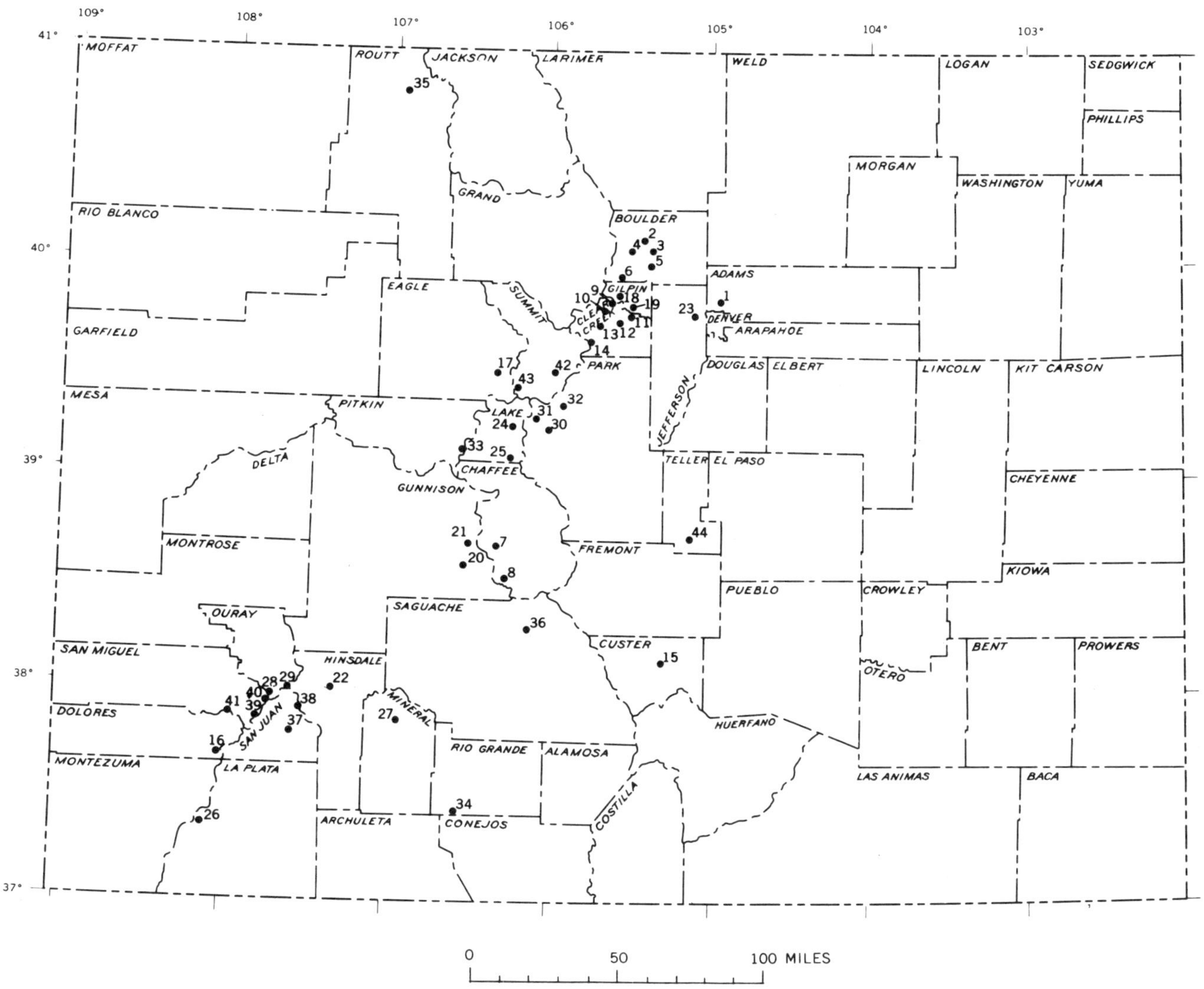

FIGURE 10.—Gold-mining districts of Colorado.

Adams County:
1, Clear Creek placers.

Boulder County:
2, Jamestown; 3, Gold Hill-Sugarloaf; 4, Ward; 5, Magnolia; 6, Grand Island-Caribou.

Chaffee County:
7, Chalk Creek; 8, Monarch.

Clear Creek County:
9, Alice; 10, Empire; 11, Idaho Springs; 12, Freeland-Lamartine; 13, Georgetown-Silver Plume; 14, Argentine.

Custer County:
15, Rosita Hills.

Dolores County:
16, Rico.

Eagle County:
17, Gilman.

Gilpin County:
18, Northern Gilpin; 19, Central City.

Gunnison County:
20, Gold Brick-Quartz Creek; 21, Tincup.

Hinsdale County:
22, Lake City.

Jefferson County:
23, Clear Creek placers.

Lake County:
24, Leadville; 25, Arkansas River valley placers.

La Plata County:
26, La Plata.

Mineral County:
27, Creede.

Ouray County:
28, Sneffels-Red Mountain; 29, Uncompahgre.

Park County:
30, Alma; 31, Fairplay; 32, Tarryall.

Pitkin County:
33, Independence Pass.

Rio Grande County:
34, Summitville.

Routt County:
35, Hahns Peak.

Saguache County:
36, Bonanza.

San Juan County:
37, Animas; 38, Eureka.

San Miguel County:
39, Ophir; 40, Telluride; 41, Mount Wilson.

Summit County:
42, Breckenridge; 43, Tenmile.

Teller County:
44, Cripple Creek.

761), the existence of gold in South Park was recorded in a report delivered in secret to General Zebulon Pike in 1807 at Santa Fe, N. Mex., where he was being held prisoner by the Spaniards. Cherokee Indians of Oklahoma reportedly brought gold from the headwaters of the South Platte River to residents along the lower Missouri River from 1849 to 1857.

In the spring of 1858, the Russell brothers, placer miners from Georgia and later from California, led a party who prospected along Cherry and Ralston Creeks and the South Platte River near the present site of Denver. They were guided to the area by Cherokee Indians. Although they only found gold in very small quantities, news of the discoveries spread and a rush to the "Pikes Peak Country" followed. By Christmas of 1858 about 1,000 men had arrived, and several settlements were founded in the Denver area. In January 1859 the first commercial gold placers in Colorado were discovered by George A. Jackson near the mouth of Chicago Creek near Idaho Springs. This news spread and precipitated a rush of prospectors into the surrounding mountains. In May 1859, John Hamilton Gregory found outcrops of veins with residual deposits of gold in the drainage basin of North Clear Creek near Blackhawk, and in early June, W. G. Russell discovered placer gold in Russell Gulch near Central City. Throughout 1859 prospectors spread to many of the streams emerging from the Front Range, to the headwaters of the South Platte River and its tributaries in South Park, and up the Arkansas River and its tributaries as far as California Gulch to what was to become the Leadville district (Henderson, 1926, p. 1–9; Finch and others, 1933, p. 761–768; Bastin and Hill, 1917, p. 67–69). This activity led to many rich and significant discoveries in the following few years. Placers generally were found first; then gold-bearing veins or disintegrated oxidized residue of gold-bearing veins, the "mother lodes," were found soon afterward.

In the first few years frenzied activity reigned in the newly discovered gold fields. During 1858–67 Colorado produced about $14,924,000 in placer gold and about $10 million in lode gold (Henderson, 1926, p. 69). When mining had depleted the rich placers and the free-milling oxidized ores and reached the underlying sulfide ore, which was not amenable to amalgamation or simple devices of concentration, many mines closed and mining waned (Bastin and Hill, 1917, p. 153–163). This condition was in part remedied in 1868 when the Hill smelter opened in January at Blackhawk in Gilpin County. It successfully treated sulfide ores from many districts, and the lode-mining industry in Colorado was revived (Henderson, 1926, p. 69).

Railroads also stimulated mining in Colorado during the 1860's and 1870's with the completion of the Union Pacific Railroad to Cheyenne, Wyo., in 1867, the Denver Pacific from Denver to Cheyenne in 1870, the Kansas Pacific to Denver in 1870, and a narrow-gage railroad to Blackhawk in 1872 (Henderson, 1926, p. 61).

Prospectors soon spread to all parts of the State and discovered in rapid succession many of Colorado's most famous mining camps. Discovery of gold in the San Juan Mountains in southwestern Colorado in 1870 triggered a stampede of prospectors into this region—to Summitville in 1873 and Silverton in 1874. In 1875 major ore discoveries were made at Lake City, Ouray, and Telluride. In the middle and late 1870's rich ore deposits were discovered on the east side of the Sawatch Range in the Monarch and Chalk Creek districts, in the Rosita Hills in Custer County, in the Kokomo and Breckenridge districts in the Tenmile Range, and at Aspen on the west side of the Sawatch Range. The placer deposits in California Gulch were depleted in 1867, and the area was abandoned, but in 1877 rich lead-silver ore was discovered and the Leadville district at the south end of the Mosquito Range was founded. In 1891 rich gold ore was discovered at Cripple Creek and lead-silver ore was discovered at Creede; these were the last of Colorado's famous gold-mining camps to be established.

Except for only a few years, gold production in Colorado exceeded 100,000 ounces annually from 1860 through 1954. It gradually rose from 97,500 ounces in 1873 to about 201,000 ounces in 1890 (Henderson, 1926, p. 69). The Cripple Creek district boosted production to a peak of about 1,393,000 ounces in 1900 (fig. 11). Thereafter production declined at an uneven rate to about 213,700 ounces in 1929. When the price of gold was raised to $35 per ounce in 1934, production again rose to 380,000 ounces in 1941. It again declined abruptly when the mines were closed during World War II. After the war the annual gold output reached a maximum of about 150,000 ounces in 1947, but during 1954–65 it was below 100,000 ounces. Gold output reached a low of 33,605 ounces in 1963.

The mineral belt of Colorado trends obliquely to the mountain ranges and crosses the San Juan Mountains in the southwestern part of the State and the Sawatch, Mosquito, Gore-Tenmile, and Front Ranges in the central and north-central parts of the State. This belt is coincident with a belt of intrusive stocks, dikes, and sills of porphyritic

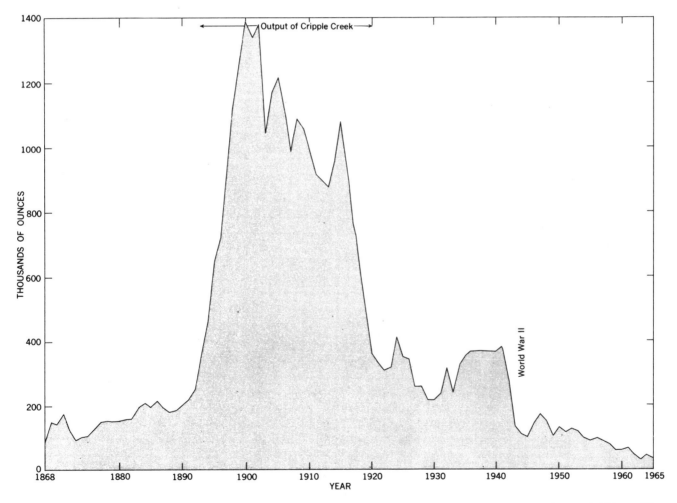

Discoveries of gold deposits in Boulder County, which date from 1858 (Henderson, 1926, p. 38–40, 105–106), were among the first in the State. Though placers were worked first, most of the gold mined before 1869 was from oxidized free-milling lode ore, and when this was depleted, many mines closed. Through 1868 the annual production was less than $50,000 in gold. The construction of a new smelter at Blackhawk in 1868 stimulated activity in the mining camps, new veins were discovered, and mines and camps developed rapidly. Gold production increased from about $100,000 (4,838 ounces) in 1870 to $683,941 (33,089 ounces) in 1891 and to a peak production of $982,988 (47,556 ounces) in 1892 (Henderson, 1926, p. 106). After the panic of 1893, when the price of silver dropped, gold production fluctuated but generally declined; only $16,516 (799 ounces) in gold was produced in 1930. The rise in the price of gold in 1934 stimulated gold mining, and 33,621 ounces was produced in 1940. Activity again declined during World War II and decreased even more after the war.

Boulder County has many mining camps and districts, but to 1959 only five had a total gold output in excess of 10,000 ounces: Jamestown (Central), Gold Hill-Sugarloaf, Ward, Magnolia, and Grand Island-Caribou.

GOLD HILL-SUGARLOAF DISTRICT

The Gold Hill-Sugarloaf district, the largest gold producer in Boulder County, contains several small mining camps within an area of about 12 square miles in the central part of the county, 3 to 8 miles northwest of Boulder. The largest of these is Gold Hill; others are Sugarloaf, Rowena, Salina, and Sunshine. Gold was the chief metal produced in the district, although in most deposits silver is associated with the gold.

Placer gold was discovered in this district in January 1859, very early in the history of mining in the State, and $100,000 (4,838 ounces) worth of gold was worked from these placers during the first summer (Goddard, 1940, p. 106). Gold-bearing veins were discovered nearby during the summer of 1859, and in consequence several thousand people flocked to the district. The oxidized surface ore yielded free gold and recovery was made by sluice, arrastre, and stamp mill. When these ores were mined out after a few years, activity in the district declined sharply. Mining activity increased markedly in 1872 when the gold-silver telluride, petzite, was discovered at the Red Cloud mine at Gold Hill. In 1873 telluride ore was discovered in the Cold Spring mine. The ore was extremely rich, yielding an average of $1,500 per ton, and in 2 years these two mines produced about $600,000 in gold from about 400 tons of ore (Henderson, 1926, p. 39). Many more veins were found from 1875 to 1880 and activity was sustained at a high level until 1904, after which mining declined (Goddard, 1940, tables p. 108–109). The district was rejuvenated in the middle and late 1930's but slumped sharply during World War II; after the war it failed to regain its former importance and was almost inactive during 1950–59.

The lode-gold production from the Gold Hill-Sugarloaf district from the time of discovery through 1903 could not be ascertained. According to Henderson (1926, table, p. 106), Boulder County from 1859 through 1903 produced about $13,435,000 worth of gold. It seems reasonable to assume that the Gold Hill-Sugarloaf district produced at least one-fourth of this amount—about $3,360,000 or 162,500 ounces. The minimum total output of the district through 1959 was about 412,000 ounces, mostly from lodes. The placer production probably did not exceed 3,000 ounces (Lovering and Goddard, 1950, p. 240).

The following brief description of the geology and ore deposits of the district is mostly from Goddard (1940, p. 110–139).

Schists and gneiss of the Idaho Springs Formation are intruded by a batholith of Boulder Creek Granite and dikes of Silver Plume Granite, all Precambrian in age. Sedimentary rocks of Pennsylvanian age unconformably overlie the Precambrian rocks about 2 miles east of the district. The Precambrian rocks have been cut by a series of porphyry dikes of Laramide age that range in composition from diabase to alaskite. The mineral deposits are chiefly in the northern part of the Boulder Creek batholith; most of the veins are in the granite and a few in the western part of the district extend into the schist.

The distribution of ore deposits was strongly influenced by conspicuous silicified, hematite-stained breccia zones, called breccia reefs. The most prominent of these are nearly vertical and trend N. 25°–50° W.; others can be grouped into sets that trend N. 70°–80° W., N. 60°–75° W., and N. 5°–30° E. The gold deposits are in telluride and pyritic veins that occupy fissures, most of which strike northeast. Ore is localized where these veins cross the breccia reefs. Most of the productive veins are more than half a mile long and from 1 to 5 feet wide, but some are from 10 to 30 feet wide. The order of deposition of the veins is not certain. Silver-lead veins appear to be the oldest in the district; these are followed by the gold telluride veins, and then by the pyritic gold veins. A few of the silver-lead veins, however, seem to be related to the pyritic gold veins.

Gold tellurides, the most abundant of which are petzite and sylvanite, are the most important ore minerals in the Gold Hill-Sugarloaf district, but free gold is also abundant. Other tellurides occurring in small amounts are hessite, altaite, and coloradoite. Fine-grained pyrite and very small amounts of galena and sphalerite are associated with the ore minerals. Horn quartz and sugary quartz are the chief gangue minerals. Roscoelite is closely associated with the tellurides and free gold. Ankerite and other carbonates also are associated with the telluride ores but are younger than the telluride minerals.

In the pyritic gold veins, pyrite and chalcopyrite are the most abundant ore minerals, but free gold is abundant in some veins. The chief gangue mineral is sugary to glassy quartz; ankerite is found in some veins.

GRAND ISLAND-CARIBOU DISTRICT

The Grand Island-Caribou district is in southwest Boulder County, about 17 miles west of Boulder and 4 miles northwest of Nederland.

Silver is the chief metal produced in the district, but moderate amounts of lead and some lode gold have also been produced. Prospectors discovered veins near Caribou in about 1860 (Henderson, 1926, p. 38); however, they did not recognize the silver ore until 1869, when one of them, after seeing some silver ore from Nevada, returned to the district and made the first location. Other claims were staked the same year, and by the end of 1871 most of the rich lodes in the district had been found and production increased rapidly. Ore was produced from the district until 1893, when a drop in the price of silver forced most mines to close; however, some of the richer gold mines resumed operation in 1898. Since 1900 activity in the area has been limited to sporadic attempts to reactivate certain mines or to mill dump material from some of the larger mines (Moore and others, 1957, p. 521–522). The district was almost dormant from 1952 through 1959.

Nearly all the output of the district has come from lead-silver veins containing a little gold, though some gold-silver ore has been mined in outlying areas. The ore in the upper levels of many of the mines was very rich in silver, probably because of secondary enrichment (Moore and others, 1957, p. 521).

There is no record of the early gold production from the Grand Island-Caribou district. It has been estimated (Moore and others, 1957, p. 522) that the total value of lead and silver produced before 1924 was about $6 million, but no figures are given from which to estimate the gold production, though it was probably small. The gold production from 1932 through 1959 was 10,006 ounces.

The eastern and western parts of the district are underlain by schist and gneiss of the Idaho Springs Formation and by small bodies of Boulder Creek Granite. These rocks, which are of Precambrian age, were intruded by a composite stock of calcic monzonite and quartz monzonite which occupies the central part of the district. A striking feature is the occurrence of numerous masses of pyroxenite, titaniferous magnetite, and hornblendite in the stock (Smith, 1938, p. 171, 174).

Lead-silver veins in the monzonite stock in the vicinity of Caribou Hill have been the most productive in the district. The gold veins are in the Precambrian rocks and are older than the lead-silver veins. Quartz, pyrite, chalcopyrite, covellite (?), and minor galena and sphalerite are the predominant minerals of the gold veins. The lead-silver veins chiefly contain quartz, pyrite, sphalerite, galena, chalcopyrite, argentite, pyrargyrite, carbonates, and secondary azurite, malachite, native silver, and limonite (Moore and others, 1957, p. 526–528).

JAMESTOWN DISTRICT

The Jamestown (Central) district is in the Front Range in central Boulder County, about 9 miles northwest of Boulder. Gold ore was discovered in 1865 (Lovering and Goddard, 1950, p. 255), and sometime between 1876 and 1881 the town of Jamestown was founded (Henderson, 1926, p. 40). Little else is known of the early development of the district, even though it is one of the major gold-producing areas in Boulder County. The Jamestown, Gold Hill, and Ward districts were the chief gold producers in the county from 1883 to 1912. Many mines were closed thereafter but were reopened during 1934–42. From World War II through 1959 gold mining again declined. The total gold production from the district through 1959 was about 207,000 ounces. This figure includes an estimate by E. N. Goddard (in Vanderwilt and others, 1947, p. 324) of $4,700,000 worth of gold ore produced through 1943.

The geology of the district is summarized chiefly from E. N. Goddard (in Vanderwilt and others, 1947, p. 323–327) and Lovering and Goddard (1950, p. 255–279).

The Jamestown district, at the northeast end of

the Colorado mineral belt, is underlain chiefly by schist of the Idaho Springs Formation and by some hornblende gneiss, intruded by the Boulder Creek and Silver Plume Granites. These Precambrian rocks have been intruded by stocks and a variety of dikes of porphyritic igneous rocks of early Tertiary age. The rocks are cut by silicified brecciated zones known as breccia reefs, which are older than the Tertiary porphyries, and by normal faults, the vein fissures, which are younger than the porphyries.

An early set of vein fissures, trending northwestward, contains lead-silver and fluorspar deposits, and a later set, trending northeastward, encloses pyritic gold and gold telluride deposits. The ore deposits appear to be genetically related to a small quartz monzonite porphyry stock. Though their distribution around the stock is irregular, there is, nevertheless, a rough mineralogical zoning of the deposits. The lead-silver and fluorspar deposits are close to the border of the stock and the pyritic gold and gold telluride deposits are successively farther away.

The chief minerals in the pyritic gold veins are pyrite and chalcopyrite in a quartz gangue. The gold is free or is intricately associated with chalcopyrite and in small amounts with pyrite. Galena and sphalerite are present in some veins. Silver is usually present in about equal amounts with the gold.

The telluride veins consist of jaspery quartz, finely disseminated pyrite, free gold, and a variety of telluride minerals—predominantly krennerite and petzite, smaller amounts of sylvanite and altaite, and locally small amounts of hessite, coloradoite, and native tellurium.

The pyritic gold veins range in width from a few inches to 3 feet, but some shoots occur in mineralized zones 10 to 30 feet wide. The telluride veins are as much as 10 feet wide, and some shoots at vein junctions are as much as 30 feet wide. The deepest workings are only about 500 feet below the surface, and on many veins the deepest workings are only 100 to 200 feet deep. Many veins are as strong at the bottom level as at the surface and are considered favorable for exploration at greater depth (E. N. Goddard, in Vanderwilt and others, 1947, p. 327).

MAGNOLIA DISTRICT

The Magnolia district, about 4 miles southwest of Boulder along the east side of the Front Range, is small, and most of the productive veins crop out in an area of less than 1 square mile.

Gold telluride ore was discovered in the district in 1875, 3 years after the discovery of gold telluride in the Gold Hill camp (Wilkerson, 1939, p. 82), and most of the known veins were being worked by 1877. Small amounts of tungsten ore also have been mined. The productive life of the district was largely spent by 1905, and even the increased price of gold in 1934 failed to excite more than a spark of revival. The production of the district before 1906 was valued optimistically at $2,815,000 and was mostly in gold (Lovering and Goddard, 1950, p. 227). Total gold production through 1959 was about 130,000 ounces.

Almost all the district is underlain by gneissic Boulder Creek Granite of Precambrian age, which is cut by numerous aplite and pegmatite dikes (Wilkerson, 1939, p. 84). Most of the ore deposits are in gold telluride fissure veins that trend west or northwest, and ore seems to be localized at intersections of fissures.

The Magnolia district, whose ore minerals consist chiefly of gold tellurides, was the first in Colorado to produce considerable quantities of telluride ore. Much of the ore was very rich. The district is of interest also because of the variety of the telluride minerals and the unusual association of gold tellurides with tungsten, vanadium, and molybdenum minerals (Lovering and Goddard, 1950, p. 228). Sylvanite is the main ore mineral but it is almost everywhere accompanied by one or more of the following tellurides: calaverite, hessite, petzite, coloradoite, and altaite. Other minerals found in the district are native gold, lionite, magnolite, nagyagite, henryite, tellurite, ferro-tellurite, melonite, native tellurium, ferberite, molybdenite, and roscoelite, and some galena, sphalerite, pyrite, marcasite, calcite, and fluorite (Lovering and Goddard, 1950, p. 228). Gangue minerals are present in only minor amounts and consist mainly of light- to dark-colored varieties of extremely fine grained quartz or "horn."

WARD DISTRICT

The Ward district is in western Boulder County, west of the Gold Hill-Sugarloaf district and about 9 to 13 miles northwest of Boulder. It comprises 12 square miles in the headwaters of Lefthand and Fourmile Creeks and includes the mining camps of Sunset and Copper Rock.

Gold was first discovered in 1861, and by 1870 most of the major lodes had been located. The Niwot and Columbia mines were the largest gold producers; however, Worcester (1920, p. 56) noted that there were more than 50 mines in the district that had produced more than $5,000 worth of ore. Gold mining in the district declined after 1893; it revived briefly during 1936–42, but it waned from 1943 through 1959. The exhaustion of the rich oxidized ores left only low-grade sulfide ores that have thus far resisted all attempts at successful treatment.

The early gold output of the Ward district can only be estimated. Using Henderson's (1926, p. 106) figure of $15,954,999 for Boulder County from 1859 to 1923 and Worcester's (1920, p. 70) assumption that Ward produced 20 to 24 percent of the total dollar value of Boulder County mineral production through 1915, we can credit the district with a minimum of $3,191,000 or about 154,400 ounces of gold through 1923. Total gold produced through 1959 was roughly 172,000 ounces, mostly from quartz veins. The small placer deposits were exhausted long ago.

The country rock in the Ward district is largely Precambrian in age. Gneiss and schist of the Idaho Springs Formation predominate in the southern part of the district, whereas Silver Plume Granite is the major bedrock in the northern part. Several stocks of diorite and monzonite porphyry and smaller masses of sodic andesite and diorite porphyry and a wide variety of dikes of Tertiary age intrude the Precambrian rocks throughout the district (Lovering and Goddard, 1950, p. 203).

Nearly all the ore in the Ward district occurs in veins or in shoots or chimneys that appear to be local enlargements of veins. Most of the productive veins are in the granite or granite gneiss; many veins feather out in the schist. The veins either follow or are closely associated with felsite, dacite, quartz monzonite, latite, or quartz latite dikes. Gold, silver, and lead have been mined in appreciable quantities; and copper, zinc, and tungsten have been produced in small amounts. Most of the gold has been derived from quartz veins rich in chalcopyrite; lesser amounts have come from quartz-pyrite veins with minor molybdenite and wolframite. Native gold and gold alloyed with silver occur in small amounts in ores that contain sphalerite and argentiferous galena as the chief constituents. Gold telluride ores are found in mines in the eastern part of the district (Lovering and Goddard, 1950, p. 203–207).

CHAFFEE COUNTY

Chaffee County is near the central part of Colorado. It borders the Continental Divide on the west and extends eastward across the valley of the upper Arkansas River. Through 1959 the county produced about 370,500 ounces of gold, mostly from lode deposits. Placers and base-metal ores yielded small quantities of gold.

Among the earliest gold discoveries in Colorado were placer deposits in early 1859 near the headwaters of the Arkansas River in Chaffee County and along Cache and Clear Creeks near Granite (Henderson, 1926, p. 9). By late 1860 most of the stream valleys in the county probably had been prospected, and gold placers were reported in places along the Arkansas River from Buena Vista southeast for 25 miles to the Fremont County line and in the northern part of the county near Granite and northward into Lake County. Other placers were found along Lost Canyon Gulch, Chalk Creek, Cottonwood Creek, Pine Creek, Bertscheys Gulch, Gold Run Gulch, Gilson Gulch, Oregon Gulch, and Ritchey's Patch. The relative importance of these stream placers is not given, but through 1869 Chaffee County is credited with a production of placer gold amounting to $400,000 (Henderson, 1926, p. 107). The small estimated annual production—$80,000 or less through 1904—indicates that there were no rich placers, and the large number of placer deposits listed above indicates that few if any of them had a large production. The deposits along the Arkansas River and Cache Creek near Granite probably were the most productive, but whether they produced more than 10,000 ounces cannot be ascertained. Some of this production probably came from placers just north of Granite in Lake County.

The date of the first discovery of lode deposits in Chaffee County has not been recorded. There was some lode mining in 1867–68 and the lode mines at Granite produced $60,000 in gold in 1870 (Henderson, 1926, p. 43, 107). The large lode deposits were not discovered until the early 1870's and later, and very little work was done on these deposits until 1883, when railroad facilities became available. Mining activity was accelerated during the 10 years following 1883 and continued at a high level until the close of World War I, after which production decreased rapidly. Gold mining remained at a low ebb through 1959.

About 15 districts in Chaffee County have produced gold, but of these probably only the Chalk Creek and Monarch districts have produced more than 10,000 ounces. Henderson (1926, p. 107) credited Chaffee County with a gold production through 1923 valued at $7,401,354 (358,072 ounces), of which $1,548,179 (74,900 ounces) represented placer gold and $5,853,175 (283,172 ounces), lode gold. Most of this production was achieved before 1904 when reliable and fairly complete records were not kept, and the source of much of this gold can only be conjectured. Total gold production of Chaffee County through 1959 was about 370,500 ounces.

Most of the lode gold came from the Chalk Creek district, but an appreciable amount, probably 50,000 to 75,000 ounces, came from many small mines and districts scattered throughout the county.

CHALK CREEK DISTRICT

The Chalk Creek district is in western Chaffee County near the headwaters of Chalk Creek, 16 miles west of Nathrop along the Arkansas River. The ores of the district contain gold, silver, lead, zinc, and a little copper. The Chalk Creek district probably is the only one in the county that has produced more than 100,000 ounces of gold.

The date of discovery of ore in the district probably was in the late 1860's. The Mary Murphy mine, the largest and most important in the district, is believed to have been in continuous operation from 1870 to 1925; thereafter it was operated intermittently (Dings and Robinson, 1957, p. 98). Although there are at least 20 other mines in the district, records of their history are fragmentary; most of them were inactive from 1901 through 1959.

The Mary Murphy mine, from which has come about 75 percent of the output of the district, produced a total of about 220,400 ounces of gold in addition to large amounts of silver, lead, zinc and a little copper (C. S. Robinson, oral commun., 1961). Total gold production of the district through 1959 was roughly 275,000 ounces.

Two masses of Tertiary quartz monzonite are the most abundant bedrock of the Chalk Creek district: the Mount Pomeroy, which is the older, and the Mount Princeton. In the southern part of the district, bodies of Tertiary andesite, quartz latite porphyry, quartz monzonite porphyry, and granite aplite cut these rocks; along the western edge of the district a large dike of quartz monzonite porphyry cuts the Mount Princeton Quartz Monzonite (Dings and Robinson, 1957, pl. 1).

The ore deposits in the district are veins chiefly in the Mount Princeton Quartz Monzonite, although veins also occur in the other intrusive rocks. Most of the ore mined was from pyritic quartz veins which range from mere stringers to lodes 50 feet thick and more than a mile long. The Mary Murphy vein has been worked through a vertical range of about 2,200 feet. Galena and sphalerite are the principal ore minerals and occur in streaks 1 to 12 inches wide within the pyritic quartz lodes. Some chalcopyrite is generally present. Free gold is reported to occur in much of the ore and probably occurs chiefly in the oxidized ore. The chief gangue mineral is white quartz, locally accompanied by calcite, rhodonite, rhodochrosite, barite, and fluorite. A few veins have been developed as molybdenum prospects, and these consist of white quartz with small amounts of molybdenite, molybdite, pyrite, magnetite, beryl, and muscovite (Dings and Robinson, 1957, p. 95–101).

MONARCH DISTRICT

The Monarch district is centered around the town of Garfield about 17 miles west of Salida. The district has produced chiefly silver, lead, and zinc, some copper, and a small amount of byproduct gold.

The first ore was discovered in the Monarch district in 1878. Other discoveries followed shortly, and by 1882 most of the large ore deposits in the region had been found. Transportation difficulties inhibited early development, but by 1883 a railroad was built to Monarch which permitted cheap and rapid transportation to the smelter at Pueblo. Oxidized ore rich in silver and lead was mined during the next 10 years, and production was large. In 1893, when the price of silver dropped, most mines were closed, and the district was nearly deserted (Crawford, 1913, p. 195–196). A demand for zinc revived the district, and in 1906 shipments of zinc carbonate ore began and continued for many years (Henderson, 1926, p. 43), especially during World War I. Between 1924 and 1940 activity was only intermittent. During World War II a few mines reopened, but these were closed again shortly after the war.

The Madonna mine, which is credited with almost 50 percent of the total output of the district, produced 4,652 ounces of gold between 1883 and 1911 (Crawford, 1913, p. 239). Total gold production of the district through 1959 was probably from 15,000 to 20,000 ounces.

The bedrock of the district is of three ages—metamorphic and igneous rocks of Precambrian age, sedimentary rocks of Paleozoic age, and intrusive rocks of Tertiary age. The Precambrian rocks are schists and gneisses and intrusive masses of Pikes Peak and Silver Plume(?) Granites. The Paleozoic rocks, which contain productive ore horizons, are about 6,000 feet thick and range in age from Cambrian to Permian(?). The sedimentary rocks have been eroded from a large part of the area, but patches have been preserved in synclines and in down-faulted blocks. The intrusive rocks of Tertiary age, the largest of which is the Mount Princeton batholith, are chiefly of quartz diorite and quartz monzonite composition (Dings and Robinson, 1957, p. 5–27).

The ore deposits in the Monarch district are replacement bodies, chiefly in the Paleozoic limestone and dolomite beds, and fissure veins. The Manitou Dolomite of Ordovician age and beds in the upper part of the Leadville Limestone of Mississippian age are especially favorable host rocks. The largest and richest replacement deposits are along faults in these beds near or adjacent to the Mount Princeton batholith. The chief sulfide minerals are galena, pyrite, sphalerite, some chalcopyrite, and local pyrrhotite. Much of the pyrite is gold bearing, and practically all the galena carries some silver, in places large amounts. The gangue consists of quartz and recrystallized limestone or dolomite. The bulk of all ore mined was at least partially oxidized, and the ore in the replacement deposits was more thoroughly and deeply oxidized than the ore in veins. Oxidation in the replacement deposits extends to a depth of 1,000 feet or more, whereas the oxidized ore in the veins is only a few feet deep.

Most of the veins in the Monarch district occur in the Mount Princeton Quartz Monzonite and in the sedimentary rocks of Pennsylvanian age; a few are found in some of the older sedimentary rocks and in the Precambrian rocks. The mineral assemblage in the veins is very similar to that of the replacement bodies. The unoxidized parts of the veins consist chiefly of galena, sphalerite, and pyrite, and some chalcopyrite in a gangue of white quartz. Silver is present in most of the ores, but gold is erratically distributed (Dings and Robinson, 1957, p. 81–85).

CLEAR CREEK COUNTY

Clear Creek County is in north-central Colorado in the Front Range, west of Denver, and immediately east of the Continental Divide.

Clear Creek County ranks seventh among the gold-producing counties of Colorado with a total of about 2,400,000 ounces through 1959, yet gold is second to silver in the value of minerals mined in the county. Substantial amounts of lead, zinc, and copper are also produced. Most of the precious metals have been recovered from siliceous ores in lodes, but in some deposits they were byproducts of base-metal ores. From 1859 to 1864 gold was almost wholly derived from placer deposits or from the hydraulicking of decomposed outcrops of veins.

Prospecting parties working westward from the first gold discoveries in Colorado near Denver discovered gold in Clear Creek County in early April 1859 along Chicago Creek, just above its junction with Clear Creek near Idaho Springs. Prospectors stampeded to the region, and shortly afterwards the first gold-bearing lodes were discovered and located. Later that year lodes were discovered in the Empire district and as far west as Georgetown. In the middle 1860's discoveries of silver veins in the Argentine and Georgetown-Silver Plume districts drew many mining people to western Clear Creek County (Spurr and others, 1908, p. 173).

When the free-milling oxidized ores were mined out, the mining industry waned until 1868 when the Blackhawk smelter opened and successfully treated the sulfide ores. The ever-widening network of railroads also encouraged mineral exploitation at this time. After 1900 mining activity was accelerated during World War I and in the 1935–41 period.

The country rock in Clear Creek County is a complex of Precambrian metamorphic and igneous rocks cut by Tertiary stocks and numerous dikes of porphyries. The most common porphyries range in composition from quartz monzonite to bostonite and alaskite. The ore deposits are also Tertiary in age and are genetically related to the porphyries.

The following six districts in the county have each produced more than a total of 10,000 ounces of gold: Alice, Empire, Idaho Springs, Freeland-Lamartine, Georgetown-Silver Plume, and Argentine. Of these the Idaho Springs district is the largest producer.

ALICE DISTRICT

The Alice district is about 7 miles west-northwest of Central City in north-central Clear Creek County and extends into southwest Gilpin County.

Most of the production of the district has come from the Alice mine, though little is known about its early history. The deposit probably was first mined in 1883. It was first worked as a placer by hydraulicking, and it yielded $60,000 in gold (2,903 ounces). Later the oxidized ore was treated in a stamp mill, and part of the free gold was recovered by amalgamation. The mill operated at a profit for 3 years until the oxidized ore was exhausted. Attempts to treat the unoxidized ore by concentration met with indifferent success; only about $10,000 (484 ounces) in gold concentrates was shipped (Bastin and Hill, 1917, p. 120, 325–326). The only other production recorded from the district is that of the North Star-Mann mine, which produced ore worth about $116,000 (about 5,610 ounces) through 1916 (Bastin and Hill, 1917, p. 329).

Apparently the district was abandoned for many years after the oxidized ore had been removed. The increased price of gold caused a brief revival from 1935 to 1941, during which time the upper enriched part of the sulfide zone was mined (Lovering and Goddard, 1950, p. 164). The district was largely idle from 1943 through 1959. Total gold production was at least 23,000 ounces through 1959.

The country rock of the Alice district consists mainly of schist of the Idaho Springs Formation which is interfingered with granite gneiss and Boulder Creek Granite, all of Precambrian age. A stock of quartz monzonite porphyry of Tertiary age intrudes the Precambrian rocks. The Alice mine ore body is a gold-bearing pyritic stockwork in the quartz monzonite porphyry; other mines in the district are in quartz-pyrite veins in the Precambrian rocks. The deposits were oxidized near the surface and contained 1 to 2½ ounces of gold per ton. A zone of supergene sulfide enrichment, containing 0.20 ounce of gold per ton, was found beneath the oxidized zone. The primary sulfide zone, beneath the supergene zone, contains only 0.03 ounce of gold per ton and is of too low grade to mine. Quartz and pyrite, some chalcopyrite, a little arsenopyrite, and local bismuth sulfide are the constituents of the primary ore. Sooty chalcocite and bornite are locally abundant in the supergene zone (Lovering and Goddard, 1950, p. 164–165; Bastin and Hill, 1917, p. 323–330).

ARGENTINE DISTRICT

The Argentine district, located at the heads of Leavenworth and Stevens Creeks in southwestern Clear Creek County, is 6 to 8 miles southwest of Georgetown and Silver Plume, just east of the Continental Divide. The mineralized area is on Kelso and McClellan Mountains. Lovering and Goddard (1950, p. 135) also included in the district an area in Summit County at the head of Peru Creek on the west side of the Continental Divide, but this area has produced insufficient gold to be considered in this report.

The early wave of frenzied gold prospectors overlooked the potential wealth of silver in Colorado; consequently, silver lodes lay unnoticed until 1864 when the Belmont silver lode in the Argentine district was discovered. A rush to the area ensued, resulting in additional discoveries in the Georgetown-Silver Plume district and in the Montezuma district in Summit County to the west. The Belmont and Baker mines were developed, slowly at first, but after 1869 they showed enough promise to attract numerous prospectors to the district. The district flourished during the 1870's, but activity declined and became intermittent thereafter (Lovering, 1935, p. 66–67, 69, 73).

Production records for the Argentine district are fragmentary. According to incomplete mine production figures listed by Lovering (1935, p. 68–116), the district had a minimum gold output through 1928 of 21,990 ounces. From 1932 through 1957 the district had a recorded production of 3,373 ounces of gold, or a total minimum of 25,400 ounces, all of which was a byproduct of silver ores.

The Argentine district is underlain by schist and gneiss of the Idaho Springs Formation into which were intruded masses of Silver Plume Granite, of Precambrian age. Dikes and plugs of Tertiary quartz monzonite porphyry and rhyolite and dacite porphyry cut the Precambrian rocks. The ore bodies are in veins that trend north-northeast and contain galena, pyrite, sphalerite, chalcopyrite, silver sulfantimonides, and gold (Lovering and Goddard, 1950, p. 135–136). Quartz, carbonates, and locally occurring fluorite are the most common gangue minerals.

EMPIRE DISTRICT

The Empire district is in north-central Clear Creek County about 9 miles west of Idaho Springs and 4 to 5 miles south-southwest of the Alice district. It includes an area of about 8 square miles, but the main productive veins are about 1½ miles north of Empire.

Oxidized and disintegrated gold-bearing quartz veins were discovered in the district in 1860 by prospectors from the Central City district (Spurr and others, 1908, p. 172–173). The disintegrated material could be easily sluiced and treated the same way as placer gravel and these operations proved very profitable. The oxidized material extended to a depth of about 40 feet and there gave way to sulfide ore which carried some free gold. Amalgamation of the sulfide ore presented difficulties, and after 1875 activity declined, although sporadic activity continued to 1924 (Henderson, 1926, p. 31). The district gained prominence again in 1934 when a group of veins north-northwest of Empire was developed in the Minnesota mine. Production increased from 272 ounces in 1932 to 16,693 ounces in 1940. The mines closed during World War II, and there was only minor sporadic production from 1945 through 1957. Total minimum gold production of the district was 165,000 ounces, roughly half of which came from the Minnesota mine from 1934 through 1943.

The following summary of the geology and ore deposits of the district was taken from Spurr,

Garrey, and Ball (1908, p. 383–386) and from Lovering and Goddard (1950, p. 156–161).

The country rock of the Empire district consists chiefly of Precambrian rocks intruded by stocks and dikes of early Tertiary age. The Precambrian rocks include schist of the Idaho Springs Formation, hornblende gneiss, granite gneiss, and both the Boulder Creek and Silver Plume Granites. The Boulder Creek Granite occupies the greater part of the area. The Tertiary stocks are quartz monzonite, and the dikes range in composition from bostonite to alaskite.

The ore deposits of the district are in pyritic quartz veins that are chiefly in the Boulder Creek Granite near the contact of the granite with a quartz monzonite stock. The chief metal produced is gold but in some veins copper also is of value. Few veins have been traced for more than 1,000 feet along the surface or to depths greater than 500 feet. The chief minerals are pyrite, chalcopyrite, and quartz, although small amounts of sphalerite and galena are found in some veins. The gold seems to be associated with the chalcopyrite. The ore ranges from about 0.2 to 0.4 ounce of gold per ton, and silver ranges from a few ounces to 20 ounces per ton.

FREELAND-LAMARTINE DISTRICT

The Freeland-Lamartine (Trail) district includes about 4 square miles of the Colorado mineral belt and is about 3 miles west of Idaho Springs in central Clear Creek County.

Soon after the discovery of gold placers near the mouth of Chicago Creek in 1859 (Spurr and others, 1908, p. 311), the search for gold spread to the area along Trail Creek, which lies north of Chicago Creek. The first veins were discovered in 1861, but these were not developed until 1868, after the successful smelter operation at Blackhawk. In 1870 railroad facilities became available to the region, and mining activity was stimulated still further. From about 1910 through 1933, mining in the district was intermittent and generally on the decline (Harrison and Wells, 1956, p. 36), but it was revived when the price of gold was increased in 1934. The mines in the district were relatively idle from 1944 through 1959.

Almost all production has come from lode deposits in the Lamartine and Freeland mines. Harrison and Wells (1956, p. 74) estimated that from 1868 to 1905 ore valued at about $5 million was produced, and the output from 1905 to 1953 was valued at $13 million in gold, silver, copper, lead, and zinc. Total gold production through 1959 was about 220,000 ounces, about 100,000 of which was mined from the Lamartine and Freeland mines between 1905 and 1953 (Harrison and Wells, 1956, p. 74).

The country rock in the district consists of the Idaho Springs Formation, which is composed of schist and gneiss of sedimentary origin and is intruded by quartz diorite, granite, and pegmatites, all of Precambrian age. During Tertiary time the Precambrian rocks were intruded by dikes and plugs of porphyries that range in composition from quartz monzonite and bostonite to alaskite. The structure is complex and involves two periods of Precambrian folding and Tertiary arching, fracturing, and faulting (Harrison and Wells, 1956, p. 37–67).

The ore deposits of the district are Tertiary mesothermal fissure veins deposited in fractures near porphyritic intrusive rocks. Two principal varieties of veins are recognized—pyrite-gold and galena-sphalerite. Locally, as observed in the Lamartine tunnel, a transition zone between the two types contains composite ore. The primary minerals of the pyrite-gold veins are pyrite (partly auriferous), chalcopyrite, tetrahedrite-tennantite, and minor galena and sphalerite in a gangue of quartz and carbonate. The galena-sphalerite veins contain galena (partly argentiferous), sphalerite, and pyrite, with subordinate amounts of chalcopyrite and tetrahedrite-tennantite, and quartz-carbonate gangue. Native gold is present in both types (Harrison and Wells, 1956, p. 74, 75).

GEORGETOWN-SILVER PLUME DISTRICT

The Georgetown-Silver Plume (Griffith) district consists of about 25 square miles centered around the towns of Georgetown and Silver Plume, in western Clear Creek County.

Precious metal lodes were first discovered near Georgetown in 1859, soon after the placer discoveries along Chicago Creek near Idaho Springs. In 1864 when rich silver ores were found in the Argentine district, southwest of Silver Plume, many prospectors were attracted to the region and uncovered significant silver deposits in the Georgetown area. With the successful introduction of smelting at Blackhawk, the sulfide veins were mined after the surface ores were exhausted. As the mines reached greater depths, silver and lead were the main commodities, whereas the surface ores were richer in gold. By 1880, the district was the principal silver producer in Clear Creek County. This trend was maintained, reaching a peak in 1894, after which a gradual decline began (Spurr and others, 1908, p. 173–175). Zinc became a major component of the metal output after 1903, especially during World Wars I and II. Between the two wars the base-metal and silver mines were mostly idle, and most of the sporadic activity was from gold mines. The raise in the price of gold in 1934 failed to effect any marked increase in gold production. From the end of World War II through 1959 the lead-silver mines yielded a few ounces of gold annually.

The total gold output of the district through 1959 was about 145,000 ounces, most of which was mined before 1900.

Bedrock in the Georgetown-Silver Plume district is generally similar to that in the other mining districts in Clear Creek County. Contorted schist of the Idaho Springs Formation is cut by several types of Precambrian igneous rocks, including dikes and sheets of hornblende gneiss, bodies of gneissic quartz monzonite resembling Boulder Creek Granite, and large masses of Silver Plume Granite which makes up about half the bedrock in the district. Stocks and dikes of Tertiary dacite, quartz monzonite porphyry, alaskite porphyry, and granite porphyry were intruded into the Precambrian rocks (Lovering and Goddard, 1950, p. 138–140).

The ore deposits of the district are of two mineralogical types: silver-lead-zinc veins and pyritic gold veins. The rich silver-bearing veins are found chiefly in the very productive area just north of Silver Plume, but some are also found south and northeast of Georgetown. The gold-bearing veins lie in a narrow belt between the two silver belts. North of Silver Plume, the veins carry silver, lead, and zinc, and almost no gold, whereas the gold-bearing veins contain some silver and locally their silver content is higher than gold. The most abundant minerals of the silver-lead-zinc ores are galena, sphalerite, and pyrite. These ores commonly contain less than 0.10 ounce of gold per ton. The chief gangue minerals are quartz and brown carbonates. The principal minerals in the pyritic gold deposits are pyrite, chalcopyrite, gold, small amounts of silver minerals, and quartz gangue. Small amounts of galena and sphalerite are in most of these veins, but where galena is more abundant the veins contain larger amounts of gold and silver. Locally hessite and argentite have been found, and in one mine platinum and iridium were noted (Lovering and Goddard, 1950, p. 141–142).

IDAHO SPRINGS DISTRICT

An unbroken succession of gold deposits extends from Idaho Springs in Clear Creek County to Central City and Blackhawk in Gilpin County. The deposits form a geologic entity, separated into the Idaho Springs and Central City districts only by the county line. The area has been the largest source of gold in both counties and includes the Chicago, Ute, and Cascade Creek camps.

Gold placers, which were found in early 1859 along Chicago Creek near Idaho Springs, attracted many prospectors who combed the nearby gulches and surrounding mountains and who soon uncovered additional placers in Nevada and Illinois gulches and Missouri Flats, as well as rich gold quartz veins, notable among which were the Gregory, Russell, Bates, Bobtail, and Mammoth lodes (Henderson, 1926, p. 27, 28). After the oxidized ores were depleted, the mines were shut down. In 1868 the Blackhawk smelter began treating the sulfide ores; the district was rejuvenated and experienced a long period of intense activity, exemplified by the 4½-mile-long Argo tunnel, which was started in 1904. By 1918 a marked decline was evident, and this trend continued until 1932. The period 1932–42 was one of high production, and it was followed by a period of steady decline after World War II.

The total minimum gold production of that part of the district in Clear Creek County was about 1,805,000 ounces (R. H. Moench, written commun., 1963). The production of the Central City part of the district, in Gilpin County, is given in the Gilpin County section of this report (p. 100).

The area is underlain by interlayered metamorphic gneiss, migmatite, and roughly concordant sheets of granodiorite similar to Boulder Creek Granite and granite similar to Silver Plume Granite (Moench and others, 1962, p. 37–38), all of Precambrian age. These Precambrian rocks are intruded by a variety of Tertiary plutons and dikes of porphyritic igneous rocks of the granodiorite, quartz monzonite, bostonite, and hornblende granodiorite groups (Wells, 1960, p. 232).

Two episodes of Precambrian deformation are recognized: a plastic deformation that recrystallized the rock minerals and produced large open folds whose axes trend north-northeast, and a younger cataclastic deformation that was characterized by asymmetrical folds whose axes trend N. 55° E., weak recrystallization of minerals, and intense granulation. The major structures near Central City are the Central City anticline and smaller subparallel folds formed in the older period (Moench and others, 1962, p. 39–54). The younger folding is recognized only near Idaho Springs as part of a belt of shearing called the Idaho Springs-

Ralston Buttes cataclastic zone (Tweto and Sims, 1960, p. B8). Large northwest-trending faults of Precambrian ancestry, displaying Laramide movement, and three sets of small faults of Laramide age also cut the Precambrian rocks.

Most of the ore deposits are mesothermal sulfide veins in fault fissures. Veins are grouped according to their mineral assemblages into (1) pyrite-quartz veins, (2) pyritic copper veins containing quartz, pyrite, chalcopyrite, tennantite, and minor galena and sphalerite, (3) pyritic lead-zinc veins containing quartz, pyrite, galena, sphalerite and subordinate chalcopyrite and tennantite, and (4) lead-zinc veins containing quartz, carbonates, galena, sphalerite, and small amounts of chalcopyrite, tennantite, and pyrite (Sims, 1956, p. 743–744; R. H. Moench, written commun., 1963). All four types contain gold, but the most important mines are in the pyritic lead-zinc veins. Gold occurs partly as discrete fine particles and is partly tied up in the sulfide minerals. A few gold telluride veins are found in the southeast part of the Central City district in Gilpin County.

The veins are arranged in a concentric pattern of zones with pyrite and pyritic copper veins occupying an elliptical central area which is 2 to 3 miles wide and extends from Blackhawk south to the Idaho Springs district. This is surrounded by successive zones containing pyritic lead-zinc veins and galena-sphalerite veins (Sims, 1956, p. 744–745; R. H. Moench, written commun., 1963).

About a mile southwest of Central City is the well-known "stockwork" named "The Patch"—a pipe or chimney of brecciated country rock cemented by ore minerals. This mineralized body extends from the surface to a depth of 1,600 feet where it is intersected by the Argo tunnel. At this depth the pipe has not decreased in size, but the grade of ore is diminished. The ore is of two types: one is characterized by pyrite, chalcopyrite, quartz, and a little tetrahedrite; and the other, by galena, sphalerite, chalcopyrite, and subordinate pyrite (Bastin and Hill, 1917, p. 96–97).

CUSTER COUNTY

Custer County lies in south-central Colorado, west of Pueblo. Its western boundary is formed by the crest of the Sangre de Cristo Range, and its central and eastern parts include segments of the Wet Mountain Valley and the Wet Mountains.

Custer County through 1959 produced about 107,300 ounces of gold and ranks 17th in gold production in Colorado. It has also produced silver and lead and small amounts of copper and zinc. Nearly all the gold has been derived from silver-gold lodes and some is a byproduct of lead-silver ore.

The first significant ore discovery was in 1872, when rich silver-lead ore was found in the Rosita Hills district, though ore specimens had been found earlier in the county by herdsmen searching for stray cattle (Emmons, 1896, p. 412–416). Prospectors flocked to the Rosita Hills; in 1874 silver-copper ore was found in the Humboldt-Pocahontas vein, and in 1877 the rich gold ore of the Bassick mine was discovered. In 1878, important silver discoveries were made in the Silver Cliff area, a few miles northwest of Rosita Hills. Great excitement was generated by the ore discoveries in Custer County, and for a few years the properties were developed with much vigor, but the boom was short lived. For a variety of reasons—transportation problems, overoptimism, unsuccessful mining methods, and reduction techniques—many of the ventures failed, and by 1892, production for the county was valued at only a few thousand dollars (Emmons, 1896, p. 412–420). Some of the mines were reactivated during World War I and at brief intervals thereafter. For the most part, the mineral wealth of Custer County was earned before 1900. Gold production of the county through 1959 was about 84,700 ounces, all of which is credited to the Rosita Hills district.

ROSITA HILLS DISTRICT

The Rosita Hills district, in the low western foothills of the Wet Mountains about 7 miles southeast of Westcliffe, has produced gold, silver, lead, copper, and a small amount of zinc.

The district was most active during 1877–90. Thereafter the mines were operated only sporadically; from 1932 through 1959 they were virtually dormant. The minimum total gold production through 1959 was about 84,660 ounces, most of which came from the Bassick mine.

The rocks of the Rosita Hills district consist of tuffs, breccias, agglomerates, and flows of andesite, rhyolite, and trachyte, all of Tertiary age, which overlie Precambrian gneiss, schist, and granite. The Bassick mine is in an elliptical volcanic pipe about 1,200 feet wide and 2,000 feet long that is enclosed in gneiss. The pipe is composed of andesitic agglomerate in which are embedded fragments and boulders of granite and gneiss. A dike of limburgite cuts the agglomerate.

Most of the smaller ore bodies are in veins in the volcanic rocks; however, the Bassick ore body is a body of mineralized agglomerate about 30 feet wide,

100 feet long, and at least 1,500 feet deep. The ore consists of thin concentric shells of minerals deposited on boulders. The minerals noted were sphalerite, galena, jamesonite, tetrahedrite, smithsonite, calamine, native gold, quartz, chalcopyrite, and gold-silver tellurides (Cross, 1896, p. 338–344; Emmons, 1896, p. 430–434).

DOLORES COUNTY

Dolores County, in southwestern Colorado, contains deposits of silver, lead, and zinc in the mountainous eastern part, which is a dissected laccolithic dome. The western part of the county is within the Colorado Plateaus. A relatively unimportant gold mining area, Dolores County has had a total gold production through 1959 of about 104,500 ounces; almost all production has been a byproduct of silver, lead, and zinc deposits of the Rico district.

RICO DISTRICT

The Rico (Pioneer) district lies near the southwest end of the Colorado mineral belt (Fischer and others, 1946) near the headwaters of the Dolores River.

Prospectors first came into the region in 1861 (Ransome, 1901a, p. 240–242), but the first claims were not located until 1869. In 1872 the first smelting furnace was erected and produced three bars of bullion. The early results were not encouraging, however, and the area was abandoned. Prospectors came into the region again in 1877 and, in the spring of 1879, discovered rich oxidized silver ore on Nigger Baby Hill and in the Chestnut vein on Newman Hill. Prospectors from neighboring camps rushed to the region, and the town of Rico was founded. Other major discoveries were made soon afterward, smelters and mills were built, and in 1880 the Rio Grande Southern Railroad reached Rico. The rich Enterprise blanket deposit was found in 1887, which insured some permanence to the district (Ransome, 1901a, p. 240–242). Mining was almost continuous through 1959 but it fluctuated considerably. Metal production was relatively high during the periods 1889–94, 1924–29, and during World War II. Before 1904 silver was of greatest value in the ore (Ransome, in Cross and Ransome, 1905, p. 14), but after 1904 lead and zinc were the important products. Most of the gold, which was a byproduct, was produced before 1910, especially between 1889 and 1894 (Henderson, 1926, p. 117). After 1910, gold production declined at an irregular rate, and for most years through 1959 it was below 500 ounces.

The total gold production of the Rico district is unknown, but of the 104,000 ounces credited to Dolores County through 1959, it seems reasonable to credit the Rico district with about 100,000 ounces.

The Rico district is in the central part of a laccolithic dome comprising the Rico Mountains in the southeast corner of Dolores County. In the central part of the uplift, Precambrian quartzite and schist are exposed. These are flanked on all sides by sedimentary rocks of Cambrian, Devonian, Mississippian, Pennsylvanian, Permian(?), Triassic, and Jurassic ages. All the rocks are intruded by sheets and sills of hornblende monzonite porphyry and by a stock of quartz monzonite of Tertiary(?) age. The central part of the dome is complexly faulted (Cross and Ransome, 1905, p. 2–11).

Much of the ore mined in the district has come from mineralized solution breccia in gypsum beds of the Hermosa Formation of Pennsylvanian age. These are known as blanket deposits. Other ore deposits are replacement bodies in Devonian and Pennsylvanian limestone beds and fissure veins. The age of the mineralization is thought to be late Tertiary (Cross and Ransome, 1905, p. 14–19).

The ore is of two general types: (1) pyritic ore, most of which is of too low grade to be mined, and (2) silver-bearing galena ore, in which galena, sphalerite, chalcopyrite, pyrite, argentite, proustite, polybasite, and silver-bearing tetrahedrite are the characteristic minerals. Much of this silver ore contains small amounts of gold that is associated with sphalerite and chalcopyrite and locally is associated with tellurium and bismuth (Cross and Ransome, 1905, p. 14–15).

EAGLE COUNTY

Eagle County, in mountainous west-central Colorado, produced about 359,900 ounces of gold through 1959.

Although some prospecting was done in Eagle County in the 1860's it was not until 1879, after the great rush in 1877–78 to the Leadville district about 20 miles to the south (Henderson, 1926, p. 41), that rich oxidized silver-lead carbonate ore was discovered on Battle Mountain in the Gilman district. Many claims were located that year, and in 1880 silver valued at $50,000 was produced (Henderson, 1926, p. 47). In the early 1880's prospectors swarmed over the county and opened small silver and gold mines here and there, but most of these early camps were short lived. Only the Gilman district became a major producer. More than 99 percent of the total metal output credited to Eagle County has come from this district.

GILMAN DISTRICT

The Gilman (Battle Mountain, Red Cliff) district, in southeastern Eagle County on the northeast flank of the Sawatch Range, is between Gilman and Red Cliff, about 20 miles north of Leadville. Gold has been extracted from pyritic gold ores and as a byproduct of base-metal ores.

The initial discovery in 1879 of silver-lead ore in limestone was followed in 1884 by finds of gold ore in the underlying quartzite. The relative importance of the metals mined varied periodically in the history of the district. Before 1905 silver and gold were the major commodities, whereas lead and copper were of minor importance. From 1905 to 1930 zinc was the principal product and from 1931 to 1941 silver-copper ore containing considerable gold was mined. Zinc again regained importance from 1942 through 1959. The total gold production of the district through 1959 was roughly 348,000 ounces.

Precambrian granite, schist, and gneissic diorite are exposed in the bottom of Eagle Canyon and are overlain by thin lower Paleozoic formations that include the Sawatch Quartzite of Cambrian age, the Harding Sandstone of Ordovician age, the Chaffee Formation of Devonian age, and the Leadville Limestone of Mississippian age. Overlying these units is a thick section of Pennsylvanian and Permian(?) sedimentary rocks. A sill of Cretaceous or Tertiary quartz latite appears a few feet above the Leadville Limestone throughout the district. The sedimentary rocks dip about 12° NE. and are cut by bedding-plane faults and a few weak high-angle faults (Ogden Tweto and T. S. Lovering, in Vanderwilt and others, 1947, p. 379–381).

Ore bodies occur in (1) veins in Precambrian rocks and in the Sawatch Quartzite and (2) in replacement deposits in quartzite and limestone of Devonian and Mississippian age. Most production has come from replacement bodies in the Leadville Limestone and the Dyer Dolomite Member of the Chaffee Formation. The veins in the Precambrian rocks contain pyritic gold and complex sulfide ores in which sphalerite, chalcopyrite, galena, and pyrite are the chief minerals. The pyrite-gold veins are almost entirely of pyrite with a little gold. Most of the veins terminate or become thin at the base of the Sawatch Quartzite, but those that extend into the quartzite contain scattered pockets of gold-silver tellurides, chief among which are petzite and hessite.

A large part of the early output from the Gilman district came from oxidized manto or bedding-vein deposits in a breccia zone in the Sawatch Quartzite, about 180 feet above the base. Two distinct stages of mineralization are recognized in these deposits. The first deposited largely pyrite, a very little chalcopyrite, and inconsequential amounts of gold and silver. During the second stage, manganosiderite, pyrite, chalcopyrite, galena, sphalerite, and pyrite were deposited. Gold and silver are chiefly associated with the chalcopyrite of the second stage.

The replacement deposits in the limestones consist of chimneys of pyritic silver-copper ore and mantos of base-metal sulfide ores. The chimneys are downward-tapering pipes that extend from the ends of manto ore bodies near the top of the Leadville Limestone downward into the Parting Quartzite Member of the Chaffee Formation. The chimneys are roughly circular or elliptical and are as much as 300 feet in diameter at the top and taper downward. There is no physical break between the two types of ore bodies, but there is a pronounced mineralogic difference. The chimney ore, the chief source of the gold, consists of a core of pyrite containing minor quantities of other minerals which make them valuable for silver, copper, and gold. The chief copper mineral is chalcopyrite. Silver and gold are associated with chalcopyrite, galena, and with a group of late copper and silver minerals including tetrahedrite, freibergite, polybasite, stromeyerite, bournonite, and schapbachite. Late accessory minerals include manganosiderite, dolomite, barite, apatite, and quartz. The galena contains small inclusions of hessite and a little petzite, and the petzite contains minute blebs and veinlets of free gold.

The manto ore bodies are valued mainly for zinc. The minerals of these deposits are sphalerite, pyrite, manganosiderite, minor galena, and accessory chalcopyrite, barite, dolomite, and quartz. Oxidized parts of these deposits contain considerable lead, silver, and gold. The mantos are 50 to 300 feet wide, 5 to 150 feet thick, and as much as 4,000 feet long. All are in the Leadville Limestone (Ogden Tweto and T. S. Lovering, in Vanderwilt and others, 1947, p. 381–385).

GILPIN COUNTY

Gilpin County, on the east slope of the Front Range in north-central Colorado about 30 miles west of Denver, ranks second among the counties of Colorado in gold production. Through 1959 it produced, in round numbers, 4,255,000 ounces of gold valued at $89,785,000. Of this production, 4,207,000 ounces was lode gold and 47,900 ounces was placer gold.

Some of the first significant gold discoveries in Colorado were in Gilpin County. In May 1859, John H. Gregory found a rich and easily worked, oxidized, gold-bearing lode at the Gregory diggings near

Blackhawk. Early in June 1859, W. Green Russell discovered gold placers and decomposed outcrops of lodes in what is now called Russell Gulch. By July 1, 1859, about 100 sluices were at work in the vicinity of Gregory's discovery, and toward the end of September about 890 men were at work in Russell Gulch. Some lodes averaged $100 a day for months at a time and yields as large as $400 for a day's work were not uncommon.

In June 1859 the miners at the Gregory diggings met and adopted resolutions defining the boundaries of the district (now known as the Central City district) and the conditions under which claims could be taken and held. In July a provisional local government was formed at the Gregory diggings.

All the veins of the region were oxidized and gold bearing at the surface, and the decomposed ores could be easily and cheaply mined and treated in sluices and crude stamp mills. The underlying sulfide ores, which commonly contained silver and base metals as well as gold, were not amenable to such simple treatment, and many mines were closed when the oxidized ore gave way to sulfide ores at depths of 40 to 100 feet. Stamp mills saved only about one-fourth of the gold and wasted all the other metals in the sulfide ores (Henderson, 1926, p. 30).

In 1868, the Hill matting smelter at Blackhawk opened and the first matte was shipped that same year. The successful smelting of ores stimulated the mining industry and made possible a long period of development and production from lodes. In 1872, additional impetus was given to mining in Gilpin County when the Colorado Central (later the Colorado and Southern) Railway was completed from Denver to Blackhawk.

Records show that Gilpin County had a steady output of gold from 1859 through 1908, a peak production valued at $3,237,346 being recorded in 1871 (Henderson, 1926, p. 122). From 1909, output gradually declined and in 1920 it dropped below $100,000 for the first time since gold was discovered in the county. Production rose in the late 1920's and during the depression in the early 1930's, and after the price of gold was raised in 1934 there was a marked increase in output. Since 1944, mining in the county has been on a reduced and fluctuating scale.

There are many small mining camps in the county but they are in general grouped into two districts referred to as the Northern Gilpin district and the Central City district.

CENTRAL CITY DISTRICT

The Central City district is along the southern border of Gilpin County in the vicinity of the towns of Central City and Blackhawk. This district is the northern segment of the rich chain of ore deposits between Central City and Idaho Springs.

Both the mining history and geological setting of Idaho Springs and Central City are so entwined that they are considered an entity and are discussed together in the Clear Creek County section of this report (p. 96).

The production of the Central City district rightfully belongs under the Gilpin County heading. The district is credited with 95 to 99 percent of the $84,114,389 worth of gold mined in the county through 1923 (P. K. Sims, oral commun., 1959). Total gold production through 1959 was about 4,200,000 ounces; all but about 30,000 ounces was from lode mines.

NORTHERN GILPIN DISTRICT

The Northern Gilpin district lies north of North Clear Creek in the central part of the county and extends north to the Boulder County line. The most important mines are just south of Apex and in the vicinity of Gilpin.

Gold was first discovered in the district in June 1859 in Gamble Gulch in the Perigo area, and lodes in both the Dirt and Perigo mines were discovered in 1860 (Bastin and Hill, 1917, p. 68, 197–198). Some of the ore was very rich near the surface, and within a short time 10 or 12 stamp mills were operating (Henderson, 1926, p. 31). However, the rich and easily worked ore was soon exhausted and in 1867 only four or five companies were still operating in the district. After 1868 the camp was almost deserted until 1879 when the Perigo mine again became active and continued activity at least until 1888. The district was revived briefly during the 1930's, but from 1943 through 1959 very little activity was reported.

There was some placer mining near Rollinsville in 1897 (Henderson, 1926, p. 31). Many of the gulches in the district have placer ground, but production was small until 1937–39, when dredging operations along South Boulder Creek recovered 7,724 ounces of gold.

Though the early production is unknown, it was probably small, and the total amount of gold mined in the district through 1959 was probably 35,000 ounces.

The bedrock of the district is a complex of Precambrian rocks, comprising schist of the Idaho Springs Formation and quartz monzonite gneiss, cut by Boulder Creek Granite and by quartz diorite. The Precambrian rocks are intruded by irregular stocks and dikes of quartz monzonite porphyry and dikes of bostonite porphyry of Tertiary age.

The ore deposits are pyritic gold veins in fractures, most of which trend northeast; a few strike west or northwest. The primary ores are in general low grade and contain less than half an ounce of gold and 1 ounce or less of silver to the ton, but some veins have higher grade ore in the supergene-enriched upper parts. Many of the deposits are discontinuous lodes along shear zones that carry pyrite disseminated through several feet of sheared rock; however, fissure fillings are more abundant. Besides pyrite the ore contains variable amounts of chalcopyrite and locally, some galena and sphalerite. Quartz is the common gangue mineral in the veins (Lovering and Goddard, 1950, p. 193–194).

GUNNISON COUNTY

Gunnison County, in west-central Colorado west of the Continental Divide, produced about 130,000 ounces of gold through 1959. Although the first ore discoveries were placer deposits, most of the gold produced in the county has been a byproduct of silver-lead ore.

Ore was first discovered in 1861 when placer gold was discovered simultaneously along Taylor River in the Tincup district and in Washington Gulch in the northern part of Gunnison County (Henderson, 1926, p. 44, 124). By 1867 placer deposits had been discovered along other gulches. Lode deposits also were known, but little work was done on them until 1872 when silver-bearing rock was discovered in the Elk Mountains. In 1878 discoveries were made in the Gold Brick-Quartz Creek district (Henderson, 1926, p. 125), and the years 1879 and 1880 saw the first rush of miners to southeastern Gunnison County. Several towns, including Ohio City and Pitkin, were founded between 1878 and 1882. In the fall of 1881 the Denver and Rio Grande Railroad was completed to Gunnison and later to Crested Butte. During the next 4 to 5 years, ore was discovered over a wide area, and several smelters and concentrating mills were built. The most productive years for gold mining were between 1908 and 1913. The period 1934 through 1942 was one of increased activity, but from 1943 through 1959 most of the mines were closed.

The Gold Brick-Quartz Creek district has been the leading gold producer of the county, and the Tincup district is the only other district that has yielded more than 10,000 ounces.

GOLD BRICK-QUARTZ CREEK DISTRICT

The Gold Brick-Quartz Creek district, which includes Box Canyon, is in southeast Gunnison County, 1 to 4 miles north and northeast of Pitkin. Much of the gold mined in this district was a byproduct of lead-silver ores.

After the discovery in 1879 of a boulder of rich silver ore at the mouth of Gold Creek, prospectors flocked to the area and staked many claims in 1879 and 1880. The town of Ohio City was founded in 1881, and the following year the Denver, South Park, and Pacific Railroad reached the new town. Though few of the early claims were successful, lucrative deposits of lead and silver were found later, especially in the 1880's and early 1890's. By 1893 most of the shallow ore bodies were worked out and the price of silver fell at this time; consequently, there was little incentive to keep the mines open (Crawford and Worcester, 1916, p. 12–13). The district remained virtually deserted until 1934 when the increased price of gold stimulated activity, resulting in considerable gold production from 1934 through 1942. From 1943 through 1959 the district was again dormant.

Early records, though incomplete (Crawford and Worcester, 1916, p. 92–111), indicate that the district produced at least 80,000 ounces of gold through 1959.

The following summary of the geology and ore deposits of the district has been compiled from the reports by Crawford and Worcester (1916) and Dings and Robinson (1957).

The bedrock of the Gold Brick-Quartz Creek district consists of gneiss, schist, and granite of Precambrian age, sedimentary rocks of Paleozoic age, and intrusive rocks of Tertiary age. The Paleozoic rocks range in age from Cambrian to Pennsylvanian. The Tertiary rocks are chiefly intrusive sheets and dikes and range from rhyolite to andesite and diorite porphyry (Crawford and Worcester, 1916, p. 22–68).

The ore deposits are chiefly fissure veins in the Precambrian rocks. Replacement deposits occur in some of the Paleozoic limestone and dolomite, but very little is known about them (Dings and Robinson, 1957, p. 63) and the amount of gold derived from them probably has been very small. The greatest values in the veins have been in silver, gold, and lead, and the lesser values, in copper and zinc. A few veins contain molybdenum and tungsten. Gold and silver vary in relative abundance. The bulk of the ore produced was limonitic quartz, and only a few mines produced sulfide ore; most mines have not reached a depth below the zone of at least partial oxidation, which extends to a depth of about 1,300 feet. Sulfide minerals found include galena, sphalerite, pyrite, chalcopyrite, arsenopyrite, tetrahedrite, argentite, and ruby silver in a gangue of quartz and local barite. Huebnerite and molybdenite are found in some veins (Crawford and Worcester, 1916, p. 82–83; Dings and Robinson, 1957, p. 62–63).

TINCUP DISTRICT

In the Tincup district in northeastern Gunnison County, about 25 miles northeast of Gunnison, gold has been obtained mainly as a byproduct of silver-lead ores, although a considerable amount has come from placers. Most of the mines are at the head of Willow Creek on the southeast side of Taylor Park.

One of the first reported gold discoveries in the county was in 1861 when a man named Taylor, searching for strayed horses, found good color in what became known as Tincup Gulch. During the next 18 years there was sporadic placer mining in Tincup Gulch. In 1879 the lode source of the placer gold was found, and soon miners streamed into the area. The town of Tincup had a population of nearly 4,000 by the end of 1880. The boom lasted until the price of silver dropped in 1893. A second period of prosperity began in 1904, which attracted about 2,000 people to the district. This was short lived, and by 1912 the mines were again inactive (Goddard, 1936, p. 552–554). From 1912 through 1959 the district was virtually idle; even the increased price of gold in 1934 did not renew activity.

Total gold production of the district through 1959 was about 16,400 ounces, most of which was produced before 1932.

The rocks exposed in the Tincup district are of three ages: schist and granite gneiss of Precambrian age, sedimentary rocks about 1,000 feet thick of Paleozoic age, and intrusive rocks of Tertiary age. The Paleozoic rocks are chiefly limestone, with some shale and quartzite, and range in age from Cambrian to Pennsylvanian. The Tertiary rocks consist of quartz monzonite porphyry and hornblende diorite porphyry which form dikes, sills, and a stock. The rocks were folded into a north-trending monocline that dips to the east. Along the east side of the district, the sedimentary rocks are in contact with the Precambrian schist along the Tincup thrust fault that trends about N. 25° W. Another strong thrust of the same trend appears in the southwest part of the district. Numerous small high-angle faults, younger than the thrusts, cut the rocks (Goddard, 1936, p. 557–565).

The most productive ore deposits have been silver-lead-gold blanket deposits and silver-lead-gold veins. Of slight importance are molybdenum-tungsten veins and iron blanket deposits. The metals produced, in the order of their value, are silver, lead, gold, and small amounts of copper. The blanket deposits have been the most productive. These occur at the contacts between limestone and dolomite near intersections with steeply dipping faults or fractures. The chief primary ore minerals are silver-bearing galena and pyrite and small amounts of chalcopyrite and sphalerite. The gold is probably associated with the pyrite. The chief gangue minerals are quartz and calcite. All the ore of the blanket deposits is at least partly oxidized, and much of the ore consists of cerussite and anglesite, usually associated with some galena, in a limonitic and siliceous gangue. Oxidation of the ore bodies extends to a depth of more than 500 feet.

The vein deposits, which cut the Precambrian granite gneiss and the sedimentary rocks, range from 1 to 6 feet in width and from 600 to 1,000 feet in length. The minerals and character of the ore are similar to those in the blanket deposits (Goddard, 1936, p. 565–569).

HINSDALE COUNTY

Hinsdale County lies in southwestern Colorado in the western San Juan Mountains. Lake City, the county seat, lies at the junction of Henson Creek and Lake Fork. The mines are concentrated along Henson Creek for a distance of about 10 miles west of Lake City and for about 5 miles along Lake Fork south of Lake City. Silver and lead are the chief metals produced, but the county has also produced considerable gold and some copper and zinc.

The first significant ore discovery in the county was made in 1871 when silver-lead veins, called the Ute and Ulay veins, were discovered along Henson Creek about 4 miles west of Lake City. News of mineral wealth attracted many prospectors to the region, but all the land of the San Juan region belonged to the Ute Indians, who resented encroachment on their domain by prospectors. In 1874, to avoid open hostilities, a treaty was made with the Utes, and the San Juan region was opened to settlement (Irving and Bancroft, 1911, p. 12–14). In August 1874, the rich Golden Fleece vein, about 4 miles south of Lake City, was discovered, and prospectors flocked to the region and made numerous discoveries. As development and production increased, Lake City became a center of activity, and smelters and concentrating works were built. Although rapid progress was made in the late 1870's, the area lacked railroad transportation and was generally inaccessible. This situation brought on a decline in activity in the late 1880's which was alleviated in 1889 by construction of a branch of the Denver and Rio Grande Railroad to Lake City. The period from 1891 to 1902, inclusive, was the most productive in the county (Henderson, 1926, p. 51; Irving and Bancroft, 1911, p. 15–16).

Depletion of the higher grade oxidized and enriched ores decreased the annual output to $100,000 or less by 1903. After 1903 the output fluctuated, but for most years it was worth less than $100,000. Flotation units were installed in several mills during the 1920's and in 1937, but renewed activity was brief. Hinsdale County produced an estimated 70,243 ounces of gold ($1,451,921) during 1875–1923 (Henderson, 1926, p. 128), and 1,123 ounces of gold was produced during 1924–59. A total of about 71,365 ounces was produced through 1959.

Except for a relatively small amount of ore which is credited to several small outlying districts, the Hinsdale County production came entirely from the Lake City district in the northern part of the county (W. S. Burbank, in Vanderwilt and others, 1947, p. 439).

LAKE CITY DISTRICT

The Lake City district, which includes Henson Creek, Galena, and Lake Fork, is in northern Hinsdale County along Lake Fork and Henson Creek a few miles west and south of Lake City.

The district is on the margin of the Lake City caldera, an oval-shaped downfaulted block of volcanic rocks which is bounded roughly by Henson Creek on the north and Lake Fork on the south. Precambrian rocks are exposed along the south and west sides of the caldera, but elsewhere the prevailing rock types are Tertiary volcanics. The Silverton Volcanic Series, consisting of rhyolite, andesite, and latite lavas, tuffs, and breccias, occupies much of the caldera and surrounding areas. Younger Tertiary rocks, including the Sunshine Peak Rhyolite, Hinsdale Formation, Fisher Latite-andesite, and Potosi Volcanic Series, cover higher parts of the area. Small bodies of intrusive rhyolite, latite, and quartz monzonite porphyry occur in the caldera and in the volcanic rocks within 4 or 5 miles from the margin of the caldera (W. S. Burbank, in Vanderwilt and others, 1947, p. 438).

The ore deposits are in veins whose distribution is related to the structural weakness around the margin of the caldera. Three types of veins are recognized: (1) quartz-sphalerite-galena veins, rich in silver, (2) tetrahedrite-rhodochrosite veins, valued for silver and lead, and (3) the telluride veins, characterized by krennerite, sylvanite, and petzite, and important for silver and gold (W. S. Burbank, in Vanderwilt and others, 1947, p. 440–441).

JEFFERSON COUNTY

Jefferson County lies in north-central Colorado immediately west of Denver. The western two-thirds of the county is in the Front Range, and the northeastern third is in the Great Plains. Although placer gold was first discovered along Cherry Creek, east and southeast of Denver, the early prospectors worked along the streams west from there into the mountains, and in 1859 gold placers were discovered along Clear Creek near Golden in what is now Jefferson County (Henderson, 1926, p. 27, 129). No production was recorded from the county until 1885. The county is credited with a production of $32,769 (1,585 ounces) in placer gold during 1885–1905 and with $29,527 (1,428 ounces) in lode gold during 1895–1904 (Henderson, 1926, p. 130). No production was recorded for 1906–31, but a consistent, though small, annual production during 1932–59 totaled 12,478 ounces of placer and 435 ounces of lode gold. Total county gold production through 1959 was about 15,900 ounces.

Lode gold in Jefferson County probably has been derived as a byproduct from several small copper deposits found in Precambrian rocks near Evergreen, notably in the Malachite mine. The deposits are in or very close to amphibolite schists and gneisses, which may be metamorphosed diorite. The deposits probably are Precambrian in age (Lovering and Goddard, 1950, p. 67–68).

Most of the production from Jefferson County has come from the placers along Clear Creek. Immediately west of Golden, Clear Creek is a narrow stream and the yardage of sand and gravel is limited. East of Golden the gravel is more extensive. In recent years most of the gold production, as in Adams County, has come as a byproduct from sand-and-gravel operations (Vanderwilt, in Vanderwilt and others, 1947, p. 122). It appears reasonable to credit the entire placer production of the county, which was about 14,000 ounces, to this district.

LAKE COUNTY

Lake County lies near the center of Colorado in a mountainous area that extends from the crest of the Mosquito Range on the east to the crest of the Sawatch Range on the west. The Arkansas River heads in Lake County and flows south across the middle of the county.

Colorado's most important mining districts, Leadville and Climax, are in Lake County; however, only Leadville is important as a source of gold.

Relatively small amounts of gold have come from placers in the Arkansas River valley. Through 1959 Lake County produced about 2,983,000 ounces of gold as well as large amounts of silver, molybdenum, lead, zinc, and copper.

ARKANSAS RIVER VALLEY PLACERS

Most of the placer gold production in Lake County has come from California Gulch in the Leadville district, but some has come from many other tributaries of the Arkansas River. The more productive of these were Box and Lake Creeks, which enter the Arkansas River valley from the Sawatch Range in southern Lake County.

Although many of the gold placers in the Arkansas River valley were found in 1859 and in the early 1860's, their discovery and subsequent history and production were obscured by news of the richer discoveries in California Gulch; consequently, early production is unknown. No placers were worked in Lake County during 1886–1914. From 1915 to 1924 a bucket dredge, known as the Derry Dredge, operated successfully along the valley of lower Box Creek (Vanderwilt, in Vanderwilt and others, 1947, p. 126). These and later operations along Box Creek yielded about 39,000 ounces of gold. Total production of the district through 1959 was about 41,000 ounces. The placers were virtually idle from 1948 through 1959.

LEADVILLE DISTRICT

The following brief history of the Leadville mining district and its production was abstracted from reports by Henderson (1926, p. 40–43, 130–176). The early history of Lake County is virtually the history of mining in the Leadville district.

The first ores found and mined in Lake County, as in most of the mining camps in Western United States, were gold placers. At the time of the "Pikes Peak excitement," some of the early prospectors, searching for gold in stream gravels, wandered across the Rampart, Tarryall, and Mosquito Ranges into South Park and the Arkansas River valley. Early in the spring of 1860, placers were discovered in Iowa and California Gulches, tributaries of the Arkansas River, in what was to become the Leadville district. News of the rich discoveries spread with amazing rapidity, and by July 1860 the placer camp called Oro City boasted a population of 10,000. The placers, though rich, were quickly depleted, and within 3 or 4 years only a few hundred of the more persistent souls remained. It was reported that $2 million in gold was taken out the first summer, and the placers continued to be productive, but at a diminishing rate, until 1886.

In June 1868 gold lodes were discovered which were mined with great success until 1877, after which gold production was overshadowed by silver and lead.

The mining of rich silver-bearing lead carbonate ore began in the summer of 1874 and brought great prosperity to the Leadville district, especially from 1876 until 1902, which was the most productive period in its history. The first railroad to reach Leadville was the Denver and Rio Grande in August 1880. The Colorado Midland Railway, running westward from Colorado Springs and across South Park, reached Leadville in September 1887. The period of general prosperity, however, was marred by declining silver content of the ores, by the financial depression of 1893, and by labor troubles. As a result, there was increased prospecting for gold which culminated in increased gold production from the Breece Hill area after 1893. Gold continued to be an important commodity through 1917, though its proportion of the total output of the district was overwhelmed by the development of the huge zinc ore bodies after 1903 (Emmons and others, 1927, p. 111–133). The Leadville mines closed in 1957, and from 1957 to 1959 only small amounts of gold were recovered from fluxing material. The total gold output of the district through 1959 was about 2,970,000 ounces.

According to Behre (1953, p. 18–60), the bedrock in the Leadville district consists of a Precambrian basement complex of gneiss, schist, and granite, overlain by about 500 feet of Cambrian, Ordovician, Devonian, and Mississippian sedimentary rocks and 2,500 feet of Pennsylvanian sedimentary rocks. The Precambrian and Paleozoic rocks are intruded by numerous sills and dikes and by a few stocks of porphyry and pipelike bodies of volcanic breccia, all of Tertiary age. The igneous rocks are chiefly quartz monzonitic, but some are granitic or rhyolitic. Several irregular, roughly funnel-shaped pipes of Tertiary agglomerate have been partly outlined by mine workings.

The rocks in the Leadville district have been tilted and extensively faulted. According to Tweto (1960), all the porphyries are older than the ores, and nearly all of the faults originated before the ore, although many faults were reactivated after mineralization.

The original or hypogene ore deposits in the Leadville district have been classified into three main groups: (1) silicate-oxide deposits, (2) mixed sulfide veins, and (3) mixed sulfide replacement bodies (G. F. Loughlin and C. H. Behre, Jr., in Vanderwilt and others, 1947, p. 360–365).

The silicate-oxide deposits are of little economic value; only small amounts were mined in the early days for smelter flux. These deposits are mixtures of magnetite and hematite in a gangue consisting mainly of serpentine, and are replacement deposits in dolomite. The only ore mined has come from pyritic gold veins that cut these deposits and enriched the adjacent wallrocks.

The mixed sulfide veins occur mainly in siliceous sedimentary rocks which predominate in the eastern part of the district, where numerous sill-like bodies of porphyry intrude the grit and shale of Pennsylvanian age near the Breece Hill porphyry stock. The largest veins have been productive to a depth of about 1,300 feet below the surface. Some veins are too small to mine but expand into small replacement bodies where they cut dolomite. The veins that cut siliceous sedimentary rocks consist mainly of pyrite with a little interstitial chalcopyrite in a gangue of quartz. Where they grade into replacement deposits, pyrite and quartz persist for a short distance laterally but grade into a mixture of sphalerite and galena in dense quartz or jasperoid. The veins and the pyritic parts of the replacement deposits have been valuable mainly for gold, some of which is primary but much of which has resulted from enrichment in the secondary sulfide zone. The gold is accompanied by some silver and locally by copper.

Replacement deposits of sulfides in dolomite are common in the western part of the district. These replacement bodies lie along fractures or sheeted zones, known locally as contacts, beneath impervious covers such as sills. The largest replacement bodies are at the top of the Leadville Dolomite (Mississippian), and some are more than 2,000 feet long, 800 feet wide, and 200 feet thick.

The mixed sulfide replacement bodies consist of sphalerite and galena with pyrite. The ore contains a few ounces of silver and 0.03 to 0.05 ounce of gold to the ton, but here and there small shoots have been found that are unusually rich in silver and gold and also contain bismuth. Intergrowths of argentite, bismuthinite, and a little galena have been found in this rich ore and also in veins cutting large bodies of the mixed sulfide ore. Tetrahedrite, chalcopyrite, and arsenopyrite also occur locally.

Oxidation and supergene enrichment of the various types of hypogene sulfides produced ores of variable mineralogy. Some of the ores are rich in cerussite and cerargyrite; others, in smithsonite and hemimorphite, manganese-iron-bismuth oxides, chalcocite-covillite-gold-silver, and argentite-silver. Much of the coarse gold in the placers of California Gulch is believed to be of reworked supergene origin.

LA PLATA COUNTY

La Plata County is in southwestern Colorado just north of the New Mexico State line. The mineral deposits lie in the mountainous west-central part of the county, on the southwest end of the mineral belt of Colorado. Gold has been the most valuable mineral mined in the county, but silver and small amounts of lead and copper have also been recovered. The total metal production through 1959 was valued at about $6,230,000, of which about $4,825,000 (215,375 ounces) represented its gold production. The sole important gold-producing district in the area has been the La Plata district in the La Plata Mountains (Henderson, 1926, p. 52).

LA PLATA DISTRICT

Spanish explorers who visited the La Plata Mountains in the 18th century may have found gold, but mining in the region did not begin until 1873 when placer gold was found along the Animas River near the present site of Durango (Eckel, 1949, p. 51). In that same year placer gold was discovered along La Plata River. Production during the early years in the La Plata district is not known, but it was probably small. Lode gold, which has been the chief commodity of the district, was also discovered in 1873, and by the end of 1881 many locations had been made. The output from lodes was small through 1901, but with the discovery of new deposits in 1902, output increased sharply, and through 1914 annual gold production exceeded $100,000 (5,000 ounces). Thereafter production fluctuated considerably and rarely exceeded $100,000 annually (Eckel, 1949, p. 54). Since 1938, mining activity has declined and, except for a few years, output usually has been less than 500 ounces annually. The total gold production of the district through 1959 was about 215,000 ounces, chiefly from lodes.

The La Plata district lies within the La Plata Mountains, a rugged mountain group about 15 miles in diameter, between the San Juan Mountains to the east and the Colorado Plateau on the west. The La Plata Mountains were carved from a domal uplift of sedimentary rocks caused by intrusion of numerous stocks, dikes, and sills of igneous rocks. Superimposed on the general dome is a curving open anticline whose horseshoe-shaped axis opens southward. Several faults of large displacement cut the outer parts of the dome, and within the dome there are many small faults and fractures.

The sedimentary rocks exposed within the district are more than 4,500 feet thick and range in age from Pennsylvanian through Late Cretaceous. From oldest to youngest they are the Hermosa Formation of Pennsylvanian age, the Rico and Cutler Formations of Permian age, the Dolores Formation of Late Triassic age, the Entrada Sandstone, Wanakah Formation, Junction Creek Sandstone, and Morrison Formation of Jurassic age, and the Dakota (?) Sandstone and Mancos Shale of Cretaceous age (Eckel, 1949, p. 7–31).

The igneous rocks, which are of Late Cretaceous or Tertiary age, are of two general types—porphyritic and nonporphyritic. The more abundant porphyritic rocks are intermediate between diorite and monzonite in composition; the nonporphyritic rocks consist of syenite, monzonite, and diorite. The country rocks were silicified during the doming and intrusion of the nonporphyritic stocks, which occurred later than the intrusions of porphyritic bodies (Eckel, 1949, p. 50–51).

Most of the output of the district has come from veins and replacement deposits of gold- and silver-bearing telluride ores. Of lesser importance are disseminated deposits of platinum-bearing chalcopyrite, gold-bearing contact-metamorphic bodies, replacement and breccia bodies of pyritic gold ore, veins of mixed base-metal sulfides with silver or native gold, chalcocite veins, and veins of ruby-silver ore. The gold-bearing placers have not been very productive (Eckel, 1949, p. 60).

MINERAL COUNTY

Mineral County is in southwestern Colorado near the center of the San Juan Mountains. Mining has been conducted in three general areas in the county, the Creede district, the Spar City district, and the Wagon Wheel Gap fluorspar district, but only the Creede district has had significant production of gold. Ores in the Creede district are valuable chiefly for silver, lead, and zinc, but byproduct gold is important locally. From 1891 through 1959 the district produced about 149,200 ounces of gold.

CREEDE DISTRICT

The Creede and the Cripple Creek districts were the last of the famous mining districts in Colorado to be discovered, and the significant discoveries in both districts were made in 1891. In the 1880's the upper Rio Grande valley was a route of transportation between Wagonwheel Gap and the flourishing mining camps near Silverton and Lake City (Emmons and Larsen, 1923, p. 3–5). Some of the prospectors traveling this route located promising claims at Sunnyside, about 2 miles west of the present site of Creede, in 1883, and in 1884 a claim was located on the Amethyst or Big vein near Creede. Interest in the area was aroused in 1889 when the Holy Moses vein was discovered on East Willow Creek, and, in 1891, when rich ore was found on the Amethyst vein in the Last Chance, Amethyst, and New York mines. Within a few months, late in 1891 and in 1892, about 10,000 people swarmed into the infant town of Creede (Emmons and Larsen, 1923, p. 4). In late 1891 the Denver and Rio Grande Railroad was extended from Wagonwheel Gap to Creede, and in 1893 the Creede district had its largest annual production, consisting chiefly of silver but also some lead and gold and having a total value of $4,150,946. Because of the continued drop in the price of silver, production declined sharply in 1894, but there was a fair recovery in 1897, and the district maintained a fairly steady annual output worth about $1 million through 1910. Thereafter production declined and the district was virtually idle between 1930 and 1933. From 1934 through 1959, annual production of silver, lead, zinc, and gold ranged from less than $300,000 to more than $1 million. Gold production was greatest from 1900 through 1911 when the output was about 92,000 ounces and was valued at $1,899,560 (Emmons and Larsen, 1923, p. 9–10). Total gold production of the district through 1959 was about 149,200 ounces.

The following brief description of the geology of the Creede district has been abstracted from a report by Steven and Ratté (1960a), and the summary of the ore deposits is from a report by Emmons and Larsen (1923).

The bedrock exposed in the Creede district consists of Tertiary volcanic rocks. The ore deposits are localized along faults in a complex graben that extends outward from the Creede caldera, a subcircular subsided mass of volcanic rocks about 10 miles in diameter. Within the caldera, quartz latitic welded tuff at least 6,000 feet thick is exposed. Surrounding the caldera is a mass of volcanic rocks at least 4,000 feet thick which accumulated from several volcanic centers and consists of rhyolitic and quartz latitic welded tuffs, nonwelded pumiceous tuff, and locally interlayered quartz latitic and dacitic lava flows and breccias. Stream and lake sediments and travertine, collectively called the Creede Formation, accumulated along the margin of the caldera.

Known ore deposits of the district occur chiefly as veins along three of the main faults in the graben. A small amount of ore has been mined from disseminated deposits in the basal beds of the Creede Formation where it rests on a highly faulted segment of the caldera margin. The faults in the graben were active many times during caldera subsidence; however, mineralization did not take place until the last main period of movement. The mines along the Amethyst fault zone produced $55 million worth of metals; all the other veins produced about $2,800,000, and the disseminated deposits in the Creede Formation yielded about $800,000 worth of metals.

The ore deposits in Creede are silver-lead-zinc veins. The unaltered ore is composed mainly of sphalerite, silver-bearing galena, and pyrite in a gangue of amethystine quartz, barite, and chlorite (thuringite). Fluorite, rhodochrosite, chalcopyrite, and native gold are sparingly present. Much of the ore is oxidized, and in some deposits enrichment is pronounced.

Gold as a primary mineral is presumably very finely divided and is probably included in pyrite, galena, sphalerite, and other minerals. The richest gold ore consists of gold in a gangue of manganese oxide in veinlets cutting the older sulfides, and ore with such veinlets may carry as much as 1 or 2 ounces of gold per ton (Emmons and Larsen, 1923, p. 98–103). The gold is not uniformly distributed in the veins; for example, most of the ore mined from the north end of the Amethyst vein contained 0.03 to 0.25 ounce of gold per ton, whereas ore from the south end of the Amethyst lode contained negligible amounts of gold.

OURAY COUNTY

Ouray County is in southwestern Colorado in an area drained by the headwaters of the Uncompahgre River, a tributary of the Gunnison River. The mineralized areas are in the southern part of the county within the San Juan Mountains and include the Sneffels-Red Mountain and the Uncompahgre mining districts.

Ouray County was originally part of territory that was owned by the Ute Indian Tribe and that was ceded to the United States in 1873. Until 1873 the area had been little explored, but after the treaty was ratified, settlers and prospectors overran the county (Henderson, 1926, p. 24). By 1874 nearly four-fifths of the claims were on silver lodes; however, rich deposits of gold as well as silver were found in 1875 in the Mount Sneffels area, and the famous Camp Bird mine, the largest gold producer in the region, was located in 1877 (W. S. Burbank, in Vanderwilt and others, 1947, p. 403). The area developed rapidly, and additional discoveries were made in the Red Mountain area. By 1896, however, increased mining costs, a drop in the price of silver, and depletion of the rich surface ores caused many of the mines to close, although the Camp Bird continued to be a significant producer until 1917. The mine was reopened in 1926 and was operated sporadically through 1956. Total gold production of Ouray County through 1959 was about 1,911,000 ounces, more than half of which came from the Camp Bird mine.

SNEFFELS-RED MOUNTAIN DISTRICT

The Sneffels-Red Mountain district is in southern and southwestern Ouray County, 8 to 12 miles from Ouray. The Sneffels camp is at the head of Canyon Creek in Imogene Basin west of Hayden Mountain, and the Red Mountain camp is at the head of Red Mountain Creek east of Hayden Mountain.

The district is the principal gold producer in Ouray County and one of the leading producers in the San Juan region, but little is known about its production in the early years. According to W. S. Burbank (in Vanderwilt and others, 1947, table 8, p. 404–405), deposits of late Tertiary age in Ouray County to 1945 produced about 1,693,000 ounces of gold, most of which came from the Sneffels area. The Camp Bird mine, the principal producer of metals in Ouray County until it closed at the end of 1956, produced, from 1896 to 1916, gold, silver, lead, and copper valued at $27,269,768, of which at least $21,884,894 (1,058,774 ounces) was in gold (Henderson, 1926, p. 185). Production of other mines in the district has been small and sporadic. Total gold output of the district through 1959 was indicated to be about 1,723,000 ounces.

The Sneffels-Red Mountain district and the adjoining Telluride district to the southwest, in San Miguel County, are geologically contiguous, and therefore they are treated as a geologic entity in the following description.

The main geologic feature of the area is the Silver volcanic basin which Burbank (1941, p. 151) divided into two distinct parts or provinces: (1) an interior downfaulted circular block, the caldera, which may be subdivided into a hub of tilted and locally faulted rocks, surrounded by a ring of highly faulted rocks, and (2) an exterior unit of relatively undisturbed but fissured rocks. The Sneffels and Telluride districts are in the exterior unit, on the northwest flank of the caldera; the Red Mountain area is in the northern part of the highly faulted outer ring.

Most of the rocks exposed throughout the area are Tertiary volcanic rocks; however, the older underlying formations are exposed at lower elevations. In the Telluride district, sedimentary rocks ranging from the Cutler Formation of Permian age to the Dakota Sandstone of Cretaceous age are exposed, and in the Sneffels-Red Mountain district older Paleozoic as well as Mesozoic sedimentary rocks are found. The unconformable blanket of Tertiary rocks, which is 4,000 to 6,000 feet thick, consists of, from oldest to youngest, the Telluride Conglomerate, San Juan Tuff, Silverton Volcanic Series, and Potosi Volcanic Series. During the outpouring of these volcanic rocks, subsidence occurred in the caldera, and a network of circular faults and radial fractures was formed. Bodies of rhyolite, andesite, quartz latite porphyry, diorite, and quartz monzonite porphyry were injected into the country rocks; some were guided by the preexisting fractures, and others domed and fractured the rocks still more. Mineralizing solutions followed the emplacement of intrusive rocks (W. S. Burbank, in Vanderwilt and others, 1947, p. 419–424).

The ore deposits are directly related to geologic structures and also to the forms of the intrusive bodies. Ores of the Red Mountain area are chimney deposits, which are vertical cylindrical bodies a few feet to a few tens of feet in diameter in and near volcanic pipes filled with breccia, quartz latite porphyry, and rhyolite. The common ore minerals are pyrite, enargite, chalcopyrite, tennantite, chalcocite, covellite, stromeyerite, bornite, sphalerite, and galena. Gold is associated with the copper minerals (Burbank, 1941, p. 178–209).

The ore deposits of the Telluride and Sneffels areas are in veins whose distribution is controlled by a zone of crustal sag extending northwestward from Red Mountain to Stony Mountain and Mount Sneffels. Many of the veins, such as the Smuggler-Union in the Telluride district, follow a swarm of dikes that trend northwest; a few, such as the Camp Bird in the Sneffels district, trend north or northeast. The most productive veins are in the San Juan Tuff, and some are remarkably persistent; the Smuggler-Union, for example, has been mined for a horizontal distance of 8,000 feet. The veins contain variable amounts of pyrite, sphalerite, chalcopyrite, galena, tetrahedrite, tennantite, and pearcite in a gangue of quartz, barite, sericite, ankerite, rhodochrosite, rhodonite, calcite, fluorite, adularia, and clay minerals. Silver is derived mainly from tetrahedrite, galena, and tennantite. Gold is found in the quartz (Burbank, 1941, p. 209–261).

UNCOMPAHGRE DISTRICT

The Uncompahgre district covers about 15 square miles near the town of Ouray, where most of the mine workings are in the canyon walls of the Uncompahgre River.

The headwaters of the Uncompahgre River and Poughkeepsie Gulch were prospected in 1874, and many claims near Ouray were located within the next few years (Henderson, 1926, p. 54). In 1875 gold-bearing lodes were discovered in the Permian and Pennsylvanian rocks in the canyon walls near Ouray, and a little later silver-lead deposits were found in the Leadville Limestone of Mississippian age. Early records of the district are incomplete, but according to Burchard, as quoted by Henderson (1926, p. 184), considerable development was done in 1884, but because of the low grade of ore and the lack of economical transportation, only a few mines shipped ore. In 1889 phenomenally rich gold ore was discovered in the Dakota Quartzite at the American Nettie mine which, together with adjoining properties, accounted for most of the district's gold output (W. S. Burbank, in Vanderwilt and others, 1947, p. 409). Silver-lead ore bodies, which had been known for many years, were not worked until 1892 when the Bachelor ore body, the major silver producer, was discovered. For a few years production of silver and lead was high, but it declined after 1895. Since that time the main effort has been to treat lower grade ores by milling.

The total gold production of the district was about 200,000 ounces, most of which was mined before 1900.

The canyons of the Uncompahgre River and its tributaries expose a vertical section of rocks nearly 6,000 feet thick which reveals many features of Precambrian to late Tertiary geology.

The Precambrian rocks are exposed south of Ouray in the Uncompahgre gorge and consist of a compressed sequence of 3,000 feet of quartzite and shale called the Uncompahgre Formation. The Precambrian rocks are overlain with marked angular discordance by a thick section of sedimentary rocks that includes the Elbert Formation and Ouray Limestone of Devonian age, the Leadville Limestone of Mississippian age, the Molas and Hermosa Formations of Pennsylvanian age, the Dolores Formation of Late Triassic age, the Entrada Sandstone, Wanakah and Morrison Formations of Jurassic age, and the Dakota Sandstone and Mancos Shale of Cretaceous age. The rocks were folded and faulted several times—in late Paleozoic and late Mesozoic or early Tertiary time—and then were covered by Tertiary rocks consisting of the Telluride Conglomerate, San Juan Tuff, Silverton Volcanic Series, and Potosi Volcanic Series. Late Cretaceous or early Tertiary intrusive rocks are found in a northeast-trending zone just north of Ouray. The most prominent of these are laccolithic masses of granodiorite porphyry that intruded the Dakota-Mancos contact; these intrusive bodies were probably connected at depth by a central conduit now filled with a small stock that is exposed about a mile north of Ouray and is known as the Blowout (Luedke and Burbank, 1962).

The ore deposits are of two ages—Late Cretaceous or early Tertiary and late Tertiary. Most of the production has come from the older deposits which are genetically associated with the granodiorite intrusions and consist of (1) low-grade contact-metamorphic deposits containing some gold, (2) pyritic base-metal deposits containing silver and gold tellurides and native gold, and (3) siliceous and baritic lead-zinc deposits containing silver and gold. These older deposits are fissure veins and flat-lying replacement deposits in the Paleozoic and Mesozoic sedimentary rocks. The late Tertiary deposits are weakly mineralized gold-quartz and silver- and gold-bearing base-metal veins distributed around the margins of the district (Luedke and Burbank, 1962).

PARK COUNTY

Park County is in the mountainous central part of Colorado and includes a central broad basin, called South Park, rimmed on the east and north by the Front Range, on the west by the Mosquito Range, and on the south by an unnamed range of low hills. The county is drained by the South Platte River and its tributaries, most of which head in the Mosquito Range.

Gold is the principal mineral mined in the county, which ranks eighth in the State in gold production. Gold, silver, and other metals totaling $49,172,800 in gross value had been produced through 1959. Of this total about $36,725,000 (1,364,430 ounces) represents gold—$27,305,000 in lode gold and $9,417,000 in placer gold. Most of the production has come from the northwest part of the county along the east slope of the Mosquito Range.

Placer gold was discovered in Park County in 1859; this was one of the earliest mineral discoveries in Colorado. Prospectors, some arriving by way of the Arkansas River and others arriving by way of the South Platte River, found gold in the streams of South Park and later rich lodes at the headwaters of the South Platte and its tributaries. Nearly all the lode gold has come from the Alma district, and the placer gold has come from the Fairplay, Tarryall, and the Alma districts.

ALMA DISTRICT

The Alma district lies east of the Leadville district along the east slope of the Mosquito Range and includes the Mosquito-Buckskin, Montgomery, Horseshoe, and Alma placers.

The earliest discoveries in the Alma district appear to have been of lode deposits along the headwaters of Buckskin Gulch and the South Platte River (Henderson, 1926, p. 36–38). The Phillips lode in Buckskin Gulch was discovered in 1860, and other lodes were discovered in rapid succession soon after. The gold obtained from the lodes from 1860 to 1867 was worth about $710,000 (Henderson, 1926, p. 37, 196). After the easily disintegrated and oxidized ores near the surface were exhausted, the mines were closed because the sulfide ores at depth could not be successfully treated by amalgamation.

In the summer of 1871, silver ore was discovered on Mount Lincoln and Mount Bross, and mining activity in the district increased. Silver was the chief metal mined through 1885, and high silver production was maintained until 1892 when the price of silver began to drop. In later years production of silver fluctuated considerably. In 1873, outcrops of the London vein were discovered (Singewald and Butler, 1941, p. 36), but the London mine was not located and opened until 1875. It became the largest producer in the district and, though production fluctuated, it operated almost continuously until 1942.

The output of lode gold of the Alma district through 1959 was about 1,320,000 ounces valued at about $27,275,000.

Gold placers in the Alma district are found along the South Platte River east of Alma. These were first mined in the early 1870's, and during the first 3 years they produced $19,000 in gold (Singewald, 1950, p. 145). The greatest productivity was from 1904 to 1942 when about 27,600 ounces was recovered. There was some production during 1947–52, but the amount has been reported with that of other districts. The placers were virtually inactive from 1952 through 1959. Probably less than 200 ounces of gold has come from some of the other streams in the district. The total minimum placer production is about 28,000 ounces.

Exposed bedrock in the district is of Precambrian, Paleozoic, and Tertiary(?) ages. The Precambrian rocks are contorted gneiss, schist, and granite. They are overlain by Paleozoic sedimentary rocks consisting of the Sawatch Quartzite of Cambrian age, the Manitou Limestone of Ordovician age, the Chaffee Formation of Devonian age, the Leadville Limestone of Mississippian age, the Minturn Formation of Pennsylvanian age, and the Maroon Formation of Pennsylvanian and Permian age. Intrusive sills and dikes of quartz monzonite porphyry of Tertiary (?) age cut the older rocks. The stratified rocks dip eastward, but the dip is locally modified by folds and faults. The largest fault is the London, a reverse fault along which the beds have been displaced 1,600 feet. Most of the major ore deposits are near the London fault or the Cooper Gulch fault, another major reverse fault (Singewald and Butler, 1941, p. 7–28).

The principal types of ores are (1) gold-bearing sulfide veins in or adjoining porphyry sills near the base of the Lower Pennsylvanian strata, (2) silver-lead deposits in limestones, and (3) gold deposits in the Sawatch Quartzite of Cambrian age. The gold deposits, both in the porphyry sills and in the Sawatch Quartzite, are flanked by small silver-lead deposits.

The gold-bearing sulfide veins are composed of milky quartz with subordinate pyrite, sphalerite, galena, and chalcopyrite, and native gold which is seen only in exceptionally rich ore. The gold deposits in the Sawatch Quartzite contain the sulfides previously mentioned in a gangue of quartz and iron and manganese-bearing dolomite. The silver-lead deposits in limestones are unimportant as a source of gold (Singewald and Butler, 1941, p. 38–40).

The gold placers are glacial outwash deposits. The mineralized area on North Star Mountain, near the head of South Platte River along the Continental Divide, probably contributed to the bulk of the gold in the Alma placer as well as in minor placers farther north (Singewald, 1950, p. 149).

FAIRPLAY DISTRICT

Gold production from the Fairplay (Beaver Creek) district was entirely from placer deposits and included production from the Snowstorm and Fairplay placers along the South Platte River and small placers along Sacramento and Beaver Creeks.

Gold placers were discovered in the district about 1859, and through 1872 their output was valued at about $1 million (48,380 ounces) (Henderson, 1926, p. 36–38). From 1872 through 1938 the placers were worked sporadically without any spectacular results. From 1939 to 1951, the district was rejuvenated and about 125,000 ounces of gold was produced. These operations were terminated in 1952, and the district was virtually idle from 1952 through 1959. The minimum total gold yield of the district through 1959 was about 202,000 ounces.

By far the most productive placers are outwash gravels which extend downstream from the moraines formed by the South Platte glacier; smaller deposits have been found upstream (Singewald, 1950, p. 146–161).

TARRYALL DISTRICT

Almost all the gold production from the Tarryall district has come from placer deposits along the upper reaches of Tarryall Creek and its tributaries, northwest of the town of Como. Placer gold was discovered in August 1859, probably a little earlier than the discovery in the Fairplay district. These placers are credited with an output from 1859 to 1872 of about $1 million (48,380 ounces) (Henderson, 1926, p. 36, 187). Unrecorded and probably small-scale activity continued into the early 1900's. A brief resurgence occurred in 1941–42 and again in 1947, but the district was dormant from that time through 1959. The total minimum gold production from the Tarryall placers through 1959 was about 67,000 ounces. Lode mines in the district yielded less than 250 ounces of gold.

The placer deposits are of two kinds: glacial moraines and outwash gravel deposits downstream from the moraines (Singewald, 1950, p. 147–148, 162–168). The bulk of the gold has been mined from outwash deposits where the gold is concentrated just above bedrock; however, all the gravel contains some gold.

The gold in the placers was probably derived from lodes in the mineralized area at the heads of Montgomery and Deadwood Gulches, tributaries of Tarryall Creek (Singewald, 1950, p. 148).

PITKIN COUNTY

Pitkin County, in mountainous west-central Colorado and west of the Continental Divide, has produced silver, lead, and zinc valued at more than $100 million, but only about 28,200 ounces of gold has been produced. The Aspen district was the major source of this mineral wealth; however, the bulk of the gold came from the Independence Pass district.

INDEPENDENCE PASS DISTRICT

The Independence Pass district is in southeastern Pitkin County, about 20 miles southeast of Aspen.

In 1879, miners from Leadville crossed the Sawatch Range and found ore in this district on West Aspen Mountain (Henderson, 1926, p. 45). In the same year a belt of gold-bearing veins was found which, during 1881–82, yielded $190,000 (9,192 ounces) in gold.

The veins apparently terminated abruptly, either against a fault or contact, and mining was halted. The mines were reopened in 1891, again in 1897–99, and possibly for a short period in 1900 (Henderson, 1926, p. 45). Although the output of the district is unknown for these years, Pitkin County is credited with a gold production valued at $300,000 (Henderson, 1926, p. 201); much of this probably came from the Independence Pass district. There were only small sporadic operations in the district from 1932 through 1959. Total gold production through 1959 was probably about 25,000 ounces.

The formations of the Independence Pass district consist of Precambrian gneiss and granite covered by Tertiary breccia or rubble and rhyolite flows, all intruded by a granite porphyry stock (Vanderwilt and Koschmann, 1932).

Not much is known about the veins. They occur in the Precambrian rocks or in the Tertiary intrusive rocks. Howell (1919, p. 75–102) described some of the veins in the Twin Lakes district east of the county line which are probably similar and are genetically related to those in the Independence Pass district. They consist of gold-bearing quartz associated with pyrite and galena and locally associated with some chalcopyrite and sphalerite. Silver is present in small amounts.

RIO GRANDE COUNTY

Rio Grande County is in south-central Colorado in the southeastern San Juan Mountains, on the west side of the San Luis Valley. The Rio Grande River crosses the northern part of the county.

In the early 1880's Rio Grande County ranked third in the State in the production of gold, the county's chief metal. Gold output of the county through 1947 was about 257,600 ounces (about $7 million worth); however, from 1949 through 1958 it was only 135 ounces. Small amounts of silver, copper, and lead valued at about $330,000 have been recovered from the gold ores.

SUMMITVILLE DISTRICT

The Summitville district is in the southwest corner of Rio Grande County, high in the San Juan Mountains.

The earliest discoveries of gold in the San Juan Mountains were in 1870 in the Summitville district and in Arrastre Gulch in San Juan County. The news of these finds started a rush to the region, and within a few years most of the major mining camps were established. The early discoveries in the Summitville district were of placer gold, but available records indicate that placer production in the area was minor, probably less than $10,000 worth. The first lodes were located in 1871, the richest deposits were located by 1873, and large-scale mining began in 1875.

The ore near the surface was oxidized, rich, and easy to beneficiate. By the end of 1887 most of the known oxidized ore had been mined out, and the underlying sulfide ores were much lower grade and more difficult to mill and concentrate. During 1873–87 the Summitville district produced, mostly from the Little Annie mine, about $2,064,000 in gold and silver, 95 percent of which was gold (Steven and Ratté, 1960b, p. 6). Production declined sharply in 1888 and fluctuated considerably in the years through 1925. A deposit discovered in 1926 in the Little Annie group of mines produced, by 1930, about $500,000 in gold from 864 tons of sorted ore. This ore shoot was mined out by the end of 1930, and during 1931–33 the total metal production from the district was only slightly more than $5,000.

In 1934 most of the properties in the district were brought under one control, and the most productive period in the history of the district followed. From 1934 through 1947 the total production of the district exceeded $4 million, most of which was in gold (Steven and Ratté, 1960b, p. 6–7). Although considerable exploration work was done after 1947, there was little or no production from 1948 through 1959.

The total gold production of the district from 1873 through 1959 was about 257,600 ounces.

According to Steven and Ratté (1960b, p. 9–10), bedrock in the Summitville district consists of volcanic rocks and related shallow intrusive rocks, all of middle or late Tertiary age. The oldest rocks, known as the Conejos Formation, are a thick succession of dark, fine-grained porphyritic rhyodacite flows cut by a large quartz monzonite stock. The north margin of the stock and the adjacent flow rocks were intensely altered by solfataric action. Erosion dissected the area and produced relief of at least 2,000 feet. Volcanic eruptions were renewed and quartz latite lavas known as the Fisher Quartz Latite were extruded on the irregular erosion surface. These rocks were intruded by dikes of similar composition, altered by hydrothermal solutions, and in part covered by later eruptions of quartz latite and rhyolite flows. Mineralization was related to the second period of alteration, and all known ore deposits are in the Fisher Quartz Latite (Steven and Ratté, 1960b, p. 38–40).

The ore bodies are resistant pipes and veinlike masses of vuggy quartz and quartz-alunite rock that commonly contain pyrite and enargite and some galena and sphalerite. The resistant veins are surrounded by irregular envelopes of soft argillized ground in which illite, montmorillonite, and locally occurring kaolinite are the most abundant minerals. Beyond the argillized envelope the rocks are pervasively bleached, owing to the extensive alteration of the matrix and ferromagnesian minerals to montmorillonite, chlorite, and quartz; only the quartz and feldspar phenocrysts are relatively unaltered (Steven and Ratté, 1960b, p. 41–48).

ROUTT COUNTY

Routt County is in north-central Colorado along the Wyoming boundary.

Prospectors, in search of gold, entered what is now Routt County early in the 1860's and discovered placers in the Hahns Peak area in 1865 (George and Crawford, 1909, p. 221). These deposits were the chief source of gold in the county and were mostly developed before 1900. Total gold production of the county through 1959 was about 19,000 ounces.

HAHNS PEAK DISTRICT

Much of the mining history of the Hahns Peak (Columbine) district, near Hahns Peak in north-central Routt County, is obscure. After the initial discoveries in 1865, the placers were worked intermittently for several years and yielded gold worth $200,000 to $500,000 according to conservative estimates (George and Crawford, 1909, p. 221). Lodes were also developed, but their returns were disappointing. In 1959, the district had been virtually inactive for 30 years or more. Total gold production probably was between 15,000 and 20,000 ounces.

The bedrock of the district consists mainly of Dakota Sandstone and Mancos Shale of Cretaceous age and laccoliths and sills of rhyolite, latite, and andesite porphyry intruded into these formations. The rocks are folded and faulted, and older rocks of Jurassic and Carboniferous age are locally exposed. Small irregular veins and impregnations, containing lead, silver, gold, and copper, occur in the porphyry (Vanderwilt, in Vanderwilt and others, 1947, p. 186–189).

SAGUACHE COUNTY

Saguache County lies in south-central Colorado. Its east boundary is the crest of the Sangre de Cristo Mountains, and its western part includes the northeastern San Juan Mountains. The north end of the San Luis Valley occupies the central part of the county. Through 1959, Saguache County produced about 20,590 ounces of gold and significant quantities of silver, lead, zinc, and copper. Most of the gold has come from the Bonanza district.

BONANZA DISTRICT

The Bonanza (Kerber Creek) district is about 12 miles north of Saguache in the northeastern part of the county.

The first mineral-bearing lode was located in the district in May 1880 on Kerber Creek, where large silver-lead fissure veins were discovered (H. C. Burchard, in Henderson, 1926, p. 208). After the discovery, prospectors swarmed into the area, and the town of Bonanza was founded. Most of the mining operations were small, however, and by 1882 the town had lost most of its population (Patton, 1915, p. 10). In 1911–12 the Rawley drainage tunnel was driven to tap the silver-lead-copper-zinc ore shoot of the Rawley vein (W. S. Burbank, in Vanderwilt and others, 1947, p. 445), and in 1912 annual production increased from $9,600 to $80,000. Most of the ore in the Rawley shoot above the tunnel level was mined and milled between 1923 and 1930. District production dropped abruptly in 1931 but was revived in the late 1930's and early 1940's. The mines were relatively inactive from 1952 through 1959. Total gold production through 1959 was about 17,000 ounces; virtually all production was a byproduct of base-metal and silver ores.

Though Tertiary volcanic rocks cover much of the Bonanza district, older rocks are discernible in places, and they consist mainly of Precambrian schist, gneiss, and granite overlain unconformably by a thick succession of Paleozoic formations ranging in age from Ordovician to Permian. The Tertiary rocks overlie the older rocks with pronounced unconformity. They are about 4,000 feet thick, are chiefly lava flows, and include the Rawley Andesite, Bonanza Latite, Squirrel Gulch Latite, Hayden Peak Latite, Brewer Creek Latite. These rocks are cut by dikes and small intrusive bodies of granite porphyry, diorite, monzonite, rhyolite, and latite. Numerous small closely spaced faults cut the Tertiary rocks, and most of the ore deposits are in fissure fillings along these faults in the Rawley Andesite, the basal unit of the Tertiary section (Burbank, 1932, p. 5–60).

The ore deposits of the Bonanza district are chiefly complex base-metal ores containing pyrite, sphalerite, galena, chalcopyrite, bornite, enargite, tennantite, and stromeyerite in a gangue of quartz, calcite, rhodochrosite, and barite. Two principal classes of ore deposits have been distinguished: (1) quartz veins of rather high sulfide content that contain lead, zinc, copper, silver, and a little gold, and (2) quartz-rhodochrosite-fluorite veins, valuable mainly for their silver, with only minor quantities of sulfides. A few veins in the northern part of the district contain small shoots of gold and silver tellurides (Burbank, 1932, p. 60).

SAN JUAN COUNTY

San Juan County is in the western San Juan Mountains in southwestern Colorado, just south of Ouray County.

The county produced about 1,665,000 ounces of gold through 1959 and large quantities of silver, lead, copper, and zinc. The bulk of the gold came from lodes in the Animas (Silverton) and Eureka districts. There are no extensive placer deposits in the county.

Some prospecting in the county was carried on in the 1860's, and the first gold ore was mined in 1870 while the region was still part of the Ute Indian Reservation. The main rush to the region did not begin until 1874, after a treaty with the Ute Indians opened the region to settlement (Ransome, 1901b, p. 19–20). About 2,000 men came into the district during the summer of 1874, and at least that many claims were staked. San Juan County was formed in 1876 with the county seat at Silverton.

During the 1870's, the chief route into the region was by trail from Del Norte 125 miles away on the Rio Grande River and transportation was by pack train and wagon. Both transportation and ore treatment charges were high; consequently, only rich ore could be mined. The area, nevertheless, was actively prospected, and many lodes which subsequently proved valuable were located. In July 1882, the Denver and Rio Grande narrow-gage railroad was completed to Silverton, which reduced transportation rates and permitted the mining of lower grade ores. There followed a brief but turbulent period marked by unscrupulous promoting, squandering of large sums of money on fruitless mining ventures, and repeated failures to treat successfully the complex San Juan ores (Ransome, 1901b, p. 21–24). In 1890, treatment of low-grade ores by concentration and amalgamation at the Sunnyside and Silver Lake mines near Silverton started a new period in mine development. The first large-scale selective flotation mill, which successfully separated lead and zinc from ores from the Sunnyside mine, began operation in 1917–18 (W. S. Burbank, in Vanderwilt and others, 1947, p. 403).

Silver and lead ores were mined almost continuously in San Juan County from 1873 through 1923 (Henderson, 1926, p. 216). Gold production, which began in 1873, increased steadily, and with few exceptions after 1894 the value of gold produced exceeded that of silver. Profitable operations continued until 1953, when the Shenandoah-Dives mill near Silverton closed. The metal output of the county was small from 1953 through 1959.

ANIMAS DISTRICT

The Animas (Silverton) district is in north-central San Juan County near Silverton.

The total gold production of the district is not recorded, but D. J. Varnes (written commun., 1960) estimated that the mineral output before 1901 was valued at $8,200,000, of which 65 percent (about 258,000 ounces) was in gold. Varnes (1963, table 6) credited the south Silverton mining area with a total of 616,000 ounces of gold from 1901 through 1957. The total output through 1959 was at least 874,000 ounces and it may have exceeded 1 million ounces.

The mineralized area of the district is along and south of the south rim of the Silverton caldera, the major features of which are discussed under the Sneffels-Red Mountain district in the Ouray County section (p. 107).

Overlying a dissected terrane composed of Precambrian and Paleozoic sedimentary rocks is the Telluride Conglomerate, the lowermost unit of a thick section of dominantly volcanic Tertiary rocks. This conglomerate is succeeded, in ascending order, by the San Juan Tuff and the Silverton Volcanic Series. After an interval of faulting and subsidence in the caldera, the rocks in the zones of fractures were intruded by dikes of andesite and latite and small bodies of porphyritic quartz monzonite (Burbank, 1933, p. 138–155).

The ore deposits are in veins that fill fissures radial to the rim of the caldera and in veins that diverge from the radial fissures. Some of the fractures that intersect the radial system at high angles are filled with dikes and are mineralized in places.

The largest veins of the area are the Shenandoah-Dives, the Aspen, Silver Lake-Nevada, and the Highland Mary. They are located in Arrastre Basin, Silver Lake Basin, and Cunningham Gulch. These veins are valuable mainly for silver and lead, but some parts contain appreciable amounts of gold with pyrite and chalcopyrite. Locally these veins are rich in specularite and fluorite. The main veins in the upper part of Cunningham Gulch contain galena, sphalerite, and chalcopyrite in a gangue of quartz and some calcite. Near the mouth of Cunningham Gulch, however, in the vicinity of a quartz monzonite stock, the ores change character and consist predominantly of siliceous and pyritic gold-bearing ores with lesser amounts of base-metal sulfides (D. J. Varnes, in Vanderwilt and others, 1947, p. 432–433).

EUREKA DISTRICT

The Eureka district is in northeastern San Juan County, at the head of the Animas River drainage basin, and includes mines in the Animas Forks, Cement Creek, and Mineral Creek areas.

Silver, gold, lead, and zinc ores worth a total of $50 million have been mined from this district, chiefly from the Sunnyside and Gold King mines (W. S. Burbank, in Vanderwilt and others, 1947, p. 433). Total gold production of the district through 1959 was at least 500,000 ounces.

The district is on the north side of the Silverton caldera along a northeast-trending graben that extends from the Silverton caldera to the Lake City caldera in Hinsdale County. Part of the district extends into the central downfaulted block of the Silverton caldera, the major features of which are discussed under the description of the Sneffels-Red Mountain district in Ouray County (p. 107).

Most of the rock exposed in the district belongs to the Silverton Volcanic Series of Tertiary age; in addition a few small bodies of intrusive rhyolite and latite are present (W. S. Burbank, in Vanderwilt and others, 1947, p. 434).

The ore deposits are fissure fillings, most of which are in the southwest part of the graben within 1 mile of the crescentic faults that outline the central block of the Silverton caldera. Some of the larger fissures, however, are mineralized in places along a length of 6 miles. Veins in the Sunnyside mine display several stages of mineralization—quartz-pyrite, base-metal sulfides, and rhodonite. Gold-bearing quartz cuts the base-metal sulfides and rhodonite (W. S. Burbank, in Vanderwilt and others, 1947, p. 434). Ore deposits in the Cement Creek area are quartz-pyrite-gold veins characteristic of the Gold King mine, tungsten-bearing quartz veins, and chimney deposits rich in lead, silver, and a little gold (D. J. Varnes and W. S. Burbank, in Vanderwilt and others, 1947, p. 435, 436).

SAN MIGUEL COUNTY

San Miguel County is in southwestern Colorado and extends from the west boundary of Ouray County to the Utah-Colorado border.

From 1875 through 1959 the county produced 3,837,000 ounces of gold in addition to large quantities of silver, lead, zinc, and copper. It ranks third among the gold-producing counties of the State.

The first recorded discoveries of gold and silver in San Miguel County were in 1875 on the Smuggler vein (Purington, 1898, p. 755–756). After this discovery many additional mineral locations were made, but because of the inaccessibility of the area and distance from railroad transportation very little ore was mined or shipped before 1881. Prior to 1882 production was less than $50,000 annually (Henderson, 1926, p. 226), but by 1888, output had increased to $1 million annually. Mining activity was stimulated further in 1890 when the Rio Grande Southern Railroad was completed from Ridgeway to Telluride. The panic of 1893, during which the price of silver dropped, caused a minor decline, but mining again increased in 1895 and gold production alone was valued at $1,421,159 (68,755 ounces), almost double that in 1894. This was the first year the value of gold production exceeded $1 million; from 1901 through 1919 it generally averaged more than $2 million annually (Henderson, 1926, p. 226), and from 1920 through 1926 more than $1 million annually. The lowest gold production in the county since 1882 occurred during the depression years, 1929 through 1933, when the annual production dropped below $100,000 (4,838 ounces). From 1934 through 1959 the annual production for most years has exceeded $700,000 (20,000 ounces).

Placers in San Miguel County have been of minor importance and have yielded only about 9,700 ounces from 1878 through 1959.

Three districts in San Miguel County are important sources of gold—the Ophir, the Telluride, and the Mount Wilson.

MOUNT WILSON DISTRICT

The Mount Wilson district is in southeastern San Miguel County on one of the western spurs of Mount Wilson.

The Silver Pick mine, which was the only property of importance in the district, was located in 1882 and was worked steadily until 1909. Its period of greatest productivity was from 1882 to 1906, when ore worth $750,000 was mined. Purington (1898, p. 847) noted that some ore was worth as much as $100 to $150 per ton, with gold as the major constituent and silver and lead as minor constituents. The Silver Pick and most of the smaller mines were idle from 1909 through 1959, except for small-scale activity from 1932 through 1941 when about 520 ounces of gold was produced. Total gold production of the district through 1959 was roughly 24,800 ounces.

The oldest rock unit of the district is the Mancos Shale of Cretaceous age. This is overlain in turn by the Telluride Conglomerate, the San Juan Tuff, and the Silverton Volcanic Series, all of Tertiary age. The main mass of Mount Wilson is a stock which ranges in composition from granogabbro to quartz monzonite. The intrusive cuts rocks as young as the Silverton Volcanic Series, and thus is the youngest bedrock unit of the district (C. S. Bromfield, oral commun., 1963).

The ore deposits are in quartz veins containing pyrite, chalcopyrite, arsenopyrite, galena, sphalerite, tetrahedrite, stibnite, and calcite. Most of the gold is believed to be contained in chalcopyrite, galena, and arsenopyrite. The most productive veins, including the Silver Pick, are in the stock; however, a few veins of minor importance are in the invaded sedimentary rocks near the intrusive contact (C. S. Bromfield, oral commun., 1963).

OPHIR DISTRICT

The Ophir district, in eastern San Miguel County, includes the area south of San Miguel River, west of Bridal Veil Creek, and the Ophir Valley on the south. This district includes the Iron Springs, Ames, and South Telluride mining areas.

Mines in the Ophir Valley were operating as early as 1878, and the ore was shipped to the Silverton smelter (Henderson, 1926, p. 53). In 1879 two arrastres were built in the vicinity of Ophir. In 1883 a small smelter was built at the old town of Ames, but it was unsuccessful and was operated for only a year (Henderson, 1926, p. 216). According to H. C. Burchard, as quoted by Henderson (1926, p. 217–218), several mines including the Alta, the largest producer in the district, were developed as early as 1881. According to D. J. Varnes (in Vanderwilt and others, 1947, p. 427), the history of the district has been one of intermittent production except for a few large mines which operated fairly continuously. Most of the ore mined early from this district was rich in silver, and activity of the camp depended in part on the price of silver. Some mines, which were idle most of the time, became substantial producers during times of favorable metal prices. The district was almost idle from 1930 through 1936, was substantially active from 1937 through 1948, and was idle again from 1949 through 1959.

Production records are fragmentary and the amount of gold is usually included with the value of other metals (D. J. Varnes, in Vanderwilt and others, 1947, p. 427). The total gold output of the district through 1959 was probably a minimum of 200,000 ounces.

The Ophir district is 5 to 7 miles west of the Silverton caldera, and its ore deposits are in structures related to the caldera. Paleozoic and Mesozoic sedimentary rocks are exposed in the bottoms of the deeper valleys and are overlain, in ascending order, by the Telluride Conglomerate, the San Juan Tuff, and the Silverton Volcanic Series. These are all intruded by small igneous bodies ranging in composition from quartz monzonite to diorite. The rocks are cut by a network of fissures and veins. The most productive veins trend westerly and contain pyrite, galena, sphalerite, chalcopyrite, and freiburgite as the more common sulfide minerals. Hematite and magnetite also are present, and the gangue minerals are chiefly quartz, with some calcite, manganiferous iron carbonate, and barite. Some veins in the Ophir Valley trend north and northeast, and the minerals of these consist of quartz and pyrite carrying free gold and some silver. Gold also occurs in the altered and pyrite-impregnated country rock adjacent to the veins. The veins in the San Juan Tuff and overlying andesite commonly are more sharply defined than those in overlying volcanic rocks. Veins also occur within the sedimentary rocks. Replacement deposits are rare and of small extent (Cross and Purington, 1899; D. J. Varnes, in Vanderwilt and others, 1947, p. 425–427).

TELLURIDE DISTRICT

The Telluride (upper San Miguel) district is along the east border of San Miguel County immediately southwest of the Sneffels-Red Mountain district in Ouray County. The geology is described on pages 107–108; only the history and production will be discussed in this section.

The first discoveries in the Telluride district were made on the Smuggler vein in 1875 (Purington, 1898, p. 752–754). There was only a small production through 1882, but in 1883 a shipment of 4 tons of high-grade ore from the Smuggler vein yielded 800 ounces of silver and 18 ounces of gold per ton and thereafter production increased rapidly. Since 1898, the large output of the Telluride district has come chiefly from the mines of three large companies—the Liberty Bell, Smuggler-Union, and the Tomboy (Henderson, 1926, p. 53, 224–225). The Liberty Bell mine, which produced only silver and gold, was operated from 1898 to 1921 and during that period had an output of 633,021 ounces of gold (Henderson, 1926, p. 225). The Tomboy group of mines closed in 1927 and the Smuggler-Union closed in 1928 after operating 52 years (W. S. Burbank, in Vanderwilt and others, 1947, p. 421). In 1940 the Smuggler-Union group of mines and the Tomboy holdings were organized as the Telluride Mines, Inc., which was still active in 1959. Total production of gold through 1959 was at least 3 million ounces; thus Telluride is one of the 25 leading gold-producing districts in the United States. Large quantities of silver, lead, zinc, and copper have also been produced.

SUMMIT COUNTY

Summit County, in north-central Colorado, is bounded on the west by the crest of the Gore Range, on the northeast by the crest of the Williams River Mountains, and on the southeast by the Front Range.

Summit County produced, through 1959, gold, silver, lead, and zinc, all having a gross value of about $74,177,600. Of this total, a minimum of $21,673,180 (1,010,670 ounces) represents gold—$15,644,143 (739,511 ounces) in placer gold and $6,024,769 (271,159 ounces) in lode gold. Summit County ranks first in Colorado in placer gold production and tenth in the State in total gold production. Almost the entire output has come from the southern part of the county, in which the Breckenridge and Tenmile are the major districts.

BRECKENRIDGE DISTRICT

The Breckenridge (Blue River) district includes the upper valley of the Blue River which lies between the Front Range on the east and the Tenmile Range on the west. The district has produced large amounts of placer and lode gold, silver, lead, and zinc. It is credited with an output of about 1 million ounces of gold, of which about 735,000 ounces came from placers and the remainder from gold lodes and as a byproduct of silver-lead-zinc ores.

Rich gold placers were discovered along Georgia Gulch on the north side of Farncomb Hill in 1859, and soon afterward placers were discovered along many streams and gulches in the district (Ransome, 1911, p. 16–20). From 1859 to 1862, the Georgia Gulch placers reportedly yielded $3 million in gold; most of the $5½ million worth of placer gold produced in Summit County from 1860 to 1869 is credited to the Breckenridge district (Henderson, 1926, p. 33, 245). Production of placer gold decreased in the 1880's and 1890's but in 1908 it was rejuvenated by dredging operations. By 1909, four dredges were operating in the district (Henderson, 1926, p. 35). After the late 1930's activity declined, and after 1947 there was only small sporadic placer production.

In 1880, about 20 years after the discovery of the placer deposits, gold was found in lodes on Farncomb Hill and elsewhere in rapid succession. Lodes were the chief source of gold in the Breckenridge district from about 1885 until 1908, when the large-scale placer dredging operations began.

Some gold in the Breckenridge district has also been derived as a byproduct from silver-lead-zinc ore, chiefly from the Wellington mine, which became an important producer in 1910 (Lovering, 1934, p. 3). This mine operated continuously to 1929 and sporadically thereafter until 1958. Lode mines in the district were virtually inactive in 1959.

Precambrian schist, gneiss, and granite, which underlie the sedimentary rocks of the district, are exposed in only a few places. The Maroon Formation of Pennsylvanian and Permian age rests directly on the Precambrian rocks. It is overlain by the Morrison Formation of Jurassic age and the Dakota Sandstone, Benton Shale, Niobrara Formation, and Pierre Shale, all of Cretaceous age. Folding and faulting at the end of Cretaceous time was accompanied by intrusion of sills and dikes of monzonite and a small stock of quartz monzonite porphyry. The sedimentary rocks were folded into an asymmetric syncline that generally dips to the west (Lovering, 1934, p. 3–22).

Ransome (1911, p. 124–157) recognized three major types of ore deposits in the district: zinc-lead-silver-gold veins, gold-silver-lead stockworks and veins, and the gold veins of Farncomb Hill. The zinc-lead-silver-gold veins are in a stock of quartz monzonite porphyry and in the surrounding country rocks. Chief minerals are sphalerite, argentiferous galena, and pyrite in a gangue of carbonate and very little quartz. Gold is in the pyrite. The Wellington mine is the chief producer in this group. The gold-silver-lead stockworks are masses of quartz monzonite porphyry interlaced with a network of veinlets of pyrite, sphalerite, and galena in a gangue of sericitized porphyry. The Farncomb Hill gold veins are in shale country rock near a mass of quartz monzonite porphyry on Farncomb Hill. Though some veins enter the porphyry, ore bodies do not. The Farncomb Hill veins are remarkably persistent considering their narrowness. They are rarely more than one-half inch wide, and some have been traced for distances of 300 feet. These veins are noted for their rich pockets of native gold which have supplied specimens of wire and leaf gold to museums and collectors throughout the world. The vein mineralogy is simple; pyrite, chalcopyrite, sphalerite, and galena are in a calcite gangue. Native gold occurs in local thickenings or pockets and also is embedded in calcite, sphalerite, or galena.

Placers, according to Ransome (1911, p. 175), are of three types—bench or high-level placers, deep or low-level placers, and shallow gravels in gulches. The gulch gravels, notably those on Farncomb Hill, were the first placers worked. The bench gravels were mined by hydraulic methods and were largely worked out by 1900. The deep placers, which are along the Swan and Blue Rivers, have been worked by dredges and were the source of most of the placer gold of the district after 1900.

TENMILE DISTRICT

The Tenmile district includes the mining camps of Kokomo, Robinson, and Frisco, which lie in the Tenmile valley on the west side of the Tenmile Range. The district has chiefly produced silver, lead, and zinc. Small amounts of gold have been recovered as a byproduct from the base-metal ores, and small amounts have been derived from placer deposits in McNulty Gulch near Kokomo.

Gold placer deposits were discovered in McNulty Gulch in 1861 (Hollister, 1867, p. 326), and some time later oxidized gold ore in lodes was discovered in the Tenmile Range on the east side of the valley. Neither the placers nor lodes proved significant, and no important mining development took place until 1879–80 after the discovery of rich silver deposits in 1877 in the Leadville district 12 miles to the south (Emmons, 1898, p. 1). Rich silver ore was discovered on the west side of the Tenmile valley during the summer of 1878, and as a result of this discovery many claims were located and the district developed rapidly (Henderson, 1926, p. 11, 36). By the spring of 1881 most of the properties that were to become the large producers had been located. The total mine output in 1881 was estimated to be worth about $2 million, and the district became the leading producer in Summit County (Henderson, 1926, p. 237). The blanket of oxidized and secondarily enriched ore in the district was rapidly mined out between 1880 and 1890 and as a consequence the bonanza period of the camp came to a close.

In 1896, the Wilfley table was put into operation. This device separated the components of the lead-zinc sulfide ores and enabled these ores to be exploited profitably. The district entered a long period of prosperity that lasted until 1923 (Koschmann and Wells, 1946, p. 55–56). The demand for base metals during World War II rejuvenated the mines, and from 1942 through 1949 the district was one of the most productive in the State. Falling metal prices caused most of the mines to close in 1950, and the district was virtually inactive from 1950 through 1959. Total gold production through 1959 was about 52,000 ounces, most of which was a byproduct of base-metal ores. An unknown but small amount of gold was mined from placers.

The Tenmile district is in a belt of folded and faulted Paleozoic sedimentary rocks bounded on the east and west by high mountain ranges of Precambrian gneiss, schist, and granite (Koschmann and Wells, 1946, p. 57–96). The Paleozoic rocks are of sedimentary origin and lie unconformably on a Precambrian basement. Because of tectonic activity during Paleozoic time, the Paleozoic section is incomplete from place to place. The most persistent sedimentary rocks are the Minturn Formation of Pennsylvanian age and the Maroon Formation of Pennsylvanian and Permian(?) age. Tertiary intrusive rocks, which are predominantly sills and a few small irregular bodies of several textural varieties of quartz monzonite, cut the Paleozoic formations.

The rocks were folded into a north-trending syncline that plunges north. The east limb of the syncline is cut by the north-trending Mosquito fault, one of the major faults in the region.

The ore deposits of the Tenmile district are of two types: massive sulfide replacement bodies in limestone beds of the Minturn Formation and sulfide veins in Tertiary igneous rocks and Precambrian rocks. The most productive ore has been in the replacement deposits which consist of aggregates of pyrite, pyrrhotite, marcasite, sphalerite, galena, and chalcopyrite. Quartz and siderite are the chief gangue minerals. The veins are in fissures and faults and contain galena, sphalerite, pyrite, and local molybdenite in a gangue of calcite, barite, and quartz (Koschmann and Wells, 1946, p. 100–105).

TELLER COUNTY

Teller County is in the southern part of the Front Range, west of the city of Colorado Springs. The famous Cripple Creek district is the source of nearly all the mineral wealth of the county.

CRIPPLE CREEK DISTRICT

The Cripple Creek district is about 45 miles southwest of Colorado Springs, in the shadow of Pikes Peak. The leading gold producer of Colorado and the second most productive gold-mining district in the United States, Cripple Creek had a total gold output of 19,100,867 ounces through 1959.

Though prospectors were active in the Pikes Peak region as early as 1859, they overlooked the ores of

Cripple Creek. In 1874, a few fragments of gold ore were found in the Mount Pisgah area, but they generated little sustained interest. Between 1880 and 1890, Robert Womack, an itinerant prospector and rancher, found gold ore in numerous shallow pits and diggings in the Cripple Creek area, which at that time was a cattle ranch. Womack's persistence finally roused the curiosity of others, who bought his claims in 1891. At about this time W. S. Stratton became interested in the discoveries and noted that much of the ore which the prospectors considered to be galena was in reality a gold-bearing mineral that was later found to be the gold telluride, sylvanite. Stratton continued his investigations, and on July 4, 1891, he located the Washington and Independence claims on a barren, granitic-appearing outcrop that proved to be gold ore worth $380 per ton (Lindgren and Ransome, 1906, p. 130–132). Within a few months the hills swarmed with prospectors, and in February 1892 the town of Cripple Creek was founded. By 1893 many of the major mines of the district, among them the Portland, Independence, Granite, and Strong, were in production. Labor strife in 1894 caused a temporary setback, but new mines, including the Vindicator, Golden Cycle, Victor, Isabella, and Cresson, were opened in the following few years. Peak production was in 1900, when 878,167 ounces of gold were mined (Henderson, 1926, p. 247). Activity slowly declined until 1934, when the price of gold was raised. The revived production in the late 1930's was further stimulated by construction of the Carlton drainage tunnel in 1941, which relieved many of the pumping difficulties found in the deeper mines. Output declined during World War II and increased thereafter, but it did not increase to the prewar level. Only a few mines were operating in the district in 1959.

The following brief description of the geology and ore deposits has been abstracted from reports by Lindgren and Ransome (1906), Loughlin and Koschmann (1935), and Koschmann (1949).

The ore deposits of the Cripple Creek district are within or at the margin of an irregular mass of Miocene fragmental rocks composed of stratified terrigenous sediments and volcanic breccia, collectively known as breccia according to local usage. These rocks occupy a steep-walled basin or caldera about 4 miles long and 2 miles wide, in granite, gneiss, and schist of Precambrian age. Locally the surrounding Precambrian rocks are capped by sandstone, grits, and volcanic rocks that are older than the fragmental rocks in the basin. As the breccia accumulated in the basin, it subsided intermittently along steep faults. Subsidence also produced shear zones in the breccia and adjacent Precambrian rocks, and these were filled with dikes and irregular masses of latite-phonolite, syenite, phonolite, and alkaline basaltic rocks (lamprophyres). A small pipe of basaltic breccia, known as the Cresson blowout, cuts the fragmental rocks in the south-central part of the caldera.

The subsurface structure and configuration of the basin can be deciphered only in a general way. Available data show that the basin is composite in structure and comprises three minor basins or subbasins separated by buried granite ridges and spurs. The basin walls, as determined from underground exposures, are irregular but in general steep. In most places their average slopes range from 46° to 80° toward the center of the corresponding subbasin. In places, however, notably along the southwest wall, they overhang, and in places along the northeast wall they slope as little as 23°; in still other places they consist of gently sloping benches with steep walls above and below.

Three stages of mineralization followed the recurrent fissure formation. The first stage is characterized by quartz-fluorspar veins and coarse pyrite. Gold tellurides, silver and copper tellurides, pyrite, sphalerite, galena, tetrahedrite, and the gangue minerals quartz, fluorspar, dolomite, ankerite, celestite, and roscoelite, mark the second stage. During the third stage, open fractures were filled with quartz, chalcedony, fine-grained pyrite, calcite, and local cinnabar.

The ore deposits in the Cripple Creek district occur in relatively short individual veins along narrow long vein zones. Many of these vein zones lie close to the margin of the breccia mass; others persist into the breccia; some cross the contact and extend into the adjacent Precambrian rocks for 2,000 feet or more. Most of the known vein zones are related in position and strike to the abrupt bends or recessions along the basin walls or to buried granite spurs or ridges within the basin.

GEORGIA

The gold deposits of Georgia occur in several northeast-trending mineralized zones in the crystalline schists and gneisses that underlie the northern third of the State. Intruded into the foliated rocks are many bodies of granitic rock ranging from dikes to stocks. The gold deposits are associated with the dikes (Pardee and Park, 1948, p. 18). In this gold belt are about 500 properties reported to contain gold (Pardee and Park, 1948, p. 124), but only three localities—the Creighton mine in Cherokee County, the Dahlonega district in Lumpkin County, and the Nacoochee district in White County—have had significant production.

Gold was discovered in Georgia in 1829 in the Nacoochee River valley in White County, near Dahlonega in Lumpkin County (Jones, 1909, p. 17), and in Habersham County (Becker, 1895, p. 257). Thousands of people flocked to these areas to wash gold from the surficial deposits along creeks and streams. By 1838, production was large enough for the Government to establish a branch of the mint at Dahlonega. Although the richer and more accessible placers were soon exhausted, the mint remained operative until 1861, when Georgia seceded from the Union (Jones, 1909, p. 17). The Civil War halted mining in Georgia, but after the war, activity was resumed, with emphasis on lode mining, and a few thousand ounces of gold was produced annually until the early part of World War I. During 1916–34 only a few hundred ounces was produced annually. When the price of gold was increased in 1934, most mines were reactivated for a brief period. In 1942 the mines were closed by Federal order, and when controls were lifted in 1945, few were able to reopen under the prevailing high costs. Production of only 156 ounces of gold was reported during 1942–52, and none was reported during 1953–59.

Before 1900, Georgia produced an estimated $16 to $17 million in gold and silver, mostly from the Dahlonega district in Lumpkin County (Lindgren, 1906b, p. 122); from 1830 through 1959 the State produced about 870,665 ounces of gold (fig. 3).

CHEROKEE COUNTY

The Creighton (Franklin) lode mine, 7 miles southeast of Ball Ground on the Etowah River in eastern Cherokee County, was one of the oldest and most successful lode properties in the State; it was worked successfully as early as 1840. Early operations were restricted to mining the residual mantle of decomposed bedrock (McCallie, in Yeates and others, 1896, p. 176); after these ores were exhausted, the sulfide ore in the unweathered bedrock was successfully mined. The mine was active in the early 1900's when it was considered the most important in the State, but in 1909 it was flooded by a cave-in beneath the dammed Etowah River (Pardee and Park, 1948, p. 129). No record could be found of any subsequent mining. Total gold production of the property was between $750,000 and $1 million (about 35,400 to 48,500 ounces) (Pardee and Park, 1948, p. 129).

Pardee and Park (1948, p. 129), who summarized the findings of earlier workers, noted that the country rock in the mine area is mica schist with layers of amphibole gneiss. Two major lodes or vein systems, the Franklin and McDonald, occur. The Franklin was the more productive. The deposits consist of aggregates of quartz stringers parallel to the strike and dip of the foliation of the schist and gneiss. Auriferous pyrite is a constituent of the stringers and also occurs in the wallrock. Calcite, muscovite, and chalcopyrite are minor minerals in the ore.

LUMPKIN COUNTY

Gold was discovered in Lumpkin County in 1828 or 1829 near the town of Dahlonega in the Dahlonega district, in the south-central part of the county, and it was actively mined until 1849 when many miners drifted on to California (Yeates and others, 1896, p. 271–274). In the post-Civil War period, lode mining and dredging operations produced steadily, though not at the prewar scale. The mines revived markedly in the mid-1930's because of the increased price of gold, but by 1938 their activity was sporadic and on a small scale.

Lumpkin County and especially the Dahlonega district produced most of the total gold output of the State. Exact figures could not be found, but the total production through 1959 probably was between 400,000 and 500,000 ounces. The Findley mine, one of the most important of the Dahlonega district, produced $200,000 in gold before the Civil War (Yeates and others, 1896, p. 373).

Four general rock types can be recognized in the district—mica schists, feldspathic gneisses, hornblende schist, and granite (Eckel, 1903, p. 58–59). The mica schists and feldspathic gneisses are the oldest rocks and are regarded as of Precambrian or early Paleozoic age. They were intruded by diorite which later was metamorphosed to the hornblende schist. The granite which is exposed in some of the mines is the least sheared rock in the area and may therefore be the youngest.

The earliest deposits worked were stream placers. Later the free-milling gold of the entire saprolite was mined by hydraulic methods. This gold has been released by weathering from the sulfides with which it had been associated in the quartz veins at depth. The quartz veins in the fresh rock seem to be best developed and richest in gold along the contact of the mica schist with either granitic rock or the sheared hornblende schist.

WHITE COUNTY

The first discovery of gold in White County—and probably in Georgia—was in 1829 near the town of Nacoochee, in the Nacoochee district, at the junction of the Nacoochee and Chattahoochee Rivers in the east-central part of the county (King, in Yeates and others, 1896, p. 33).

The Nacoochee district may be considered the northeastward extension of the Dahlonega gold belt, which crosses the county from southwest to northeast. Small-scale sporadic production continued until the outbreak of the Civil War and was resumed after the war on a slightly more ambitious and better organized level. In the early and mid-1930's (Pardee and Park, 1948, p. 141–143), a few lode mines were opened in the district, and some of the alluvial placers were worked by hydraulic methods. From 1940 through 1959, however, no production was reported from the Nacoochee district. The total production of this district could not be ascertained with any degree of accuracy. Estimates by King (in Yeates and others, 1896, p. 33–79) of production from a few mines in the district range from $600,000 (30,000 ounces) to $1 million (50,000 ounces) in gold. No further record appears until the mid-1930's, when the mines in White County, presumably in the Nacoochee district, produced 2,235 ounces of gold from 1935 to 1940. Total production of the district through 1959 probably was 35,000 to 52,000 ounces.

The gneisses, mica schists, and hornblende schists in the district strike northeast, grade into one another along strike, and are cut in places by a coarse-grained granitic rock (King, in Yeates and others, 1896, p. 35). Most of the exposures are saprolitic, but in some of the stream valleys fresh rock can be found (Pardee and Park, 1948, p. 142). The gold deposits are in saprolite, alluvial placers, and lodes. The lodes consist of closely spaced gold-bearing quartz stringers in the schist.

IDAHO

Gold placers were discovered in Idaho in 1852 along the Pend Oreille River (Ross, 1930b, p. 2); however, Staley (1946, p. 5) considered the placer discovery at Pierce City in 1860 as the earliest discovery of consequence in the State. Other placers were discovered in Elk City, Orofino, and along the Salmon River in 1860 and 1861, and a year later discoveries were made at Florence, Warren, and Boise Basin.

Placers were the major source of gold in Idaho before 1900 (fig. 12); however, most of them were exhausted after the period of feverish exploitation from 1860 to 1870. Ross (1930b, p. 3) estimated that the value of placer gold produced to 1864 was about $20 million (about 1 million ounces).

With a slight decline of placer mining after 1870, lode deposits, which had been known and worked on a small scale since 1861, became more important, though placering was rejuvenated in 1897 by cheaper dredging operations and it continued to furnish most of the gold. After a lull in mining from 1870 to 1880, the industry revived, but after 1900 gold declined in importance among the mineral commodities mined in Idaho (Ross, 1930b, p. 3).

From 1863 to 1965 Idaho produced 8,322,930 ounces of gold. If the 1 million ounces that was produced before 1864 is added to this amount, the total gold production was about 9,300,000 ounces (fig. 13).

The lode gold deposits of Idaho are related to the huge Idaho batholith, a mass of granitic intrusive rocks that occupies much of the central part of the State. Most of the deposits are near the contact of the batholith, either in the granitic rocks or in intruded rocks which consist of sedimentary, metasedimentary, and volcanic rocks.

It is almost impossible to ascertain accurately the gold production of individual counties in Idaho. Much of Idaho's gold was produced before 1864, when the area became a territory and was politically subdivided. Counties were formed gradually, and many of the younger counties were formed from parts of older ones; consequently, some mining districts were originally in one county but later in another, and part of their production was reported by both counties. Further complicating the issue is the lack of any county production data before 1880, except for Boise and Idaho Counties. Total recorded production for all counties accordingly is less than that for the State.

ADA COUNTY

BLACK HORNET DISTRICT

In Ada County, in the southwest part of the State, the only important gold production came from the Black Hornet district in the northeast corner of the county about 10 miles east of Boise. Lode mines in this district probably were developed in 1862, at the time discoveries were being made in the Boise Basin, but the earliest record of production was in 1895–96, when gold ore valued at $24,000 was shipped from the district (Lindgren, 1898, p. 704). Small amounts of gold were produced annually through 1955, but during 1942–59 the output was only 119 ounces. Total recorded production from 1880 through 1959 was 21,431 ounces.

The geology of the district, according to Lindgren (1898, p. 704), is fairly simple. The country rock consists of granite of the Idaho batholith, which is cut locally by granite porphyry dikes. The ore deposits are gold-bearing quartz veins that contain variable amounts of pyrite, arsenopyrite, sphalerite, and galena (Ross, 1941, p. 5). The granite adjacent to the veins has been sericitized.

BINGHAM COUNTY

Gold has been mined from placers at several localities along the Snake River in Bingham County. Staley (1946, p. 13) credited the county with a total of 24,242 ounces of gold since 1885, all presumably from the Snake River placers. These deposits were not worked from the mid-1930's through 1959.

BLAINE COUNTY

Prospectors, drawn to central Idaho by the rich gold strikes in the Boise Basin in 1862, went from there into what is now Blaine County. Silver-lead deposits were found in the Wood River region in 1864, but these were ignored for a few years, because the chief interest was in gold (Umpleby and Ross, in Umpleby and others, 1930, p. 81). Gold deposits in the Camas district southwest of Hailey were developed in 1879. By 1880 the Wood River silver-lead deposits were worked, and gold was yielded as a byproduct. A decline in mining in the county began in the early 1900's and, except for a few brief revivals, continued until the early 1940's, when a period of high productivity of base-metal ores with gold as a byproduct commenced. Mining in the county slowly declined from the late 1940's through 1959.

Production of gold from 1874 through 1942 was 176,262 ounces (Staley, 1946, p. 13); total production from 1874 through 1959 was 212,638 ounces.

CAMAS DISTRICT

The Camas (Hailey, Mineral Hill) district is in west-central Blaine County, 5 to 15 miles southwest of Hailey in T. 1 N., Rs. 16 and 17 E.

Gold was first discovered in this district in 1865 at the site of the Camas 2 mine, but there was no production until 1879 (Anderson and Wagner, 1946, p. 9). Other discoveries were made in 1880, and the period from 1880 to the early 1900's was one of great prosperity in the district. The chief mine, the Camas 2, produced ore valued at $1¼ million before it was closed in 1898 (Anderson and Wagner, 1946, p. 9). Most of the mines in the district remained closed, but the Camas 2 and the Hattie were reopened for short periods in the 1930's, 1940's, and 1950's.

Production records are not complete, especially for the years of peak activity before 1900. Of the 175,770 ounces of gold produced in Blaine County from 1874 to 1900, Anderson and Wagner (1946, p. 9–10) estimated that more than half of it came from the Camas district. Umpleby and Ross (in Umpleby and others, 1930, p. 84) listed a total of 7,019 ounces produced from the Mineral Hill camp between 1902 and 1926; 7,161 ounces were produced from 1932 through 1959. Total gold production, including the estimate of Anderson and Wagner (1946, p. 9), was about 102,000 ounces. Much silver, lead, and zinc was mined also.

The district is underlain by granodiorite and quartz monzonite of the Idaho batholith of middle Cretaceous age, which is cut by many aplite and pegmatite dikes and a few lamprophyre dikes (Anderson and Wagner, 1946, p. 4–9). Remnants of a once-extensive cover of Tertiary basalt that buried an erosion surface carved into the granitic rock are found at a few places. The gold occurs in quartz veins along gently dipping faults in the batholith. The veins are generally rich in silver and carry two to four times as much silver by weight as gold. Some contain moderately large amounts of sulfides (Anderson and Wagner, 1946, p. 10).

In the northeastern part of the district, near Hailey, the country rock consists of tightly folded Paleozoic sedimentary rocks—the Milligen (Mississippian and Devonian) and the Wood River (Pennsylvanian) Formations. These have been faulted and intruded by several stocks, which are probably related to the Idaho batholith (Ross, 1941, p. 13). Most of the deposits are in shear zones in the Mississippian sedimentary rocks, which largely are thin-bedded carbonaceous argillites. The ore minerals are argentiferous galena, sphalerite, and tetrahedrite, with minor pyrite in a gangue of altered and crushed country rock, siderite, and a little quartz (Ross, 1941, p. 13).

WARM SPRINGS DISTRICT

The Warm Springs district, between lat 43°35′ and 43°50′ N. and long 114°10′ and 114°30′ W., near Ketchum, is predominantly a silver-lead district; gold is produced as a byproduct.

Though the initial discoveries were made in 1864, the district was not developed until 1880. Production was high from 1880 to 1887, when many of the richer ore bodies were exhausted. Depletion

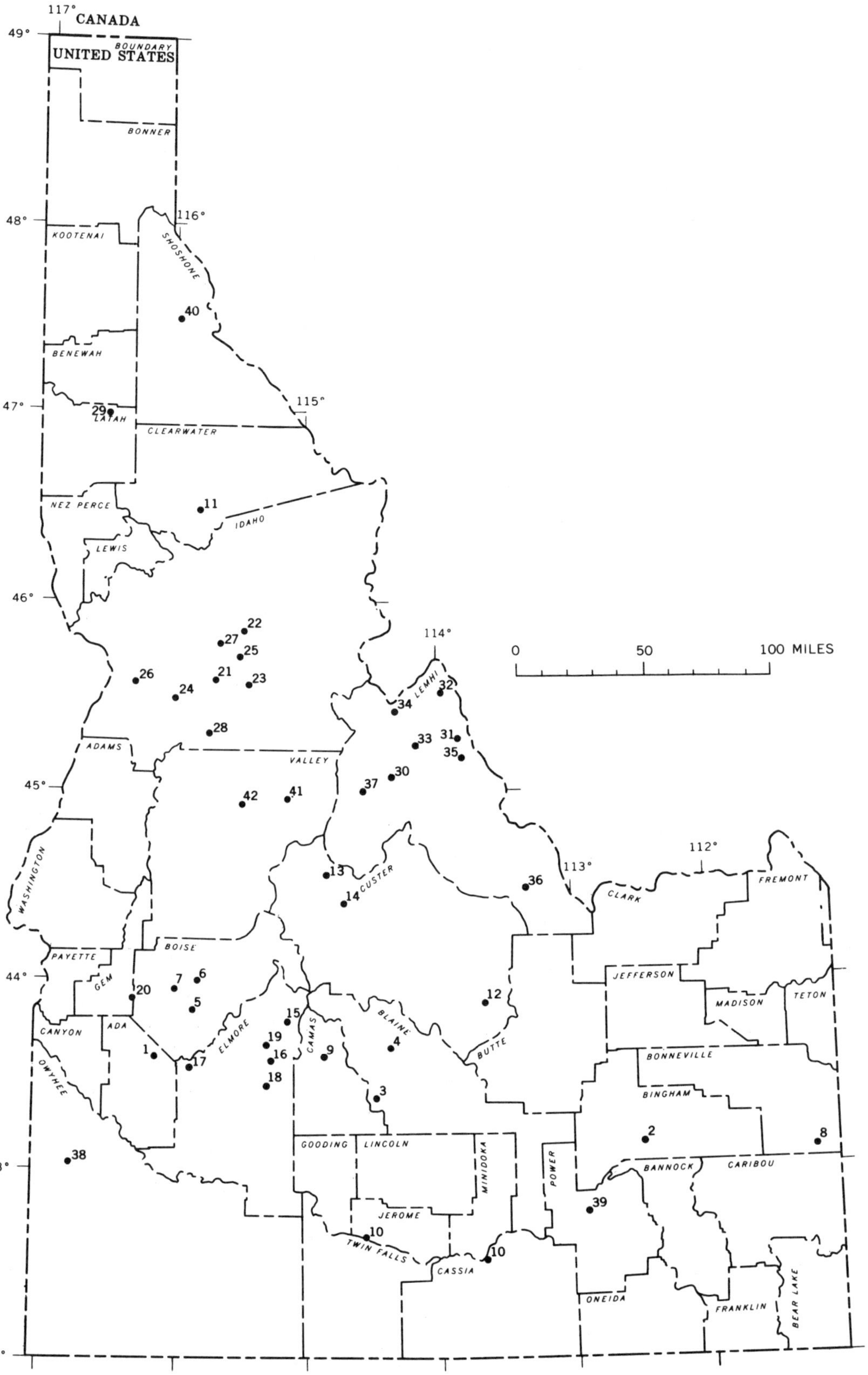

Figure 12.—Gold-mining districts of Idaho.

of ore and a decrease in the price of silver forced closure of many of the mines. Activity in the district gradually decreased through the 1900's, although the Triumph mine, which was reopened in 1927 and which became the largest producer of base-metal ore in the district, continued to be productive until 1957, when the ore bodies were mined out and the mine was abandoned.

Value of gold produced before 1902 is not known, although Ross (1941, p. 15) credited the district with more than $3 million worth of combined metals from 1880 to 1902. From 1902 through 1926, the district produced 6,069 ounces of gold (Umpleby and Ross, in Umpleby and others, 1930, p. 84). From 1932 through 1959, a total of 70,570 ounces was produced; almost all production was from the Triumph mine. Total recorded gold production was 76,639 ounces, a byproduct of the silver-lead ores.

Metasediments composing the Hyndman and East Fork Formations of Algonkian(?) age are the oldest rocks in the district and are exposed in the mountainous areas in the eastern part. Overlying these is a thick series of Paleozoic sedimentary rocks consisting of the Phi Kappa Formation of Ordovician age, the Trail Creek Formation of Silurian age, the Milligen Formation of Devonian(?) and Mississippian age, and the Wood River Formation of Pennsylvanian age (Westgate and Ross, in Umpleby and others, 1930, p. 9–34).

Numerous masses of plutonic rocks ranging in composition from granite through quartz monzonite to granodiorite cut the Paleozoic rocks. Tertiary and Quaternary andesite, basalt, and rhyolite lavas interbedded locally with tuffs cover large parts of the district (Westgate and Ross, in Umpleby and others, 1930, p. 43–61). Pre-Tertiary rocks are complexly folded and faulted, and some of the faults offset Tertiary rocks.

The important ore deposits are in Mississippian and Pennsylvanian sedimentary rocks, according to Umpleby and Ross (in Umpleby and others, 1930, p. 88–112), and are of two general types: lodes in shear zones in sedimentary and granitic rocks, and contact metamorphic deposits in calcareous beds adjacent to intrusive bodies. The shear-zone deposits, from which most of the production came, contain argentiferous galena, sphalerite, tetrahedrite, pyrite, and variable amounts of gold in a gangue of crushed and altered country rock, siderite, and quartz.

The contact metamorphic ore deposits are a skarn of garnet, epidote, diopside, augite, actinolite, and wollastonite through which is disseminated variable amounts of argentiferous galena, sphalerite, chalcopyrite, pyrrhotite, magnetite, and pyrite.

BOISE COUNTY

Placers were discovered in Boise County in 1862 about 25 miles northeast of Boise in Boise Basin, an area of about 300 square miles. The placer operations led to the discoveries of lodes at the heads of streams, and some of these lodes were mined as early as 1863 (Anderson, 1947, p. 176). The lodes were never developed to sustain any extended yield; first one district would be active for a few years, then another. Placers, on the other hand, had a less erratic history and remained highly productive through the 1890's. In the early 1900's they were

Ada County:
1, Black Hornet.
Bingham County:
2, Snake River placers.
Blaine County:
3, Camas; 4, Warm Springs.
Boise County:
5, Boise Basin; 6, Pioneerville; 7, Quartzburg.
Bonneville County:
8, Mount Pisgah.
Camas County:
9, Big and Little Smoky-Rosetta.
Cassia, Jerome, and Minidoka Counties:
10, Snake River placers.
Clearwater County:
11, Pierce.
Custer County:
12, Alder Creek; 13, Loon Creek; 14, Yankee Fork.
Elmore County:
15, Atlanta; 16, Featherville; 17, Neal; 18, Pine Grove; 19, Rocky Bar.
Gem County:
20, Westview.
Idaho County:
21, Buffalo Hump; 22, Elk City; 23, Dixie; 24, French Creek-Florence; 25, Orogrande; 26, Simpson-Camp Howard-Riggins; 27, Tenmile; 28, Warren-Marshall.
Latah County:
29, Hoodoo.
Lemhi County:
30, Blackbird; 31, Carmen Creek-Eldorado-Pratt Creek-Sandy Creek; 32, Gibbonsville; 33, Mackinaw; 34, Mineral Hill and Indian Creek; 35, Kirtley Creek; 36, Texas; 37, Yellow Jacket.
Owyhee County:
38, Silver City.
Power County:
39, Snake River placers.
Shoshone County:
40, Coeur d'Alene region.
Valley County:
41, Thunder Mountain; 42, Yellow Pine.

FIGURE 12.—Continued.

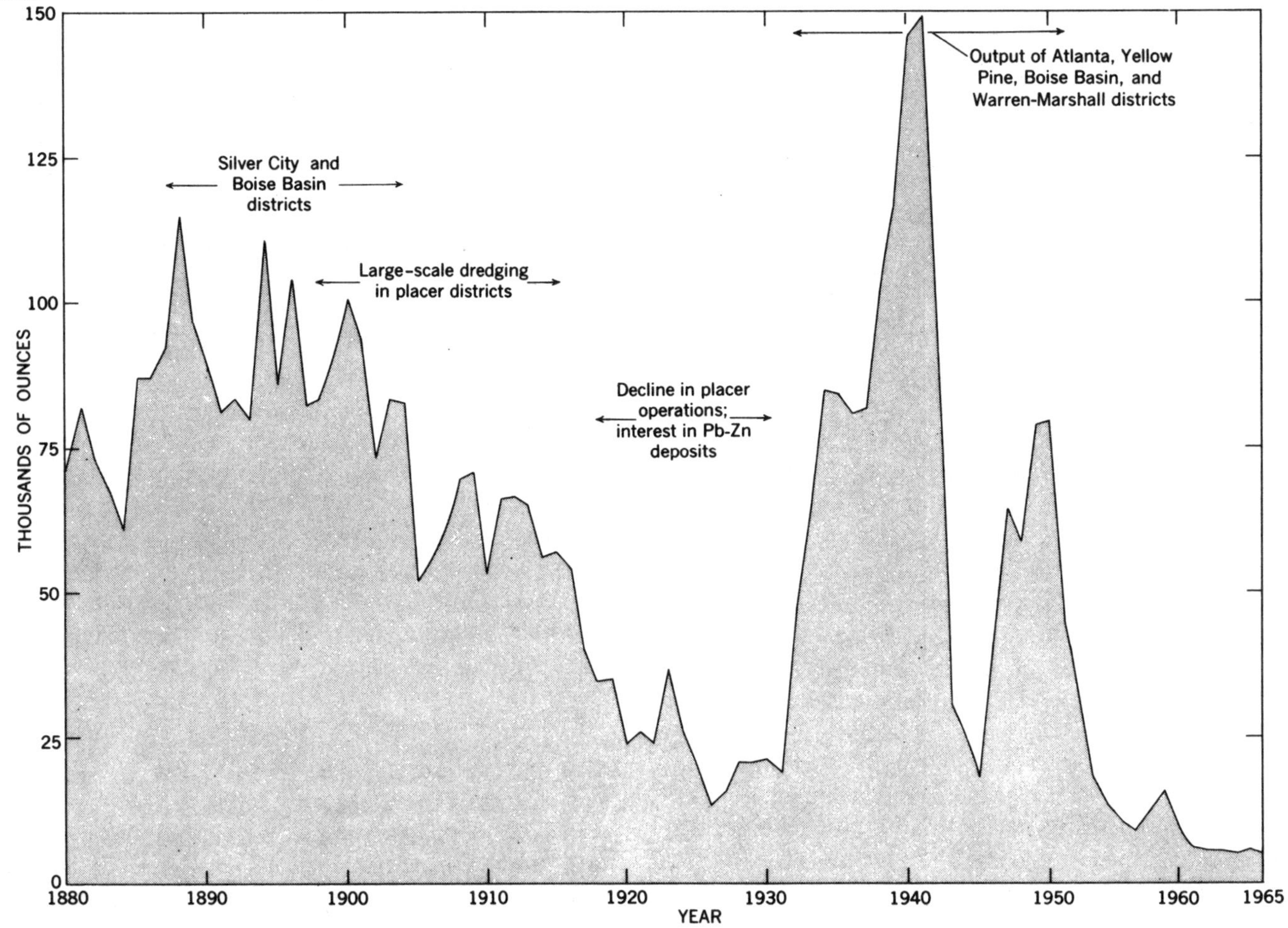

FIGURE 13.—Annual gold production of Idaho, 1880–1965. Sources of data: 1880–1923 from U.S. Geological Survey (1883–1924); 1924–65 from U.S. Bureau of Mines (1925–34; 1933–66). Production reported in dollar value was converted to ounces at prevailing price per ounce.

worked by dredges, and some time later, by large-scale hydraulicking (Ballard, 1924, p. 31–32).

The Boise Basin is divided into many mining districts. In this report that part of the basin that includes the Idaho City, Moore Creek, Gambrinus, and Centerville camps is referred to as the Boise Basin district. The Pioneerville (Summit Flat, Grimes Pass) and Quartzburg (Gold Hill, Granite, Placerville) districts are considered separately.

In general, bedrock in the mineralized parts of Boise County consists of quartz dioritic and quartz monzonitic facies of the Idaho batholith, which are cut by groups of porphyry dikes of Tertiary age. Certain areas are covered by Tertiary lake beds, by basalt lavas of the Columbia River Basalt of Miocene age, or by Quaternary alluvial deposits (Anderson, 1947, p. 129).

Recorded production in the county began in 1863 (Jones, 1917, p. 86). Total gold production for the county from 1863 through 1959 was 2,891,530 ounces, about 95 percent of which came from the Boise Basin.

BOISE BASIN DISTRICT

The Boise Basin (Idaho City, Moore Creek, Gambrinus, Centerville) district is in the central and southern part of the Boise Basin.

All the districts in the Boise Basin have a common history related to the original placer discoveries in 1862 and subsequent development of both placer and lode gold mines. The first placer discoveries in Boise County were made in this area in 1862. Most of the county's gold production came from the rich placers during the first few years of mining. Estimated production from 1863 to 1896 from the Idaho City camp was valued at $44,651,-800 (2,167,500 ounces) (Lindgren, 1898, p. 655). The district produced 129,038 ounces from 1939 through 1958; its total production was about 2,300,000 ounces, mostly from placers.

Lode mines in the Gambrinus area were active from time to time. Two of the most productive were the Illinois and Gambrinus with outputs valued at $225,000 and $263,000 respectively (Lindgren, 1898, p. 685–686).

Most of the Boise Basin is underlain by a quartz monzonite facies of the Idaho batholith of middle Cretaceous age (Anderson, 1947, p. 130–132). In the Gambrinus area, many thin aplite dikes, dikes and stocks of diorite and granodiorite, and several lamprophyre dikes, all of early Tertiary age, cut the quartz monzonite. Near Idaho City and Centerville, patches of lake beds are interstratified with basalt lava and volcanic ash. This sequence is considered lower Miocene (Anderson, 1947, p. 153). Alluvial deposits of two ages, Pleistocene and Recent, cover much of the district. The younger deposits are more restricted to the present stream valleys, whereas the older deposits cover low ridges and form terraces over a considerably wider area. The younger gravels were the source of most of the placer gold (Anderson, 1947, p. 156–159).

The lode deposits, which are mainly in the Centerville and Gambrinus area, are of early Tertiary (?) age. They consist of fissure fillings in fracture zones in the quartz monzonite. The fissures were formed by reverse faults, in contrast with the fissures formed by horizontal movement, which characterize the lodes of Miocene age in the Pioneerville and Quartzburg districts (Anderson, 1947, p. 181).

The vein mineralogy is simple, consisting of quartz and small amounts of pyrite, arsenopyrite, sphalerite, tetrahedrite, chalcopyrite, galena, and stibnite. Gold occurs with quartz or with the sulfides (Anderson, 1947, p. 183).

PIONEERVILLE DISTRICT

The Pioneerville (Summit Flat, Grimes Pass) district is at about lat 44°00′ N. and long 115°50′ W., near the settlements of Grimes Pass and Pioneerville, in the northern part of the Boise Basin. This has been predominantly a lode-mining district; its mining history is closely associated with that of Boise Basin. The district was most active before 1920. The Golden Age mine produced ore worth $200,000 between 1895 and 1920, and the Mammoth mine, $472,000 in the early days (Ballard, 1924, p. 75–76, 95). Most of this was in gold, although it included considerable silver and some lead. Only 3,340 ounces of gold was produced from 1939 through 1959. Total production for the district from 1895 through 1959 was about 25,000 ounces.

The Pioneerville district is at the north end of the "porphyry belt" discussed by Ross (1933a, p. 330–333) and Anderson (1947, p. 191). The country rock is quartz monzonite of the Idaho batholith which is cut by a zone of northeast-trending dikes of dacite porphyry, rhyolite, granophyre, granite porphyry, and diabase. These were intruded along preexisting shear zones in the quartz monzonite. The ore deposits are closely associated with the porphyry dikes and were emplaced in fissures that resulted from later movements along the old shears. The principal metallic minerals of the veins are pyrite, tetrahedrite, chalcopyrite, arsenopyrite, galena, and sphalerite. These occur in a gangue of sericitized dike rock and quartz monzonite, quartz lenses, and some calcite. Native gold occurs most abundantly in quartz or in or near the bismuth minerals galenobismutite, bismuthinite, and tetradymite. Some deposits, characterized by abundant miargyrite and pyrargyrite, are mined for silver alone. Electrum, containing about equal amounts of silver and gold by weight, is the chief ore mineral at the Comeback mine (Anderson, 1947, p. 195–203).

QUARTZBURG DISTRICT

The Quartzburg (Gold Hill, Granite, and Placerville) district is in T. 7 N., R. 4 E., near the town of Quartzburg.

Soon after the initial placer mining rush to the Boise Basin, lode mining began in the Quartzburg district. The Gold Hill mine, discovered in 1863, was worked almost continuously until 1938 (Anderson, 1947, p. 176). Other important producers were the Mountain Chief and Belshazzar mines.

Ross (1941, p. 20) mentioned a total of $8 million (about 400,000 ounces) in gold from this district; however, the district was virtually idle from 1940 through 1959. Production since 1932 must have been combined with production reported from other districts because this district does not appear in the annual volumes of "Minerals Yearbook."

The Quartzburg district is at the southwest end of the "porphyry belt" that crosses the northern part of Boise Basin. The country rock is quartz monzonite of the Idaho batholith which was cut by northeast-trending shear zones, which in turn were intruded by porphyry dikes during Miocene time (Anderson, 1947, p. 129–150; Jones, 1917, p. 89–97; Ross, 1933a, p. 330–331). The gold lodes are fissure veins and small stockworks in or along the dikes and in adjacent quartz monzonite. The deposits are extensively oxidized, and most of the early production came from this easily treated ore which had high gold content. The hypogene minerals are pyrite, galenobismutite, arsenopyrite, native gold, sphalerite, tetradymite, pyrrhotite, stibnite, chalcopyrite, and either tetrahedrite or tennantite. Gangue consists primarily of altered host rock and quartz (Ross, 1933a, p. 339–341).

BONNEVILLE COUNTY

MOUNT PISGAH DISTRICT

The total recorded gold production of Bonneville County, about 16,600 ounces, was from the Mount Pisgah district, in T. 4 S., R. 44 E., in the Caribou Mountains.

Both placer and lode mines were productive, but all the recorded production was from placers, which in the 1870's yielded $250,000 in gold annually (Mansfield, 1927, p. 348). In later years mining in the district declined, although some time after 1920 several unsuccessful attempts were made at dredging. From 1939 through 1959 only 459 ounces of gold was produced.

The geology of the district was outlined briefly by Ross (1941, p. 26), who stated that most of the country rock consists of Mesozoic sedimentary rocks cut by dioritic dikes and sills. The deposits were described as large tabular masses of quartz that were shattered and then mineralized with calcite and auriferous pyrite. In most of the deposits, the pyrite is oxidized and the gold is free.

CAMAS COUNTY

The only gold-producing district in the area now included in Camas County—the Big and Little Smoky-Rosetta district—was most active before Camas County was formed, and its production was credited largely to Blaine County, which was originally known as Alturas County, a large area covering many of the present counties.

The Big and Little Smoky-Rosetta district covers about 150 square miles near Carrietown in eastern Camas County. Ores rich in silver, lead, and zinc were discovered in this district in the early 1880's. For about 10 years mining flourished, then it declined rapidly, and by 1900 most of the properties were abandoned (Ross, 1930a, p. 19).

From 1917 through 1942 gold production in the district was 8,249 ounces (Staley, 1946, p. 16). The total gold production is not known, but the gross value of the ores, estimated at $1,200,000 by Ross (1930a, p. 19), indicates that possibly as much as 10,000 ounces of gold was recovered as a byproduct.

The district is underlain mostly by granitic rock of the Idaho batholith and sedimentary rock of the Wood River Formation of Pennsylvanian age. The ore deposits are in impure quartzite and limestone in the Wood River Formation. Dikes of granophyre and porphyry cut both the granite and sedimentary rocks. Large areas in the southern part of the district are covered by the Challis Volcanics of Tertiary age (Ross, 1930a, p. 23).

Most of the ore deposits are replacement bodies in shear zones in the sedimentary rocks near the contacts with the granitic rock. A few are in the granitic rock. The dominant ore minerals are galena, sphalerite, pyrite, and tetrahedrite in a gangue of quartz, siderite, and altered country rock (Ross, 1930a, p. 23).

CASSIA, JEROME, AND MINIDOKA COUNTIES

At several localities along the Snake River in Cassia, Jerome, and Minidoka Counties (fig. 12), placer deposits were productive in earlier years. The gold production of the counties is extremely difficult to ascertain because of the haphazard nature of early reporting and also because of the creation of new counties from old ones. For example, Cassia and Jerome Counties were formed from part of Lincoln County, so that a certain amount of Lincoln County's early gold production must be credited to the placer districts in the newly formed counties. At any rate, Staley (1946, p. 30) credited about 22,000 ounces of gold to Snake River placers of Cassia County, 1,736 ounces to Jerome County, and 133 ounces to Minidoka County.

CLEARWATER COUNTY

PIERCE DISTRICT

Clearwater County, which was formed in 1911 from parts of Nez Perce, Shoshone, and Idaho Counties, had a total gold production through 1942 of about 29,136 ounces (Staley, 1946, p. 18); from 1943 through 1959, it produced 1,001 ounces. Most of the gold credited to Clearwater County came from the Pierce district in Tps. 36 and 37 N., Rs. 4 and 5 E. However, most of the gold mining in this district occurred before Clearwater County was in existence; hence, the early production is included with other counties.

In the fall of 1860, E. D. Pierce led a party of 12 miners into the upper Clearwater River region, a territory then guarded by the Nez Perce Indians. Within a short time, substantial amounts of gold were found in the gravels of Orofino Creek, a tributary of the Clearwater River. Before the end of the year, the town of Pierce was founded, and enough gold was mined to attract a horde of prospectors despite forceful Indian objections (S. M. Barton,

M. W. Wells, and E. Oberbillig, written commun., 1958). The placers of this district were the first in Idaho to be worked on a large scale, and their development accelerated interest in gold prospecting throughout the State.

Unlike many other districts that collapsed completely after the initial boom, the Pierce district continued to be active, though after 1875 the pace was slower. Ross (1941, p. 37) estimated a total production of between $5 and $10 million in gold before 1875. Lindgren (1904, p. 102) reported the production before 1902 in this manner: "A guess may be hazarded that the total output of Pierce is in the vicinity of $5 million." According to S. M. Barton, M. W. Wells, and E. Oberbillig (written commun., 1958), the most productive period was between 1861 and 1867, when gold with an estimated value of $3,400,00 was produced. A noticeable decline in production began in 1866 because lower grade deposits were being mined by Chinese labor employed at low wages. In later years the district was rejuvenated periodically by large-scale dredging operations. Some time before 1905 lode mines were developed and yielded about $250,000 in gold. The most important of these was the Wild Rose mine (Thomson and Ballard, 1924, p. 114). The placers were worked on a moderate scale through the 1930's, but after 1941 they produced only a negligible amount. Total production of the district through 1959 was about 385,000 ounces.

The Pierce district is underlain by granitic rocks of the Idaho batholith, Precambrian metasedimentary rocks of the Belt Series, and Columbia River Basalt (Ross, 1941, p. 37). The lode deposits are discontinuous fissure fillings of quartz, auriferous pyrite, free gold, and some arsenopyrite. They are distributed in or near gneissic bodies and are closely associated with pegmatite, aplite, and diabase dikes.

The placers are in stream channels and on terraces as much as 500 feet above present streams. Terrace deposits possibly were formed along stream channels dammed by the Columbia River Basalt (Ross, 1941, p. 37) and were left in their present perched positions by subsequent erosion of later diverted drainage systems. Perched or bench placer deposits are characteristic of much of the area in central Idaho.

CUSTER COUNTY

The major gold-producing districts of Custer County are in its western part.

From 1881 through 1942, the county produced 252,879 ounces of gold (Staley, 1946, p. 18); total production through 1959 was 329,586 ounces. The Yankee Fork district was the most productive, although the Loon Creek district also produced considerable gold. Small amounts of gold were produced as a byproduct of the copper ores of the Alder Creek district and the lead, zinc, and copper mines in the Bayhorse district. Placers were worked at several localities along the Yankee Fork of the Salmon River.

ALDER CREEK DISTRICT

The Alder Creek district is in southeastern Custer County near Mackay and includes Tps. 6 and 7 N., Rs. 23 and 24 E.

Ores rich in copper were discovered in this district in 1884, after the rich lead-silver discoveries at Nicholia to the northeast at the site of the district's chief mine, the Empire (Ross, 1930a, p. 7). After many failures to produce copper and after the expenditure of about $3 million, success was finally achieved in 1905 (Umpleby, 1917, p. 93), and the mine remained active through 1929. Sporadic production was also reported from 1940 through 1951. Mining resumed in 1957 and was continuing in 1959.

From 1884 to 1913 the Empire produced about $100,000 (about 5,000 ounces) in byproduct gold (Umpleby, 1917, p. 94). The Empire and Horseshoe mines produced 24,710 ounces from 1912 through 1928 (Ross, 1930a, p. 8–9), and the district produced 3,770 ounces from 1939 through 1959. Total gold production for the district through 1959 was about 33,500 ounces.

The district is underlain by folded Paleozoic sedimentary rocks, intrusive granitic and monzonitic rocks, and volcanic rocks of the Challis Volcanics. The Paleozoic rocks are mostly thick-bedded dolomitic limestone containing Mississippian fossils (Ross, 1930a, p. 13). In the Empire mine area the limestone is intruded by a large mass of granitic rocks and by a swarm of porphyritic dikes that follow a broad zone of regional faulting.

Ore deposits in the district are largely of the contact-metamorphic type and are along the limestone-granite contact. Some ore bodies of the Empire deposit are in large blocks of limestone isolated well within the granite (Umpleby, 1917, p. 97). The primary ores contain intergrowths of garnet and chalcopyrite and subordinate amounts of pyroxene, pyrite, and pyrrhotite. Oxidized ores, which were highly productive, contain a mixture of chrysocolla, azurite, malachite, and cuprite. Secondary copper sulfides are rare (Umpleby, 1917, p. 98–99).

LOON CREEK DISTRICT

The Loon Creek district is between lat 44°32′ and 44°38′ N. and long 114°45′ and 114°52′ W., in the Loon Creek drainage area.

The first mineral discoveries in this area were in 1869 when gold placers were found along Loon Creek near the abandoned town of Casto (Ross, 1934, p. 117). During the next 10 years the placers were worked out, having yielded between $1½ and $2 million in gold.

Lode mining became significant in the district about 1902 when the Lost Packer gold-copper prospect was developed. Despite transportation difficulties, the mine remained operative through 1917, but was mostly inactive after that time. Ross (1934, p. 118) reported a production of $600,000 worth of ore for this mine, but he did not mention the amount of gold.

Considering the more conservative estimates of early placer production and assuming that at least half of the lode output of the Lost Packer mine was in gold, the total production of the district through 1959 was about 40,000 ounces. This, however, is a conservative estimate, and the production may have been several times that amount.

The geology in the vicinity of the Lost Packer mine was described by Ross (1934, p. 120, pl. 8). The ore body is in contorted Precambrian schist that was intruded by dikes and irregular bodies of aplite, lamprophyre, dacite porphyry, granophyre, and quartz monzonite. Elsewhere in the district, large areas are covered by flows and tuffs of the Casto Volcanics of Permian(?) age and the Challis Volcanics of Oligocene(?) age.

Chalcopyrite is the principal ore mineral in the lodes, which occupy steplike fissures in the schist. Also present are small amounts of tetrahedrite, pyrite, and pyrrhotite, and near the surface is bornite, native copper, and oxidized iron and copper minerals (Ross, 1934, p. 121–123). Gold is associated with the chalcopyrite and in some veins, with quartz.

YANKEE FORK DISTRICT

The Yankee Fork district is between lat 44°20′ and 44°30′ N. and long 114°40′ and 114°50′ W., in northwestern Custer County.

Gold was discovered in the gravels of Jordan Creek in the mid-1870's, but these yielded only about $50,000 in gold (Umpleby, 1913a, p. 89). Ores from silver-gold lode deposits, the first of which was discovered in 1875, proved to be extremely rich. The General Custer mine alone produced $8 million before 1900 (Anderson, 1949, p. 14). However, these high-grade deposits proved to be shallow, and the district began to decline in the 1890's, and its mill closed in 1905. There were sporadic attempts to revive some properties, but no significant activity occurred until the reopening of the Lucky Boy mine in 1939. Placer mining along the Yankee Fork was also renewed about that time. World War II curtailed activities, but a few properties were reopened in 1946 and 1947. Production in the late 1940's was almost entirely by a dredge that operated along the Yankee Fork, although some small-scale production from lode deposits continued through 1957 (T. H. Kiilsgaard, written commun., 1962). The most productive placers in the district were along the Yankee Fork of the Salmon River, from the mouth of Jordan Creek almost to the mouth of the Yankee Fork.

Anderson (1949, p. 14) credited the district with a total production of gold and silver valued at $13 million to about 1948. Of this, $12 million was mined before 1910. Umpleby (1913a, p. 78) estimated that about 40 percent of this was in gold (about 252,400 ounces). From 1948 through 1959 the district produced 14,253 ounces; most of it was from dredging operations. Total gold production through 1959 was about 266,600 ounces.

Bedrock in the Yankee Fork district, according to Anderson (1949, p. 8–11), consists of contorted Paleozoic and Mesozoic sedimentary and volcanic rocks that are intruded by quartz monzonite and granodiorite of Mesozoic age. The Paleozoic rocks are the Wood River Formation of Pennsylvanian age and the Casto Volcanics of Permian(?) age. These are cut in the northwest part of the district by quartz monzonite of the Idaho batholith. The Paleozoic rocks were subjected to two periods of deformation—one at the close of the Jurassic and one at the close of the Cretaceous. During Oligocene time the Challis volcanic flows covered most of the older rocks, and these were intruded in Miocene time by relatively small masses of dacite and rhyolite porphyry (Anderson, 1949, p. 8–10). The Challis Volcanics were gently warped and fractured, and these fractures were filled by epithermal silver-gold deposits. Most of the lodes are simple fissure fillings, but where the rock was complexly fractured, the ore minerals are disseminated and the deposits resemble stockworks (Anderson, 1949, p. 15). Typical veinfilling is quartz which may be fine grained, coarse comb, or drusy. Veins characteristically contain pyrite, chalcopyrite, sphalerite, tetrahedrite, arsenopyrite, enargite, galena, stephanite, miargyrite, pyrargyrite, argentite, aguilarite, gold, and electrum; some calcite may be present. In the weathered zones, native silver, argentite, cerargyrite, azurite, malachite, chalcocite, and covellite are present in variable amounts (Anderson, 1949, p. 16–17).

ELMORE COUNTY

Most of the gold-producing districts in Elmore County are clustered in its northeastern part, in an area underlain by granitic rocks of the Idaho batholith. Shear zones that trend nearly east contain lode deposits of gold and silver, which have yielded most of the gold produced in Elmore County, although placers were important in the Featherville and Rocky Bar districts, especially before 1900.

Gold lodes were discovered in 1862 in the Rocky Bar district and soon afterward at Atlanta. The 1870's and 1880's were years of intense lode-mining activity, but by the early 1900's many of the mines closed. Gold mining in Elmore County, with the exception of that in the Atlanta district, continued to decline, although by 1956 the Atlanta district also ceased significant production. Gold production for the county from 1889 through 1942 was 381,396 ounces (Staley, 1946, p. 19) and from 1943 through 1959 it was 60,300 ounces. A total of 441,696 ounces was produced through 1959.

ATLANTA DISTRICT

The Atlanta (Hardscrabble, Middle Boise, Yuba) district is in T. 5 N., Rs. 11 and 12 E., in rugged, mountainous country 65 to 70 miles east of Boise.

Gold was first discovered in the district in 1864, in veins on Atlanta Hill, but extreme inaccessibility of the area hindered its development for almost 10 years (Ballard, 1928, p. 7–8). The greatest activity was in the 1870's and 1880's. Ballard (1928, p. 10) reported that the Monarch Mining Co. shipped ore valued at $700,000 in the period 1876–78. Mining declined after the 1880's but was rejuvenated in 1929 (Ross, 1941, p. 51) and increased steadily until 1956.

The total gold production of the Atlanta district is difficult to ascertain because figures for both gold and silver were combined in the early reporting. According to Ross (1941, p. 51), total metal production to 1936 was valued at $6 million, but the amount of this in gold was not stated. From 1932 through 1959 the district produced 243,175 ounces of gold. If at least half of the early production worth $6 million was in gold, most of which was from lode deposits, total district gold production may have been 385,000 ounces. Placers were worked in the district, but their yield was not great (Ballard, 1928, p. 9).

The country rock in the district is granite of the Idaho batholith which was fractured and intruded by aplite and porphyry dikes. These fractures and dikes are arranged in a zone about 1½ miles wide that trends northeastward. The ore deposits are in veins filling the fissures (Ballard, 1928, p. 13–18). The chief vein is the Atlanta on which most of the workings of the district are located. Stephanite and pyrargyrite are silver minerals characteristic of the ores that were mined in the early days. Ore mined more recently contains auriferous pyrite (Ross, 1941, p. 51).

FEATHERVILLE DISTRICT

The Featherville district is in T. 3 N., R. 10 E., along the South Fork of the Boise River.

This placer district has only a partial production record. From 1922 to 1927, dredging operations produced a total of 32,777 ounces of gold (Ross, 1941, p. 48). No additional production data were noted except for 1951 when 33 ounces was reported.

NEAL DISTRICT

The Neal district is in Tps. 2 and 3 N., R. 5 E., about 15 miles southeast of Boise, near the Arrowrock Dam.

This district, discovered in 1889, was noted chiefly for its lode mines, but small amounts of gold were also produced from intermittently worked placers. Since 1911 the district has been virtually inactive.

Estimates of the early production vary widely. Lindgren (1898, p. 699) noted that about $200,000 worth of gold was produced from the district between 1889 and 1896. Ross (1941, p. 49) later estimated that $2 million in gold was produced, but much of this could have been produced from 1906 to 1911, when the district was fairly active.

The predominant country rock is granodiorite of the Idaho batholith. It is cut by numerous dikes of porphyry and lamprophyre, and the veins seem to be closely associated with the lamprophyre dikes. Vein minerals consist of quartz, pyrite, gold, galena, sphalerite, arsenopyrite, and local garnet, in altered granitic rock (Ross, 1941, p. 49).

PINE GROVE DISTRICT

In the Pine Grove district, which is in Tps. 1 and 2 N., Rs. 9 and 10 E. near the town of Pine, gold and silver have been produced from lode mines and on a small scale from placers.

The principal mine was the Franklin, which produced $750,000 in gold and silver before it was closed in 1917 (Ross, 1941, p. 49). No other details on history or production are available.

The country rock in the Pine Grove district is granite, presumably of the Idaho batholith (Ballard, 1928, p. 18–19). This is cut by numerous northeast-trending dikes of diorite, rhyolite, and diabase. The veins occupy a zone 1¼ miles wide that trends north-northwest. The upper parts of the veins are oxidized and contain free gold and iron and manganese oxides. Primary ore contains pyrite, galena, sphalerite, and some arsenopyrite and chalcopyrite in a gangue of quartz.

ROCKY BAR DISTRICT

The Rocky Bar district is in T. 4 N., R. 10 E., near the town of Rocky Bar. Placers discovered in 1862 on Bear Creek produced from 1863 until about 1873 (Ballard, 1928, p. 22). The gold in the placers was traced to lode deposits which were quickly developed; the principal mines were the Elmore and Pittsburg. According to Ross (1941, p. 47), the quartz mines of the district produced about $2 million in gold and silver and the placers, about $2 million in gold to 1882. Ballard (1928, p. 25) estimated a total production of ore worth from $3¼ to $3¾ million, presumably in gold, from the Elmore and Pittsburg mines alone. About 1900 the district became inactive and remained so except for small operations in 1938 and 1939, which yielded no gold.

Granitic rock, part of the Idaho batholith, forms the bedrock here, as in most of the other gold districts of Elmore County. Numerous aplite, rhyolite, diorite porphyry, and mafic dikes, all trending east-northeast, cut the granite (Ballard, 1928, p. 22). The major veins strike eastward and consist of quartz gangue and auriferous pyrite. Small amounts of galena and sphalerite are in some veins.

GEM COUNTY

WESTVIEW DISTRICT

The gold production of Gem County is virtually equivalent to that of the Westview (Pearl-Horseshoe Bend) district, which sprawls across the Boise-Gem County line, about 18 miles north-northwest of the city of Boise.

Gold was mined chiefly from lodes in the Westview district. According to Anderson (1934, p. 17–18), the first development of note was at the Red Warrior in 1870, although greatest activity occurred between 1900 and 1907. Thereafter, interest waned as the easily milled oxidized ores were depleted. Lindgren (1898, p. 708) estimated that the district produced $80,000 in gold (about 4,000 ounces) to 1896, but Anderson (1934, p. 18) listed an estimate (by R. N. Bell) of ores worth more than $1 million. Including Lindgren's estimate for the early production, the minimum total gold production for this district was about 20,000 ounces.

Country rock in the Westview district consists of a batholithic mass of quartz diorite and granodiorite (Anderson, 1934, p. 5–12). An elongate mass of diorite cuts the granodiorite and a large number of porphyry dikes cut both the granodiorite and diorite. These dikes, which are in a belt that trends east-northeast, are composed of dacite porphyry, granite porphyry, syenite porphyry, and rhyolite porphyry; some are moderately mafic in composition. The ore deposits are mineralized fissures in the dike zone, and they may be in granodiorite, diorite, or in or along the dike contacts (Anderson, 1934, p. 18). The deposits are stringers of arsenopyrite and pyrite and contain subordinate sphalerite and galena and small amounts of chalcopyrite, tetrahedrite, boulangerite, and stibnite. Small amounts of quartz, dolomite, and calcite gangue accompany the ore minerals, but the chief gangue component is broken and altered wallrock. Gold accompanies the sulfides and is extremely fine grained (Anderson, 1934, p. 19).

IDAHO COUNTY

Many districts throughout Idaho County—such as Buffalo Hump, Dixie, Elk City, Orogrande, Simpson, Tenmile, and Warren-Marshall—have made the county the second largest producer of gold in the State.

The first gold discoveries in this general area were made in 1857 along Orofino Creek, in what is now Clearwater County, by Jean deLassier, a trapper. Later, E. D. Pierce made the well-known discoveries at Pierce, and a rush to the region followed. By 1861 a group from the Orofino area explored the unknown country to the south and found placer gold along the South Fork of the Clearwater River at Elk City, in what is now Idaho County. In a few months more than 2,000 people rushed to the new area. Other discoveries were made in 1861 at Florence by another group from Orofino, and at almost the same time placers were found at Newsome, Dixie, and along the Salmon River. By 1872 the richest placers were depleted, and the Chinese took over most of the workings. After 1900, low-grade placers were worked at several localities, but it was not until the 1930's that a real revival of the placers was made possible by higher prices, development of new mining equipment, and improved transportation facilities (Lorain and Metzger, 1938, p. 6–8, Thomson and Ballard, 1924, p. 13–14).

Gold-bearing veins were worked as early as 1866

in the Warren district (Ross, 1941, p. 62), but the important lode mines at Elk City, Dixie, and Buffalo Hump were developed in the 1880's and 1890's. After a few years of intense activity, lode mining declined in Idaho County and reached a low in 1920 (Lorain, 1938, p. 7). Activity increased in the 1930's because of higher prices and improved transportation, but a general decline in both lode and placer activity was again dominant from 1950 through 1959.

Total gold production before 1904 was estimated at from \$35 to \$55 million by Lindgren (1900, p. 233, 238; 1904, p. 84) and at \$47 million by Thomson and Ballard (1924, p. 13). Production from 1905 through 1936 was 101,354 ounces of placer and 122,008 ounces of lode gold (Lorain and Metzger, 1938, p. 9). From 1905 through 1959 a total of 455,554 ounces of gold was produced in Idaho County. Staley (1946, p. 20, 21) presented yearly production data from 1862 through 1942 that totaled 2,176,550 ounces.

In general the oldest rocks in Idaho County are gneisses, schists, quartzites, and limestones of the Belt Series of Precambrian age (Shenon and Reed, 1934, p. 10). These were intruded by the Idaho batholith, a granodiorite and quartz monzonite body that underlies much of central Idaho and most of Idaho County. Unconformably overlying these rocks at low altitudes are remnants of the Columbia River Basalt, basaltic lavas which were poured out on a mature erosion surface during Tertiary time. Gold-bearing fissure veins occur in both the metasedimentary rocks of the Belt Series and in the granitic rocks of the Idaho batholith near intrusive contacts (Shenon and Reed, 1934, p. 24).

BUFFALO HUMP DISTRICT

The Buffalo Hump district is between lat 45°30′ and 45°40′ N. and long 115°35′ and 115°45′ W., in the west-central part of Idaho County.

Gold was discovered in this remote district in 1898 at the Big Buffalo property which developed into its chief producer. The rush to this new area was more frantic than to most areas and the lawlessness and excesses, for which it became known, were perhaps intensified by its remoteness and primitiveness. Several towns were built, and despite almost impassable roads, machinery was brought in and mining flourished (Thomson and Ballard, 1924, p. 98, 103). But metallurgical problems, high costs, relatively small deposits, and transportation problems were obstacles too large to overcome, and the boom collapsed after a few years. Except for small-scale operations, the mines have been idle for many years.

According to Shenon and Reed (1934, p. 4) and Ross (1941, p. 52), the Buffalo Hump district produced ore valued at about \$700,000, most of which was in gold, with undetermined amounts of silver and copper. From 1939 through 1941 the district produced 2,307 ounces of gold, but no activity has been reported since that time. Total gold production through 1959 was about 27,000 ounces.

The bedrock in the district consists of quartzite and schist of the Belt Series and quartz monzonite of the Idaho batholith. The metasedimentary rocks were folded into a northwest-trending overturned anticline and then invaded by the quartz monzonite. The veins, about 20 in all, occupy an area 5 miles long and ½ to 1¾ miles wide in a shear zone along the crest of the anticline (Shenon and Reed, 1934, p. 26). Individual veins usually are less than half a mile long and terminate by horsetailing and splitting into thin stringers. Pyrite, tetrahedrite, sphalerite, chalcpoyrite, galena, and native gold are the common ore minerals of the veins. Small amounts of arsenopyrite, stibnite, molybdenite, and tellurides may be present, and quartz is the dominant gangue mineral (Shenon and Reed, 1934, p. 27).

DIXIE DISTRICT

In the Dixie district, which is in Tps. 25 and 26 N., R. 8 E., about 20 miles south of Elk City, gold placers were discovered in 1861 and were extensively and successfully mined during the early years. Lode deposits were developed in 1891 (Thomson and Ballard, 1924, p. 73), but their exploitation was hampered by the remoteness of the area. There has been very little activity in the district in recent years.

Production data for this district are incomplete. Lorain and Metzger (1938, p. 50) noted that \$270,500 (13,000 ounces) worth of placer gold was shipped from the district from 1861 to 1863 and that the total production of the placers was probably less than \$1 million (48,500 ounces). Thomson and Ballard (1924, p. 13), however, estimated \$1½ million (72,800 ounces) in gold as the production of the district. Lode mines, according to Ross (1941, p. 55), produced gold worth about \$50,000 (2,400 ounces). Total production for the district through 1959 was approximately 40,000 to 75,000 ounces.

The geology of the Dixie district is similar to that of the Elk City district. Quartz monzonite or granodiorite of the Idaho batholith is the dominant rock. Numerous inclusions of the older country rock—schist, gneiss, and quartzite—are incorporated in the igneous intrusion and are exposed locally (Thomson and Ballard, 1924, p. 73). The ore deposits are in quartz veins containing pyrite and gold.

ELK CITY DISTRICT

The Elk City district is in parts of Tps. 29 and 30 N., R. 8 E., near Elk City.

The first gold discovery in Idaho County was at Elk City in 1861. Here rich placers attracted 2,000 people the first year, but by 1872 the best ground was worked out, and the Chinese took over the operations. In 1870 gold-quartz veins were found at the Buster property, but very little gold was mined until 1902. The Buster mine became the largest lode producer in the district and produced about $300,000 in gold between 1907 and 1909 (Lorain, 1938, p. 28). The mines produced fairly steadily from the early 1900's through the 1930's, but since World War II they have been inactive. Placers, on the other hand, were active through 1957.

The early gold production of the district was estimated at $5 to $10 million by Lindgren (1904, p. 84) and at $18½ million by Thomson and Ballard (1924, p. 13). From 1902 to 1939 the lodes produced more than $725,000 in gold (Ross, 1941, p. 55); from 1933 to 1959 lodes and placers produced 75,575 ounces. Total production, including the early estimates, was about 550,000 to 800,000 ounces.

Bedrock in the Elk City district consists of granite gneiss, a kind of gneissic shell formed along the contact of the Idaho batholith with metasedimentary rocks of the Belt Series (Thomson and Ballard, 1924, p. 22–23, 60). Small patches of the quartz monzonite of the batholith are exposed at various localities near Elk City, and Tertiary sediments underlie the valley at Elk City.

The veins are quartz lenses as much as 20 feet thick and 300 feet long. They are arranged in a radial pattern in the gneiss, near the quartz monzonite contact (Shenon and Reed, 1934, p. 24–26), and most of them trend at right angles to the foliation in the gneiss. The ore minerals of the veins are native gold, pyrite, tetrahedrite, sphalerite, chalcopyrite, and galena.

The placers of the district are in so-called high-level gravels of Tertiary age (Reed, 1934, p. 8–16).

FRENCH CREEK-FLORENCE DISTRICT

The French Creek-Florence district is in T. 25 N., Rs. 3 and 4 E., about 42 miles from Grangeville, the nearest supply point.

In the 1860's this area was one of the most productive in the State; the gulches and stream beds swarmed with miners working the rich gravels. The gravels were only 4 to 10 feet thick, and the richer parts soon were exhausted, after which the Chinese took over and reworked the tailings. The total output of the district, most of which was produced in the 1860's, was valued between $15 and $30 million (Lindgren, 1900, p. 233). By the 1880's, production had dropped to between $30,000 and $45,000 worth of gold per year (Lindgren, 1900, p. 233). A few small lode properties were developed in later years but the district has been deserted for a long time except for a brief revival in the late 1930's. Total production through 1959 was about 1 million ounces; nearly all production was from the early placers.

Bedrock in the district consists of soft, decomposed quartz monzonite which is cut by numerous small, but rich, gold-quartz veins (Lorain and Metzger, 1938, p. 47). These veins were the source of the gold in the stream gravels.

OROGRANDE DISTRICT

The Orogrande district is in T. 27 N., R. 7 E., about 12 miles southwest of Elk City.

Lode mines were developed in the late 1890's; however, the largest mines, the Orogrande-Frisco and the Gnome, were not productive until 1902 and 1932 respectively (Shenon and Reed, 1934, p. 52). The Gnome produced 11,582 ounces of gold from 1932 to 1937, when it was closed (Lorain, 1938, p. 44). The district produced small quantities of gold annually through 1957 and through 1959 its total was 32,000 ounces; almost all production was from lodes.

Country rock in the Orogrande district consists of quartz monzonite and granodiorite of the Idaho batholith and schist of the Belt Series (Shenon and Reed, 1934, p. 30, 31, pl. 1). The ore deposits are of two types: gold-pyrite disseminated through a silicified shear zone in the schist, and small veins and stringers of quartz and sulfides in granodiorite and dacite. The dacite intruded the granodiorite and the mineralization is related to the dacite. Ore minerals consist of pyrite, chalcopyrite, galena, tetradymite, molybdenite, native gold, gold telluride, wolframite, and scheelite.

SIMPSON-CAMP HOWARD-RIGGINS DISTRICT

The Simpson-Camp Howard-Riggins placer district, in Tps. 24 to 28 N., R. 1 E., along the Salmon River between Riggins and Freedom, has been intermittently productive since the 1860's. Most of the activity immediately followed the initial discoveries; from 1862 to 1866 an estimated $575,000 in gold was produced (S. M. Barton, M. W. Wells, and E. Oberllig, written commun., 1958). In the 1930's, large-scale but unsuccessful mining methods were introduced (Lorain and Metzger, 1938, p. 80). The district, which was still active in 1959, produced a total of 9,578 ounces of gold from 1903 through 1959.

The placer deposits are in bench and stream gravels. The bench gravels, which have been more productive (Lorain and Metzger, 1938, p. 82–85), occur along the main stream canyon as much as several hundred feet above present stream level. The stream gravels consist of small bars along the present river course.

TENMILE DISTRICT

The Tenmile district is between lat 45°33′ and 45°55′ N. and long 115°31′ and 115°44′ W., immediately north of the Buffalo Hump district and west of the Elk City district.

Both placer and lode deposits were worked in this district, but the placers were more productive. Gold was discovered in 1861 in Newsome basin in the gravels of Newsome Creek. Most of the gravels were soon exhausted, but they yielded approximately $2 million (about 100,000 ounces) in gold (Ross, 1941, p. 61). Lode properties were developed as early as 1888 (Lorain, 1938, p. 30), and they emerged in recent years as the more important sources of gold. The lode mines produced an estimated minimum of 18,400 ounces of gold to about 1932 (Shenon and Reed, 1934, p. 71–82). From 1932 through 1959 the district produced 28,671 ounces. Total estimated gold production was about 147,000 ounces.

Bedrock in the area consists of gneiss and quartzite of the Belt Series and granodiorite and quartz monzonite of the Idaho batholith. The granitic rocks intrude the gneiss. The ore deposits are in quartz veins that fill fractures and faults in gneiss, quartz monzonite, and quartzite. Variable amounts of the sulfides, pyrite, chalcopyrite, arsenopyrite, chalcocite, galena, covellite, and sphalerite occur in the veins, and gold is associated with the sulfides (Shenon and Reed, 1934, p. 71–82).

WARREN-MARSHALL DISTRICT

The Warren-Marshall (Resort) district is in southern Idaho County between Tps. 20 and 24 N., and Rs. 4 and 8 E.

Rich placers were discovered in Warren Meadows in 1862 shortly after the discoveries at Florence; rich lode deposits were found as early as 1866 (Lindgren, 1900, p. 238–239). Before 1900 an estimated $15 million in gold was mined from the district; most of it, from placers. After the initial boom period which lasted through the 1860's, activity continued on a much-reduced scale, especially from 1902 to 1932 (Reed, 1937, p. 25). Bucket dredges were introduced in 1932, and large-scale placer production re-created on a lesser scale the booming days of the 1860's. Production from placers gradually diminished through the 1950's.

Detailed production data for the district from 1902 through 1936 were listed by Reed (1937, p. 25). From 1902 through 1928, the combined output of lodes and placers was 21,581 ounces of gold. From 1929 through 1935, lode mines yielded $37,992 (about 1,765 ounces) and placers $1,593,062 (about 56,640 ounces). From 1936 through 1959 the district produced 98,519 ounces. Total gold production, including Lindgren's estimate of early production, was about 906,500 ounces.

The oldest rocks in the Warren-Marshall district are quartzite, gneiss, and schist of the Belt Series of Precambrian age. These rocks are intruded by quartz monzonite of the Idaho batholith, the predominant bedrock in the district (Reed, 1937, p. 8); over most of the district, the quartz monzonite is deeply weathered. Locally, lamprophyre dikes of middle Miocene age also intrude the older rocks.

The gold lodes are known collectively as the Warren vein system, consisting of quartz veins in a strong set of northeast-trending joints in the quartz monzonite. Mineralization probably occurred in Late Cretaceous time before the intrusion of the lamprophyre dikes. The primary vein minerals are gold, galena, sphalerite, tetrahedrite, stibnite, and pyrite in a gangue composed mainly of quartz and locally abundant calcite and muscovite. Arsenopyrite, ruby silver, chalcopyrite, and scheelite may be found at some localities, and silver is rare (Reed, 1937, p. 35–37).

The most productive placers in the district occur in unconsolidated deposits called younger gravels by Reed (1937, p. 13–15) and in Recent alluvium. These are distinguished from older gravels which are believed to be middle Miocene to Wisconsin in age (Reed, 1937, p. 12). The younger gravels include bench gravels and high meadow deposits; the Recent alluvium consists of broad sand and gravel deposits along present streams. The older gravels have been mined locally but have sustained no large production.

LATAH COUNTY

Early settlers who were attracted to Latah County by visions of mineral wealth soon found that lumbering, cattle raising, and agriculture were far more rewarding. Gold placers that were found in the Hoodoo district in 1860 produced more than 10,000 ounces of gold and were the chief sources of mineral production in the county; gold and copper lodes were also worked on a small scale (Hubbard, 1957, p. 10).

Across the northern part of the county, Precambrian metasedimentary rocks of the Belt Series are exposed in a 6- to 12-mile-wide zone; on the east edge of the county they crop out in another zone 4 to 8 miles wide. The central part of the county is underlain by granodiorite of the Idaho batholith which intrudes the Belt rocks. About one-third of the county is underlain by upper Tertiary Columbia River Basalt and younger lavas interlayered with lacustrine deposits composing the Latah Formation. Auriferous quartz veins with variable amounts of copper sulfides occur in both the granodiorite and the metasedimentary rocks near stocks of the granodiorite or near diorite bodies (Hubbard, 1957, p. 4–5, 9–14).

Though placer gold mining began in 1860, production figures are available only since 1904. Hubbard (1957, p. 7) listed annual production of Latah County from 1904 through 1955 which totaled 17,165 ounces of placer gold and 76 ounces of lode gold. In 1956 the county produced only 4 ounces of gold, and during 1957, none.

HOODOO DISTRICT

The Hoodoo district, about 28 square miles in T. 42 N., Rs. 1 and 2 W., in the Hoodoo Mountains in northeastern Latah County, has been the chief gold producer in the county. Most of the gold came from placers along the Palouse River and Poorman Creek.

Gold was first found in the district in 1860 in Hoodoo Gulch, along the South Fork of the Palouse River (Hubbard, 1957, p. 10). These placers were quickly exhausted, but Chinese reworked the deposits in the 1870's. The district then declined and was dormant until the mid-1930's when a dredge was installed on the North Fork of the river (Hubbard, 1957, p. 10–11). Production was curtailed during World War II. Attempts were made in 1950 to revive the placers, and small quantities of gold were produced for a few years; however, in 1959 the district was again inactive.

LEMHI COUNTY

In 1866, prospectors from the Elk Creek area found gold on Napias Creek in the unexplored north-central part of Lemhi County. The town of Leesburg was soon founded and became a base from which discoveries were made in the northern part of the county at Gibbonsville, Moose Creek, Bohannon Bar, and Yellow Jacket (Umpleby, 1913b, p. 21). Gold placers and then lode deposits were discovered at Yellow Jacket in 1868. Nearly all the gold discoveries in Lemhi County were made before 1900, and most of the production, which was largely from placers, occurred in the early days. In recent years byproduct gold from copper-cobalt ores in the Blackbird district caused a significant increase in gold output.

Umpleby (1913b, p. 21) estimated that the total gold production of Lemhi County to 1911 was worth $13,702,256 (about 665,060 ounces), of which $6 million represented the output of placers before 1881.

Staley (1946, p. 22) listed annual gold production data for Lemhi County from 1874 through 1942. Total output for this period was 514,430 ounces. From 1942 through 1958, the county was credited with 56,295 ounces of gold. Total production through 1959 was 570,725 ounces, according to Staley's data, or 720,000 ounces, according to Umpleby's estimate.

The oldest rock is Archean granitic gneiss, exposed around Shoup, in the northwestern part of Lemhi County. This is unconformably overlain by argillites, phyllites, and quartzites of the Belt Series of Precambrian age. In the southern part, the Precambrian rocks are overlain by Cambrian quartzite and Ordovician, Silurian, Devonian, and Mississippian limestones and dolomites (Umpleby, 1913b, p. 30–35). Farther north in the Leesburg quadrangle, Ordovician quartzite lies unconformably on the Belt Series (Shockey, 1957, p. 10). Lake beds of Miocene age, occupying an area 8 miles wide and 90 miles long, occur in the valley of the Lemhi River near the east boundary of the county. At several localities in the northern part, granitic rocks probably related to the Idaho batholith cut the pre-Tertiary rocks (Umpleby, 1913b, p. 42–43). Numerous dikes, ranging from granite porphyry to lamprophyre, are associated with the larger intrusives. The dominant igneous rocks of Tertiary age are lava flows and welded tuffs that cover much of the central part of the county. These are known regionally as the Challis Volcanics of Oligocene age (Shockey, 1957, p. 12).

The gold lodes are fissure veins and replacement deposits along shear zones. There are two recognized periods of mineralization: Late Cretaceous or early Eocene, and late Miocene or early Pliocene (Umpleby, 1913b, p. 49).

BLACKBIRD DISTRICT

The Blackbird district, about 35 miles southwest of Salmon, was discovered in 1893. Ores were first worked for gold, with discouraging results, but copper was found in 1896 and cobalt in 1901 (Umpleby, 1913b, p. 160). Before 1957 the district produced only 1,205 ounces of gold. However, increased activity at the Calera cobalt-copper mine yielded 3,683 ounces of gold in 1957, a total of 9,506 ounces in 1958, and an undisclosed amount in 1957; all production was a byproduct of cobalt-copper ore.

Rocks of the Blackbird district are metamorphosed sedimentary rocks of the Belt Series of Precambrian age, intruded by granitic rocks of the Idaho batholith (Vhay, 1948, p. 2). At the Calera mine, the only significant producer in the district, quartz-biotite and garnet-chloritoid schists are the favorable host rocks for copper-cobalt deposits. These rocks are contained in a structural unit, the Blackbird block, which is 5 miles long, 2 miles wide, and is elongate northward. Copper-cobalt mineralization is controlled by north-trending shear zones and north-plunging folds; deposits are in veins and lenses formed by replacement. The ore minerals are chalcopyrite, cobaltite, safflorite, and gold; the gold is present in trace amounts to a few hundredths of an ounce per ton.

CARMEN CREEK-ELDORADO-PRATT CREEK-SANDY CREEK DISTRICT

Carmen Creek, Eldorado, Pratt Creek, and Sandy Creek are contiguous small camps in the northeastern part of Lemhi County along the flanks of the Beaverhead Mountains. The Kirtley Creek camp is also in this area but it will be considered separately.

Mining first began in the 1870's in the Eldorado area, where Chinese were mining the gravels on Bohannon Bar. From 1895 through 1911, the placers produced $350,000 in gold (Umpleby, 1913b, p. 123–124). Lode mines were also developed but were not very successful.

In the Carmen Creek camp, only small amounts of bullion were produced (Umpleby, 1913b, p. 125). The only property of significance was the Oro Cache mine, opened about 1897. At Pratt Creek, gold lodes were found in the early 1890's at the Goldstone mine. According to Ross (1941, p. 68), total production from all camps was about $1 million, including $500,000 in gold credited to the Kirtley Creek camp (Anderson, 1956, p. 64). Considering that about $350,000 came from the Eldorado camp, the Pratt Creek, Carmen Creek, and Sandy Creek camps produced about $150,000 in gold. In the 1930's and 1940's this area was active, but only small amounts of gold were mined. Total gold production through 1959 was about 24,500 ounces.

The rocks underlying this district are quartzites, quartzitic slates, and schists of the Precambrian Belt Series which are covered in the valleys by Miocene lake beds. The Precambrian rocks are cut locally by diorite dikes and granitic intrusions (Umpleby, 1913b, p. 121–127; Ross, 1941, p. 68). Most of the lode deposits are found in the metasedimentary rocks and are fissure fillings of quartz with variable amounts of pyrite, chalcopyrite, galena, and sphalerite. Gold occurs with the sulfides.

GIBBONSVILLE DISTRICT

The Gibbonsville district, at the northern apex of Lemhi County, was discovered in 1877. Gold placers were worked extensively and several lode properties, particularly the A. D. and M. mine, were very productive (Umpleby, 1913b, p. 128). From the time of a disastrous fire in 1907 through 1959 mining was sporadic. Total production, according to Ross (1941, p. 70), was about $2 million in gold, about half of which came from the A. D. and M. mine (Umpleby, 1913b, p. 132).

Bedrock in the district consists of thick beds of quartzite, quartzitic slate, and micaceous slate, which strike northwest and dip steeply to the east (Umpleby, 1913b, p. 129). Ross (1941, p. 70) assigned these rocks to the Belt Series of Precambrian age. Diorite dikes which cut the Precambrian rocks were believed to be Precambrian in age by Umpleby (1913b, p. 129) and Mesozoic by Ross (1941, p. 70).

The gold lodes occur in the quartzite and slate as narrow east-trending veins that are broken by numerous faults. The primary vein minerals are auriferous pyrite and chalcopyrite in a gangue of quartz and local calcite.

KIRTLEY CREEK DISTRICT

The Kirtley Creek district, in Tps. 21 and 22 N., R. 23 E., about 6 miles east of Salmon, was for a short time the most productive placer area in the State. Gold-bearing gravels were found along Kirtley Creek some time before 1890, and extensive hydraulic operations were conducted in them between 1890 and 1894. Production in the district declined in the late 1890's but was revived in 1910 when a dredge was brought in which successfully mined the gravels until the deposits were depleted in 1918 (Anderson, 1956, p. 63–64). From 1932 through 1959 the district was active for short periods on a small scale.

During 1910–18 about $500,000 (about 24,300 ounces) in gold was dredged from the placers (Anderson, 1956, p. 64). No data were found on the production before 1910. Production from 1932 to 1947 was 2,146 ounces; none was reported from 1947 through 1959.

Some gold-quartz veins at the head of Kirtley Creek were worked (Umpleby, 1913b, p. 124–125). At the White House mine, $40,500 in gold was produced. The veins contain pyrite, chalcopyrite, galena, and free gold in a quartz gangue.

Total minimum production from the district was about 27,500 ounces, mostly from placers.

MACKINAW DISTRICT

The Mackinaw (Leesburg) district is about 10 miles west of Salmon, near lat 45°14′ N. and long 114°10′ W.

In 1866 gold placers were discovered at Wards Gulch along Napias Creek, and for the next 14 years these placers were worked on a large scale. The population of the town of Leesburg in the district was 7,000 during this period, but by 1911 it had dwindled to 25 (Umpleby, 1913b, p. 145–146). Lodes were productive in this district, though on a much smaller scale than the placers. The vein deposits were first developed in 1870 but were worked for only a few years (Umpleby, 1913b, p. 146); however, the placers were worked intermittently to about 1954. The district was inactive from that date through 1959.

Umpleby (1913b, p. 146) estimated the value of placer production of the district at not more than $5 million and the lode output at about $250,000. Shockey (1957, p. 32, 33) listed annual production from 1902 through 1954, which totaled 7,635 ounces from placers and 1,146 ounces from lodes. Total gold production through 1959 from all sources, including the estimate of early production, was about 271,200 ounces.

The oldest rocks in the area are phyllite and quartzite of the upper(?) Belt Series of Precambrian age (Shockey, 1957, p. 7–20). These are overlain by the Kinnikinic Quartzite of Ordovician age. Intrusive into these metasedimentary rocks are quartz monzonite apophyses of the Idaho batholith. After a long period of erosion, the rocks were buried by early Tertiary conglomerate and later by the Challis Volcanics. Parts of the Leesburg basin are underlain by Tertiary lake beds, and these sediments are overlain by late Tertiary volcanic ash deposits. Prior to Ordovician sedimentation, the Precambrian rocks were deformed, and afterward the Precambrian and Ordovician rocks were faulted and compressed into a northwest-trending synclinorium some time before the monzonitic intrusion. During Tertiary time minor warping occurred.

The lode deposits, according to Umpleby (1913b, p. 150–152), are of five types: (1) quartz veins and stockworks in quartz monzonite, containing pyrite, sphalerite, specularite, and a little galena; (2) replacement veins along fault planes in metasedimentary rocks and quartz monzonite, containing quartz and pyrite as the chief constituents; (3) replacement deposits along a shear zone in schist, containing garnet, epidote, and magnetite; (4) mineralized lenses in schist and probably monzonitic rock, possibly the source of much of the placer gold; and (5) quartz veins along biotite monzonite dikes, containing chalcopyrite, sphalerite, and subordinate pyrite and galena. All five types are of equal economic importance as lode-gold producers (Ross, 1941, p. 73).

The placers were distributed along Moose Creek, Beaver Creek, and Napias Creek and its tributaries; most of the production was from the Leesburg basin, an area drained by Napias Creek. Umpleby (1913b, p. 150) regarded some of the placers as of Miocene and Pliocene age, but Ross (1941, p. 74) was of the opinion that much of the auriferous gravel was Pleistocene or younger.

MINERAL HILL AND INDIAN CREEK DISTRICT

The Mineral Hill and Indian Creek district is in Tps. 23 and 24 N., Rs. 17, 18, and 19 E., in northwestern Lemhi County, near the town of Shoup.

Most of the gold mined in the district was from lodes, but small amounts came from placers along Boulder Creek (Lorain and Metzger, 1939, p. 70–71). In the Mineral Hill area most of the lode properties were discovered and developed in the 1880's. These include the Kentuck and Grunter mines which were discovered in 1882. In the Indian Creek area there was some activity in 1895, but no extensive development occurred until 1901 when the Kittie Burton and Ulysses lode mines became operative (Umpleby, 1913b, p. 134, 139). Most of the production of the district was before 1910. The early production—which in addition to gold included an undisclosed amount of silver and small amounts of base metals —was estimated at $1,350,000 by Umpleby (1913b, p. 135, 139) and at $1,400,000 by Ross (1941, p. 74). From 1932 through 1959 the district produced only 21,937 ounces of gold.

The rocks of this area, as summarized by Ross (1941, p. 74), consist of schist and quartzite of the Belt Series and intrusive gneissic granite that Umpleby (1913b, p. 139) believed to be Precambrian in age but Ross (1941, p. 74) believed to be related to the Idaho batholith. Much of the southern part of the district is underlain by granitic rocks of the Idaho batholith. Mineral deposits occur as fissure fillings and also as replacement deposits in both the schistose and granitic rocks. Quartz, pyrite, arsenopyrite, galena, sphalerite, and some calcite, magnetite, and muscovite are the predominant vein minerals. Gold occurs with the pyrite (Umpleby, 1913b, p. 141).

TEXAS DISTRICT

The Texas district is in parts of Tps. 13 and 14 N., Rs. 26 and 27 E., near Gilmore.

In the early 1880's prospectors swarmed over the east slope of the Lemhi Range in search of lead-silver deposits similar to those discovered at Nicholia to the southeast. Some promising deposits were found in the area known as the Texas district, but after about 10 years of occasional activity, the district became dormant for 10 to 12 years. After the discovery of large ore bodies at the Pittsburg-Idaho mine in 1902, the future looked bright for the Texas district; however, transportation difficulties hampered any major activity. In 1910, a railroad was constructed that linked the mines to a smelter (Umpleby, 1913b, p. 90–91); large-scale mining then began and continued through 1929. After a decline for a few years, the district again became active, and infrequent small-scale operations continued through 1956.

Production which was mainly in silver and lead from the Pittsburg-Idaho mine, was small during 1903–10; data before 1903 were not found. Total gold production from 1903 to 1959 was 21,745 ounces.

Most of the district is underlain by eastward-dipping sedimentary rocks of Cambrian, Ordovician, Silurian(?), Devonian(?), and Mississippian age (Umpleby, 1913b, p. 92). With the exception of the Cambrian rocks, which are quartzite, all the Paleozoic strata are limestone or dolomitic limestone. Unconformably overlying the Paleozoic rocks in the eastern part of the district are Miocene lake beds.

The ore deposits occur in the belt of calcareous rocks, an area bounded by the Cambrian quartzite on the west and the lake beds on the east. They are in flat and steeply dipping veins, parallel with the strike of the country rocks; some of the larger and more productive deposits occur at the intersection of the steep and flat veins (T. H. Kiilsgaard, written commun., 1962). Most of the ore is valued for its lead and silver, but one deposit, the Martha vein, was mined for gold alone. Almost all the workings were in oxidized ore containing cerussite, anglesite, smithsonite, calamine, cerargyrite and iron, and manganese oxides.

YELLOW JACKET DISTRICT

The Yellow Jacket district is at about lat 44°58′ N. and long 114°31′ W., near the settlement of Yellow Jacket, in west-central Lemhi County.

Lode deposits were discovered in the district in 1868, and they were worked in the early 1870's, but their greatest production was during 1893–97 (Anderson, 1953, p. 15). Activity throughout the district declined with the closing of the Yellow Jacket mine in 1897, and except for intermittent activity during 1911–14, in the late 1920's, and in the 1930's, the district never approached its pre-1900 production.

Umpleby (1913b, p. 170) estimated production from the Yellow Jacket mine at $450,000 (about 21,840 ounces) in gold. Ross (1934, p. 108) listed a total of $121,761.56 in bullion from the Yellow Jacket mine for 1893–97. From 1902 through 1949 the district produced 3,855 ounces of gold (Anderson, 1953, p. 17), and from 1949 through 1959, only 8 ounces. Gold has been the chief commodity, but small amounts of silver, copper, and lead have also been recovered. Total gold production, according to Umpleby's estimate, was about 25,000 ounces.

The Yellow Jacket district is underlain by sedimentary, metasedimentary, and igneous rocks that were folded and faulted into a complex pattern and then mineralized (Anderson, 1953, p. 4–11). The oldest sedimentary rocks consist of two subdivisions of the Belt Series—the Yellowjacket Formation, which is composed of argillite and calcareous quartzite, and the Hoodoo Quartzite. In the western part of the district these are overlain by Challis Volcanics of Oligocene age. Intrusive rocks of three ages are in the district: dikelike and stocklike bodies of gabbro of Precambrian(?) age; a large body of hornblende-biotite diorite and smaller bodies of syenite, diabase, diorite, and gabbro, all of Late Cretaceous or early Tertiary age; and dikes of granophyre, granite porphyry, and vitrophyre, all of Miocene age (Anderson, 1953, p. 6–11). The older rocks were deformed and fractured by several diastrophic events.

Most of the lodes are either fissure fillings or replacement deposits in breccia zones. The Yellowjacket Formation, which has been deformed most extensively, contains most of the ore deposits (Anderson, 1953, p. 18). Primary minerals in the deposits are quartz, calcite, siderite, and barite in the gangue, and the ore minerals are pyrite, specularite, chalcopyrite, tetrahedrite, galena, and gold. The ores are somewhat oxidized near the surface: much of the early production was from these free-milling oxidized ores (Anderson, 1953, p. 19–23).

OWYHEE COUNTY

Gold deposits in Owyhee County are grouped in the Silver City district, in the northwestern part of the county. Placers along the Snake River also yielded gold, but the quantity yielded and the locations of the placers are not known.

Total gold production of Owyhee County from 1863 through 1942 was 1,058,694 ounces (Staley, 1946, p. 25); from 1943 through 1959 it was 44,851 ounces—a total of 1,103,545 ounces from 1863 through 1959.

SILVER CITY DISTRICT

The Silver City district, which includes the De Lamar, Flint, and Florida Mountain-War Eagle Mountain camps, is in parts of Tps. 3, 4, and 5 S., Rs. 1, 2, 3, and 4 W., in northwestern Owyhee County.

The first mineral discoveries were gold placers found along Jordan Creek in 1863. That same year, prospectors followed the Jordan Creek placers to their source—the lodes on War Eagle Mountain. By 1865 the richest placers were exhausted, but the Chinese continued lower grade placer mining for a number of years. After the discovery of rich oxidized gold-silver ores at the Poorman and Orofino mines in 1865, the district erupted into a period of frantic activity accompanied by so much violence and disorder that federal troops were called in to quell the disturbances. The area prospered, developed, and grew despite extremely high costs engendered by poor transportation facilities. Silver City, with a population of 4,000, was the largest settlement, but the towns of Ruby City, Fairview, Booneville, and Wagontown were also thriving communities (Piper and Laney, 1926, p. 51–52).

By the early 1870's much of the rich oxidized ore was mined out, and in 1876, when the Bank of California failed, financial support was withdrawn and mining in the Silver City area collapsed. Thus the first phase of mining in the Silver City district ended with a production of $12½ million in gold and silver (Piper and Laney, 1926, p. 53).

In 1889, discoveries at the Black Jack mine at Florida Mountain and the De Lamar mine at Wagontown started a second boom of greater magnitude but with less hysteria than the first. This was a period of consolidation and systematic development. By 1914, after $23 million in precious metals had been mined, the ores were depleted, and the activity again ended (Piper and Laney, 1926, p. 55–56). Since then, there has been no major revival; operations have been sporadic and on a small scale. Piper (in Piper and Laney, 1926, p. 58) estimated the gold production of Owyhee County (which would in effect be the production of Silver City) as 900,000 ounces. Ross (1941, p. 81) estimated the total gold production of the district at "over 1,000,000 ounces." Recorded gold production from 1941 through 1959 was only about 8,500 ounces and would not greatly change Ross' estimate.

Metasedimentary rocks consisting of graphite and biotite schists are the oldest rocks in the district, though they are present in only a few outcrops. The most abundant rock unit is a granodiorite stock probably related to the Idaho batholith. The granodiorite is cut by aplite, dacite, and diorite porphyry dikes, which may or may not be genetically related to the stock (Ross, 1941, p. 81). During Miocene time, basaltic lavas were poured onto an erosion surface cut on the granodiorite, and rhyolite flows covered the basalt (Piper and Laney, 1926, p. 20–36).

The rocks of the Silver City district are cut by faults of several ages. The oldest are a set of high-angle fractures and joints in the stock. After extrusion of the rhyolite flows, the rocks were dislocated by a second system of fractures that strike northwest and are nearly vertical (Piper and Laney, 1926, p. 39–40). The youngest faulting occurred after the ore deposits were formed.

The veins of the district are fracture fillings and may be classified into four types (Piper and Laney, 1926, p. 63): (1) veins characterized by white or milky quartz as in the Flint district, (2) veins composed of lamellar quartz typical of the De Lamar district, (3) silicified shear zones such as the Poorman, and (4) quartz-cemented breccias of which the Orofino-Golden Chariot vein is an example. All types are remarkably persistent and are traceable for thousands of feet along strike and as much as 2,500 feet below the surface (Ross, 1941, p. 81).

The ore minerals are argentite, electrum, jamesonite, ruby, silver, naumannite, owyheeite, stibnite, and tetrahedrite. Arsenopyrite, galena, pyrite, and marcasite occur in minor amounts (Ross, 1941, p. 81). Included in the gangue are quartz, barite, calcite, chalcedony, and valencianite, a rare variety of orthoclase occurring as gangue in some ore deposits (Lindgren, 1900, p. 166–167).

POWER COUNTY

Founded in about 1912, Power County was formed from the part of Oneida County that bordered the Snake River.

In the late 1800's and early 1900's, placers were worked along the Snake River near American Falls. Staley (1946, p. 30) listed gold production of 17,039 ounces for Oneida County from 1880 through 1912 and 1,446 ounces from Snake River placers in Power County from 1913 to 1942. This total of 18,485 ounces represents probably only a small fraction of the total yield, for as Staley (1946, p. 30) noted, the poorly kept records do not do justice to the actual production of the placers. In the 1950's these placers were inactive.

SHOSHONE COUNTY

The important mineral deposits of Shoshone County are in the Coeur d'Alene Mountains, along its northeast boundary. This mineralized area covers about 500 square miles and includes about eight mining districts, known collectively as the Coeur d'Alene region.

The county's gold production from 1881 through 1942 was 393,088 ounces (Staley, 1946, p. 27); from 1943 through 1959 it was 41,113 ounces—a total of 434,201 ounces for 1881–1959.

COEUR D'ALENE REGION

The Coeur d'Alene region is in northeastern Shoshone County between lat 47°25′ and 47°40′ N. and long 115°40′ and 116°10′ W., and includes the districts of Beaver, Eagle, Evolution, Hunter or Mullan, Lelande or Burke, Placer Center or Wallace, Summit, and Yreka. Wallace is its principal town.

The first mineral discoveries were lodes in 1878, but it was not until rich placers were discovered along Prichard and Eagle Creeks in the early 1880's that any concentrated interest was shown in the area. The town of Murray was founded in the placer area, and it soon became the county seat of Shoshone County. In 1885 rich deposits of lead and silver were discovered along the South Fork of the Coeur d'Alene River; at the same time the placers at Murray began to decline (Ransome and Calkins, 1908, p. 78–80). A railway into the region was completed in 1887, and by that time many properties—among them the Bunker Hill and Sullivan, Mammoth, Tiger, Morning, Poorman, and Granite—were producing substantial amounts of ore. The succeeding decade was marked by strife between the miners' unions and the mine owners, and several times troops were called in to restore order (Ransome and Calkins, 1908, p. 81). Meanwhile the Murray placers experienced a revival. The bench gravels were worked, and several new lode properties began producing. By 1911 the lead-zinc mines at Murray reached their peak, and many continued operating until 1933, when all of them closed (Shenon, 1938, p. 15). The region became slightly active again in the mid-1930's and remained so through 1959.

Most of the early gold production of the region was from placers and gold-quartz veins near Murray; the lead-zinc ores at Murray contained only negligible amounts of gold. A total of 227,890 ounces of gold was produced in the region from 1884 to 1905 (Ransome and Calkins, 1908, p. 82). From 1906 through 1934 the Murray area produced 66,092 ounces of placer and 3,154 ounces of lode gold (Shenon, 1938, p. 17), and from 1935 through 1951 a total of 16,275 ounces of placer and lode gold was produced (Hosterman, 1956, p. 740). Mines in the Coeur d'Alene region, including the Murray district, produced a total of $7,180,151 (348,550 ounces) in gold from 1884 through 1931 (Ross, 1941, p. 85). Total gold production of the region through 1960 was about 439,000 ounces (Shenon, 1961, p. 1).

The geology of the region was described in detail by Ransome and Calkins (1908, p. 23–77), and the following was abstracted from their report. The oldest and most abundant rocks underlying the district are Precambrian sedimentary rocks of the Belt Series. These are subdivided into six formations, from the oldest to youngest: Prichard Formation, Burke Formation, Revett Quartzite, St. Regis Formation, Wallace Formation, and Striped Peak Formation. All these formations, except the Striped Peak, are intruded along a northeast-trending belt by bodies of quartz monzonite. The intruded rocks, especially the calcareous types, are metamorphosed extensively along the contacts. In addition to quartz monzonite, other igneous rocks of the district are dikes of diabase and lamprophyre.

The age of the intrusions and deformation is not clearly revealed. The rocks were folded and then faulted, but the intrusions may have occurred at any time during or prior to the faulting, as some faults cut the monzonite.

The rocks are thrown into several large asymmetrical folds which trend west-northwest, north, or northeast. Complicating the structure are smaller folds superimposed on the limbs of the major ones. The rocks are extensively dislocated by normal and reverse faults, the main group of which strikes nearly east and a smaller group, north to slightly west of north. The Osburn, Placer Creek, Big Creek, and White Ledge faults are examples of the first group; the Dobson Pass, Carpenter Gulch, and O'Neil Gulch faults are typical of the second.

Mineral deposits in the Coeur d'Alene region primarily contain silver-lead-zinc ores, and some copper and gold are recovered as byproducts. Gold lodes have been mined near Murray. The silver-lead-zinc ores are mostly in the main part of the region, between Mullan and Kellogg. They are in veins and in tabular replacement bodies most of which are in the Revett and Burke Formations (Ransome and Calkins, 1908, p. 106). Argentiferous galena, pyrite, pyrrhotite, chalcopyrite, sphalerite, and local tetrahedrite are the most abundant metallic minerals; siderite and locally occurring quartz are the dominant gangue minerals (Ransome and Calkins, 1908, p. 107–111).

Gold deposits occur in four different structural environments: (1) mineralized shear zones with steep dips, (2) quartz veins along bedding planes, (3) quartz veins along low-angle thrust faults, and (4) placers (Shenon, 1938, p. 18). Of these, the placers were the most productive, followed by the bedding-plane veins, then by the mineralized shear zones and thrust-fault deposits. All the gold lodes occur in beds of the Prichard Formation. Bedding-plane veins usually are found in argillite. They contain quartz and some ankerite, sericite, albite, chlorite, and apatite. The ore minerals, which form as much as 5 percent of the vein material, are arsenopyrite, pyrite, galena, chalcopyrite, specularite, scheelite, and gold. Selenium is sparse (Shenon, 1938, p. 20). The shear-zone deposits are mineralogically similar to the bedding-plane veins except that they also contain pyrrhotite and sphalerite but no scheelite or specularite (Shenon, 1938, p. 19). The minable thrust-fault deposits are restricted to only one mine, the Wakeup Jim. The mineralogy also is similar to that of the bedding-plane veins.

Although copper deposits in this region are classified as a distinct type occupying an area in the southeast part of the district, they were worked by only one mine, and it was closed in 1915. The ores are disseminations of bornite, chalcocite, and chalcopyrite in the Revett Quartzite (Ransome and Calkins, 1908, p. 150). Gold is a minor constituent.

VALLEY COUNTY

Valley County, in west-central Idaho, was formed in 1917 and is one of the newest counties in the State. The early gold production of the area now known as Valley County was reported under Idaho or Boise Counties. Staley (1946, p. 28) credited Valley County with 96,578 ounces of gold from 1917 through 1942. Total gold production from 1917 through 1958 was 324,460 ounces, most of which was mined from lode deposits of antimony-gold ore in the late 1940's. The gold districts are in the northeastern part of the county in a triangular-shaped area with Edwardsburg at the apex and the Yellow Pine and Thunder Mountain districts at the southwest and southeast corners respectively. Each side of the triangle is about 15 miles long. Edwardsburg, however, had only minor gold production and will not be discussed here.

THUNDER MOUNTAIN DISTRICT

The Thunder Mountain district is in T. 19 N., R. 11 E., on Monumental Creek, in northeastern Valley County.

Discovered in 1896, the Thunder Mountain district is a typical example of the effect of rumor on the gold-fever-ravaged minds of that day. Accounts of wondrously rich gold ore attracted several thousand people to the district in 1902, and the towns of Belleco and Roosevelt sprang up; Roosevelt was the principal business center (Shenon and Ross, 1936, p. 18). The boom lasted until 1907 when the principal producer, the Dewey mine, closed regular operations. In 1909 a landslide destroyed the town of Roosevelt, and this disaster stifled the enthusiasm of those still remaining in the district (Shenon and Ross, 1936, p. 19). After 1909 there were only intermittent operations in the district, chiefly at the Dewey and Sunnyside mines.

The total value of production of the district to about 1940 was $400,000, most of which came from the Dewey and Sunnyside mines (Ross, 1941, p. 96). Although most of this was in gold, silver was also important as evidenced by the Dewey mine production record of 14,342 ounces of gold and 8,484 ounces of silver from 1902 to 1919 (Shenon and Ross, 1936, p. 38). Total gold production of the district through 1959 was probably about 17,500 ounces.

Bedrock in the Thunder Mountain district consists of tuffaceous and rhyolitic rocks interbedded with sandstone, shales, and breccias, all considered part of the Challis Formation of late Oligocene or early Miocene age (Shenon and Ross, 1936, p. 10). Locally, patches of basalt cap the higher areas.

The ore bodies are in altered rock, usually in the more permeable beds; at the Dewey mine, for example, the ore is in altered rhyolitic tuff, sandstone, rhyolitic lava, and breccia, in a steeply dipping shear zone. Pyrite and pyrargyrite were the only recognized ore minerals, and the gold was associated with pyrite irregularly concentrated in the rocks. The host rocks are highly silicified (Shenon and Ross, 1936, p. 39). At the Sunnyside mine the ore occurs in flow breccia overlain by interbedded sandstones, shales, and conglomerate; a mudflow overlies much of the area. At some places where the mudflow is close to the breccia, blanketlike ore bodies are formed. Apparently the mud acted as an impermeable barrier to the upward-moving ore solutions. The ore is highly oxidized although patches of pyrite can be found locally.

YELLOW PINE DISTRICT

The Yellow Pine district is between lat 44°50′ N. and long 115°00′ and 115°30′ W., near the town of Stibnite.

In about 1900, during the rush to the Thunder Mountain district, deposits of quicksilver, antimony, and gold were found in the Yellow Pine district. No work of any consequence was done, however, until 1917, when the demand for quicksilver encouraged development of several properties, notably the Fern and Hermes mines (Cooper, 1951, p. 152). Gold-antimony deposits were developed in 1929 at the Meadow Creek mine, but this property was closed in 1938. The Yellow Pine deposit, the major producer of the district, was discovered in the early 1900's but was not mined until 1937. At first only gold and antimony were recovered, but in 1941 scheelite was found. Activity accelerated, and during World War II the Yellow Pine mine became the largest tungsten producer in the United States. The tungsten ore was exhausted by 1945; nevertheless, large-scale mining of the antimony-gold ore continued (Cooper, 1951, p. 174–175). At the end of 1952, the Yellow Pine mine was shut down and virtually no gold was produced from the district afterward. The nearby town of Stibnite was almost deserted by 1958. The Hermes mine remained active, however, and was still producing mercury in 1959.

The gold production of the Yellow Pine and Meadow Creek mines through 1945 was 101,437 ounces (Cooper, 1951, p. 155). Little if any gold was produced from any of the other properties. Total district gold production through 1959 was 309,734 ounces.

The oldest rocks in the Yellow Pine district are quartzite, quartzitic conglomerate, mica schist, altered limestone, dolomite, and tactite, all probably Ordovician in age (Cooper, 1951, p. 156). These rocks were folded and faulted, then intruded by a mass of quartz monzonite related to the Idaho batholith of middle Cretaceous age. There was also some postintrusion faulting that dislocated the igneous rocks (Cooper, 1951, p. 162–163). Dikes ranging from basalt to rhyolite in composition cut the quartz monzonite and fill many of the faults and shear zones.

Ore deposits, according to Cooper (1951, p. 164), are of two types: deposits of low-grade disseminated gold ore containing local concentrations of antimony, silver, and tungsten; and deposits of quicksilver. Currier (1935, p. 16–17), on the other hand, classified three types: arsenical gold ores, antimony-gold-silver ores, and mercury ores.

The gold-bearing deposits are characterized by auriferous pyrite and arsenopyrite, scheelite, and stibnite. Cooper (1951, p. 165) noted a zoning of the deposits. East of a north-south line, 1 mile east of Stibnite, only mercury deposits are found; west of the line the important tungsten-antimony-silver-gold deposits are found. All deposits are localized along faults; the zoning is probably due to depth below the land surface at the time of mineralization (Cooper, 1951, p. 165). Most of the deposits consist of a network of small mineralized fractures and disseminations in the adjacent wallrock.

MICHIGAN

The only significant output of gold in Michigan came from a small area in the Upper Peninsula about 3 to 5 miles west-northwest of Ishpeming on the north side of the Marquette Range in Marquette County. This area yielded gold bullion valued at about $625,000, of which about $605,000 came from the Ropes mine (Allen, 1912, p. 358). The ratio of gold to silver is not known, but ore produced from the Ropes mine in 1895 yielded $34,838 (1,686 ounces) in gold and $1,373 in silver—a ratio in value of about 25 to 1. Total gold production of Michigan through 1959 probably was about 29,000 ounces.

Gold in upper Michigan was probably first discovered in the early 1840's by Dr. Douglass Houghton, Michigan's first State geologist, who found gold in a streambed while studying the geology of the Upper Peninsula (Allen, 1912, p. 356), but the exact location of this discovery is not known. Gold mining in Michigan began with the discovery of the gold-bearing quartz vein in the Ropes mine in 1880 and continued until 1897, when the mine was closed (Allen, 1912, p. 355–356). Very small amounts of gold that were reported periodically after 1897 were derived from reworking of tailings. The workings of the Ropes mine reached a depth of about 850 feet but none of the other mines exceeded 80 feet in depth.

The ores in the Ropes mine are in veins in peridotite in the Keewatin (Precambrian) rocks (Allen,

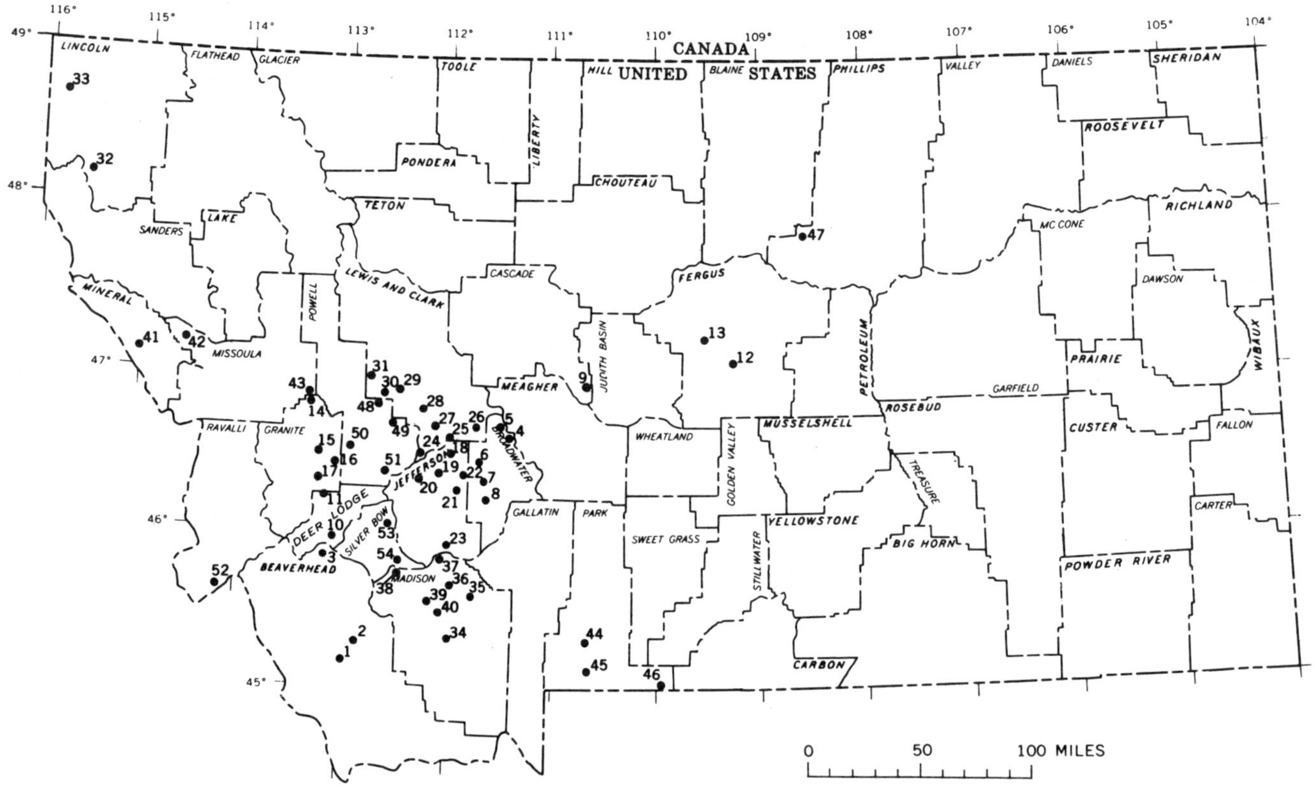

Figure 14.—Gold-mining districts of Montana.

Beaverhead County:
1, Bannack; 2, Argenta; 3, Bryant.

Broadwater County:
4, Confederate Gulch; 5, White Creek; 6, Winston; 7, Park; 8, Radersburg.

Cascade County:
9, Montana.

Deer Lodge County:
10, French Creek; 11, Georgetown.

Fergus County:
12, Warm Springs; 13, North Moccasin.

Granite County:
14, First Chance; 15, Henderson Placers; 16, Boulder Creek; 17, Flint Creek.

Jefferson County:
18, Clancy; 19, Wickes; 20, Basin and Boulder; 21, Elkhorn; 22, Tizer; 23, Whitehall.

Lewis and Clark County:
24, Rimini-Tenmile; 25, Helena-Last Chance; 26, Missouri River-York; 27, Sevenmile-Scratchgravel; 28, Marysville-Silver Creek; 29, Stemple-Virginia Creek; 30, McClellan; 31, Lincoln.

Lincoln County:
32, Libby; 33, Sylvanite.

Madison County:
34, Virginia City-Alder Gulch; 35, Norris; 36, Pony; 37, Renova; 38, Silver Star-Rochester; 39, Tidal Wave; 40, Sheridan.

Mineral County:
41, Cedar Creek-Trout Creek.

Missoula County:
42, Ninemile Creek; 43, Elk Creek-Coloma.

Park County:
44, Emigrant Creek; 45, Jardine; 46, Cooke City.

Phillips County:
47, Little Rocky Mountains.

Powell County:
48, Finn; 49, Ophir; 50, Pioneer; 51, Zosell.

Ravalli County:
52, Hughes Creek.

Silver Bow County:
53, Butte; 54, Highland.

1912, p. 355). The veins are lenticular, and they are associated with talcose slate that probably was formed from sheared and altered peridotite. Free gold occurs with galena, pyrite, and copper ore minerals in a gangue of quartz. The mined ore ranged in value from $2 to $6 per ton. Some gold-bearing quartz veins in the district are also in diorite and granite.

MONTANA

In Montana, 54 mining districts distributed in 17 counties (fig. 14) each have produced more than

10,000 ounces of gold. Four districts—Butte, Helena, Marysville, and Virginia City—have produced more than 1 million ounces, and 27 other districts produced between 100,000 and 1 million ounces. Montana generally is credited with lode and placer gold production of 17,752,000 ounces from 1862 through 1965. Almost two-thirds of the total was mined before 1900 when records were poorly kept; thus a large part is estimated. Figure 15 shows annual gold production of Montana from 1900 through 1965.

In 1852 gold was first discovered in Montana in gravels along Gold Creek in Powell County (Lyden, 1948, p. 118). The influx of prospectors, however, started with the discovery in 1862 of placers along Grasshopper Creek, near Bannack, in Beaverhead County (Winchell, 1914a, p. 18). Other discoveries, both placer and lode, came in rapid succession. In May 1863, the very rich deposits along Alder Gulch near Virginia City in Madison County were discovered; these proved to be the most extensive and the most productive placers in Montana. The Last Chance placers on the present site of Helena in Lewis and Clark County, among Montana's most productive placers, were discovered in the summer of 1864 (Knopf, 1913, p. 15) as were the placers in the Butte district in Silver Bow County (Lyden, 1948, p. 144–145). These rich discoveries stimulated a rush of prospectors to Montana who searched the valleys and gulches for gold-bearing gravels. Placer mining flourished during the 1860's. Some of the deposits were quickly worked out, but others were worked on a substantial scale up to World War II. Winchell (1914a, p. 19) described this extended activity as follows:

> By the gradual installation of ditches, flumes, and hydraulic and sluicing apparatus the life of the placer-mining industry has been extended for half a century, though with decreasing yield at nearly all places, except where new and virgin ground was opened by late discovery or by bringing water upon ground previously too dry to work. * * * The introduction of dredges increased the annual output to about half a million dollars, though the newness of the method and the many difficulties that had to be overcome caused for a time great fluctuations in the yield. Since about the first of the century, however, the product has been large and increasing, and, despite the marked decrease in the amount of gold won by other placer methods, the annual placer production has formed an important portion of the total gold output of the State.

In 1895 dredging was first attempted in Montana on Grasshopper Creek near Bannack (Winchell, 1914a, p. 21). Dredges operated by electric power have been used since 1906. Since World War II very little placer mining has been done.

Although placer deposits were the first to be discovered in most districts, lode deposits were discovered soon afterward or even contemporaneously, and in the 1870's lode production became significant. Among the first rich lode discoveries in 1864 were the Whitlatch-Union in the Helena district (Knopf, 1913, p. 15), the Black Chief (Travona) lode in the

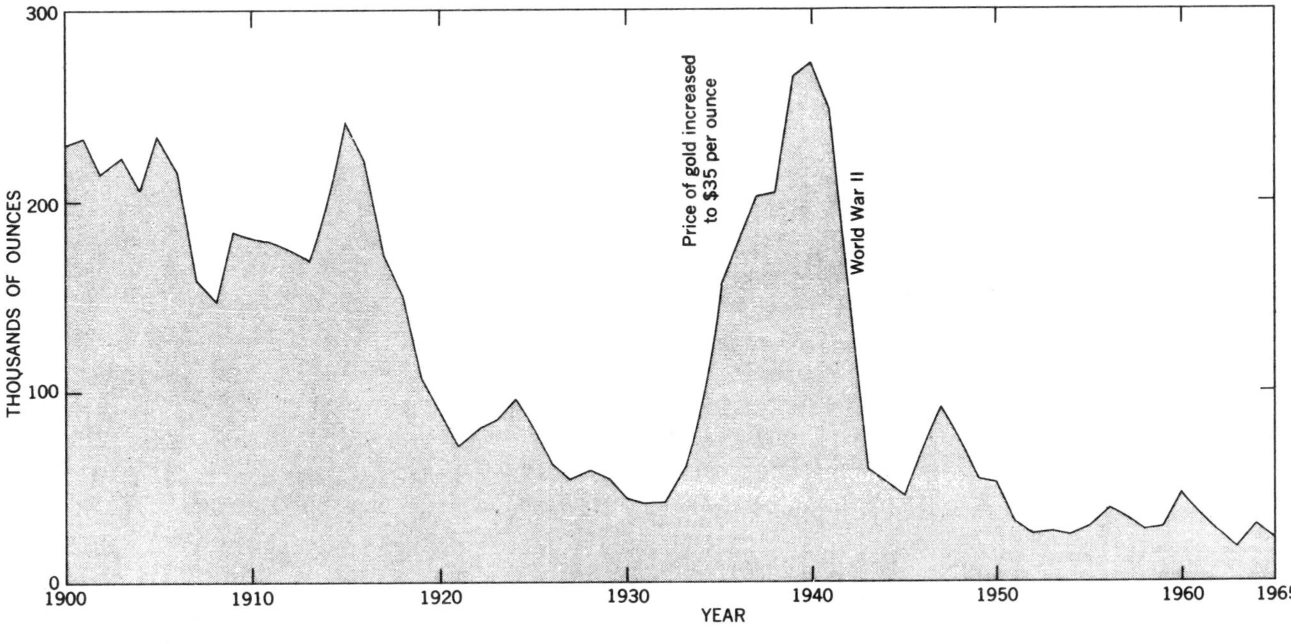

FIGURE 15.—Annual gold production of Montana, 1900–65. Sources of data: U.S. Geological Survey (1883–1924); U.S. Bureau of Mines (1925–1934; 1933–1966).

Butte district (Weed, 1912, p. 18), and several lodes in the Blue Wing and Sheridan districts (Winchell, 1914a, p. 69, 133). Lodes were found in the Silver Star district in 1867 (Winchell, 1914a, p. 139–140).

Early development of the mines was impeded by lack of an adequate transportation system. By 1870 the placers had been largely exhausted, and a period of inactivity followed because lode mining was hindered by high freight charges (Knopf, 1913, p. 16). Mining supplies and equipment had to be brought in by wagon train in the early years; consequently, only the richest ore could be mined. Railroad transportation in the region became available in 1882 on completion of the Utah and Northern Railway, a part of the Union Pacific Railroad system, from Ogden, Utah, to Silver Bow, near Butte, Mont. (Winchell, 1914a, p. 20). In 1883 the main line of the Northern Pacific Railway was completed across the State, and a spur was built from Garrison through Silver Bow to Butte (Winchell, 1914a, p. 20).

The principal mining districts in Montana are scattered in the southwestern part of the State and are associated with the Boulder batholith and nearby stocks and dikes of Late Cretaceous or early Tertiary age (Pardee and Schrader, 1933, pl. 1). The ore deposits are found in the margins of the granitic rocks or in the wallrocks.

BEAVERHEAD COUNTY

Beaverhead County, in the southwest corner of the State, had a recorded gold production of about 370,000 ounces through 1959, but early production records are incomplete and total output may be considerably larger. Before 1900 production from placers probably was considerably larger than from lodes; however, from 1904 through 1958 the county produced about 116,350 ounces of lode gold and only about 14,800 ounces of placer gold.

Rich gold placer deposits were discovered at Bannack along Grasshopper Creek in 1862. These deposits were the first significant ore discoveries in Montana and started the first rush of prospectors to Montana. The first lode mine in Montana, also in the Bannack district, was located in 1862, soon after discovery of placer gold (Shenon, 1931, p. 27).

The placer deposits along Grasshopper Creek have been the most productive in the county and probably are the only placers that have produced more than 10,000 ounces of gold. Gold has been recovered from placers along many of the other streams in the county (Lyden, 1948, p. 8–12), but operations have been intermittent and, according to available records, none of these placers yielded more than 3,000 ounces.

The lode deposits are chiefly in the north half of the county where the Mount Torrey granitic stock and several smaller satellite bodies (Corry, 1933, fig. 6) intrude Precambrian, Paleozoic, and Mesozoic sedimentary rocks. Most of the deposits are in or near the granitic intrusives and are valuable chiefly for silver and lead, but significant amounts of gold and copper have also been recovered. Gold production from lode deposits has come mainly from the Bannack, Argenta, and Bryant (Hecla) districts.

ARGENTA DISTRICT

The Argenta district, about 12 miles west of Dillon, has produced gold, silver, and lead, and smaller amounts of copper and zinc, mostly from lode deposits. After the discoveries of placer deposits in the Bannack district in 1862, some placer deposits were discovered near Argenta in the early 1860's, but apparently (Winchell, 1914a, p. 66) these were successfully mined on a small scale for only a short time in the 1870's. No figures are available as to the amount of placer gold produced. Lode deposits in the district were discovered in the spring of 1865 (Shenon, 1931, p. 57), and the early lode discoveries presumably consisted of rich argentiferous lead ore which carried only small amounts of gold. According to fragmentary early mining records, eight furnaces were built at Argenta in the first few years. The ore bodies were soon depleted, and by 1875 the district was almost deserted. The next 50 years was a period of dormancy, broken by brief periods of activity (Winchell, 1914a, p. 66). In 1926 the Ermont deposits were discovered and the bulk of the gold production of the district has come from them (W. B. Myers, written commun., 1947). The amount of gold produced prior to 1904 has not been ascertained but it probably was very small. From 1904 through 1957 the district produced about 65,350 ounces of gold.

The geology and ore deposits of the Argenta district were briefly described by Shenon (1931, p. 44–77) and by Winchell (1914a, p. 65–69).

The Argenta district is underlain by folded and complexly faulted sedimentary rocks of Precambrian and Paleozoic age that are intruded by a stock of quartz monzonite and by sills and dikes of andesite and dacite of Late Cretaceous or Tertiary age.

The ore occurs chiefly in contact metamorphic deposits in limestone, in pipelike bodies in limestone, in tabular shoots along bedding planes in limestone, and in veins in both the sedimentary rocks and in the quartz monzonite. The deposit at the Ermont mine, the most productive in the district, is in andesite along the Ermont fault and in shale beneath an andesite sill. The ore is oxidized and contains gold and limonite which is pseudomorphic after pyrite (W. B. Myers, written commun., 1947).

BANNACK DISTRICT

The Bannack district, about 22 miles west-southwest of the town of Dillon, is best known for the rich placer deposits discovered along Grasshopper Creek in 1862, but lode deposits on both sides of Grasshopper Creek have produced significant amounts of gold, silver, lead, and copper. Winchell (1914a, p. 19, 75) credited the placer deposits along Grasshopper Creek with a gold production prior to 1905 of about $2½ million (120,950 ounces) to $3 million (145,140 ounces), most of which was mined during the 1860's, whereas Shenon (1931, p. 28, 43–44) reported the total placer production for about the same period to be about $8 million (387,034 ounces). Winchell (1914a, p. 75) reported that the Bannack district produced about $1½ million (72,569 ounces) in gold bullion from its lode deposits, whereas Shenon (1931, p. 28) listed the gold production from lodes to be over $2 million (96,760 ounces). Total gold production through 1959 was at least 240,400 ounces—132,000 ounces from placers and 108,400 ounces from lodes. The district was virtually idle from 1950 through 1959.

The Bannack district is underlain by the Madison Limestone of Mississippian age, the Quadrant Quartzite of Carboniferous age, and red beds of Triassic(?) age. These rocks were intruded by several small masses of granodiorite. The eastern part of the district is covered by Tertiary volcanic rocks. The sedimentary rocks are folded and cut by faults, the most prominent of which is a thrust fault along which Madison Limestone overrides folded Triassic (?) red beds (Shenon, 1931, p. 14–26).

The ore deposits are chiefly irregular replacement bodies in the Madison Limestone near the granodiorite (Shenon, 1931, p. 39). They have yielded silver and gold and smaller amounts of lead, zinc, and copper. Much of the ore is oxidized. The most common ore minerals are native gold, tetrahedrite, chalcopyrite, galena, sphalerite, pyrite, specularite, and magnetite, and their oxidation products—malachite, azurite, chrysocolla, cerussite, anglesite, smithsonite, and manganese and iron oxides. The gangue minerals include calcite, quartz, siderite, garnet, epidote, and vesuvianite (Shenon, 1931, p. 39–40).

BRYANT DISTRICT

The Bryant (Hecla) district, in northeastern Beaverhead County about 12 miles west of Melrose, produced chiefly silver and lead and minor amounts of copper, gold, and zinc. Mining began with the first discovery of rich silver-lead ore in 1873 (Winchell, 1914a, p. 86) and continued through 1920, although production declined sharply after 1904 and was intermittent and small during the 1920's. After the price of gold was raised in 1934, the district again was active through 1949, but since then it has been idle. From 1873 through 1912 ore valued at about $15,425,000, chiefly in silver and lead, was mined, including 11,744 ounces of gold valued at $242,800 (Winchell, 1914a, p. 86). Total gold production through 1959, all from lode deposits, was about 17,440 ounces.

Paleozoic and Cretaceous sedimentary rocks and a stock of quartz monzonite and basic dikes of Late Cretaceous or Tertiary age underlie the district. The rocks were warped into a dome and subjected to compressive forces that produced overturned folds, thrusting, and tear faults. Later, probably at the end of Tertiary time, the rocks were offset by normal faults (Karlstrom, 1948, p. 15–50).

Most of the ore deposits are replacement shoots and pockets in dolomitic limestone of Cambrian age near the quartz monzonite intrusive. Small deposits have also been found in the quartz monzonite and along dikes (Winchell, 1914a, p. 79–86). Most of the ore is oxidized, but sulfides are found in the lower levels of some mines. The oxidized ores contain native silver, gold, cerargyrite, cerussite, malachite, azurite, chrysocolla, cuprite, smithsonite, and calamine; the sulfide ores contain galena, tetrahedrite, argentite, pyrite, sphalerite, chalcocite, and chalcopyrite. The gangue consists chiefly of calcite, dolomite, hematite, and quartz (Karlstrom, 1948, p. 50–51).

BROADWATER COUNTY

Broadwater County, in west-central Montana, was noted for its gold placers, which were among the most productive in the State. Though production before 1904 was not recorded, it was large. The estimated placer gold production of Confederate Gulch alone was about $12 million (580,550 ounces) (Pardee and Schrader, 1933, p. 172–173), and significant production has also come from placers along White, Avalanche, Beaver, Indian, and Crow Creeks (Lyden, 1948, p. 17–20). Early lode production is also unrecorded, but it probably was small. Total gold production for the county from 1901 through 1959 was approximately 362,000 ounces—about 327,500 ounces from lodes and 34,500 ounces from placers; from the beginning of mining through 1959 the total probably was about 1 million ounces.

CONFEDERATE GULCH DISTRICT

The Confederate Gulch (Backer) district is along Confederate Gulch, a tributary of the Missouri River in northern Broadwater County, about 11 miles north of Townsend. Gold has been mined chiefly from placer deposits along Confederate Gulch and its tributaries; only a little production has come from lode deposits. The placers along Confederate Gulch were discovered in 1864 and proved to be exceedingly rich; they were higher in grade, though lower in tonnage, than the well-known placers along Alder Gulch in Madison County and along Last Chance Gulch in Lewis and Clark County. The total yield is estimated to be worth about $12 million (580,550 ounces), most of which was achieved in the first 5 years of mining. After 1869 placer mining declined rapidly and by 1880 only a few miners remained in the district (Pardee and Schrader, 1933, p. 171–173). Lode production in the early years was of little consequence, but from 1908 through 1951 lodes were worked continuously on a small scale, except during World War II. No activity was reported in either lodes or placers from 1953 through 1959.

The total gold production of the district through 1959 was between 550,000 and 600,000 ounces; all but about 10,000 ounces was from placers.

The placers are in stream terrace gravels believed to be Pleistocene in age (Pardee and Schrader, 1933, p. 174–175). They were deposited at several levels by streams during the process of excavating the Confederate Gulch drainage basin. Pardee concluded that the distribution of the gold-bearing gravel indicates that the chief, if not the only, source of the gold is the quartz lodes on Miller Mountain at the head of Montana Gulch.

Most of the district is underlain by Precambrian shaly, slaty, and calcareous rocks of the Belt Series. These are disconformably overlain by Paleozoic sedimentary rocks that include the Flathead Quartzite, Wolsey Shale, and unnamed limestone and shale, all of Cambrian age; limestone and shale of Devonian age; and the Madison Limestone, Quadrant Quartzite, and Phosphoria Formation, all of Carboniferous age. These rocks were folded into a large northwest-trending anticline, exposing the Precambrian rocks in the eastern part of the district and steeply dipping bands of Paleozoic rocks in the western part. The rocks were also cut by prominent thrust faults and were intruded during Late Cretaceous or early Tertiary time by sills, dikes, and small stocks of quartz diorite and quartz monzonite (Pardee and Schrader, 1933, p. 123–132). Gold-quartz veins are along fractures in the quartz diorite and bedding planes in adjacent Precambrian shale. A few lodes are replacement bodies in the quartz diorite. Quartz, pyrite, and galena are characteristic minerals of both types of lodes. The oxidized parts of the deposits contained quartz, iron oxides, and small specks of native gold (Pardee and Schrader, 1933, p. 139–146).

PARK DISTRICT

The Park (Indian Creek, Hassel) district, on the east side of the Elkhorn Mountains between Winston and Radersburg, has produced lode and placer gold, silver, and a little lead and zinc. Placer deposits were discovered about 1860 along Indian Creek near Hassel, and gold veins were discovered later (Stone, 1911, p. 90). The placers yielded about $50,000 (2,370 ounces) in 1871, but little else is known of the early placer operations (Lyden, 1948, p. 19). There was placer mining in 1911–15, 1933–43, and again in 1945–49.

Records of the early lode mining are meager. According to Stone (1911, p. 90), tunnels and open-pit mining along some large mineralized zones produced about $500,000 (23,690 ounces) in gold, probably prior to 1908. With few exceptions there was some production every year from 1908 through 1957. The district was idle from 1957 through 1959. M. R. Klepper (written commun., 1962) summarized gold production as follows: 1864–1904, $850,000; 1905–28, $50,000; 1929–56, $1,250,000. Production from 1864 to 1904 was mainly from placers and from some lode mines in the Hassel area. From 1929 to 1956, production was mainly lode gold from the Marietta mine. Total production for all three periods was about 80,300 ounces of gold valued at $2,150,000.

Most of the lode deposits in the Park district are quartz veins in andesite which is intruded by quartz monzonite. The ore consists chiefly of auriferous pyrite accompanied by arsenopyrite and galena; the principal value is in gold (Stone, 1911, p. 89–91).

RADERSBURG DISTRICT

The Radersburg (Cedar Plains, Crow Creek) district, on the east side of the Elkhorn Mountains in southern Broadwater County, was the largest producer of lode gold in the county; it also produced some placer gold and significant amounts of silver, copper, lead, and a small amount of zinc.

Placer and lode deposits were discovered in 1866 (Winchell, 1914a, p. 173, 182). By the late 1870's the easily worked oxidized gold ores were depleted, and most of the mines closed. In 1883 railroad connections were made with the large smelters at Butte and Helena that treated sulfide ores at low costs. The mines at Radersburg were reactivated and continued in operation through 1956. The district was idle from 1956 through 1959.

Placer deposits are found for several miles along Crow Creek and Johnny Gulch near Radersburg. Old residents of the district estimated the placer production from 1866 to 1904 at $500,000 (24,380 ounces) to $1 million (48,379 ounces) (Winchell, 1914a, p. 182). Placer production after 1904 was about 850 ounces. The total gold production of the district through 1959, including both lode and placer, was about 325,000 ounces.

The principal gold deposits in the Radersburg district are in veins in andesitic volcanic rocks and associated intrusive diorite porphyry of Late Cretaceous age (M. R. Klepper, written commun., 1962). A stock of monzonite cuts these rocks about a mile south of the major mines. Ore deposits, which are valued mainly for silver, lead, and zinc, are along or near contacts of intrusive rocks with Paleozoic and Mesozoic sedimentary rocks. The most valuable deposits are gold-bearing pyrite veins containing a very small amount of chalcopyrite and very little quartz or other gangue material. A few veins contain quartz and small amounts of sphalerite, arsenopyrite, chalcopyrite, and galena. The ore along or near the igneous contacts is accompanied locally by calcite, siderite or ankerite, limonite, and pyrolusite. Cerussite, wulfenite, and hematite are in the oxidized parts of a few deposits.

WHITE CREEK DISTRICT

The White Creek district, in northern Broadwater County northwest of Confederate Gulch, includes the drainage basins of White Creek, Avalanche Creek, and upper Magpie Gulch, all of which are tributaries of the Missouri River. Production of the district consists chiefly of placer gold and a small amount of lode copper. Gold was discovered in the gravel along White Creek in 1865, and the placers along the upper part of White Creek and Johnny Gulch, a tributary, were mined for about 20 years (Pardee and Schrader, 1933, p. 179). The deposits were rich but production data are not available. Johnny Gulch was mined for a mile or more, and below its mouth in White Creek, drift mining was undertaken for a mile or more. Based on the amount of gravel moved, Pardee (in Pardee and Schrader, 1933, p. 179) estimated the yield at about $1 to $1½ million worth of gold. The Avalanche Creek placers yielded at least $100,000 and Magpie Gulch yielded about $330,000 in gold (Lyden, 1948, p. 18, 73). Most of the production was before 1904; only a few ounces was reported in the 1920's and 1930's from desultory diggings along White Creek and Magpie Gulch. Total gold production through 1959 was between 68,000 and 92,000 ounces.

The country rock of the White Creek district is almost the same as in the Confederate Gulch district and consists of folded and faulted Precambrian and Paleozoic sedimentary rocks and intrusive diorite and quartz diorite, chiefly dikes, of Cretaceous or Tertiary age (Pardee and Schrader, 1933, pl. 15). The placer gold along White Creek was derived from the same gold quartz veins on Miller Mountain that supplied the gold of Confederate Creek (Pardee and Schrader, 1933, p. 162–163, 174, 179). The source of the placer gold in Magpie Gulch and its tributaries and in Avalanche Gulch is considered to be the quartz veins that are associated with diorite dikes in the area (Lyden, 1948, p. 74; Pardee and Schrader, 1933, p. 179).

WINSTON DISTRICT

The Winston (Beaver Creek) mining district is in north Broadwater County in the drainage basin of Beaver Creek, a tributary of the Missouri River. Production of the district has come chiefly from lode mining of gold and mixed sulfide ores; placer gold mining, which began about 1866, has been relatively unimportant. According to Lyden (1948, p. 19), there is no record of placer mining since 1915.

The first lode was discovered in 1867 on the East Pacific property; there were other early discoveries, but apparently little mining was done until 10 to 20 years later (Pardee and Schrader, 1933, p. 211–212, 216). After 1900 the greatest activity was during 1908–18 and 1926–53. The district was idle from 1953 through 1959.

Early production records are fragmentary, but the production of precious and base metals through 1928 was estimated to be at least $3 million, of which about $2½ million was mined before 1908 (Pardee and Schrader, 1933, p. 212). Though the amount of gold was not stated, it must have been a major constituent, especially of those ores that were oxidized. Total gold production through 1959 was worth about $2,750,000, of which 90 percent was from lodes and 10 percent from placers (M. R. Klepper, written commun., 1962). This amounts to roughly 106,000 ounces from lodes and 12,000 ounces from placers.

In the Winston district (Stone, 1911, pl. 3), small stocks of quartz monzonite of probable Late Cretaceous age intrude a thick sequence of andesite flows, tuffs, and breccias of Late Cretaceous age (M. R. Klepper, oral commun., 1962). The ore deposits are in quartz veins in the andesite and in quartz monzonite. The ore minerals are pyrite and locally occurring galena, sphalerite, chalcopyrite, or their oxidation products. Arsenopyrite and tetrahedrite are rare components (Pardee and Schrader, 1933, p. 214). Gold occurs in all the veins and is the main valuable constituent in oxidized ores; it is relatively less abundant in unoxidized ores, where it is associated with the sulfide minerals.

CASCADE COUNTY

Gold production in Cascade County has been almost entirely from lode deposits in the Montana (Neihart) district.

MONTANA DISTRICT

The Montana (Neihart) district in the southeast corner of Cascade County, in the central Little Belt Mountains just east of Neihart, has produced chiefly silver and lead, some copper and zinc, and gold as a byproduct. Rich silver ore was discovered in 1881, and the district had an estimated gold production of $800,000 (38,703 ounces) from 1881 to 1898 (Weed, 1900, p. 404). The gold production from 1902 to 1948 inclusive (Robertson, 1951, table 3) was 28,010 ounces, and from 1949 through 1952, about 188 ounces. There was no recorded production from 1952 through 1959. Total recorded gold production through 1959 was about 67,000 ounces.

The oldest rocks of the Montana district are contorted Precambrian gneiss and schist and a Precambrian diorite phacolith. They are overlain by rocks of the Precambrian Belt Series of which the basal unit, the Neihart Quartzite, forms the country rock in the southeastern part of the area (Schafer, 1935, p. 6–12, pl. 2; Weed, 1900, p. 371–381, pl. 41). All the rocks are intruded by stocks, laccoliths, and dikes of granite porphyry and quartz porphyries and black mafic dikes, all probably of early Tertiary age.

The economically important deposits occur in veins in the gneisses and schists and in the diorite, along contacts of these rocks with the Tertiary intrusive rocks, and locally as disseminated low-grade deposits in the brecciated Tertiary intrusive bodies (Robertson, 1951, p. 18–19). In the Snow Creek area gold is an important constituent of veins that cut the Neihart quartzite and Tertiary porphyry (Schafer, 1935, p. 15, 26–29).

The common ore minerals are galena, pyrite, sphalerite, polybasite, argentite, pyrargyrite, native silver, gold, and chalcopyrite; the gangue minerals are quartz, barite, and ankerite (Weed, 1900, p. 405–410).

DEER LODGE COUNTY

Deer Lodge County in southwestern Montana has produced large amounts of silver and both lode and placer gold. The total production of the county has not been accurately determined, for records of early production, especially placer production, were not kept. Although there was a large placer output in the 1860's and 1870's, the deposits were soon depleted and have been virtually dormant since 1900. Production prior to 1904 was probably between $3½ (169,330 ounces) and $8¼ million (399,135 ounces), of which about $2½ to $3 million represents lode production and the remainder represents placer gold. From 1904 through 1952, the county produced about 303,000 ounces of lode gold and only 2,243 ounces of placer gold. The total minimum gold production of the county through 1959 was about 470,000 ounces. Most of the gold mined in Deer Lodge County came from the Georgetown and French Creek districts. Georgetown yielded almost all the lode gold; French Creek yielded the placer gold.

FRENCH CREEK DISTRICT

The French Creek district is in southern Deer Lodge County about 12 miles south of Anaconda. The gold of the district came from placer deposits near the headwaters of French Creek and its tributaries. The total placer gold has not been ascertained, and the estimates of the early production vary considerably. The deposits were discovered in 1864 and, according to Lyden (1948, p. 24), they were credited by R. W. Raymond with having produced about $1 million (48,380 ounces) to the end of 1869, but other estimates listed by Lyden (1948, p. 24) credited the district with a yield of $5 million during the same period. Between 1900 and 1902, a dredge and several hydraulic installations were operating in the district, but their productivity was not recorded. The deposits were again worked in the 1930's, but only a few ounces of gold was recovered. The district was inactive from 1940 through 1959. Total gold production probably was between 50,000 and 250,000 ounces through 1959.

GEORGETOWN DISTRICT

The Georgetown district, which includes the Cable mine and placer deposit, is in the northwestern part of Deer Lodge County in the upper drainage basin of Warm Springs Creek about 10 to 15 miles northwest of Anaconda and about 10 miles southeast of Philipsburg. Gold is the most valuable commodity mined in the district, but small amounts of silver and copper are also obtained. Virtually the entire output of lode gold of Deer Lodge County has come from the Georgetown district.

The Cable mine, the most productive in the district, was located in 1866, and a mill to treat the ore was built the following year (Emmons and Calkins, 1913, p. 221–222). The production of the mine to 1872 was worth about $400,000. In 1877, the mine changed ownership and a new mill was built. From 1877 until 1891, more than $2 million (96,760 ounces) in gold was recovered. The ore shoots were supposedly exhausted in 1891, and the mine closed. Under new management the mine was developed to deeper levels; additional ore was found and production was sustained for some time. The Southern Cross mine, another large gold producer in the district, was also located in 1866, but the claim was allowed to lapse. It was relocated in the early 1870's, and ore worth a total of $600,000, mainly in gold, was mined intermittently through 1905 (Emmons and Calkins, 1913, p. 231). The lode mines were moderately active until 1943. Production ceased for the following 6 years, and only a few hundred ounces of gold was produced from 1950 through 1959.

Significant amounts of placer gold were mined in the early years, chiefly from the Cable placer, near the Cable mine, and from the Georgetown placers. The Cable placer was a bonanza deposit. In 1872 and 1873 it yielded $51,000 in gold, and it was worked for many years during which the total returns probably amounted to several hundred thousand dollars (Emmons and Calkins, 1913, p. 264). The Georgetown placers, near Georgetown, produced about $40,000 (1,935 ounces) in gold in 1870. No other figures have been found covering placer production through 1934, and only 96 ounces was recorded from 1935 through 1959.

The total gold output of the district through 1959 was at least 460,000 ounces, most of which was from lode mines.

Faulted and folded sedimentary rocks, mainly of Paleozoic age, are intruded by a small stock and several smaller bodies of granitic rock (Emmons and Calkins, 1913, p. 221). The most productive mines are in the sedimentary rocks near the intrusive contacts, but some deposits are a mile or more from such contacts and some are in the intrusive rock. The deposits include gold-copper replacement deposits of contact-metamorphic origin, gold-bearing replacement veins in sedimentary rocks, and gold-bearing veins in granite (Emmons and Calkins, 1913, p. 221–242). The chief ore minerals are pyrite, pyrrhotite, chalcopyrite, gold, and magnetite in a gangue of quartz, calcite, and garnet. The ore bodies at the Cable mine are large irregular replacement deposits in a large limestone block nearly surrounded by granite. In most of the other mines the ore deposits are chiefly replacement veins in limestone and calcareous shale.

FERGUS COUNTY

Fergus County in north-central Montana is east of the main mining area of the State. Gold accounts for about 99 percent of the value of metals produced in the county. From 1886 through 1950 the total gold production of Fergus County was about 653,000 ounces; all but 500 to 1,000 ounces was from lodes. The periods of greatest activity were 1901–22 and 1936–42. The bulk of the gold production from Fergus County has come from the Warm Springs district in the Judith Mountains and from the North Moccasin district near Kendall in the North Moccasin Mountains.

NORTH MOCCASIN DISTRICT

Located in the North Moccasin Mountains in west-central Fergus County about 15 to 18 miles north-northwest of Lewistown, the North Moccasin (Kendall) district produced about 425,000 to 450,000 ounces of gold through 1959, about two-thirds of the county production. In 1903 and 1904, when Fergus County was the leading gold producer in Montana, nearly all the gold came from this district.

These deposits were discovered in 1893, about 13 years after the discovery of gold ore in the Judith Mountains, but they were not developed until about 1900, when a cyanidation plant was built to recover the gold from the refractory ores which were not amenable to amalgamation. Mining thereafter was almost continuous through 1922, at which time the North Moccasin mine, the most productive in the district since 1911, closed (U.S. Bureau of Mines, 1924, pt. 1, p. 350). The district was practically idle until the middle 1930's. In 1936 the old Barnes-King property was reopened, a 50-ton cyanide plant was built, and there was substantial production from the district through 1942. Only small-scale operations were carried on after World War II, and the district was idle from 1948 through 1959.

The North Moccasin Mountains, which lie west of the Judith Mountains, are a single, major, dome-shaped uplift formed by the laccolithic intrusion of syenite porphyry into Paleozoic and Mesozoic sedimentary rocks. Dikes and sills are also present (Blixt, 1933, p. 5).

The gold deposits are irregularly distributed in bituminous and argillaceous layers in limestone near the top of the Madison Formation, but some ore has also been found in dikes and in sandstone and shale. Mining has centered on the eastern slope of the mountains near Kendall. The ore is oxidized and consists of finely disseminated native gold, quartz, fluorite, and limonite. Unoxidized ore in prospects contains chalcopyrite, argentiferous galena, sphalerite, and pyrite (Blixt, 1933, p. 21).

WARM SPRINGS DISTRICT

The Warm Springs (Maiden-Gilt Edge) district is near the southwest end of the Judith Mountains in the central part of the county about 10 miles northeast of Lewistown. The first ore discoveries in Fergus County, which were placer gravels in the Judith Mountains, were made in either 1879 or 1880 (Lyden, 1948, p. 28). Soon afterward gold-silver lodes were found. The placers were worked on a small scale but their output is not known. The lode mines of the district yielded gold ores worth $939,230 (about 45,400 ounces) before 1900 (Robertson, 1950, table 4, p. 10). Lode mining continued after 1900; the most prosperous period probably was 1901–21. From 1932 through 1954 activity was desultory, and the district was idle from 1954 through 1959. Total gold production through 1959 was about 200,000 ounces.

The Judith Mountains are a group of dome-shaped uplifts formed by laccolithic intrusions of Late Cretaceous or early Tertiary age into sedimentary rocks that range from Cambrian to Cretaceous in age (Weed and Pirsson, 1898, p. 457). Associated with the laccoliths are sills and dikes. The intrusive rocks are chiefly acidic porphyries. The major ore deposits are found in limestone near porphyry contacts. The ore minerals are gold and sylvanite accompanied by pyrite, galena, argentite, sphalerite, and chalcopyrite. The gangue minerals are calcite, chalcedonic quartz, and fluorite (Corry, 1933, p. 39–40).

GRANITE COUNTY

Granite County, in west-central Montana, through 1959 produced a total of 710,000 ounces of gold—376,000 ounces from silver lodes and 334,000 ounces from placers. The most prosperous period was 1881–93 when the Granite Mountain, Hope, and a few other silver mines were at their peaks. Most of the lode gold has been a byproduct of silver ores in the Flint Creek, First Chance, and Boulder Creek districts (Emmons and Calkins, 1913, p. 192).

Placers along Bear Creek in the First Chance district and along Henderson Creek in the Henderson district were also productive, mostly before 1900. Lodes and, to a lesser extent, placers continued to yield substantial amounts of gold until 1946, but their output diminished through the 1950's.

BOULDER CREEK DISTRICT

The Boulder Creek district is in the east-central part of Granite County, about 7 to 9 miles northeast of Philipsburg. Most of the gold has come from lode deposits that also yielded some silver, lead, and copper. There were intermittent placer operations along Boulder Creek and its tributaries through 1942, but production from these was small (Lyden, 1948, p. 40–41).

Although lode deposits were found in districts surrounding the Boulder Creek basin in the 1860's, important discoveries were not made on Boulder Creek and its tributaries until 1885 (Emmons and Calkins, 1913, p. 192). The district was active until 1906 when the Royal mine, the most productive in the district, was put under lease (Emmons and Calkins, 1913, p. 246–247) and thereafter activity declined. Production again increased during the 1930's after the price of gold was raised, but from 1943 through 1959, activity was minor.

The early lode production is not known. The Royal mine is credited with a production, principally in the late 1890's, of about $1 million (48,379 ounces) in gold, and a small production came from other mines (Emmons and Calkins, 1913, p. 246). Total gold production of the district through 1959 was about 58,450 ounces, including about 1,400 ounces from placers.

The country rock in the Boulder Creek district consists of extensively faulted and tilted sedimentary rocks ranging in age from Precambrian to Mesozoic and biotite granite of Tertiary age which intruded the sedimentary rocks. Some of the faults cut the granite. The ore deposits are chiefly fissure veins in the granite, in siliceous Precambrian rocks, and in Carboniferous or Mesozoic quartzite and impure limestone. A few replacement veins are in relatively pure Paleozoic limestone. The most productive deposits are gold veins that contain small amounts of silver. A few veins are silver or silver-lead veins that contain a little gold. The principal sulfides of the gold ores are pyrite and galena in quartz gangue; the silver ores carry also tetrahedrite and sphalerite (Emmons and Calkins, 1913, p. 246–250).

FIRST CHANCE DISTRICT

The First Chance (Garnet) district is in northern Granite County in the drainage basin of Bear Creek, a tributary of the Clark Fork River. Both placer and lode deposits were found in the district. The placer deposits along Bear Creek and its subsidiary gulches were the most productive in Granite County and were among the more productive of the early placer operations in Montana. The placer deposits were discovered in 1865, and up to 1917, according to Pardee (1918, p. 231–232), they produced gold valued between $5 million (241,900 ounces) and $7 million (338,660 ounces), mostly in the first few years of operation. From 1917 through 1959 the district produced a minimum of 15,200 ounces, most of which was mined during the period 1939–42. The total placer production from the district through 1959 was between 260,000 and 355,000 ounces.

The lode deposits are valuable chiefly for gold, but some copper and silver have also been produced. The first lodes were located in the district in 1867 but were not exploited to any extent until 1896 (Pardee, 1918, p. 171–172). A continuous but fluctuating production was maintained through 1942. After World War II the district had only minor activity and was virtually idle through the 1950's. The total lode gold production through 1959 was probably 85,000 to 90,000 ounces. The total lode and placer production combined is probably between 345,000 and 445,000 ounces.

The rocks of the Garnet district are quartzite and shale of the Belt Series of Precambrian age overlain by limestone of Paleozoic age. These rocks were folded into a northwest-trending arch and were intruded by a mass of granodiorite of Late Cretaceous or Tertiary age. The ore deposits are in veins in the granodiorite and along bedding planes in quartzite and schist. Quartz is the dominant vein mineral; barite and ankerite are locally abundant. The ore minerals are pyrite, tetrahedrite, chalcopyrite, galena, and in rare occurrences, gold tellurides and molybdenite. Most of the gold is associated with pyrite (Pardee, 1918, p. 172–177).

FLINT CREEK DISTRICT

Most of the mines of the Flint Creek (Philipsburg) district, which includes the Red Lion camp, are in a 3-square-mile area just east of Philipsburg. This district is the largest lode-gold producer in Granite County even though gold accounts for only 10 percent of the value of the ore. Silver forms the remaining 90 percent. Some lead, copper, and zinc have been produced but they are of no great economic importance. From 1950 through 1959 the Algonquin mine produced large tonnages of manganese ore, which yielded gold as a byproduct. The principal mines of the district are the Granite, Bimetallic, and Hope mines.

Ore was discovered at the Hope mine in December 1864, and lodes were soon located in many other places in the district and in the adjacent region (Emmons and Calkins, 1913, p. 191–193). The town of Philipsburg, just south of the Hope mine, was founded in 1867.

The Granite Mountain mine, the most productive in the Flint Creek district, was located in 1872. From 1875 to 1892 it yielded about $20 million in silver and gold and for a time was the most productive silver mine in the United States (Emmons and Calkins, 1913, p. 202–203). The Bimetallic mine, on the same ore shoot as the Granite Mountain, began operations in about 1882. Because of the fall in the price of silver, the mine was shut down in 1893 and was consolidated with the Granite mine in 1898 under the name of the Granite-Bimetallic Consolidated Mining Co. From 1898 to 1904 these mines produced silver ore valued at about $1 million a year, but in August 1905 they were again shut down because of the low price of silver and decreasing grade of the ore. In 1906 the mine was opened to leasers. With the exception of the depression years, 1930–32, the Flint Creek district maintained a substantial annual production through 1945, when activity slackened. From 1946 through 1956 only a small amount of gold was mined. No activity was reported from 1957 through 1959.

Early mining operations in the district were very expensive because of the remoteness of supply points. Milling costs were especially high; for example, salt, which was used in large quantities in silver mills, had to be transported from Utah and cost $120 a ton at Philipsburg in 1871. In 1883 the Northern Pacific Railway was completed through Drummond, only 30 miles from Philipsburg. A railroad from Drummond to Philipsburg was completed in 1887 (Emmons and Calkins, 1913, p. 192), and low-cost shipment of ore to smelters at Helena, Anaconda, and Great Falls was made possible. Some ore, however, was still treated in silver mills near the mines.

The gold production of the Flint Creek district before 1904 was estimated by Emmons and Calkins (1913, p. 201, 203) to be worth about $3,200,000, or about 155,000 ounces. Total production through 1959 was about 260,000 ounces.

The rocks exposed in the mineralized area east of Philipsburg comprise the upper part of the Spokane Formation of Precambrian (Algonkian) age and

and copper. Younger lodes in Tertiary volcanics are found in a small area along Lowland Creek. These are epithermal veins and are mined for gold and silver (M. R. Klepper, written commun., 1962).

Billingsley and Grimes (1918, p. 313) noted a tendency toward mineral zoning in veins near Basin. Veins in the upper part of the batholith and in the roofrocks contain quartz, tourmaline, and arsenopyrite. Underneath this zone, from 200 to 500 feet below the roof of the batholith, galena predominates but gives way downward to sphalerite. The deepest ore is the lowest in grade and contains pyrite and copper minerals.

CLANCY DISTRICT

The Clancy district is in the northern part of the county, about 10 miles south of Helena. Though primarily a placer district, most of the gold produced in the district before 1900 was a byproduct of flourishing silver mines.

Placer mining began about 1865 along Prickly Pear Creek and the following year rich silver lodes were found. By 1910, however, most of the mines were idle, and the once-thriving town of Lump Gulch City was deserted (Pardee and Schrader, 1933, p. 227). In 1933 a dredge was installed on Prickly Pear Creek. In 1937 and 1938 additional large-scale operations, which resulted in considerable placer production through 1948, were undertaken on Prickly Pear and Clancy Creeks. From 1949 through 1957 the placer operations were suspended. In 1958 and 1959 placers were again mined on Prickly Pear Creek, but production data were not recorded.

Total gold production of the district through 1959 was about 101,000 ounces from placers and at least 2,000 ounces from lodes.

The predominant bedrock in the district is quartz monzonite and is part of the Boulder batholith of Late Cretaceous or Tertiary age. Remnants of a once-extensive cover of Tertiary rhyolite occur in the eastern and northeastern parts of the district. The lode deposits are in veins in quartz monzonite. The richest deposits contained silver-bearing galena, sphalerite, and tetrahedrite in a chalcedonic quartz gangue. Other veins produced small amounts of gold. These consisted mainly of quartz and pyrite, and small amounts of galena, sphalerite, and arsenopyrite (Knopf, 1913, p. 102–104).

ELKHORN DISTRICT

Located in the Elkhorn Mountains east of Boulder, the Elkhorn district was prospected before 1870, but the highly productive Holter lode in the Elkhorn mine was not discovered until 1875. The early economic importance of this district depended almost wholly on the Elkhorn mine (Knopf, 1913, p. 128) which produced mostly silver and lead ore and small amounts of byproduct gold. After 1911 as many as 16 mines operated in a single year, but the bulk of the more recent production came from the Golden Curry and Swissmont mines and the reworked tailings of the Elkhorn mine (Pardee and Schrader, 1933, p. 299–300). The total gold production of the district through 1953 was 70,015 ounces (Klepper and others, 1957, p. 64). From 1954 through 1959 only 97 ounces was recorded.

The Elkhorn district lies on the eastern margin of the Boulder batholith. The oldest rock in the district is metamorphosed shale of the Belt Series which is overlain by metamorphosed Paleozoic limestone, shale, and quartzite, ranging in age from Cambrian to Pennsylvanian, and by Mesozoic sandstone, shale, and impure limestone. These are overlain by a bedded series of andesitic breccias, tuffs, and lavas of Late Cretaceous age. The sedimentary and volcanic rocks are folded, faulted, and cut by small igneous masses of diverse composition that are slightly older than the Boulder batholith, by quartz monzonite of the batholith, and by aplite (M. R. Klepper, written commun., 1962).

A wide variety of ore deposits is found within the Elkorn district: magmatic sulfide deposits at the Golden Curry property, auriferous contact metamorphic deposits in the Dolcoath mine, auriferous lead-silver replacement deposits at the Elkhorn mine, and mineralized breccia pipes at the Elkhorn Queen and Skyline mines (Klepper and others, 1957, p. 64). Magmatic sulfide ore consists of a mixture of pyrrhotite and chalcopyrite intergrown with augite. The contact ore body in the Dolcoath mine consists of chalcopyrite and an auriferous sulfide and telluride of bismuth intergrown with silicates and calcite. The ore at the Elkhorn mine consists mainly of argentiferous galena, sphalerite, pyrite, and tetrahedrite as replacement bodies in dolomite beneath hornstone. At the Elkhorn Queen and Skyline mines pipelike bodies of brecciated rock are cemented by quartz, black tourmaline, pyrite, galena, sphalerite, and sparse chalcopyrite and arsenopyrite (Klepper and others, 1957, p. 64).

TIZER DISTRICT

The Tizer (Wilson Creek) district is about 20 miles southeast of Helena, immediately northeast of the Elkhorn district.

Two lode mines in this district—the Callahan and Center Reef—have produced a total of 9,536 ounces of gold (Klepper and others, 1957, p. 72–73). Klepper (written commun., 1962) estimated that other lodes in this district produced about 500 ounces of gold and that placers along Wilson and Crow Creeks produced between 500 and 1,000 ounces —a total of roughly 10,500 ounces. The Callahan property was productive as recently as 1951, but no activity was reported from 1952 through 1959.

At the Callahan mine, the ore deposits are in narrow veins in andesitic extrusive rocks of Late Cretaceous age. The veins, which are as much as 6 feet thick, consist of pyritic andesite and quartz with sparse pyrite, galena, sphalerite, chalcopyrite, and specks of gold and tetrahedrite(?).

The country rock at the Center Reef mine is similar to that at the Callahan. The ore is in a narrow vein with mineralogy similar to that of the Callahan deposit (Klepper and others, 1957, p. 72–73).

WHITEHALL DISTRICT

Located on the south end of Bull Mountain in the south-central part of the county, the Whitehall (Cardwell) district has produced lode gold, silver, and lead.

The chief mine, the Golden Sunlight, was opened in 1890 and was operated almost continuously until 1957 (Roby and others, 1960, p. 82–83). Roughly three-quarters of the recorded gold production of 71,850 ounces between 1902 and 1957 came from this mine. Production of the Golden Sunlight from 1890 to 1910 was $1½ million in gold and silver (Roby and others, 1960, p. 83). Total gold production of the district through 1959 was at least 100,000 ounces.

The rocks of the district are shales, sandstones, and sandy limestones of the Precambrian Belt Series conformably overlain by a thick sequence of Paleozoic rocks, mainly limestone. The sedimentary rocks are intruded by quartz porphyry, andesite, and basalt dikes. The ore occurs in veins in the sedimentary rocks and in the porphyry. The ore contains auriferous pyrite, galena, and sphalerite in a quartz gangue (Winchell, 1914a, p. 97–99).

WICKES DISTRICT

In the Wickes (Colorado) district, in north Jefferson County, about 20 miles south of Helena, gold has been a byproduct of rich silver-lead ores.

Lode mining began in 1864 with the discovery of the Gregory lode. Four mines—the Gregory, Alta, Comet, and Minah—have been the sources of nearly all the metals produced in the district. The most active period was from 1880 to 1893; however, the district was active almost continuously through 1959.

Gold production from 1864 to 1928 was estimated at $4,325,000 (about 210,000 ounces) from lodes and $25,000 (about 1,200 ounces) from placers (Pardee and Schrader, 1933, p. 186). Total production through 1959 was roughly 264,000 ounces from lodes and 2,200 ounces from placers.

The oldest rocks in the district are andesites and latites of Cretaceous age, which occur as roof remnants in quartz monzonite of the Boulder batholith. The quartz monzonite is intruded by large masses of aplite.

The ore deposits are in quartz veins in altered andesite or sericitized quartz monzonite or aplite. The principal ore minerals are galena, sphalerite, pyrite, chalcopyrite, tetrahedrite, and arsenopyrite. In the oxidized zone are cerussite, anglesite, bournonite, and covellite. Tourmaline is abundant in the wallrock and in the veins (Pardee and Schrader, 1933, p. 234–235).

LEWIS AND CLARK COUNTY

Lewis and Clark County produced between 4 and 5 million ounces of gold through 1959 and is one of three counties in Montana to exceed an output of 1 million ounces. Within the county two districts—Helena and Marysville—have each produced in excess of 1 million ounces, and six others have produced in excess of 100,000 ounces. The gold yield is roughly divided equally between placer and lode deposits.

The first mineral deposits discovered and mined in the county, either in 1863 or 1864, were the gold-bearing gravels along Iowa Gulch in the northern part of the Scratchgravel Hills, about 4 miles northwest of Helena (Pardee and Schrader, 1933, p. 36). The famous Last Chance Gulch placers on the present site of Helena were discovered shortly afterwards in the summer of 1864, and rich gold lodes were discovered a few miles south of Helena in September of the same year (Knopf, 1913, p. 15).

Most placer deposits and some lode deposits were quickly exhausted, and mining languished by 1900. However, after the price of gold was raised to $35 per ounce in 1934, both placer and lode districts were reactivated and gold mining again became a major industry.

The placers of the Helena-Last Chance district have been the most productive in the county, but other highly productive placer deposits occur chiefly in the western part of the county and, from south to north, include the following (Lyden, 1948, p. 54–74): Tenmile Creek and its tributaries in the

Rimini district, Sevenmile Creek in the Scratchgravel district, Silver Creek in the Marysville district, Virginia Creek in the Stemple district, McClellan Creek west of Stemple, and Lincoln Gulch in the Lincoln district. Rich placers were also exploited in the southeastern part of the county east of Helena in the York district on the western slope of the Belt Mountains along the Missouri River, York Gulch, and Oregon Gulch (Pardee and Schrader, 1933, p. 120–122, 176–182; Lyden, 1948, p. 68–74).

The chief lode deposits are in and near the Boulder batholith and its satellite stocks and in the roofrocks (Pardee and Schrader, 1933, pl. 1). The Boulder batholith, of Late Cretaceous or early Tertiary age, is 60 miles long from north to south and averages 18 miles in width. The Marysville district has been the largest producer of lode gold in the county, but sizable production has also come from the Helena, Rimini, Stemple, Dry Gulch, and Scratchgravel districts.

HELENA-LAST CHANCE DISTRICT

The Helena-Last Chance district, in the southern part of Lewis and Clark County, in and around Helena, the capital of Montana, includes the famous Last Chance Gulch placer deposits, among the richest and most productive in Montana. Placer gold was discovered in Last Chance Gulch in 1864; other placer deposits in neighboring gulches were discovered soon after, and in the fall of the same year lode gold was discovered at the Whitlatch-Union mine, the most productive lode in the district. Gold accounts for more than 99 percent of the total value of the mine production from the district.

Most of the rich placers and lodes were mined out before 1900, and mining operations after that time were intermittent and on a small scale until 1934, when the gold price increase reawakened activity. During 1935–50 a successful dredging operation yielded considerable gold. Lode mines were also reactivated and were productive to 1940 but declined thereafter (Lyden, 1948, p. 56–57). There was no recorded production from lodes or placers during 1954–59.

The estimated value of the early placer gold production, most of which was taken out before 1868, ranges from $10 to $35 million (Knopf, 1913, p. 15, 86). Pardee and Schrader (1933, p. 186) credited the district with a placer production of $17,079,000 (826,275 ounces) and with lode production of $6,304,000 (305,000 ounces) from 1864 through 1928. From 1929 through 1959 the district produced about 40,120 ounces of lode gold and about 110,600 ounces of placer gold. Thus the total production of the district through 1959 was at least 345,000 ounces of lode gold and about 940,000 ounces of placer gold.

The Helena-Last Chance district lies along the north edge of the Boulder batholith, a mass of quartz monzonite and related rocks of Late Cretaceous or early Tertiary age which has intruded a thick sequence of sedimentary rocks of late Precambrian, Paleozoic, and Mesozoic age and volcanic rocks of Late Cretaceous age. Other igneous rocks in the district are porphyry dikes and sheets of pre-Tertiary age and small intrusive masses, lava flows and tuffs of rhyolite, all of Miocene age.

The sedimentary and volcanic rocks were folded into a large dome about 25 miles in diameter which extends beyond the district. The folds were ruptured by the intrusion of the Boulder batholith, and additional faulting occurred as the intrusive forces relaxed.

The ore deposits are mainly near the contact of the batholith with the sedimentary rocks; some are in the granitic rocks, and others are in the adjacent hornfels or tactite. The ore minerals in the contact deposits are pyrite, pyrrhotite, and gold, and local chalcopyrite and galena; they occur in aggregates of lime-silicate minerals, tourmaline, quartz, ankerite, and chlorite.

The Whitlatch-Union lode, the most productive in the district, lies partly in the granite and partly in hornfels. The vein ranges in width from a thin seam to 15 feet and averages about 4 feet. The ore taken out in the early years averaged from $20 to $25 per ton in gold (Knopf, 1913, p. 99).

LINCOLN DISTRICT

The Lincoln district includes Lincoln Gulch and several other tributaries of the Blackfoot River near the town of Lincoln in the western part of Lewis and Clark County. Most of the gold mined in the district was from placer deposits; a small amount was from lodes. The gold placers, which were discovered about 1865, were rich and hastily worked, and by about the middle 1870's the camp was virtually abandoned (Pardee and Schrader, 1933, p. 115–117). Pardee and Schrader (1933) estimated that during these early years a stretch of the gulch 7,400 feet long yielded about $7 million (338,653 ounces) in gold. The placers were worked intermittently from 1904 through about 1955 and yielded at least 2,700 ounces of gold. The total placer production through 1959 was about 342,000 ounces.

Lode production, which probably totaled less than

200 ounces, was mined sporadically, mostly during the 1930's.

Low-grade gold ore, which averages $2.20 to $3 per ton, is found in a diorite dike that has intruded calcic argillite of the Belt Series (Pardee and Schrader, 1933, p. 116–117). The lode follows a shear zone and is as much as 30 feet wide. The diorite in the shear zone is largely replaced by quartz, siderite, and pyrite.

McCLELLAN DISTRICT

All production of the McClellan district, which is in the western part of Lewis and Clark County about 8 miles south of Lincoln, has been placer gold. Placer mining in McClellan Gulch dates back to 1864, and by 1875 these deposits yielded an estimated $7 million (338,653 ounces) in gold (Pardee and Schrader, 1933, p. 117). The gravels were very rich and have been reworked in places as many as two or three times since 1875. The amount of gold recovered since 1875 is not known. The total minimum production of these placers through 1959 was about 340,000 ounces. About 10 ounces of lode gold was produced in the late 1940's.

The source of the gold probably was the low-grade gold-quartz lodes that crop out on the slopes at the head of the gulch (Pardee and Schrader, 1933, p. 118).

MARYSVILLE-SILVER CREEK DISTRICT

The Marysville-Silver Creek (Ottawa) district, near the headwaters of Silver Creek about 18 miles northwest of Helena, also includes the Bald Butte area. The district has been one of the most productive precious-metal mining districts in Montana. Most of the gold has come from veins, although a smaller amount has come from placer deposits. Some mines have also produced substantial amounts of lead.

The first placer mining in the district was along Silver Creek in 1864, and these placers accounted for at least 75 percent of the placer production of the district (Lyden, 1948, p. 60). The placers were rich and were mined out in the early years; in fact, no placer activity was reported in the district from 1904 to 1933 (Lyden, 1948, p. 60). From 1938 to 1941, dredging and dragline shovel operations were undertaken.

The placer production during the early period was estimated at about $3,200,000 (154,813 ounces) (Lyden, 1948, p. 60), and the total through 1959 was about 164,500 ounces.

Lode mining dates back to 1876 and the discovery of the rich Drumlummon lode, the most productive and most steadily mined lode in the district (Knopf, 1913, p. 61–62). In the early 1890's, the Drumlummon property became involved in protracted litigation and the mine was worked only intermittently. In 1911 the mine was sold, and the new owners rehabilitated both the milling plant and mine and began exploration for new ore bodies. In later years tailings from the Drumlummon mill were also reworked (Pardee and Schrader, 1933, p. 63). The last significant lode gold production was reported in 1951. The lode production of the district before 1903 was valued at about $30 million in gold and silver (Knopf, 1913, p. 62), of which possibly 60 percent was in gold. About half of the early production was from the Drumlummon mine. Total lode gold production through 1959 was about 1,145,800 ounces. If placer production is included, the district had a total yield through 1959 of about 1,310,000 ounces.

The Marysville-Silver Creek district is centered around a small stock of quartz diorite of Late Cretaceous or Tertiary age that has intruded limestone and shale of the Belt Series of Precambrian age (Barrell, 1907, p. 7–19). The sedimentary rocks adjacent to the stock have been metamorphosed to a hard and dense-textured hornstone locally called slate, in a zone ranging from ½ to 2 miles in width. Numerous dikes of pegmatite, aplite, and diorite porphyry cut the stock and the sedimentary rocks.

The ore deposits are steeply dipping gold and silver veins around the border of the quartz diorite stock. Some veins are in the marginal part of the diorite, but most are in metamorphosed sedimentary rocks. The gold is finely divided and accompanies the ore minerals tetrahedrite, chalcopyrite, pyrite, sphalerite, and galena. The gangue minerals are chiefly lamellar quartz and calcite (Knopf, 1913, p. 64–66); the calcite contains some iron and manganese.

MISSOURI RIVER-YORK DISTRICT

Located in the southeast corner of Lewis and Clark County, on the west side of the Belt Mountains, the Missouri River-York district includes Trout Creek, York, Clark, Oregon, Cave, and Magpie Gulches—all tributaries of the Missouri River. Most of the production of this district came from placer deposits, but a significant amount came from lodes.

Placer gold was discovered in this area in 1864 about half a mile above the mouth of York Gulch (Pardee and Schrader, 1933, p. 176); placers along its tributaries and other streams in the district were discovered about the same time or a year or two later. Most of the placers were rich, and within a few years after discovery they were either mined out or the richest parts had been depleted and they were then abandoned. Years later some were worked by dredges, and again substantial amounts of gold were produced, especially during the periods 1909–13 and 1934–44. No placer production was reported from 1950 through 1959.

Authentic records of the early placer production of the Missouri River-York district have not been found. On the basis of the size of deposits and reported grades, the production to about 1928 of the individual deposits was estimated (Pardee and Schrader, 1933, p. 177–182) as follows:

		Ounces
York-Trout Creek	$500,000	24,190
Clark and Oregon Gulches	800,000	38,704
Cave Gulch	900,000	43,542
Magpie Gulch	280,000	13,546
Missouri River terraces	2,150,000	104,016
Total	$4,630,000	223,998

The figures given probably should be accepted as the minimum production of these placers. Some estimates of the output of the York-Trout Creek placers alone were as high as $5 million (Pardee and Schrader, 1933, p. 176). The production of the district from 1928 through 1950 was about 41,200 ounces. The minimum placer production of the district was therefore about 265,000 ounces.

The lode deposits occur chiefly in Dry Gulch and other tributaries of Trout Creek above the old town of York. Discovery of the first lode in the district, the gold-quartz lode of the Old Amber mine, was probably made soon after mining had begun (Pardee and Schrader, 1933, p. 120), and a mill to work the ore was built before 1870. Outcrops of gold-bearing quartz, occurring mainly in shale along a dike, attracted early attention. Numerous veins along the dike were developed, and the ore was hauled to Trout Creek or other streams where it was worked in small mills and arrastres. Several mines were active between 1895 and 1900 (Pardee and Schrader, 1933, p. 121), but after 1900 all were abandoned except the Golden Messenger mine in Dry Gulch, the most productive in the district. Mining of the Golden Messenger began in 1899 (Pardee and Schrader, 1933, p. 121, 146) and continued through 1942. The lode mines were virtually idle from 1942 through 1959.

Incomplete records credit the lode mines with production worth $450,000 to $600,000, chiefly in gold, before 1932 (Pardee and Schrader, 1933, p. 121–122). Lode production from 1933 through 1943 was about 51,440 ounces, most of which came from the Golden Messenger mine. The minimum lode production of the Missouri River-York district was about 70,000 ounces. The district can thus be credited with a total gold output through 1959 of about 335,000 ounces from lodes and placers.

The area is underlain by shaly, slaty, and calcareous rocks of the Belt Series, which are folded into a large northwest-trending anticline whose northeast limb is cut by an overthrust fault. The sedimentary rocks are cut by quartz diorite dikes and stocks of Late Cretaceous or Tertiary age (Pardee and Schrader, 1933, p. 123–134).

The lodes and the placer deposits of the Missouri River-York district are closely associated with the quartz diorite dikes. Most of the lodes are small quartz veins in fractures in diorite and along the bedding planes in the adjacent shale. The veins are valuable chiefly for gold (Pardee and Schrader, 1933, p. 139–144; 147–160); silver and lead are minor constituents. The veins consist almost entirely of quartz, a little pyrite, and scattered grains of galena. The ore shoots range from a few inches to several feet in width and from a few feet to several hundred feet in length. The ore bodies in the Golden Messenger mine are irregular replacement deposits along fractures in the quartz diorite which has been altered and more or less replaced by quartz, ankerite, and small amounts of sulfides. Pyrite is the most abundant sulfide, but galena, sphalerite, and small amounts of chalcopyrite are also present. Most of the ore mined, both in the replacement shoots and in the veins, was oxidized.

RIMINI-TENMILE DISTRICT

The Rimini-Tenmile (Vaughn) district in the valley of Tenmile Creek in the southern tip of Lewis and Clark County, about 14 miles southwest of Helena, has produced chiefly gold, silver, and lead. The first location was probably made on the Lee Mountain lode in 1864, and the first mine was a tunnel driven on the Eureka vein in 1865 (Pardee and Schrader, 1933, p. 246). Through 1957 the district had an output of about 194,000 ounces of lode gold and about 4,275 ounces of placer gold. The most active and productive period of the district was before 1907, when about 169,500 ounces of gold was mined. Thereafter the deposits were worked on a small scale until 1957, and the district was idle from 1957 through 1959.

The prevailing country rock is coarse-grained quartz monzonite and aplite of the Boulder batholith, which is intrusive into Upper Cretaceous andesitic and quartz latitic volcanic rocks. Rhyolite of

Tertiary age caps the older rocks (Knopf, 1913, p. 80–85, and pl. 1).

In the Remini-Tenmile district, two periods of mineralization are recognizable: one of Late Cretaceous and one of late Tertiary age (Knopf, 1913, p. 81). The older and more productive ore bodies are auriferous silver-lead veins in tourmalinized and sericitized quartz monzonite in the upper part of the batholith. The principal ore mineral is galena accompanied by sphalerite, pyrite, arsenopyrite, and a little chalcopyrite and tetrahedrite; most of the lodes are notably tourmaline-bearing. The Tertiary deposits are low grade and consist of altered rhyolite impregnated with gold along small fractures (Knopf, 1913, p. 82). The rhyolite rests unconformably on the eroded surface of the quartz monzonite.

SEVENMILE-SCRATCHGRAVEL DISTRICT

The Sevenmile-Scratchgravel district includes the Scratchgravel Hills which are about 4 miles northwest of Helena and immediately north of Sevenmile Creek. The ore deposits include gold placers, rich silver-lead veins, and gold veins (Pardee and Schrader, 1933, p. 35–62).

Placer deposits were discovered in Iowa Gulch, in the northern part of the Scratchgravel Hills, shortly before gold was discovered in Last Chance Gulch at Helena in 1864. These deposits were not large, and there has been little activity on them since the early days. The amount of gold produced is not known (Pardee and Schrader, 1933, p. 36). Other placer deposits along Sevenmile Creek and its tributaries, including Greenhorn Creek, were considerably more productive.

These creeks were mined for an aggregate length of 12 miles or more, and by 1930 yielded an estimated $1,200,000 (58,055 ounces) worth of gold (Pardee and Schrader, 1933, p. 59). From 1930 through 1959 the yield probably was less than 750 ounces (Lyden, 1948, p. 58–59).

The lode deposits were discovered before 1872. Some rich silver-lead ore was mined in the early years, and in 1914 rich gold ore was found in the Franklin and Scratchgravel mines. The period 1916–18 was one of great prosperity in which the lode mines, primarily the Franklin and Scratchgravel mines, produced at least $550,000 (26,600 ounces) in gold. By 1919, however, costs of supplies and labor forced these mines to close, and lode production was then limited to desultory output of several smaller mines. Total lode gold production of the district through 1959 was about 48,700 ounces; total lode and placer production through 1959 was at least 108,000 ounces.

The country rock consists of shale, sandstone, and limestone of the Belt Series of late Precambrian age and quartzite, shale, and limestone of Cambrian, Devonian, and Mississippian age. The bedded rocks are folded and are intruded by diorite and quartz monzonite, probably offshoots of the Boulder batholith, of Cretaceous or Tertiary age (Pardee and Schrader, 1933, p. 36–37; 59).

The ore deposits in the Scratchgravel Hills include contact-metamorphic deposits, gold veins, and lead-silver veins. Most of the gold deposits are gold-quartz veins in quartz monzonite. Pyrite is the most common ore mineral in the unoxidized ores, and in some veins there are scattered grains and bunches of galena and a little sphalerite. Gold can be panned from the oxidized ore (Pardee and Schrader, 1933, p. 37–58).

In the Sevenmile Creek area the lodes yielded chiefly silver, lead, copper, and gold. The lodes are irregular pockets or pipelike bodies in limestone near the quartz monzonite contact. Most of the ore was oxidized and the chief constituents were iron oxides, gold, silver-bearing galena, and copper carbonates.

STEMPLE-VIRGINIA CREEK DISTRICT

Located about 28 to 35 miles northwest of Helena in the drainage basin of Virginia Creek, the Stemple (Gould)-Virginia Creek district contained both placer and lode ore deposits. The lode ore was valued chiefly for gold; only about 5 percent of its value was silver (Lyden, 1948, p. 63). Mining began at least as early as 1878 when the Homestake lode in the Stemple area was located; in 1884 the Jay Gould, the principal mine in the district, was discovered (Pardee and Schrader, 1933, p. 77, 86). These and other mines in the district were worked intermittently. Beginning in 1922 the Jay Gould mine operated almost continuously to 1942 when all minework was suspended. A small production from the district was reported for the period 1943–51.

The gravels along Virginia Creek have been mined from Stemple to its mouth, a distance of about 8 miles. Their date of discovery has not been ascertained. The gravels were moderately rich but not very deep; prior to 1927 they yielded at least $600,000 (29,028 ounces) in gold (Pardee and Schrader, 1933, p. 86). From 1927 to 1942 small intermittent production was reported (Lyden, 1948, p. 63), but it probably totaled less than 200 ounces.

The Stemple-Virginia Creek district was most productive during the early years, but the amount cannot be definitely ascertained. The production of the Jay Gould mine to 1914 has been estimated to be worth $2½ million, more than 95 percent of which was the value of gold and the remainder, silver. The lode production of the Gould area, including some silver, through about 1927 was about $3 million (Pardee and Schrader, 1933, p. 77, 81) or about 135,000 ounces of gold. In the Stemple area the output before 1927 was about $420,000 (20,319 ounces) in gold (Pardee and Schrader, 1933, p. 86). Total production of lode gold through 1959 was about 216,000 ounces, most of which was from the Jay Gould mine. Placers yielded about 29,200 ounces, which made a district total of about 245,000 ounces.

The country rock of the district comprises shale and argillite of the Belt Series, a stock of quartz diorite, and a sill and dikes of diorite, all of Cretaceous or Tertiary age. Near the contact with the stock, the sedimentary rocks are altered to hornstone. The rocks are tilted and cut by small faults (Pardee and Schrader, 1933, p. 78).

The ore bodies are in veins in sedimentary rocks and in the quartz diorite. The Jay Gould vein cuts the metamorphosed sedimentary rocks that adjoin the stock of quartz diorite. The vein is banded, has probably filled an open fissure, and consists largely of lamellar calcite, quartz, and small amounts of chalcopyrite, argentite, and native gold distributed along streaks and bands. Small amounts of iron and manganese oxides and malachite accompany the streaks of ore minerals. The argentite and gold are closely associated. The veins in the stock consist of coarse granular quartz, with pay streaks of gold-bearing iron oxide and copper carbonate (Pardee and Schrader, 1933, p. 79–84).

LINCOLN COUNTY

Lincoln County is in the northwest corner of Montana along the Idaho border. Its most valuable mineral deposits are vermiculite deposits near Libby. Lead-silver ores are also important; gold is a minor commodity. Although both placers and lodes were worked before 1901, there are no production data on this early activity. From 1901 through 1957 a minimum of about 29,000 ounces of lode gold and 4,318 ounces of placer gold was mined. Most of the lode production came from the Libby and Sylvanite districts and the placer production came chiefly from the Libby district.

LIBBY DISTRICT

The Libby (Snowshoe) district, in southwest Lincoln County south of the town of Libby in the Libby Creek drainage basin, was the largest producer of both lode and placer gold in the county. Placer gold was discovered as early as 1867, but it was not until the early 1880's that the first mining was done, on Libby Creek (Gibson, 1948, p. 67). After 1904 these placers contributed at least 75 percent of the placer gold of Lincoln County (Lyden, 1948, p. 76–78). There was a small but steady placer production from 1931 to July 1947, when operations were suspended.

Lodes of lead-silver ore were discovered about 1887, but gold-quartz veins were not discovered until the 1890's (Gibson, 1948, p. 67), and the most productive mines were developed in the early 1900's. Production from these deposits was sporadic and small, and no lode gold production was recorded from 1945 through 1959.

From 1901 through 1937 the Libby district produced a total of about 12,400 ounces of gold (Gibson, 1948, p. 70) including about 650 ounces of placer gold. The total gold production of the district from 1901 through 1959 was about 16,300 ounces from lodes and 3,225 ounces from placers.

The following notes on geology and ore deposits of the Libby district were abstracted from the report by Gibson (1948).

The area is underlain by Precambrian sedimentary rocks of the Belt Series, consisting chiefly of quartzite, slate, and calcareous and magnesian argillite and having a total thickness of about 40,000 feet. They have been folded and faulted and intruded by metadiorite sills and dikes of Precambrian age and by stocks and dikes of granodiorite and quartz monzonite of probable Late Cretaceous or early Tertiary age.

The lodes in the Libby district are gold-quartz veins, silver-lead-zinc veins that carry some gold, and a few scattered and commercially unimportant copper veins. The lodes occupy faults and shear zones in Precambrian sedimentary rocks of the Belt Series and in metadiorite dikes and sills that intrude the Belt Series rocks. Some of the veins, especially the gold-bearing veins, have formed along bedding planes. Most of the gold has been recovered as a byproduct from the silver-lead-zinc veins, in which galena, pyrite, and sphalerite are accompanied by quartz and calcite. The gold-bearing veins are chiefly in a small area about 20 miles south of Libby. They are quartz veins with small amounts of native gold, pyrite, galena, sphalerite, and pyrrhotite. The less common minerals in these veins are chalcopyrite, arsenopyrite, tetrahedrite, magnetite, and scheelite (Gibson, 1948, p. 71–81).

SYLVANITE DISTRICT

The Sylvanite (Yaak) district is a little-known district in northwest Lincoln County. As early as 1905 Sylvanite was a ghost town; the mines were idle, presumably having been abandoned when the oxidized ore was mined out (Gibson, 1948, p. 69). From 1901 to 1930 the district produced only about 75 ounces of gold (Gibson, 1948, p. 70), but from 1932, when the mines were reactivated, through 1940 it produced about 10,850 ounces of lode gold. Since then only desultory work has been done in the district.

In the Sylvanite district gold-bearing quartz-pyrite veins are in sandstones that were intruded by mafic dikes (Emmons, 1937, p. 140).

MADISON COUNTY

The gold production of Madison County is exceeded in Montana only by that of Silver Bow and Lewis and Clark Counties. Most of its gold was produced before 1904 from the placer deposits of Alder Gulch, by far the richest placers in the State. About 40 other gulches in the county produced placer gold, but only in small amounts (Lyden, 1948, p. 80–95). After 1904, lodes became increasingly important gold sources.

Most of the gold lodes and other auriferous deposits are near the contacts of Precambrian metamorphic and Paleozoic sedimentary rocks with the Tobacco Root batholith and other smaller intrusives and satellite stocks that are probably related to the Boulder batholith (Hart, in Tansley and others, 1933, p. 23–55). Some deposits are in the igneous rocks. The more productive lode areas are the Norris, Pony, Renova, Sheridan, Silver Star-Rochester, Tidal Wave, and Virginia City districts.

The total gold production of the county through 1959 was at least 3,746,000 ounces—2,605,000 from placers and 1,141,000 from lodes. This must be considered a conservative figure, for as Lyden noted (1948, p. 80), estimates of the Alder Gulch placer production ranged from $50,612,000 to $125 million.

NORRIS DISTRICT

Located in the northeastern part of Madison County, the Norris district, which includes Norwegian, Lower Hot Springs, and Washington, has produced chiefly gold and smaller amounts of silver, copper, and lead.

Placer deposits along Norwegian Gulch and South Meadow Creek were discovered in early 1864, and Norwegian Gulch yielded $150,000 in gold by 1874 (Winchell, 1914a, p. 111). By 1902 the district had produced at least $300,000 (14,514 ounces) in placer gold (Winchell, 1914a, p. 118), and the placers were worked on a fairly large scale from 1936 through 1942.

Quartz lodes also were discovered in 1864, and within 5 years the district had at least 8 mills (Winchell, 1914a, p. 111). Production fluctuated but was almost continuous through 1953.

Winchell (1914a, p. 118) estimated that the total lode output to 1902 exceeded $3 million in combined metals. From 1902 through 1912 gold accounted for about 90 percent of the value of mine production; if the same ratio was applicable before 1902, the lode mines of the district produced about $2,700,000 (130,600 ounces) during that period. The total lode production of the district was about 235,000 ounces and the total minimum production of both lodes and placers through 1959 was about 265,000 ounces.

The geology and ore deposits were described by Winchell (1914a, p. 111–118) and by Hart (in Tansley and others, 1933).

The Norris district is on the northeast side of the Tobacco Root batholith of Late Cretaceous age. The batholith consists chiefly of quartz monzonite and is intrusive into gneiss and schist of Precambrian age. Small remnants of rhyolite and basalt of Late Cretaceous or Tertiary age intrude and cap the older rocks.

Most of the ore deposits occur in the quartz monzonite but some are in gneiss near the intrusive contact. The ore occurs in quartz veins, which are oxidized in the upper part, and contains iron oxide, gold, and silver. In the Revenue mine, the most productive in the district, the zone of oxidation extends to the 200-foot level. Some oxidized ore also carries copper carbonate and silicate minerals. Below the zone of oxidation the most common ore mineral is auriferous pyrite, but some ore also contains galena, sphalerite, chalcopyrite, bornite, and chalcocite (Hart, in Tansley and others, 1933, p. 52).

PONY DISTRICT

The Pony district, which includes Mineral Hill and South Boulder (Mammoth), is in the northeastern part of Madison County in the Willow Creek drainage basin. Almost its entire output has come from lodes which have produced chiefly gold and small amounts of silver, lead, zinc, and copper. Placer gold was noted in 1870 (Lyden, 1948, p. 89), but placer production of the district has been small. Lode deposits were discovered in the early 1870's and were actively exploited during the 1880's and 1890's (Winchell, 1914a, p. 119). Production apparently was continuous through 1918, but it declined thereafter. The district again was active from 1928 through 1944. There was no significant gold production from 1944 through 1959.

Winchell (1914a, p. 126) estimated that the mine production of the Pony district, exclusive of the South Boulder camp, through 1901 was valued at about $2,600,000. Based on production records from 1902 to 1912, it would seem reasonable that gold constituted about 90 to 95 percent of the early production or about $2,350,000 (113,690 ounces). The gold production of the South Boulder camp before 1900, all from lodes, was estimated at about $2 million (96,758 ounces) (Lyden, 1948, p. 87). From 1902 through 1930 the district produced about 76,500 ounces (Hart, in Tansley and others, 1933, p. 24), and from 1933 through 1944, about 58,950 ounces. The total gold production of the district through 1959 was about 346,000 ounces; probably less than 250 ounces was placer gold.

Most of the mines in the Pony district are in Precambrian gneiss near the contact with quartz monzonite of the Tobacco Root batholith, but some are in the marginal part of the batholith; others are associated with aplitic and pegmatitic dikes (Winchell, 1914a, p. 119–120).

The mineral deposits in the district are arranged in a rude zonal pattern (Hart, in Tansley and others, 1933, p. 25). At or near the gneiss-quartz monzonite contact, the veins consist of either (1) chalcopyrite, pyrite, and molybdenite in quartz, (2) auriferous pyrite, chalcopyrite, and quartz, or (3) tungsten-fluorite minerals. Galena and silver are the important vein constituents peripheral to these deposits, and auriferous pyrite is less abundant.

In the Clipper mine, the most productive in the district, and in the adjacent Boss Tweed mine, the ore deposits consist mostly of silicified and pyritized gneiss between two approximately parallel faults from 10 to 160 feet apart (Winchell, 1914a, p. 121–124). Some of the ore is oxidized. The economic deposits are found chiefly in shoots, but much of the gneiss between the faults contains gold.

RENOVA DISTRICT

The Renova district, which includes Bone Basin, is located in northern Madison County in the north end of the Tobacco Root Mountains. The district produced chiefly gold and some silver, most of which came from the Mayflower mine. The date of discovery of ore in the district is not known, but there was little mining activity until 1896 when the Mayflower ore body was discovered, after which the region became prominent (Winchell, 1914a, p. 97). The Mayflower mine closed in 1905, and other mines in the district operated only intermittently and on a small scale through 1912. The district again became active during the early 1930's; the Mayflower mine was reopened in July 1935 and again became the chief producer. The district reached a peak production of 21,539 ounces of gold in 1940, but activity declined sharply after 1942 and no production was recorded from 1953 through 1959.

Production prior to 1896 was probably of little significance. From 1896 through 1912 the district produced 60,023 ounces of gold valued at $1,282,052; most of this was from the Mayflower mine and was produced before 1905 (Winchell, 1914a, p. 101). From 1932 through 1953 production was 102,036 ounces, or a total of about 162,000 ounces.

The geology and ore deposits of the Renova district were briefly described by Winchell (1914a, p. 99–101). The oldest rocks are arkosic sandstone, sandy shale, and slate of the Belt Series of Precambrian age. These are overlain by rocks of Cambrian age and possibly younger rocks, consisting, in ascending order, of a basal conglomerate, quartzite, and shale, and limestone. Dikes of andesite and quartz porphyry cut the sedimentary rock.

The Mayflower ore, consisting chiefly of telluride minerals, is along a bedding fault in limestone. The ore above the 300-foot level was oxidized.

The ore in the other mines of the district is in veins that cut rock of the Belt Series. This ore is oxidized and contains free gold in iron oxide and quartz. The unoxidized ore consists of pyrite, chalcopyrite, and galena in a gangue of calcite, dolomite, and siderite.

SHERIDAN DISTRICT

Located in the western part of Madison County 10 to 12 miles northeast of Virginia City, the Sheridan district, which includes Ramshorn, is important chiefly for gold, but silver, copper, and lead have also been recovered. Small amounts of gold have been mined from placers. Quartz veins were discovered in 1864 (Winchell, 1914a, p. 133), and mills were erected as early as 1865. The district was a steady producer through about 1952, although output dropped sharply after 1948. No activity was reported in 1959.

Production data for 1864–1904 are not available (Winchell, 1914a, p. 139); however, several mines are known to have produced more during that period than after 1904. The total gold production from 1905 through 1952 was about 33,500 ounces, of which about 2,100 ounces was from placers.

The Sheridan district is underlain by Precambrian schist and gneiss interbedded with quartzites and limestones. These rocks are intruded by small stocks of quartz monzonite and dikes and sills of porphyry of Late Cretaceous or Tertiary age (Winchell, 1914a, p. 133–139; Hart, in Tansley and others, 1933, p. 40–45).

The ore deposits are veins and limestone replacement deposits in the Precambrian rocks. The chief sulfide minerals are pyrite, arsenopyrite, chalcopyrite, galena, and tetrahedrite in a gangue of quartz and small amounts of siderite. The gold occurs with the pyrite. Tellurides are not common but have been reported in the Indian Creek area (Hart, in Tansley and others, 1933, p. 41). Much of the ore was oxidized and consisted of gold in hematite with some copper oxides and carbonate.

SILVER STAR-ROCHESTER DISTRICT

Located in northwestern Madison County, west of the Jefferson River, the Silver Star-Rochester district produced ores that were valuable chiefly for gold, but silver, lead, zinc, and copper also were recovered. Though mining began in the 1860's, it did not reach its peak until 1935–42. Interest declined thereafter, and the district was virtually dormant from 1951 through 1959. The Watseca mine in the Rochester area and the Green Campbell, Iron Rod, and Broadway mines in the Silver Star area were the major mines of the district.

Incomplete records indicate that the gold output through 1903 was worth about $2 million (about 97,000 ounces) (Sahinen, 1939, p. 5–7; Winchell, 1914a, p. 144). Total production through 1959 was about 185,700 ounces, all from lodes.

The geology and ore deposits of the district were briefly described by Winchell (1914a, p. 126–132; 139–144) and Sahinen (1939), from which this summary is abstracted.

The Silver Star-Rochester district lies at the south end of the Boulder batholith. The bedrock consists dominantly of schist and gneiss of Precambrian age which in the western part of the district and in the area around Silver Star are locally overlain by sedimentary rocks that range in age from late Precambrian to Pennsylvanian. All the older rocks are intruded by quartz monzonite of the Boulder batholith, by a stock of diorite, by small aplite intrusive bodies, and by dikes and sills of acidic rocks, all of Cretaceous or Tertiary age. Remnants of andesite and basalt flows are found locally.

The most important ore deposits are northeast-trending veins in gneiss and schist (Sahinen, 1939, p. 26–34). These veins are rich in gold and silver and contain arsenopyrite, pyrite, and subordinate amounts of lead, zinc, and copper minerals in a quartz gangue. A few veins in this group are rich in lead-silver ore. Several narrow veins that trend east carry gold with small amounts of pyrite in greasy-appearing quartz. Much of the ore has been oxidized to a depth of 600 feet and consists of quartz, limonite, and oxidized copper and lead minerals.

Considerable gold has been mined from contact deposits in the Silver Star area. The ore deposits form irregular shoots in Paleozoic limestone along the quartz monzonite contact. Much of the ore was highly oxidized and consisted of jasper, gold, and oxidized minerals of iron and copper. The unoxidized ore consists of pyrite, chalcopyrite, bornite, and covellite in a gangue of quartz and contact silicate minerals.

TIDAL WAVE DISTRICT

Located in northwestern Madison County, along the western slope of the Tobacco Root Mountains, the Tidal Wave (Twin Bridges) district has produced chiefly gold, silver, and lead, and smaller amounts of copper. The initial discoveries in about 1864 were silver-lead ore but these aroused little excitement. Only gold was sought in those early days. By 1874, however, the value of the argentiferous lead ores was realized, and claims were rapidly located and developed (Winchell, 1914a, p. 145). Production records date back only to 1904, but the production during the latter part of the 19th century probably was greater than in the early 1900's (Winchell, 1914a, p. 146). The district remained active from 1904 through 1955, and the total recorded gold production through 1959 was about 33,400 ounces; nearly all production was from lodes.

The Tidal Wave district lies on the west side of the Tobacco Root batholith, a mass of quartz monzonite of Cretaceous or Tertiary age which here has intruded, faulted, and tilted Precambrian gneiss and schist and Paleozoic limestone, quartzite, and interbedded shale. These rocks also are cut locally by sills of porphyry and by aplite dikes.

The ore deposits in the district are contact deposits in limestone and lodes in gneiss and schist, and more rarely they occur in the quartz monzonite near its contact with the country rocks. Most of the veins contain gold and lesser amounts of lead, silver, copper, and zinc. A few veins in the Paleozoic limestone near the contact were mined for lead and silver, or copper and gold. The contact metamorphic deposits are valued mainly for copper and lead, with silver and gold as minor constituents (Winchell, 1914a, p. 145–158; Hart, in Tansley and others, 1933, p. 34–39).

VIRGINIA CITY-ALDER GULCH DISTRICT

The Virginia City-Alder Gulch district, which includes the Summit area, is in central Madison County at the south end of the Tobacco Root Mountains. It is the leading producer of placer gold in Montana and has also produced a small amount of lode gold. The discovery of rich gold placer deposits in Alder Gulch in 1863 marked the beginning of mining activity in Madison County. Gold-quartz veins were discovered in the district later in the year (Winchell, 1914a, p. 159). The richness of the placers attracted hordes of prospectors to the area, and within 18 months Virginia City boomed to a town of 10,000 population. Within 3 years, placer gold valued at $30 million was recovered from Alder Gulch and its tributaries (Knopf, 1913, p. 15). The Alder Creek placers, extending for about 20 miles, were the longest and most productive ever discovered in Montana. From 1863 until 1899 the gravels were worked by sluice boxes, pans, and rockers. In 1899 the Conrey Placer Mining Co. began dredging operations that lasted until 1922, when the gravels were considered mined out. The peak year of dredging, 1915, resulted in more than $800,000 in gold recovered from 6 million cubic yards of gravel (Lyden, 1948, p. 80–82). During the 14 years following 1922 only small-scale sluicing operations were undertaken. In 1935 dryland dredges were installed (Lyden, 1948, p. 82) and were successfully operated through 1942, when operations closed for the duration of World War II. Dredging was resumed in 1946 but was suspended in late 1948.

The gold-bearing gravel in Alder Gulch is 30 to 50 feet deep; the most valuable gravel is about 6 feet above the soft, plastic bedrock (Kirk, 1908, p. 330). The placer gold probably was weathered directly from the thousands of veins of the district (Lyden, 1948, p. 83).

Various estimates have been made regarding production of the Alder Gulch placers before 1904. In addition to the $30 million produced during the first 3 years (1863–66), Hart (in Tansley and others, 1933, p. 46) estimated that Alder Gulch and its tributaries yielded $42¾ million from 1867 through 1903. The Montana Bureau of Agriculture, Labor, and Industry (1900, p. 188) estimated production at $150 to $200 million in gold through 1899. Kirk (1908, p. 330) estimated the output by 1908 at $125 million. Lyden (1948, p. 80) believed that Hart's estimate was low and Kirk's was high. Almost certainly Hart's figure of $42¾ million (2,068,215 ounces) is a conservative estimate for the period 1863–1903. From 1904 through 1930 the production was 380,351 ounces (Hart, in Transley and others, 1933, p. 46), and from 1932 through 1959, about 24,500 ounces. Therefore the total production through 1959 was at least 2,475,000 ounces.

Lodes also were productive in the Virginia City district. The first lode deposits were developed soon after 1864, and by 1871 at least 8 mills had been erected to treat the gold-quartz ores (Winchell, 1914a, p. 159). Much of the early lode production came from the Oro Cache and Kearsarge mines, in the Summit camp, which produced an estimated $500,000 and $150,000 in gold, respectively by 1881 (Winchell, 1914a, p. 159). Hart (in Tansley and others, 1933, p. 46) estimated the lode production during 1867–90 at $1 million (48,379 ounces), and during 1891–1903, at $269,256 (13,026 ounces). Lode production fluctuated but continued at a moderate scale through 1914 and ranged from $131,000 in 1910 to only $12,856 in 1912 (Hart, in Tansley and others, 1933, p. 46). Thereafter, production was sporadic and it declined sharply until the price of gold was raised in 1934. Annual production after 1934, except during World War II, ranged from about 1,300 to 4,500 ounces. Very small amounts of lode gold were mined in the 1950's. Total lode production of the district was about 142,000 ounces, and the minimum total placer and lode production through 1959 was about 2,617,000 ounces.

The following brief summary of the geology and ore deposits has been abstracted from reports by Winchell (1914a, p. 159–165) and Hart (in Tansley and others, 1933, p. 47–50).

The district is underlain by gneiss and schist of Precambrian age and intrusions of aplite and andesite porphyry of Cretaceous or Tertiary age. East of Virginia City the uplands are capped by basalt flows of Tertiary age. The lode deposits are chiefly in the gneiss and schist, but one vein system is in aplite. The lodes are quartz veins and stringers that contain auriferous pyrite, galena, sphalerite, and chalcopyrite and lesser amounts of gold tellurides, tetrahedrite, argentite, and stibnite. Most of the ore shipped was oxidized and consisted of gold and free silver in quartz, iron oxides, manganese oxides, and a little locally occurring copper stain.

MINERAL COUNTY

Located in western Montana along the Idaho border, Mineral County was formed in 1914 by partition of Missoula County. All gold mined before 1914 from the area now included in Mineral County is credited to Missoula County. Almost the entire gold output came from placer deposits along the creeks that drain the east side of the Bitterroot Mountains and that flow into Clark Fork River between Tarkio and Superior. The most productive placers, and the only ones that produced more than 10,000 ounces of gold, were those along Cedar and Trout Creeks and their tributaries. Estimates by Lyden (1948, p. 98–103) suggest that placer production before 1904 may have exceeded 120,000 ounces. From 1904 through 1956 the county produced placer gold valued at about $665,000 (32,175 ounces), most of which was produced before 1942.

Lode gold production in Mineral County has been of relatively minor importance. The known lode deposits in the county are valuable chiefly for lead, zinc, silver, and copper; gold has probably been a byproduct (Wallace and Hosterman, 1956, p. 602–608).

CEDAR CREEK-TROUT CREEK DISTRICT

Cedar and Trout Creeks, about 6 miles apart, are on the east slope of the Bitterroot Mountains, southwest of Superior. The placers of Cedar Creek were discovered in 1869; those along Trout Creek, in 1872. There was some placer mining along these creeks or their tributaries almost every year up to World War II (Lyden, 1948, p. 100–102). From 1946 through 1959 operations were small scale and desultory. Estimates of early production along Cedar Creek and its tributaries ranged from $2 to $10 million in gold; Lyden (1948, p. 100) considered $2 million (96,758 ounces) to be more nearly correct. The early production of the Trout Creek placers is not known, but it was much smaller than that of Cedar Creek. The district produced about 20,000 ounces of gold from 1908 through 1959; its total production through 1959 was about 120,000 ounces.

The gold from this district was notably fine; some gold that was 982 fine was recovered and it was not unusual for it to be as high as 960 to 970 fine (Lyden, 1948, p. 102).

MISSOULA COUNTY

Missoula County, in western Montana, at one time included several adjacent counties—Ravalli, Sanders, Lincoln, Mineral, and Lake—and parts of Granite, Powell, and Flathead Counties. Only a part of the gold production of Missoula County as reported in "Mineral Resources of the United States" (U.S. Geological Survey, 1904–23) prior to 1914 came from deposits within its present boundaries (Lyden, 1948, p. 103). Gold production of Missoula County has been chiefly from placer deposits in the Elk Creek-Coloma and Ninemile districts, but an appreciable amount has also come from lode deposits in the Elk Creek-Coloma district. The total minimum gold production through 1959 was about 150,000 ounces from placers and 20,000 ounces from lodes.

ELK CREEK-COLOMA DISTRICT

The Elk Creek-Coloma district is about 30 miles east of Missoula in the southeast corner of the county. Elk Creek rises in the Garnet Range, and the district lies on the north side of the range north of the famous mining camp of Garnet in the First Chance district in Granite County. Both lodes and placers were exploited for gold in this district.

Gold placers were discovered along Elk Creek about 1865 (Pardee, 1918, p. 231), and the early production of the district came from these deposits. Reliable figures on the early production are not available, but Pardee (1918, p. 232), judging from the extent of the old placer workings, estimated that the production must have been worth between $1 million and $2 million. After the first few years of frantic activity, the rich gravels were depleted; the boom was over. Most of the claims were abandoned, though a few were worked intermittently through the 1930's. Dredging operations from 1938 to 1940 yielded about 2,500 ounces. After 1940 and continuing through 1959 the placers were again abandoned. Gold lodes, discovered about 1867 in the Coloma area, were not developed until 1897. The Comet and Mammoth mines accounted for most of the early lode production. Both mines closed after a few years of operation, and the camp has been largely idle since then. About $250,000 in gold was produced from lode mines before 1916 (Pardee, 1918, p. 195–196).

Total gold production of the district through 1959 was between 70,000 and 117,000 ounces. This included 52,000 to 100,000 ounces from placers; the remainder was from lodes.

The rocks in the Elk Creek-Coloma district are chiefly limestones of Paleozoic age and granodiorite of Late Cretaceous or early Tertiary age that intruded the limestone. Just west of Coloma the limestones are underlain by sedimentary rocks of the Belt Series (Pardee, 1918, p. 196–199, pl. 7). The veins are in granodiorite adjacent to limestone. Most of the ore was oxidized and was rich in gold.

The sulfide ore, which is relatively low grade, is banded and consists of gold-bearing pyrite, chalcopyrite, and tetrahedrite with quartz gangue.

NINEMILE CREEK DISTRICT

Located in the northwest corner of Missoula County, Ninemile Creek is a tributary of Clark Fork River. Almost the entire gold production of this district has been from placer deposits along Ninemile Creek and its tributaries. The first discoveries were made in the district in 1874 (Lyden, 1948, p. 103). Some of the deposits were rich and several miles of placer ground was quickly located and patented (Lyden, 1948, p. 103–104). The amount of gold mined in this district prior to 1908 has not been ascertained but is reported to have been several million dollars (Lyden, 1948, p. 104). Placer operations along the creek were sustained for many years, but production declined sharply after 1915 and was intermittent in the 1920's. The pace of mining increased in the 1930's and, except for the war years of 1943–45, continued at a significant level through 1948. In 1954 dredging operations recovered 1,340 ounces of gold; otherwise the district was idle from 1949 through 1959. Total production through 1959 was probably between 100,000 and 125,000 ounces.

The gold-bearing gravels of the district are reported to be either in glacial till or glacial moraine (Lyden, 1948, p. 107). The gravel is cemented with clay and is difficult to break up, and although it is gold bearing, some of the deposits have yielded little or no profit. The source of the gold is probably the scattered gold veins in the mountains at the head of the creeks (Pardee, 1918, p. 234).

PARK COUNTY

Park County, in southern Montana just north of Yellowstone Park, was organized in 1887. Gold placers were discovered in the area as early as 1862 near Gardiner, and by 1870 gold-quartz veins were found near the present site of Jardine and in the Cooke City district. The history of mining in the county is punctuated by brief periods of development and longer intervals of decline, litigation, and idleness (Reed, 1950, p. 7–9). Mineral production prior to 1887 is estimated at not more than $500,000, a large part of which was in gold. From 1887 through 1947 the county produced 250,513 ounces of gold (Reed, 1950, p. 10, table 5) and from 1948 through 1959, about 22,660 ounces. Total gold production through 1959 was roughly 295,000 ounces, more than half of which was mined from 1933 to 1953. The Emigrant Creek, Jardine, and Cooke City districts have been the major sources of gold in Park County.

EMIGRANT CREEK DISTRICT

Emigrant Creek is a tributary of Yellowstone River, which it joins about 24 miles north of Gardiner. The date of discovery of ore deposits in the Emigrant Creek district has not been ascertained, but gold lodes in the district were worked in the 1870's (Reed, 1950, p. 52). The lodes, however, never were economically important. The earliest placer production records date back to 1901 (Reed, 1950, p. 14). Prior to 1941 these gravels were worked in drift mines, or with hydraulic giants, or by ground sluicing. In 1941 a large bucket dredge was assembled on Emigrant Creek and was operated until October 1942. In April 1946 these operations were again resumed, but they were unsuccessful because of increased mining costs. The district remained dormant through 1959. These placers accounted for one-half to two-thirds of the annual production of placer gold in the county (Lyden, 1948, p. 110). Total placer production from 1901 through 1959 was 15,606 ounces. During 1901–3 the district also produced 395 ounces of lode gold (Reed, 1950, p. 14).

The placer gold was derived from the mineralized area at the headwaters of Emigrant Creek (Reed, 1950, p. 50–54). The country rock consists of Precambrian granite, gneiss, and schist, Paleozoic sedimentary rocks, and Tertiary volcanic and intrusive rocks. Small quartz stringers and veins containing galena, sphalerite, pyrite, and chalcopyrite, and small amounts of gold are found in the volcanic rocks, although a few deposits are in the Precambrian rocks. A few veins are valued chiefly for molybdenite and also contain small amounts of gold and silver.

JARDINE DISTRICT

The Jardine (Sheepeater) district is 6 miles east of Gardiner in the southern part of Park County. Gold and arsenic are its major products; tungsten has been recovered as a byproduct of gold mining.

Placer gold was discovered in the gravels along Yellowstone River near Gardiner in 1862 and near the mouth of Bear Gulch in 1866; a search for its origin led to the discovery in 1870 of gold-quartz veins at the present site of Jardine (Reed, 1950, p. 7). The early activity in the district consisted chiefly of placer operations, which produced only small amounts of gold. Little development was done on the lodes until 1884 when completion of a five-stamp mill ushered in a period of successful lode mining that lasted until the panic of 1893 (Seager, 1944, p. 6–7). From 1893 to 1902 activity was intermittent and production was relatively small. Mining activity during 1902–42 was interrupted by an extended period of litigation from 1909 to 1916 and by a shutdown from 1926 to 1932 (Reed, 1950, p. 8). Operations were temporarily suspended in 1942 because of the Federal restrictions on gold mining, but increasing war demands for arsenic led to the reopening of the mines, which operated until May 1948, when fire destroyed the cyanide plant. There was no recorded production from 1948 through 1959.

The recorded gold production from the Jardine district from 1902 through 1947 was 174,888 ounces, including 407 ounces of placer gold (Reed, 1950, p. 11). The district produced an additional 6,498 ounces of lode gold in 1948. The total gold production through 1959 was probably between 190,000 and 200,000 ounces.

The Jardine district is underlain by a complex of schist and quartzite intruded by masses of granitic rocks, all of Precambrian age. These are overlain by Paleozoic and Mesozoic sedimentary rocks and Tertiary volcanic rocks. The ore deposits are in the Precambrian schist and are the only gold deposits of Precambrian age in Montana (Seager, 1944, p. 43). In many respects these ore bodies are similar to the gold deposits in the Homestake mine, South Dakota (Seager, 1944, p. 43).

The ore deposits are in veins of two mineralogic types: quartz veins in quartz-biotite schist, and arsenopyrite (sulfide) veins in quartz-cummingtonite schist. The quartz veins are the more abundant. Both types of veins are replacements of country rock rather than fissure fillings; as a result, they are characteristically uneven in thickness, continuity, and grade, and although parallel in general with the foliation, a few veins crosscut foliation (Seager, 1944, p. 44–45). The most common ore minerals in the quartz veins in the quartz-biotite schist are arsenopyrite, pyrite, galena, gold, and scheelite. The arsenopyrite veins in the cummingtonite schist have a much higher and more uniform sulfide content and contain more gold and less tungsten than the quartz veins. They also are the chief source of arsenical ore. These veins contain variable amounts of pyrite, pyrrhotite, and gold in addition to arsenopyrite (Seager, 1944, p. 48–50).

COOKE CITY DISTRICT

Located in the southeast corner of Park County, the Cooke City (New World) district has produced silver, copper, lead, and zinc ores from which small amounts of gold have been recovered as a byproduct.

Rumors of rich lead, silver, and gold deposits in the New World district were reported as early as 1868, and in 1869 trappers, fleeing from an Indian raiding party, discovered a manganese-stained outcrop on the property which was later developed as the Republic mine. In 1870 the first claims were located in the district, although it was still part of the Crow Indian Reservation (Lovering, 1930, p. 44). A furnace was built in 1875, and lead ore was smelted until an Indian raid in 1878 terminated these efforts. In April 1882 the district was withdrawn from the Crow Indian Reservation and opened to settlement (Lovering, 1930, p. 45). This resulted in increased mining in the district, and a lead smelter and roasting furnace were erected. However, high freight rates prevented any extensive development, and finally the Republic mine, the most productive in the district, and the smelter were closed in 1887. Only sporadic exploration continued, resulting in small production of gold ore in the early 1890's (Lovering, 1930, p. 46).

From 1904 through the 1920's several properties in the district were mined for short periods, but most of these operations ended in failure; only high-grade lead-silver ore was shipped (Lovering, 1930, p. 46–47). In 1933 a concentrator was built that successfully treated low-grade pyritic gold-copper ores (Reed, 1950, p. 8–9). This activity continued through 1953, and small-scale lead-silver mining was carried on through 1957.

Early production statistics are not available but, according to Lovering (1930, p. 48), smelter records show that 438 ounces of gold was recovered in 1886 in addition to considerable amounts of silver and lead. From 1901 through 1932 only 270 ounces of byproduct gold was produced (Reed, 1950, table on p. 12). Gold recovered from 1933 through 1959 amounted to 65,245 ounces. Total gold production of the district through 1959 was at least 66,000 ounces.

The Cooke City mining district is on the southwest flank of the Beartooth-Snowy Mountain anticlinorium. Granite, gneiss, and basalt porphyry of Precambrian age are exposed in the central part of the structure. Overlying the Precambrian rocks are sedimentary rocks of Cambrian, Ordovician, Devonian, and Carboniferous age. After these rocks were folded into the large anticline and erosion had modified the relief, Tertiary lavas and pyroclastics covered the surface, and plugs, stocks, dikes, and sills of gabbro, porphyritic quartz monzonite, granodiorite, diorite, syenite, and basalt intruded the rocks (Lovering, 1930, p. 12–40).

The district contains a variety of ore deposits, most of which are clustered around two stocks—one of quartz monzonite and the other of syenite. Mineralogically, the deposits can be classified into copper-platinum, copper-lead-gold, pyritic copper, gold-quartz, copper-lead, lead-silver, lead-zinc-silver, carbonate-silver, and gold placers. Most of the gold has come from the pyritic copper deposits which were exploited from 1933 through 1953. These are veins containing quartz and pyrite and smaller amounts of chalcopyrite, galena, and sphalerite. In the higher grade ore, the value of gold ranges from $5 to $15 per ton (Lovering, 1930, p. 49–52).

PHILLIPS COUNTY

Located in north-central Montana, Phillips County is the easternmost gold-producing area in the State. Prior to 1915 Phillips County was part of Blaine County and before 1912 both were part of Chouteau County. Almost the entire metal production of the county has come from gold-silver lodes in the Little Rocky Mountains. Gold placers were discovered in 1884 and were worked intermittently for a number of years, but they yielded rather insignificant returns. Gold lodes were found in 1893 at the site of the August mine, and small amounts of gold were mined, even though the area at that time was part of the Belknap Indian Reservation. The mineral-rich land was thereupon withdrawn from the reservation; soon additional deposits were found and developed, mills were built, and by about 1906, the mines produced $950,000 worth of ore (Emmons, 1908, p. 97). Except for the periods 1919–21, 1925–29, and 1943–45, the lode mines were fairly active until 1951. The Ruby Gulch and August mines were the major gold-producing properties. From 1951 through 1959, only 6 ounces of gold was reported from Phillips County. Total gold production through 1959 was about 380,000 ounces; virtually all production was from lodes.

LITTLE ROCKY MOUNTAINS DISTRICT

The Little Rocky Mountains (Zortman-Landusky) district is in southwestern Phillips County. Its history and production are synonymous with that of Phillips County and need not be repeated here. A laccolithic dome forms the Little Rocky Mountains. Its core of Precambrian gneiss is exposed in the deeper gullies in the central part of the mountains. Overlying the Precambrian rocks are, in ascending order, the Flathead Sandstone of Cambrian age, the Emerson Formation of Cambrian and probable Ordovician age, the Bighorn Dolomite of Ordovician age, the Maywood Formation and Jefferson Limestone of Devonian age, the Three Forks Shale(?) of Devonian and Mississippian age, and the Madison Group of Mississippian age. Unconformably overlying rocks of the Madison Group is the Rierdon Formation of Jurassic age, and this is succeeded upward by the Swift and Morrison Formations of Jurassic age, the Kootenai Formation, the First Cat Creek sand (of drillers), the Thermopolis Shale, Mowry Shale, Warm Creek Shale, and the Montana Group of Cretaceous age (Knechtel, 1959, p. 726–745). These Mesozoic sedimentary rocks have an aggregate thickness of 4,000 feet.

The sedimentary formations were arched and invaded by magma which spread along bedding and formed laccolithic masses. These igneous rocks range in composition from syenite porphyry to tinguaite porphyry (Corry, 1933, p. 32). The rocks are offset by a complex system of thrusts and circular faults.

The major ore deposits are in shear zones in porphyry; other less important deposits are replacement bodies in limestone. The mineralized shear zones contain auriferous pyrite and sylvanite in a gangue of quartz and fluorite. Native gold and limonite and manganese oxides are the principal components of the oxidized deposits (Corry, 1933, p. 33–35).

POWELL COUNTY

Powell County is in west-central Montana, west of the Continental Divide and west of Lewis and Clark County. Most of the gold production has come from placer deposits in the southern part of the county. Gold-bearing gravels discovered along Gold Creek in 1852 were probably the first gold discoveries in Montana (Lyden, 1948, p. 118–120), although they were not mined until 1862. The important placers of Powell County are in the Pioneer district, which includes the Gold Creek placers, and the Ophir and Finn districts. Gold lodes were worked in the Ophir and Zosell districts. Powell County through 1959 produced about 517,000 ounces of placer gold and about 50,000 ounces of lode gold.

FINN DISTRICT

The Finn district includes Washington, Jefferson, and Buffalo Gulches. Streams in the district along the western slope of the Continental Divide, about 15 miles north of Avon, have yielded moderate amounts of placer gold, mostly before 1890 (Pardee and Schrader, 1933, p. 114). The deposits were discovered in the early or middle 1860's and according to Raymond, as quoted by Lyden (1948, p. 128), they yielded gold worth about $1½ million by 1869.

The most productive placers in the district have been those along Washington Creek. After 1890 the placers in the district were worked intermittently; the two most prominent periods were 1908–16 and 1931–42. No activity was reported from 1951 through 1959. The recorded production from 1908 through 1932 was about 1,480 ounces, and from 1933 through 1942, about 6,472 ounces. Less than 100 ounces were produced from 1942 through 1959. The total placer production of the district through 1959 was about 81,000 ounces.

From 1933 through 1959 the district also produced a little over 600 ounces of lode gold, probably from quartz lodes (Lyden, 1948, p. 128). No description of the geology of the area has been found.

OPHIR DISTRICT

The Ophir (Avon) district, which includes Nigger Hill, is on the west side of the Continental Divide and comprises several formerly productive placer deposits and lodes valuable for gold, silver, and copper.

The placer deposits were found in 1865, and the town of Blackfoot City, now called Ophir, was founded (Knopf, 1913, p. 15). The placer deposits along Carpenter Creek, locally called Ophir Creek, and its tributaries were the richest and most productive (Lyden, 1948, p. 126–128), but after 1875 they were largely exhausted and were worked in subsequent years by the Chinese. In 1934 a Yuba connected-bucket dredge was operated on Carpenter Creek, but in July 1935 it was dismantled (Lyden, 1948, p. 127). Only minor activity was reported from 1938 through 1954 and none from 1955 through 1959.

Pardee and Schrader (1933, p. 30) concluded that the value of the early placer production was at least $3½ million (169,325 ounces) and Lyden (1948, p. 127) credited the district with a production of about $5 million (about 242,000 ounces). From 1908 through 1954 a minimum production of about 9,150 ounces was recorded, of which 8,460 ounces represents the output of the dredging operations in 1934–35. The total minimum placer output through 1959 was about 180,000 ounces.

The placer deposits are in the present stream gravels and in terraces and benches. Ophir Gulch was mined for a length of 8 miles and Carpenter and Snowshoe Gulches have each been mined for a length of several miles (Pardee and Schrader, 1933, p. 31).

Mining of lode deposits in the Ophir district began as early as 1888 (Pardee and Schrader, 1933, p. 32–35) and continued on a small scale and intermittently until 1954, the greatest activity being in 1909–18 and 1936–41. Lode gold output through 1959 was about 8,250 ounces; total lode and placer production was about 188,250 ounces.

The country rock in the Ophir district is limestone, shale, and quartzite of early Paleozoic age, intruded by small stocks of quartz monzonite of Cretaceous or Tertiary age (Pardee and Schrader, 1933, p. 30–35). The lodes are irregularly shaped pipelike replacement bodies in limestone and are genetically related to the quartz monzonite. Pyrite and chalcopyrite are the principal sulfide minerals in a gangue of quartz, and garnet, diopside, magnetite, and hematite occur locally. Tetrahedrite was found in some lodes, and gold tellurides and ruby silver were reported from one lode (Pardee and Schrader, 1933, p. 31).

PIONEER DISTRICT

Located in southwestern Powell County, west of Garrison, the Pioneer district includes Gold and Pikes Peak Creeks and was the site of Montana's first gold discovery along Gold Creek in 1852. Though the initial find was not rich enough to mine, sufficient interest was aroused to attract others who found more encouraging gravels along Gold Creek in 1858, 1860, and 1861. The deposits were not rich and were neglected during the frantic stampedes to other bonanza discoveries in western Montana in the 1860's. Thus no significant development occurred until 1868–69, when a ditch 16 miles long was completed to deliver water to mine high terraces along Pikes Peak Creek (Pardee, 1951, p. 74–75). By 1871 a total of eight hydraulic giants were utilized in placer mining on Pioneer Creek and French Gulch (Lyden, 1948, p. 120), and more than $1 million in gold was recovered from terrace gravels on Pioneer Bar in the late 1870's and 1880's. By 1920 most of the favorable ground had been worked and only one large-scale hydraulic plant was active (Pardee, 1951, p. 75). About $1,350,000 worth of gold was recovered during 1933–41 from dredging operations in Pioneer Gulch. From 1942 through 1959 the district was almost inactive.

Gold production of the district through 1942 was valued at $5,667,248 (Pardee, 1951, p. 97) and included an estimate of $4 million for the period before 1897, when dependable records were not kept. Total production through 1959 was approximately 246,200 ounces.

The placers of the district, which were described in detail by Pardee (1951, p. 86–96), include creek placers, terrace or bench placers, and gold-bearing glacial drift. Some of the gold in the creek and bench placers may have been concentrated from glacial material (Lyden, 1948, p. 121).

The Pioneer district produced less than 1,000 ounces of lode gold through 1959. A small part of the district is included in the northeast corner of the Philipsburg quadrangle and is described by Emmons and Calkins (1913, p. 251). The country rock is granite of Tertiary age. The veins consist of quartz, calcite, pyrite, and chalcopyrite; some also contain a little sphalerite, galena, and gray copper. These deposits may be the source of the placer gold in the district.

ZOSELL DISTRICT

The Zosell (Emery) district is located in southern Powell County on the west slope of the Continental Divide about 8 miles east-southeast of Deer Lodge. The district includes small formerly productive placer deposits and lodes valued for gold, silver, and lead.

Gold placers were discovered in the district about 1872 and during the next 20 years yielded about $75,000 (3,625 ounces) in gold (Pardee and Schrader, 1933, p. 283). There has been no placer mining in the district since 1904.

Lode mining in the Zosell district dates back to about 1888. The chief producer has been the Emery mine, though a score of mines were operated intermittently through 1951 (Robertson, 1953, p. 2–4). The production of the lodes from 1891 to 1928 was valued at about $675,000, of which about 45 percent, $303,750 (14,695 ounces), represents the value of the gold (Pardee and Schrader, 1933, p. 270). The district was most active from 1891 to 1905 and from 1935 to 1942. Total gold production through 1959 was about 39,450 ounces from lodes and 3,625 ounces from placers.

The district is underlain by andesite and basalt flows, tuffs and breccias, probably of Late Cretaceous age (Robertson, 1953, p. 5–8). On the east, just beyond the Continental Divide, these rocks are intruded by the Boulder batholith, and a few miles south of the district, an outlier of the Boulder batholith is exposed. The volcanic rocks are warped into a west-plunging syncline and offset by faults. The ore deposits are veins that have filled open spaces along fractures; locally the veins replaced the broken rock, and several feet of wallrock are mineralized. The veins are narrow but rather persistent in length and depth (Pardee and Schrader, 1933, p. 272–283). The principal ore minerals—pyrite, arsenopyrite, sphalerite, boulangerite, tetrahedrite, chalcopyrite, and galena—are in a gangue of quartz and carbonate minerals (Robertson, 1953, p. 9–12). Oxidized ore is generally somewhat lower grade than the sulfide ore (Pardee and Schrader, 1933, p. 273).

RAVALLI COUNTY

Gold production in Ravalli County, in western Montana, has come chiefly from placer deposits along Hughes Creek. Of the 9,055 ounces of gold the county produced from 1904 through 1945, about 8,000 ounces was from these placers (Lyden, 1948, p. 132). From 1946 through 1959 the Hughes Creek district produced 336 ounces, including 36 ounces of lode gold. No production figures are available for the years before 1904; however, Lindgren pointed out (1904, p. 88) that the Hughes Creek placers were known since the early days of mining and that claims had been staked out for a distance of 15 miles from the mouth to the divide. It is therefore highly probable that the Hughes Creek district had a total output of more than 10,000 ounces of gold.

SILVER BOW COUNTY

Silver Bow County is immediately west of the Continental Divide in western Montana. It is the leading mining county of Montana and is one of the most productive mining areas in the United States. In addition to copper and gold, Silver Bow County has produced large amounts of silver, lead, zinc, and some manganese. Almost all the metals have come from the immensely rich copper deposits at Butte. The Highland district, south of Butte, has yielded a moderate amount of gold. The total gold production of the county from 1864 through 1959 was about 2,800,000 ounces.

BUTTE DISTRICT

The Butte (Summit Valley) district is in northeastern Silver Bow County in the vicinity of the city of Butte. More than 90 percent of the annual mineral output of Montana comes from the Butte district, one of the great copper camps of the world. Gold has been a byproduct of the copper ores, although some gold was mined from placers before 1875. Silver, zinc, lead, and manganese have also been recovered in substantial amounts. The total gold production of Butte through 1959 was approximately 2,725,000 ounces, which includes about 363,000 ounces of estimated production from placers in the district (Winchell, 1914a, p. 102; Lyden, 1948, p. 143–144).

The first mineral discoveries were the gold-bearing gravels found in 1864 in Missoula Gulch, at a point now within the Butte city limits. Later that same year placers were found along Silver Bow Creek and in German Gulch. These deposits were fairly profitable in the 1860's and 1870's. In the first 3 years about $1½ million worth of gold was recovered (Weed, 1912, p. 18). The placers, which were not very rich, soon declined in importance, as interest was diverted to developing the manganese-stained silver lodes which were also located in 1864. Silver mining reached its peak in 1887, at which time about 500 tons of ore, averaging $25 per ton in silver and gold, were treated daily in stamp mills and smelters in the district (Weed, 1912, p. 19). The drop in the price of silver in 1893 put an end to large silver-mining operations in the district. Copper lodes were developed slowly and gained prominence in the 1880's when railroads afforded cheap transportation. A significant event in the history of the district was the organization of the Amalgamated Copper Co. in 1899, a venture that consolidated most of the large copper mines and provided sufficient capital for future expansion. Exploration and development continued through the early 1900's. The Anaconda Co., the largest of the consolidated properties, assumed increasing importance and has been the controlling interest in the district for many years.

Bedrock in the district is mainly quartz monzonite and is part of the Boulder batholith of Late Cretaceous age or Early Tertiary age. It is cut by dikes and sheets of aplite and by dikes of quartz porphyry. A mass of dacite-rhyolite, partly intrusive into the quartz monzonite and partly extrusive, is exposed in the western part of the district and forms the butte from which the city received its name (Weed, 1912, p. 26–46). The quartz monzonite, aplite, and quartz porphyry—but not the rhyolite—are cut by numerous faults and fissures, along some of which the mineralizing solutions traveled. Extensive studies in the district (Sales, 1914; Sales and Meyer, 1948) resulted in grouping these fissures into the following systems, listed chronologically and beginning with the oldest:

1. Anaconda or east-west system (contains the most extensive and persistent veins).
2. Blue system (also heavily mineralized).
3. Mountain View breccia faults (slightly mineralized).
4. Steward system (slightly mineralized).
5. Rarus fault (barren).
6. Middle faults (barren).
7. Continental fault (barren).

Sales (1914, p. 58–61) recognized a distinct concentric zoning of the ores of the Butte district. The central zone contains veins in which chalcocite and enargite are the major copper minerals and the gangue is pyrite and quartz. Veins in the intermediate zone are characterized by sphalerite, and bornite, chalcopyrite, tetrahedrite, and tennantite are more abundant than in the central zone. Rhodonite and rhodochrosite are relatively common. The peripheral zone contains veins valued for silver, gold, and zinc. Rhodonite, rhodochrosite, galena and sphalerite are abundant; quartz is the major gangue mineral, and pyrite is common. The copper minerals chalcopyrite, tetrahedrite, tennantite, chalcocite, and bornite occur in only small amounts.

Detailed studies of the wallrock alteration of the Butte district revealed that all veins are accompanied by two types of alteration—a sericite zone adjacent to the ore-bearing fracture and an argillized zone between the sericite and fresh quartz monzonite. These changes reflect mineralogical stability ranges of the wallrock in response to a new physical and chemical environment produced by the mineralizing solutions rather than in response to abrupt changes in the composition of the solutions (Sales and Meyer, 1948, p. 25).

HIGHLAND DISTRICT

The Highland district is in southern Silver Bow County about 15 miles south of Butte, 2 or 3 miles east of the Continental Divide in the Highland Mountains. It contains both placer and lode gold deposits. Placer deposits were discovered along the upper course of Fish Creek in 1866. Lodes also were located in the early years. The town of Highland, established near the head of Fish Creek, was larger than Butte in 1869; however, the richest placer deposits were soon exhausted, and the town was virtually abandoned by 1876 (Winchell, 1914a, p. 87). The lode mines were reactivated in about 1931 and operated through 1944; their peak output was 9,945 ounces in 1939. Activity declined sharply after 1941, and there was only small sporadic production through 1959. Total gold production of the district through 1959 must have been in excess of 50,000 ounces.

The bedrock of the Highland district consists of slate and quartzite of the Belt Series of Precambrian age and contact-metamorphosed limestone, sandstone, and shale of Paleozoic age along the southeast border of the Boulder batholith (Winchell, 1914a, p. 87–89; Weed, 1912, pl. 1).

The ore deposits include veins, chimneys, and irregular contact deposits in marbleized Paleozoic limestone and irregular veins in the quartz monzonite near the contact (Winchell, 1914a, p. 89–90). The sulfide ore consists of chalcopyrite, bornite, galena, pyrite, pyrrhotite, arsenopyrite, tetradymite, argentite, and pyrargyrite. Much of the ore was oxidized and contained native gold and silver and oxidized copper and iron minerals.

NEVADA

In Nevada, gold production has been greatly exceeded by silver production; most of the gold produced has been a byproduct of silver or base-metal ores. The major gold districts are Goldfield, Silver Peak, Aurora, Rawhide, Jarbidge, National, Round Mountain, Manhattan, Delamar, Wilson, Potosi, and Lynn, although the largest gold production has come from the Comstock Lode district, principally a silver district (fig. 16).

Mining began in the State in the early 1850's, and 1859–79 was the boom era of the Comstock Lode and the Reese River districts. Mining, except in the Comstock Lode, declined steadily after 1880 until the discoveries of the silver ore deposits of Tonopah in 1900 and the bonanza gold deposits of Goldfield in 1902. These finds stimulated prospecting in new areas and rejuvenated mining activity in the State (fig. 17). The old silver-, lead-, and copper-mining camps of Pioche, Yellow Pine, Ely, and Eureka were reopened as new techniques made mining and milling more economic. From World War I through 1965, lead, zinc, and copper production dominated mining activity in Nevada, but precious-metal output regained part of its former prominence with the inception in 1938 of the large-scale opencut mining operation at the Getchell mine in the Potosi district and the opening of the Carlin mine in the Lynn district in 1965. From 1859 through 1965 a total of 27,475,395 ounces of gold was mined in the State.

Ferguson (1944, p. 78–80) has summarized the major features of the geology of Nevada. Paleozoic sedimentary rocks occur throughout the State. Mesozoic sedimentary rocks are exposed in the western part and in the west-central part as far east as Nye County. Along the west border of the State lies the huge Sierra Nevada batholith, and just east of it and related to it are numerous smaller bodies of granitic rock. Along the east, and extending southwestward through Clark County, is a belt characterized by folding and large-scale thrusting and granitic intrusions; both the deformation and intrusion are believed to be of early Tertiary age. There are many areas of granitic rocks in the central part of the State, but their geologic age is uncertain. Volcanic and nonmarine sedimentary rocks of Cenozoic age are found over wide areas. All these rocks have been dislocated by normal faults that have produced the present basin-and-range topography. Some of this faulting has continued into Recent time.

Ore deposits are associated with nearly all the rocks mentioned above. There are veins, contact metamorphic deposits, and replacement deposits associated with the granitic intrusive rocks and the invaded rocks. There are epithermal vein deposits in the Tertiary volcanic rocks.

CHURCHILL COUNTY

Churchill County, in the northern Great Basin, is characterized by many elongate, narrow mountain ranges separated by flat, relatively narrow valleys. Dry or seasonal lakes, the larger of which are in Humboldt and Carson sinks, occupy some of these valleys.

Churchill County, created in 1861, was one of the nine original counties in the State. In later years, parts of the county were used to form Lander, Lyon, and Nye Counties.

Settlers, drawn west by the lure of California gold, crossed Nevada by two main routes, both of which passed through Churchill County. The hot, dry areas occupied by Humboldt and Carson sinks were not inviting; consequently, few people lingered, and the mineral deposits of the county remained undiscovered for some time.

In the early 1860's discoveries were made at Silver Hill, Mountain Well, and Clan Alpine (Browne and Taylor, 1867, p. 128), but it is doubtful that any significant production was achieved.

The discovery at Tonopah, in Nye and Esmeralda Counties in 1900, generated considerable activity, and prospectors overflowed into Churchill County. Discoveries were made at Fairview and Wonder in the early 1900's, and these soon became the most productive gold- and silver-producing areas in the county.

Records of production before 1904 are incomplete, but the value of gold mined from 1890 to 1903 was estimated at $32,300 (about 1,600 ounces). From 1904 to 1937, a total of 12 ounces of placer gold and 123,537 ounces of lode gold was mined in the county (Vanderburg, 1940, p. 10–13). Total gold production through 1959 was 164,605 ounces.

FAIRVIEW DISTRICT

The Fairview district is in southeast Churchill County, 42 miles southeast of Fallon on the west slope of Fairview Peak.

The district was founded in 1906 and became a boom camp immediately. Activity leveled off after a few years, and the Nevada Hills mine emerged as the sustaining producing property until 1917, when it closed. After that time only sporadic small-scale activity was carried on in the district (Vanderburg, 1940, p. 23, 24). Production from 1906 through 1959 was about 53,100 ounces of gold, which was a byproduct from ores that were rich in silver and contained small amounts of lead and copper.

The rocks of the district consist of pre-Tertiary crystalline schists and limestones, intruded by granite (Greenan, 1914). Overlying these older rocks are dacite tuff, two andesite flows, tuff, and rhyo-

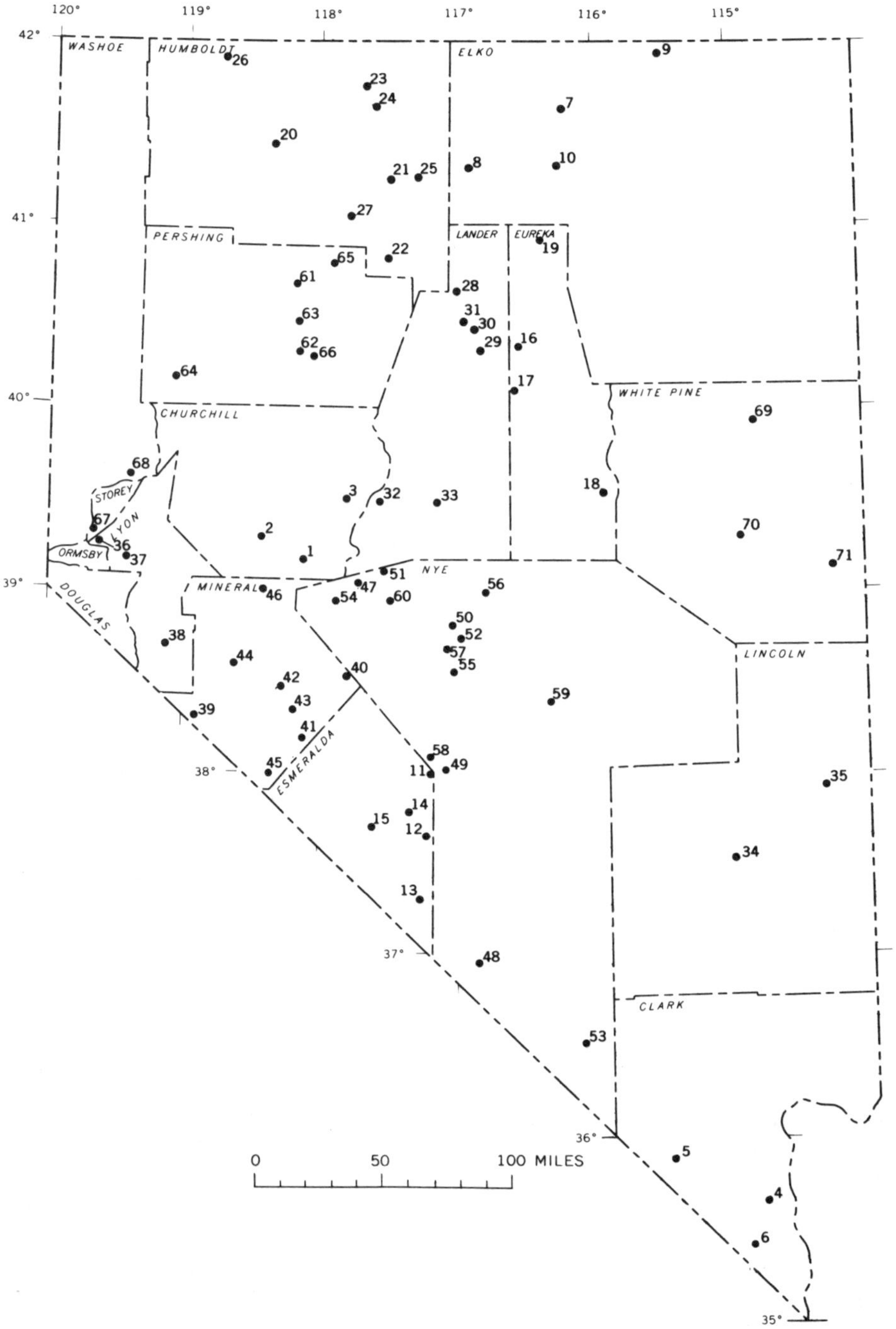

FIGURE 16.—Gold-mining districts of Nevada.

lite, all of Tertiary age. A light-gray rhyolite plug cuts all these formations.

Veins occur in fissures in the earlier of the two andesites. The more prominent veins, the Nevada Hill, the Eagle, and the Dromedary, strike northwest and dip steeply southeast. Ore minerals are argentite, stephanite, horn silver, ruby silver, chalcopyrite, pyrite, tetrahedrite, galena, sphalerite, and gold. Gangue consists of quartz, calcite, and minor rhodochrosite and pyrolusite.

SAND SPRINGS DISTRICT

Although the Sand Springs district, which is 25 to 30 miles southeast of Fallon, was prospected in 1905, its first gold production was not until 1919. To 1937 only $30,000 (about 1,450 ounces) in gold was produced, all of it from the Dan Tucker mine (Vanderburg, 1940, p. 40). From 1937 to 1951 the district yielded 20,875 ounces of gold as a byproduct of silver ores. From 1951 through 1959 no activity was reported.

The ore bodies occur in an east-trending silicified zone that cuts country rock consisting of schist, limestone, and andesite. Free gold and minor silver chloride occur in a gangue of sugary quartz and crushed andesite (Vanderburg, 1940, p. 41).

WONDER DISTRICT

The Wonder district is on the west slope of the Clan Alpine Range in east Churchill County, 55 miles east of Fallon.

The initial gold discoveries were made in 1906, and a rush began immediately (Vanderburg, 1940, p. 54–57). The Nevada Wonder mine soon became the leading producer, a position it never relinquished. The boom was short lived, and after 1919 operations declined to small-scale activities by lessees.

From 1907 through 1959 the district produced 73,890 ounces of gold which was derived from ores rich in silver. The gold-to-silver ratio was 1 to 94. Minor amounts of copper and lead were also produced.

The following description of the geology is summarized from Burgess (1917). The area is underlain by Tertiary rhyolite, dacite, andesite, and basalt. The oldest of these, the Wonder Rhyolite, contains the ore-bearing veins, grouped near small intrusives in the rhyolite. There are many small veins in the district, but only the Nevada Wonder has been productive. The vein is partly on the contact between the Wonder Rhyolite and an intrusive body of dacite.

Silver occurs in the form of argentite and the halogen salts embolite, iodobromite, and iodyrite. The gold is partly included in argentite and is partly free.

CLARK COUNTY

The mining districts of Clark County are scattered through the many north-trending mountain ranges characteristic of this part of the State.

Although there is some indication of early small-scale mining by Indians and Spanish explorers, it

---

Churchill County:
1, Fairview; 2, Sand Springs; 3, Wonder.
Clark County:
4, Eldorado; 5, Goodsprings; 6, Searchlight.
Elko County:
7, Edgemont; 8, Gold Circle; 9, Jarbidge; 10, Tuscarora.
Esmeralda County:
11, Divide; 12, Goldfield; 13, Hornsilver; 14, Lone Mountain; 15, Silver Peak.
Eureka County:
16, Buckhorn; 17, Cortez; 18, Eureka; 19, Lynn.
Humboldt County:
20, Awakening; 21, Dutch Flat; 22, Gold Run; 23, National; 24, Paradise Valley; 25, Potosi; 26, Warm Springs; 27, Winnemucca.
Lander County:
28, Battle Mountain; 29, Bullion; 30, Hilltop; 31, Lewis; 32, New Pass; 33, Reese River.
Lincoln County:
34, Delamar; 35, Pioche.
Lyon County:
36, Silver City; 37, Como; 38, Wilson.
Mineral County:
39, Aurora; 40, Bell; 41, Candelaria; 42, Garfield; 43, Gold Range; 44, Hawthorne; 45, Mount Montgomery and Oneota; 46, Rawhide.
Nye County:
47, Bruner; 48, Bullfrog; 49, Ellendale; 50, Gold Hill; 51, Jackson; 52, Jefferson Canyon; 53, Johnnie; 54, Lodi; 55, Manhattan; 56, Northumberland; 57, Round Mountain; 58, Tonopah; 59, Tybo; 60, Union.
Pershing County:
61, Humboldt; 62, Rochester; 63, Rye Patch; 64, Seven troughs; 65, Sierra; 66, Spring Valley.
Storey County:
67, Comstock Lode.
Washoe County:
68, Olinghouse.
White Pine County:
69, Cherry Creek; 70, Ely; 71, Osceola.

FIGURE 16.—Continued.

was not until 1855, when the Mormon settlers began operating the Potosi mine in the Goodsprings district, that large-scale lode mining began. The Potosi is the oldest lode mine in the State (Vanderburg, 1937a, p. 9). Gold-silver deposits were discovered in the Eldorado district in 1857, and some time later, in the Goodsprings and Searchlight districts. These three districts produced most of the metals in the county.

Total recorded county production from 1908 through 1959 was 291,770 ounces. Of this total only 200 ounces was from placers; the remainder was from lode mines or a byproduct of silver, copper, and base-metal ores.

ELDORADO DISTRICT

The Eldorado district is 6 miles wide and 12 miles long in the northern Opal Mountains in southeastern Clark County, about 25 miles south of Boulder City.

Mining began in this district in 1857, but it never received the publicity given many other areas, possibly because it was overshadowed by concurrent greater booms at the Comstock Lode, Eureka, and Ely (Ransome, 1907, p. 64). The major mines of the district were the Techatticup, Eldorado Rand, Crown Queen, Wall Street, Mocking Bird, Rambler, Rover, and Flagstaff.

The early production of the Eldorado district was estimated (Ransome, 1907, p. 65) at between $2 and $5 million, mostly in gold. From 1907 through 1959 the production was 101,729 ounces of lode and byproduct gold and 168 ounces of placer gold.

Gneiss and schist, possibly Precambrian in age, have been intruded by a mass of quartz monzonite and are flanked locally by patches of Tertiary volcanic rocks (Ransome, 1907, p. 65–68). Ores occur in fissures in the gneiss and schist and in the quartz monzonite. Most of the veins are small, but very persistent. The minerals present are pyrite, galena, and sphalerite in a gangue of quartz and some calcite. The gold and silver probably are associated with the sulfides; native gold has not been seen (Ransome, 1907, p. 76–79).

GOODSPRINGS DISTRICT

The Goodsprings (Yellow Pine) district comprises several hundred square miles in the southern

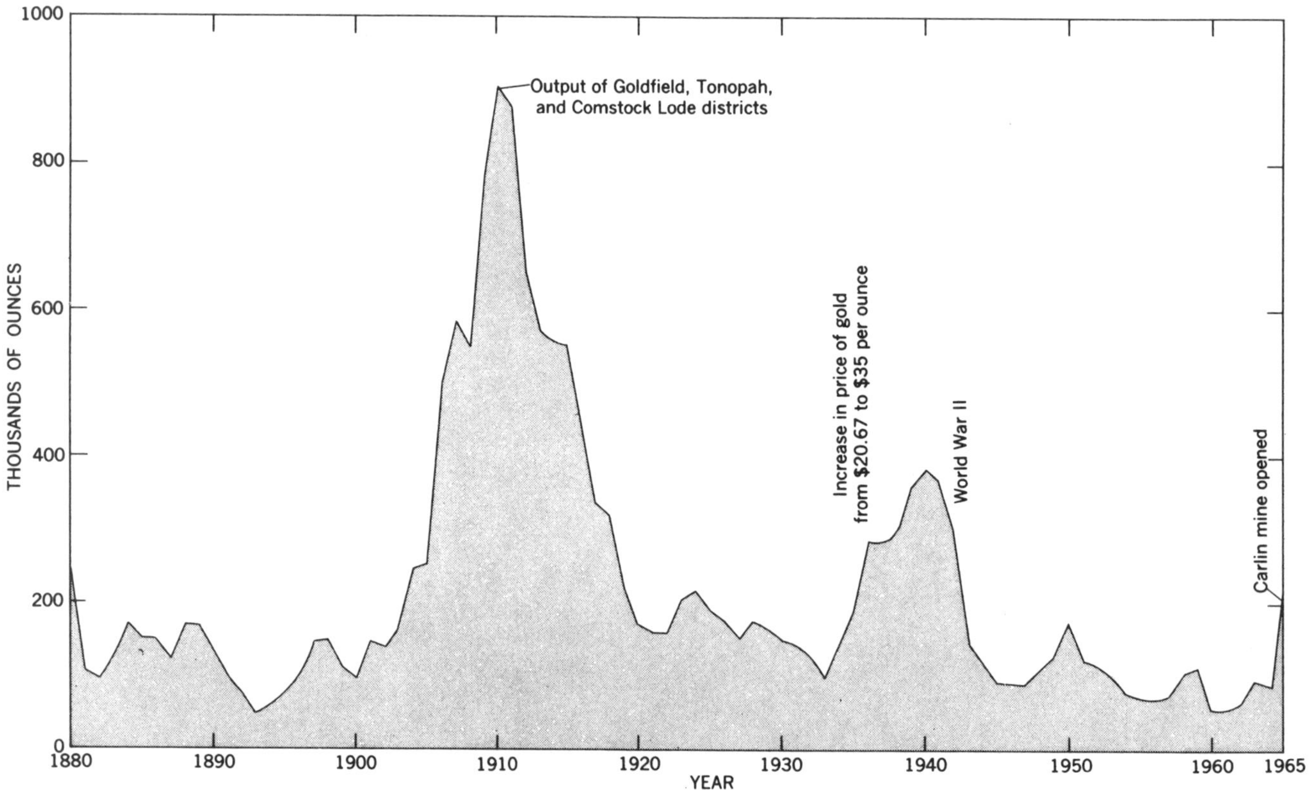

FIGURE 17.—Annual gold production of Nevada, 1880–1965. Sources of data: 1880–1923 from U.S. Geological Survey (1883–1924); 1924–65 from U.S. Bureau of Mines (1925–34; 1933–66). Production reported in dollar value was converted to ounces at prevailing price per ounce.

Spring Mountain Range, in southwestern Clark County. The town of Goodsprings, in the center of the district, is 8 miles northwest of Jean and 28 miles southwest of Las Vegas.

Mormon missionaries are credited with the first discoveries in the district, and in 1856 work was begun at the Potosi mine. After several unsuccessful attempts to smelt the ore and recover lead, work was abandoned, and for the next several decades activity in the district consisted of desultory prospecting of gold-bearing iron gossans, copper-stained gossans, and lead veins. In the 1890's the district was reactivated, and considerable gold was mined from the Keystone, Bass, and Clementine properties. In 1905 the completion of the railroad between Los Angeles and Salt Lake City provided the district with adequate shipping facilities, and the following year significant quantities of oxidized zinc minerals were recognized in the ores. These two events permitted a more orderly growth and development in the following years. Platinum was discovered in the Bass mine in 1914, but production of this element never fulfilled any of the expectations its discovery generated (Hewett, 1931, p. 69–71).

Gold is chiefly a byproduct of zinc-lead-silver ore. From 1902 through 1959 a total of 58,815 ounces of gold was produced; none of it was from placers.

The predominant bedrock consists of a thick section of Paleozoic and Mesozoic rocks that were folded, thrust faulted, and intruded by granitic dikes and sills (Hewett, 1931, p. 9–55). The Paleozoic rocks are predominantly limestone; the Mesozoic rocks are largely sandstone, shale, and conglomerate. Ores were deposited in breccia zones and fractures in limestone of pre-Permian age. Ore deposits are of three types: gold-copper with accessory cobalt, nickel-silver, and zinc-lead with accessory vanadium. Gold deposits are in fractures in and near the intrusive bodies, copper deposits are in Devonian or older beds and are more remote from the intrusive bodies, and zinc and lead deposits occur in Lower Mississippian beds (Hewett, 1931, p. VIII). The gold deposits consist of pyritic fracture fillings, weathered to free gold and iron and manganese oxides; quartz is not present (Hewett, 1931, p. 89–90).

SEARCHLIGHT DISTRICT

Located in southeastern Clark County, 40 miles south of Boulder City and 22 miles east of Nipton, Calif., the Searchlight district is one of the more recently developed in the State; the first production was recorded in 1898. The deposits have yielded gold and subordinate silver, copper, and lead.

Most of the production has come from the Duplex and the Quartette mines. The Quartette had a total yield worth well over $2,800,000 and the Duplex mine produced ore worth in excess of $650,000, mainly in gold (Callaghan, 1939, p. 161, 165).

The period of greatest activity in the district was 1902–16. After that time, activity steadily declined. Gold production from 1902 through 1959 was 246,997 ounces from the lode mines and only 26 ounces from placer workings.

The oldest rock of the district is gneiss of possible Precambrian age (Callaghan, 1939, p. 140–141). It is intruded by a large quartz monzonite body of Tertiary age and by andesite porphyry which may be an early facies of the quartz monzonite. The quartz monzonite is the most extensive rock in the district. A younger series of lava flows and volcanic(?) breccias lies on the eroded surface of the quartz monzonite and older rocks.

The veins are in fractured zones in the older rocks around the margin of the quartz monzonite. Most of the production has come from oxidized and weathered vein material which extends to depths of 800 feet, or more, in which galena is the only unweathered sulfide present. Unweathered vein material consists of a breccia of country rock cemented with vuggy quartz. Sphalerite, galena, and chalcopyrite occur in equal amounts in the quartz. The oxidized vein material contains gold, traces of copper and chalcopyrite, galena, chalcocite, quartz, chalcedony, cuprite, hematite, cerussite, malachite, calcite, brochantite, limonite, leadhillite, chrysocolla, wulfenite, vanadinite, mottramite, hemimorphite (Callaghan, 1939, p. 152–153).

ELKO COUNTY

Elko County is in the northeastern part of the State, and most of its gold production has come from districts in the northern and western parts of the county. Lode mines in the Jarbidge and Tuscarora districts have been the principal source of the gold, but in the early days considerable amounts of placer gold were mined at Tuscarora, Aura, Charleston, Gold Basin, Island Mountain, and Mountain City. Lesser amounts of lode and byproduct gold came from Gold Circle, Mountain City, Aura, and Edgemont.

The production of the county from 1903 through 1959 was 561,187 ounces—554,737 ounces from lodes and 6,450 ounces from placers. Before 1903 there was considerable production, primarily from Tuscarora and Edgemont, but no complete record could be found. From 1879 through 1896, the county produced $1,017,051 in lode gold (Nolan, 1936a, p. 13). In addition, the Tuscarora district produced about $700,000 in placer gold (Nolan, 1936a, p. 14). Total gold production through 1959 was about 614,000 ounces.

EDGEMONT DISTRICT

The Edgemont district is in northern Elko County, on the west slope of the Centennial Range, about 10 miles north of Deep Creek.

Before about 1907 the Lucky Girl and Bull Run mines yielded about $1 million in gold (Emmons, 1910, p. 75). From 1907 through 1959 the district was dormant, producing only 4 ounces in 1950 and 74 ounces in 1951.

The deposits consist of fissure veins in contorted and fractured quartzite. Gold is associated with pyrite, galena, and pyrrhotite (Emmons, 1910, p. 75–76).

GOLD CIRCLE DISTRICT

The Gold Circle district is 45 miles north of Battle Mountain, 50 miles northeast of Golconda, and 35 miles west of Tuscarora.

Gold was discovered in 1907, and a brief boom followed. This has been a gold-silver district; a total of 109,765 ounces of lode gold and 45 ounces of placer gold was produced from 1908 to 1958, mostly from the Elko Prince mine.

The country rocks—from oldest to youngest—consist of rhyolite, andesite, and postandesite rhyolite flows and tuff (Rott, 1931, p. 10). The rocks were faulted and then mineralized. Most of the veins follow northwest-trending shear zones in the older rhyolite and the fractured contact between rhyolite and andesite. Vein material is principally silicified breccia and minor calcite and adularia. The dominant minerals are pyrite, stromeyerite, and native gold. Minor constituents are tetrahedrite, proustite, chalcopyrite, and sphalerite.

JARBIDGE DISTRICT

The Jarbidge district is in northern Elko County about 60 miles west of the Utah State line and 5 miles south of the Idaho State line.

Gold ore was first discovered in 1904 (Schrader, 1912, p. 15), but the major discovery was not until 1909. A rush to the area took place the following year, and the town of Jarbidge was soon founded.

Production totaled about 217,800 ounces from 1911 through 1959.

The Jarbidge Mountains, of which the mining district is a small part, separate two major physiographic provinces: the Snake River Plain to the north and the Great Basin to the south.

The district is underlain by Tertiary volcanic rocks that were extruded on an eroded surface of Paleozoic rocks that had been intruded by granitic stocks and dikes (Schrader, 1923, p. 12–35). The Paleozoic sedimentary rocks consist of quartzite, limestone, and shale and have been considerably folded. The intrusive rock is a gray coarsely crystalline hornblende-biotite granodiorite of probable Cretaceous age. The Tertiary volcanic rocks, mostly rhyolites, are divided into two series separated by an erosion surface.

The ore deposits are gold-bearing fissure veins in the older rhyolites. These veins range from 1 to 30 feet in width and from several hundred feet to several miles in length. They are grouped into a west and east system. In the west system the veins are the more valuable; they strike north-northwestward and dip steeply eastward. In the east system the veins are narrow but persistent; they strike northward and are exposed in rocks nearer the crest of the range.

The economic metals of the district are gold and silver, and they occur as native gold, electrum, argentite, cerargyrite, and naumannite (Schrader, 1923, p. 26). Pyrite is also present. The gangue consists chiefly of quartz and adularia. Other minerals present in minor amounts are apatite, barite, calcite, chalcedony, chlorite, epidote, fluorite, hematite, hyalite, kaolin, halloysite, leverrierite, limonite, psilomelane, pyrolusite, marcasite, opaline silica, sericite, and talc.

TUSCARORA DISTRICT

The Tuscarora district is 45 miles northwest of Elko, near the headwaters of the South Fork of the Owyhee River.

Gold was discovered in the area in 1867 in stream gravels (Browne, 1868, p. 429–430), and outcrops of auriferous vein material were found soon afterward. During the following 9 years placers were mined, but there was no intense activity until 1876 when high-grade ore was found in the Grand Prize mine (Nolan, 1936a, p. 7–9). The usual boom period followed, accompanied by mismanagement, waste, litigations, and profiteering, so typical of the histories of mining camps throughout the West. By 1886 the bonanza ores were exhausted, but new discoveries to the north and west created another boom, though of lesser proportions. A third revival was created by the mining of low-grade gold ores from the Dexter mine (Nolan, 1936a, p. 9), and most of the production of the district from 1895 to 1912 was from this mine. In recent years the district declined steadily with no production reported from 1955 through 1959.

Nolan (1936a, p. 10–14) in reviewing the production history of the district noted that estimates of production before 1902 varied widely, but that a reasonable compromise would be about $10 million in gold and silver. From 1902 through 1959, a total of 15,662 ounces of gold was mined, most of it from lodes. The placer gold production of the district, most of it mined in the early days, amounted to about $700,000 (Nolan, 1936a, p. 14). Total gold production of the district through 1959 probably was at least 100,000 ounces.

The bedrock of the area consists of bedded volcanic breccias and tuffs about 5,000 feet thick and dark-green andesite porphyry that is intrusive into the pyroclastics (Nolan, 1936a, p. 14–35). The bedded rocks have been tilted to the east and southeast. The rocks are also faulted, but the nature and extent of faulting are not clear.

There are three types of deposits: (1) silver lodes rich in native silver and silver halides, argentite, stephanite, proustite, pyrargyrite, pyrite, enargite, arsenopyrite, bornite, chalcopyrite, sphalerite, and galena with quartz and calcite gangue, in the andesite masses; (2) gold deposits consisting of quartz and adularia fissure fillings and zones of quartz stringers in the bedded pyroclastics; and (3) gold placers.

ESMERALDA COUNTY

Until the discoveries at Goldfield in 1902, the gold deposits of Esmeralda County were in themselves relatively insignificant; most of the gold had been produced as a byproduct of rich silver ores. Yet, gold was the metal sought in the early days, and in at least one instance, at Gold Mountain in the Divide district, the search for gold led to the discovery of rich silver deposits.

The silver-gold deposits of the county are of two general types: veins associated with granitic bodies of Late Jurassic or Early Cretaceous age, and fissure filling in Tertiary volcanics. The deposits at Silver Peak, Windypah, Hornsilver, Lida, Montezuma, and Klondike belong to the first type; those at Divide and Goldfield to the second. Production in the county from 1903 through 1959 was 4,912,112 ounces of lode gold, mostly from Goldfield, and 2,071 ounces of placer gold.

DIVIDE DISTRICT

The Divide (Gold Mountain) district, 5 miles south of Tonopah, has been primarily a silver camp; it was founded in 1901. Between 1901 and 1917 there was only sporadic exploitation of the gold-bearing veins on Gold Mountain and the silver lodes in the Crown Divide property. Then, in 1917, a rich silver lode was discovered on Gold Mountain which immediately created a boom that lasted until 1919. The principal mines in the district are the Tonopah Divide, the Divide Extension, and the Tonopah Hasbrouck (Knopf, 1921b, p. 148–170).

Gold production from 1910 through 1959 was 26,483 ounces, mostly as a byproduct of ores mined for silver.

The predominant rock in the district is the Fraction Rhyolite Breccia (of the Siebert Formation) of probable late Miocene age. Several stocks of Oddie Rhyolite and Divide Andesite (of late Miocene age) intrude the rhyolite breccia. Latite flows of Pliocene age cap the higher peaks. The ore bodies are mineralized fracture zones in the Fraction Rhyolite Breccia. Cerargyrite is the main silver-bearing mineral; some sooty argentite is present, and molybdite and powellite are abundant locally. A few narrow gold-quartz veins have been found in the Oddie Rhyolite. Veinfilling in these consists of rhyolite fragments, quartz, and pyrite.

GOLDFIELD DISTRICT

Located near the east border of Esmeralda County, 28 miles south of Tonopah, the Goldfield district is on the south rim of a desert basin which is the southern extension of a much larger basin west of Tonopah. This rim is formed by a group of hills, known as the Goldfield Hills.

Gold was discovered in the district in 1902, but no important shipments were made until 1904 (Ransome, 1909a, p. 17) during a brief period of high production. In 1905 the district declined because of exhaustion of many of the high-grade ore shoots. In 1906 important new discoveries on the Mohawk property spurred exploration and development throughout the district. High-grading and strife between labor unions and management curtailed production and eventually assumed such proportions during this period that Federal troops were called in to maintain order. In March 1908 labor troubles were settled and soon the district settled down to a more peaceful era of development and production.

From 1903 through 1959 the district produced about 4,194,800 ounces of gold. Small amounts of silver were produced as a byproduct.

The oldest rocks in the district are dark flinty shale and quartzite of Cambrian age (Ransome, 1909a, p. 32). Intruded into these metasedimentary rocks are masses of alaskite and granite, of probable Early Cretaceous age. Overlying these rocks is a thick series of volcanic rocks and lake deposits, all of Tertiary age. Ransome (1909a, p. 36–74) divided them into the prelacustrine volcanic rocks, lacustrine rocks composing the Siebert Formation, of Miocene age, and postlacustrine volcanic rocks. Both sets of volcanic rocks consist of rhyolite, dacite, tuff, and andesite. The lake sediments consist of volcanic ash, gravel, and scattered beds of diatomaceous earth. A thick flow of mica basalt occurs in the sediments. The postlacustrine volcanics are capped by the Malpais Basalt. This entire Tertiary sequence has been warped into a dome and faulted.

Most of the ore deposits are found in topographically prominent silicified zones of small intersecting ramifying shears in the dacite, one of the prelacustrine rocks. Other deposits occur in andesite, and a few, in rhyolite (Ransome, 1909a, p. 150–155). The ores are complex sulfides consisting of pyrite, bismuthinite, goldfieldite, and a mineral resembling famatinite in a dark-gray flinty quartz gangue. Alunite is a common gangue in some ore. Native gold, commonly very fine grained, is associated with these minerals. Typical of the ore is its concentric banded character, its extreme richness, and the erratic behavior of ore shoots (Ransome, 1909a, p. 165–167).

Later work by Searls (1948) modified some of Ransome's earlier conclusions regarding the age of mineralization, the relation of faulting to mineralization, and relation of the dacite to earlier flows. Searls concluded (1) that the dacite was not intrusive into any of the earlier rocks (whereas Ransome had indicated that it was), (2) that the age of mineralization was somewhat earlier than Ransome had thought, and (3) that the Columbia Mountain fault, the major fault in the district, was the distributing agent for the mineralizing solutions. Ransome (1909a, p. 196, 197) postulated that the hot mineralizing solutions rose along complicated fissures in the dacite.

HORNSILVER DISTRICT

In the Hornsilver district, which is 20 miles south-southwest of Goldfield, prospectors were active in 1868, but their discoveries were not very productive (Ransome, 1909b, p. 41–42). In 1907 larger ore bodies were found, and the district prospered for a few years. No activity was reported from 1956 through 1959.

Total gold production from the Hornsilver district from 1903 through 1959 was about 25,000 ounces.

The rocks of the district are limestone and calcareous shale that were intruded and metamorphosed by masses of granite (Ransome, 1909b, p. 41–42). The veins strike N. 55°–60° W. and cut across the bedding of the shale. Most production has come from the Great Western and Grand Central veins. The important ore constituents are native gold and silver chloride (Ransome, 1909a, p. 41–42).

LONE MOUNTAIN DISTRICT

Located in eastern Esmeralda County, in T. 1 S., R. 41 E., the Lone Mountain district is predominantly a silver camp with a recorded production from 1903 through 1949 of 31,961 ounces of gold. No activity was reported from 1949 through 1959.

The bedrock is Cambrian limestone and shale complexly folded and intruded by masses of diorite and by dikes and sheets of diorite porphyry (Ball, 1906, p. 57, 58). Deposits containing cerussite, malachite, azurite, chrysocolla, galena, and pyrite occur in altered limonite-stained limestone near its contact with diorite porphyry sheets.

SILVER PEAK DISTRICT

The Silver Peak (Mineral Ridge) district is in central Esmeralda County, in T. 5 S., R. 39 E.

The first discoveries in this district were made in 1864. These were silver deposits which were worked for several years with rather meager returns. Some time later gold lodes were discovered, and these soon became the more important. The Drinkwater and Crowning Glory have been the major mines.

The gold production to 1905 was about 59,100 ounces (Spurr, 1906, p. 35). The interval 1906–15 was one of high production, but during 1915–31 only about $50,000 in gold was produced per year. Total production during 1903–32 was 323,085 ounces (Nolan, 1936b, p. 60). The mid-1930's to early 1940's was another period of high production, followed by the abrupt decline in production caused by World War II. From 1943 through 1959 there was only small-scale activity in the district. Total gold production of the district through 1959 was about 568,000 ounces.

The rocks of the district consist of Cambrian and Ordovician limestones, slates, and quartzites that were intruded by a Late Jurassic or Early Cretaceous alaskitic rock (Spurr, 1906, p. 9–12). The gold deposits are in quartz lenses in the limestones and probably are genetically related to the late siliceous phase of the alaskite. Native gold is finely disseminated in the quartz. Gold is also associated with scattered sulfides in the lenses.

EUREKA COUNTY

Eureka County was formed in 1873 from the eastern part of Lander County and from small parts of White Pine and Elko Counties. North-trending mountain ranges separated by wide valleys, typical of Great Basin terrain, are the predominant land forms in the county.

The first mineral discoveries were made in 1863 in the Cortez district, and the following year additional discoveries were made in the Eureka and Diamond districts. The Eureka district quickly emerged as the county's leading producer; the mining history of the county is largely a history of the Eureka district.

Gold production before 1902 is difficult to determine because of the practice in the early days of combining production of all metals and reporting it in dollar values. It can be stated, however, that a minimum of 1 million ounces of gold was mined from the Eureka district alone up to 1883 (Vanderburg, 1938a, p. 13). From 1902 through 1959 a total of 203, 597 ounces of gold was mined in the county —9,618 ounces was from placers, and the remainder was a byproduct from silver ores.

BUCKHORN DISTRICT

The Buckhorn district is in the south end of the Cortez Mountains, 5 miles northeast of Cortez.

The production of the district, which is virtually that of the Buckhorn mine discovered in 1908, was 39,632 ounces in gold from 1910 through 1959. The Buckhorn was mined for gold, and silver was a byproduct.

The highest grade ore occurs along a nearly vertical fault that disrupts country rock composed of basalt and interbedded scoria. Both sulfide and oxide ore are present. The oxide ore consists of kaolinized breccia with high gold and silver values; the sulfide ore is primarily fine grained pyrite in talc-rich rock (Vanderburg, 1938a, p. 19–21).

CORTEZ DISTRICT

The Cortez district is about 36 miles south of Beowawe at about the middle of the boundary line between Eureka and Lander Counties.

The district was founded in 1863 and was an active producer for many years. The principal mine is the Garrison mine. Silver has been the chief commodity, and lead, copper, and gold have been byproducts. From 1863 to 1903, a minimum of $500,000 (about 24,270 ounces) in gold was produced, and from 1902 to 1936, a total of 8,267 ounces of gold was produced (Vanderburg, 1938a, p. 23–24). Total recorded production of gold from 1863 to 1958 was about 48,720 ounces.

The country rock consists of Paleozoic limestone of probable Cambrian age, overlain by quartzite of probable Ordovician age (Emmons, 1910, p. 101–103). These were intruded by a mass of granite and by porphyry dikes. Ore occurs as replacement bodies in the limestone and in the quartzite. Most of it is in fissures parallel to the dikes. The ore minerals are galena, stibnite, pyrite, sphalerite, stromeyerite. Gangue minerals are quartz and calcite. The galena is rich in silver. Ore such as this is reported (Emmons, 1910, p. 104) to carry from $3 to $15 per ton in gold. Some of the ore is oxidized and consists of silver chloride, copper carbonates, and iron and manganese oxides.

EUREKA DISTRICT

The Eureka district is located at the town of Eureka, in southeastern Eureka County.

The first locations were made in 1864, but little was produced until 1869, when large ore bodies were found on Ruby Hill (Hague, 1892, p. 6). The period of greatest production was 1871–88. Hague (1892, p. 6–7) estimated that $20 million in gold was produced from 1869 to 1883. During this period two mines emerged as the major producers—the Eureka Consolidated and the Richmond. After 1888 the major ore bodies were exhausted, the smelters were shut down, and the district entered a period of inactivity broken only by sporadic small-scale mining by lessees. In 1905 the Richmond and Eureka properties were consolidated, and, after the old workings were rehabilitated, shipments of low-grade ore were made. But the low-grade ores could not be profitably mined under constantly increasing costs, and the workings were again closed except for small-scale leasing operations. Several unsuccessful exploratory ventures took place in 1919 and 1923. In 1937, however, the Eureka Corp., Ltd., discovered a new ore body. The Fad shaft was sunk to exploit this ore, but in 1949 work was halted at a depth of 2,500 feet because of the large flows of water that were encountered. Other more recent exploration in the Adams Hill area was more successful; considerable ore was mined from the T. L. shaft. There has also been a renewal of activity in the Diamond mine, about 4 miles south of Eureka (Nolan, 1962, p. 2–3).

The production of the Eureka district is difficult to ascertain, but annual production has been tabulated by Nolan (1962, p. 56–59) from what he considered to be reliable sources.

Using Hague's (1892, p. 6–7) estimate of $20 million (967,585 ounces) in gold from 1869 to 1883 and Nolan's (1962, p. 58–59) data from 1884 through 1959, we arrive at an approximate total gold production of 1,230,748 ounces, which, in view of the generalized nature of Hague's estimate, should be rounded off to 1,230,000 ounces.

The rocks of the Eureka district consist of a thick section of Paleozoic sedimentary rocks, a Cretaceous sedimentary formation, and Cretaceous and Cenozoic igneous rocks.

The Cambrian formations, which in total are about 9,000 feet thick, are, in ascending order, the Prospect Mountain Quartzite, Pioche Shale, Eldorado Dolomite, Geddes Limestone, Secret Canyon Shale, Hamburg Dolomite, Dunderberg Shale, and the Windfall Formation (Nolan, 1962, p. 5–9). Rocks of Ordovician age are about 2,200 feet thick and consist of the Pogonip Group, Eureka Quartzite, and Hanson Creek Formation. The Devils Gate Formation of Devonian age, the Chainman Shale and Diamond Peak Formation of Mississippian age, and the Carbon Ridge Formation of Permian age complete the Paleozoic sequence. Scattered outcrops of the Newark Canyon Formation of Early Cretaceous age unconformably overlie the older rocks (Nolan, 1962, p. 9–13). Igneous rocks of Cretaceous age consist of a plug of quartz diorite and a sill-like mass of quartz porphyry. Other igneous rocks range in age from Oligocene to late Tertiary or Quaternary and include hornblende andesite, rhyolite, rhyolite tuff, andesite, and basalt (Nolan, 1962, p. 13–17).

The structure, which is exceedingly complex, was considered by Hague (1892, p. 8–30) and Nolan (1962, p. 18–29) as a series of structural blocks separated from one another by faults of large displacements. Nearly all the ore bodies of the district are within the north-trending Prospect Ridge block, which is bounded on the east by the Hoosac fault and on the west by the Dugout Tunnel thrust and the Spring Valley, Sharp, and Cave Canyon faults. Recognized within the Prospect Ridge block are three thrust zones, two normal fault zones, and a transverse fault (Nolan, 1962, p. 18–26). The greater part of the deformation is thought to have occurred in the late Mesozoic, though the older structures were formed in Paleozoic time, and movement on some faults took place in Pleistocene or Recent time (Nolan, 1962, p. 27–29).

Ore bodies are grouped into five geographic groups or clusters, of which the most productive has been the Ruby Hill cluster. Most of the ore at Eureka has been mined from irregular replacement deposits in dolomite which consist of irregularly shaped masses of fine-grained anglesite, cerussite, plumbojarosite, mimetite, and galena and minor wulfenite, pyrite, arsenopyrite, hematite, sphalerite, calamine, smithsonite, calcite, aragonite, siderite, quartz, clay minerals, azurite, and malachite. Cerargyrite and native gold are present in small quantities. Gold ore from the Windfall mine is distinctive in that textures of the replaced dolomite have been preserved, and the dolomitic gangue has been converted to a "sand" by the mineralizing solutions. The Windfall ore is further characterized by relative absence of sulfides and their oxidation products (Nolan, 1962, p. 30–47).

LYNN DISTRICT

Located about 20 miles northwest of Carlin in northern Eureka County, the Lynn district was until 1962 a placer district. Gold was produced from placer deposits over a wide area, including Lynn, Simon, Rodeo, and Sheep Creeks. In 1962, however, a large lode deposit, the Carlin mine, was discovered. This mine is in a window in the Roberts Mountains thrust fault. The ore consists of very fine-grained gold, mostly less than 5 microns in size, in fractured and altered siltstone and limestone of Silurian and Devonian age below the thrust fault. In 1966, published reserves were 11 million tons of ore containing about 3.5 million ounces of gold.

Vanderburg (1936a, p. 83) reported total production of the district to about 1935 at $140,000, or approximately 6,800 ounces of gold. Total production through 1959 was only about 9,000 ounces. The opening of the Carlin mine in May 1965 brought about a large increase in production; during 1965 and 1966 the mine yielded almost 390,000 ounces of gold.

HUMBOLDT COUNTY

Mining began in Humboldt County in the early 1860's and for many years there was sporadic production from several districts. The discovery of fabulously rich gold ores in the National district in 1907 probably was the most significant event in the mining history of the county. These rich ores were soon depleted, and mining activity declined until 1935, when it increased with the discovery of ore in the Jumbo mine in the Awakening district. The Getchell mine, in the Potosi district, became active in 1938, and for several years thereafter it was the largest gold producer in the State. Most of the gold mined in Humboldt County has come from lodes, but there has also been considerable placer gold produced from the Dutch Flat district.

Vanderburg (1938b, p. 13, 14) listed production data for gold as early as 1890 and for silver and gold as early as 1870. For the period 1870–90, a total of $4.975,372 in gold and silver was produced. From 1890 through 1903 about 31,830 ounces of lode and placer gold was mined. From 1905 through 1959, a total of 811,712 ounces of lode gold and 36,720 ounces of placer gold was produced.

Humboldt County contains several north-trending mountain ranges, separated by arid undrained valleys, many of which contain playa lakes.

AWAKENING DISTRICT

The Awakening district is about 45 miles northwest of Winnemucca in the Slumbering Hills.

About 1910 mining began in this area, and there was a small production of gold and silver from 1912 to 1918. In 1935 the discovery of the Jumbo mine opened a new period of large-scale activity. The early production could not be determined, but from 1935 through 1959, a total of 25,648 ounces of gold was produced.

Metamorphosed muds and impure sandstones, now slates and schists of probable Mesozoic age, are exposed throughout most of the area (Calkins, 1938, p. 9–15). A body of quartz monzonite has intruded the Mesozoic rocks and produced zones of contact metamorphism. Aplite and pegmatite dikes are associated with the intrusive. Tertiary latite and andesite flows, underlain by lake beds, cap the higher parts of the area.

Most ore deposits are gold-bearing quartz veins in the slates (Calkins, 1938, p. 15–22). Most of the veins are less than 1 foot thick and have numerous branches. Their average strike is north and their dips are variable. The Jumbo deposit, however, is completely different from the other veins of the district. Its most characteristic feature is the abundant adularia and sparse quartz in the gangue. The veins are small and irregularly distributed, as in a stockwork (Calkins, 1938, p. 19–20).

DUTCH FLAT DISTRICT

The Dutch Flat placer district, 18 miles northeast of Winnemucca and 18 miles north of Golconda, was discovered in 1893 and produced about $75,000 in gold the first year (Vanderburg, 1936a, p. 94). Total gold production through 1959 was about 10,000 ounces.

The deposits are stream and slope-wash gravels in an area 1½ miles long and 300 to 2,000 feet wide (Willden and Hotz, 1955, p. 666). In addition to gold, significant quantities of scheelite and cinnabar occur in the placers. The ore minerals come from low-grade lode deposits in a granodiorite stock and in folded early Paleozoic sedimentary rocks. The lode deposits are of two types: gold-quartz veins that contain some sulfides and a little scheelite, and disseminated cinnabar in a shear zone that cuts metamorphosed shale and feldspathic quartzite (Willden and Hotz, 1955, p. 665).

GOLD RUN DISTRICT

Located in southeast Humboldt County, 12 miles south of Golconda, the Gold Run (Adelaide) district was organized in 1866. Gold has been a byproduct of ores mined for copper and silver. Placer gold was mined sporadically along Gold Run Creek, and total production from this source was about 2,000 ounces. Production of byproduct gold from 1907 through 1959 was 23,747 ounces.

At the Adelaide mine, the principal mine of the district (Vanderburg, 1938b, p. 24), the ore occurs as replacements of limestone beds and consists of chalcopyrite, pyrrhotite, sphalerite, and galena in a gangue of calcite, garnet, vesuvianite. Some specimens contained a little scheelite.

NATIONAL DISTRICT

The National district is in northeastern Humboldt County on the west slope of the Santa Rosa Range, 18 miles southeast of McDermitt.

Although the Santa Rosa Range had been prospected with minor success since the 1860's, it was not until 1907 that the rich deposits at National were discovered. The unusually high grade ore body at the National soon made it the leading mine in the district. Some of the ore was valued at $30 per pound. As may be expected, this attracted many individuals of questionable character, and the history of the camp is marked by numerous incidents of violence and disorder and a trial that attracted wide attention (Lindgren, 1915, p. 19, 20, 52–54). The rich ore shoots were mined out within a few years, and after about 1917 the properties were worked intermittently by lessees.

Production of the district from 1909 through 1959 was 177,000 ounces, all from lode deposits.

The northern part of the Santa Rosa Range is composed predominantly of basaltic lava flows of probable Miocene age (Lindgren, 1915, p. 21–22). At National mine, basaltic tuffs and lacustrine beds are overlain by latite, basaltic flows, and a rhyolite flow. Necks and dikes of this rhyolite cut all the older rocks. Locally basalt flows cover the rhyolite. The rocks dip 8° to 15° NE.

The ore deposits are in fissure veins that have a northward trend and steep east or west dips. The veins cut the youngest rocks in the district and are therefore believed to be Miocene or post-Miocene in age (Lindgren, 1915, p. 32). Most of the veins are rich in silver; ruby silver is the chief ore mineral. The National ore shoot is an exception. Here the ore mineral is coarse electrum irregularly distributed near the footwall of the quartz vein (Lindgren, 1915, p. 31, 32). Stibnite is the characteristic mineral of all the veins. Other sulfides present are pyrite, calcopyrite, arsenopyrite, sphalerite, and galena in a gangue of banded and vuggy quartz.

PARADISE VALLEY DISTRICT

Located on the east slope of the Santa Rosa Range, 11 miles northwest of the town of Paradise Valley, the Paradise Valley district was discovered in 1868. During 1879–91 the mines reached their peak production; then, operations ceased abruptly. Brief revivals took place in 1907–15 and 1931–35 (Vanderburg, 1938b, p. 38). From 1947 through 1959, only 10 ounces of gold was reported.

Silver is the chief commodity mined in this district; gold is a byproduct. Some placer gold was produced in 1909–15. Total gold production through 1959 was about 70,000 ounces.

The ore deposits are quartz veins in shale, calcareous slate, and porphyry. The veins, which strike north and dip steeply east, contain cerargyrite, chalcopyrite, pyrargyrite, sphalerite, and pyrite, in a gangue of quartz (Vanderburg, 1938b, p. 38–40).

POTOSI DISTRICT

The Potosi district is in T. 38 and 39 N., R. 42 E., in the northern Osgood Mountains.

Gold mining in the district was insignificant until the discovery of the Getchell ore body in 1934. Large-scale open-cut mining of the Getchell began in 1938, and during 1939–41 it was the leading gold-producer in the State. The mine was permitted to remain open during World War II in order to produce tungsten and arsenic which were in short supply. A scarcity of labor and materials forced the mine to close in 1945. Large-scale mining of gold was resumed in 1948 and continued through 1950, when attention was diverted to mining of tungsten ores. During 1952–57 the Getchell and Riley mines were the major tungsten producers in Nevada. Exploration and development of gold properties in the Getchell mine area during 1959–61 were successful, and gold mining was resumed in 1962.

Published data are incomplete and show gold production of only 116,015 ounces. Total gold production is probably worth about $17 million or roughly 485,700 ounces (R. L. Erickson, oral commun., 1963).

The geology of the district is fairly complex. The eastern part is underlain by shale, slate, and limestone of the Preble Formation of Cambrian age and by limestone, shale, and conglomerate of Pennsylvanian and Permian age. The higher central part of the district is occupied by a stock of granodiorite of Cretaceous age. Overlying the granodiorite in the north-central part of the district is a thrust plate of phyllite, calc-silicate rock, marble, and recrystallized chert, representing part of the Comus Formation of Ordovician age. North-trending normal faults dislocated the rocks after the period of thrust faulting (Hotz and Willden, 1961).

The major ore deposits, which are along the north-trending Getchell fault, are sheetlike masses that are distributed irregularly in veins along various fault branches near the surface but that coalesce at depth along the main fault. The veins consist of sheared and mineralized sedimentary rock which is cut by quartz and calcite veinlets and which contains a soft carbonaceous gumbo. Most of the gold is in the gumbo. Gangue, in addition to gumbo, consists of small amounts of barite, chabazite, gypsum, and fluorite. Pyrite, pyrrhotite, arsenopyrite, marcasite, orpiment, realgar, stibnite, ilsemannite, cinnabar, magnetite, gold, and scheelite are the major ore minerals. Gold occurs as minute particles associated with magnetite and carbonaceous material in the gumbo and also as submicroscopic particles in pyrite and marcasite. The richer gold accumulations are characterized by abundant realgar (Joralemon, 1951, p. 270–282).

R. L. Erickson (oral commun., 1963) noted a relationship of arsenic, mercury, and tungsten in geochemical anomalies in the district and suggested that these anomalies are worthy of exploration for gold.

WARM SPRINGS DISTRICT

The Warm Springs district is in northwest Humboldt County near Denio, Oreg. The first discoveries were in 1863, but production was hindered for some time by the hostile Bannock Indians, who burned a mill and drove out the miners (Vanderburg, 1938b, p. 49). The principal mine in the district is the Ashdown.

Production of the district is not known, but Vanderburg (1938b, p. 49) estimated that it was

$400,000, mostly in gold from the Ashdown mine. From 1937 through 1957, a total of 5,178 ounces of lode gold and 10 ounces of placer gold was reported. Total gold production through 1959 was about 24,000 ounces.

The country rock is slate of undetermined age and is intruded by granite and porphyry. At the Ashdown mine the ore deposit is in a quartz vein in granite. Free gold occurs in a gangue of quartz.

WINNEMUCCA DISTRICT

The first discovery in this district, which is 4 miles northwest of the town of Winnemucca, was made in 1863 by an Indian named Winnemucca (Vanderburg, 1938a, p. 51–54). The most important mine in the early days was the Pride of the Mountain, which produced an estimated $1 million in precious metals (Ferguson and others, 1951). In the early 1900's, high-grade gold ore discoveries near Barrett Springs created a short-lived rush; from 1937 through 1943 there was a renewal of activity, mainly at the Pansy Lee mine.

Production data are incomplete for the early years. During 1910–35, a total of $132,433 in gold and silver was produced (Vanderburg, 1938a, p. 51), and during 1935–59, about 10,070 ounces of gold was produced. Total gold production through 1959, including early production from the Pride of the Mountain mine, was probably 35,000 ounces.

The deposits on Winnemucca Mountain include veins and replacement deposits in hornfels and limestone of the Winnemucca Formation, of Late Triassic age. This formation locally is intruded by diorite (Ferguson and others, 1951). In the Barrett Springs area, the deposits are gold- and silver-rich quartz stringers and veins in the slates of the Raspberry Formation of Late Triassic age (Ferguson and others, 1951).

LANDER COUNTY

Lander County lies within the vast arid Great Basin, wherein narrow, northward-trending, treeless mountains rise a mile or more above sun-baked valleys.

The hordes of early gold seekers who crossed the State in 1849 and 1850 were intent on reaching the lush gold fields of the Mother Lode; they wasted no time crossing the forbidding wastes of Nevada. It was not until after the rich strike at Comstock in 1859 that Nevada was seriously considered for worthwhile prospecting.

In 1862 precious metal in Lander County first was discovered in the Reese River district. Almost immediately news of the rich silver ores started a rush. The town of Austin was formed and had a population of 6,000 by 1863 (Vanderburg, 1939, p. 11). The Reese River district flourished, and Austin was the center of mining activity. Important gold discoveries were made in the 1860's and 1870's at the Battle Mountain and Lewis districts, and, in 1905 in the Bullion district. Almost all the gold mined in the county from 1945 through 1959 came from the Bullion district.

Lander County is noted for its silver production, the great silver output of the Reese River district overshadowing the output of all other metals; nevertheless, the county has produced considerable gold, both placer and lode. Before 1890, gold and silver values were combined in production reports, and it is impossible to determine gold or silver production alone. The precious metal production of the county during 1870–89 was $16,676,405, most of which was silver from the Reese River district (Vanderburg, 1939, p. 15). Beginning in 1890, gold production and silver production were recorded separately: from 1890 through 1901, $510,270 (about 24,700 ounces) in gold was recorded; from 1902 through 1936, production was 48,899 ounces of placer gold and 75,004 ounces of lode gold (Vanderburg, 1939, p. 15–16); and from 1937 through 1959, a total of 435,325 ounces of lode gold and 23,347 ounces of placer gold was mined. Total gold production in the county through 1959 was about 607,000 ounces.

BATTLE MOUNTAIN DISTRICT

The Battle Mountain district, in northwestern Lander County, includes the Battle Mountain Range, an area 15 miles long and 12 miles wide. The town of Battle Mountain is the supply center.

The district was organized in 1866 after ores rich in silver and copper were found (Hill, 1915, p. 71–72). By 1885 the district was mostly inactive, but it revived slightly in 1900 and gold prospects created a mild flurry about 1910. The demand for copper during World War I stimulated activity, but after 1918, the copper mines were worked only intermittently. In 1932 additional gold discoveries led to increased production (Vanderburg, 1939, p. 19).

In the earlier years, the gold produced in the Battle Mountain district was a byproduct of copper and silver ores, but in more recent years the deposits were mined chiefly for their gold and the copper and silver were byproducts.

Data on gold production before 1902 were not found. From 1902 through 1936, a total of 47,633 ounces of placer gold and 27,173 ounces of lode and byproduct gold was mined (Vanderburg, 1939, p. 20). From 1937 to 1958, a total of 62,082 ounces of lode and byproduct and 12,484 ounces of placer gold was produced. Total recorded gold production through 1959 was 149,372 ounces.

The Battle Mountains are composed primarily of Paleozoic sedimentary rocks which are, from bottom to top: black shale and white quartzite, 900 to 1,000 feet thick; red sandstone, 1,500 feet thick; and limestone of probable Pennsylvanian age, 2,000 feet thick (Hill, 1915, p. 66–76). Dikes and sheets of intrusive granite porphyry, monzonite, and quartz diorite, of possible Late Cretaceous or early Tertiary age, cut the sedimentary rocks. Volcanic rocks —rhyolite and augite andesite—cap the mountains locally. The ore deposits occur along simple fissures or wide shear zones in the complexly folded and faulted sedimentary rocks. There are four mineralogic vein groups:

1. Silver-lead deposits—mostly fracture filling in the sedimentary rocks—that contain galena, sphalerite, pyrite, and tetrahedrite. Some veins contain a zone of secondary enrichment that consists of polybasite, pyrargyrite, argentite, and tetrahedrite. Near the surface these veins were oxidized, and cerussite was the most abundant ore mineral.
2. Copper deposits—slightly auriferous copper ores in fractures in sediments. The ore, some of which is oxidized, consists of chalcopyrite, pyrite, sphalerite, and galena, associated with contact metamorphic minerals.
3. Gold deposits—iron-stained quartz veins carrying free gold and pyrite.
4. Antimony deposits—quartz-stibnite veins in sediments.

BULLION DISTRICT

The Bullion district is on the east slope of the Shoshone Range, 23 miles southwest of Beowawe, in secs. 8, 9, 16, and 17, T. 28 N., R. 47 E.

Ore was first discovered in the early 1870's; silver was the chief product. In 1905 gold was discovered and a small rush to the camp of Tenabo began (Vanderburg, 1939, p. 39). Later, placer gold was found near Tenabo. In recent years the Gold Acres open pit has been the largest operation mining solely for gold in the State, but in 1958 and 1959 its production was surpassed by the Round Mountain district.

No reliable statistics on production are available for the district before 1902 (Vanderburg, 1939, p. 39). Gold production from 1902 through 1959 was 146,154 ounces of lode and 10,373 ounces of placer gold.

The country rock in the district comprises Carboniferous sedimentary rocks that have been intruded by granodiorite. Locally, patches of Tertiary andesite cap the sediments (Lincoln, 1923, p. 111). Fissure veins occur in all these rocks. Most of the ore is made up of various sulfides in which the gold probably occurs.

HILLTOP DISTRICT

The Hilltop district is on the northwest slope of Shoshone Peak, 18 miles southeast of Battle Mountain, in secs. 3, 4, 5, and 6, T. 29 N., R. 46 E.

No important discoveries were made in this area until 1907, and a rush started the following year. After 1921, however, the district declined; most of the activity was conducted by lessees. The principal mines have been the Hilltop and the Pittsburg Red Top (Vanderburg, 1939, p. 47).

Production of the district from 1909 through 1959 was 119 ounces of placer gold and 17,834 ounces of lode gold. Considerable quantities of silver and small amounts of lead and copper were produced.

The bedrock in the district consists of Carboniferous quartzite, cut by dikes of altered granodiorite (Lincoln, 1923, p. 111–112). Ore occurs in a zone of fractured quartzite that is cut by small intrusive bodies of leached porphyry. Quartz stringers that carry free gold occupy parts of the shattered zone; bodies of pyrite and galena that contain silver and gold are in other parts.

LEWIS DISTRICT

The Lewis district is 17 miles southeast of Battle Mountain, in the southeast quarter of T. 30 N., R. 45 E.

Silver deposits were discovered here in 1867, and shortly afterward the gold deposits of the Pittsburg and Morning Star mines were discovered (Vanderburg, 1939, p. 59). In the early 1920's the Betty O'Neal mine produced silver ore on a large scale, but most of the early production is attributed to the Pittsburg and Morning Star mines whose production was chiefly gold. Vanderburg estimated (1939, p. 59) that about $1,200,000 worth of ore was produced before 1903. Assuming that the bulk of this was in gold, about 48,000 ounces of gold is estimated. From 1902 through 1959 the output was 3,124 ounces, about half of which was byproduct gold from silver ores.

The rocks of the district are Carboniferous sedimentary rocks, intruded by a mass of granodiorite porphyry, and quartz porphyry dikes (Emmons, 1910, p. 122–123). The ore deposits are fissure veins that carry auriferous pyrite and occur in quartzite and granodiorite porphyry. The silver deposits are replacement bodies in limestone with barite as a gangue.

NEW PASS DISTRICT

The New Pass district is on the east slope of New Pass Range near the boundary of Lander and Churchill Counties, 31 miles west of Austin.

Gold was discovered here in 1865, but production was never large (Vanderburg, 1939, p. 65); the total through 1959 was about 16,000 ounces.

The country rocks are limestone, gabbro, and porphyry; the ore deposits are gold-quartz veins in the gabbro. Vein minerals are quartz, native gold, argentiferous galena, auriferous pyrite, copper sulfide, azurite, and malachite (Lincoln, 1923, p. 114).

REESE RIVER DISTRICT

The Reese River district is in southern Lander County near Austin.

This has been overwhelmingly a silver-producing district, but small unrecorded amounts of gold contained in the ore from the huge silver production probably qualify the district as a minor gold-producing area.

Silver was discovered in 1862 a few miles west of the present town of Austin. Production was low the first few years, but after consolidation of many properties by the Manhattan Silver Mining Co. in 1870, it increased and remained at a fairly high level until after 1910, when most of the properties were taken over by lessees (Vanderburg, 1939, p. 69). From 1935 to 1937 there was a marked increase in production and from 1947 to 1950 several companies conducted exploration in the district (Ross, 1953, p. 42–46).

The period of highest production was 1862–87, when silver ore worth an estimated $20 million was produced (Ross, 1953, p. 47). In the period 1887–1938 about $1 million worth of ore was mined. In the early days, payment was made for silver only (Ross, 1953, p. 34); the small amounts of gold and other metals present were considered impurities and served to decrease the value of the bullion.

From 1902 through 1936, a total of 2,813 ounces of gold—2,810 ounces of byproduct gold and 3 ounces of placer gold—was produced in the district.

The rocks in the northern part of the district are quartzites, tentatively assigned to the Cambrian. Underlying most of the remainder of the district is a pluton of quartz monzonite of Jurassic(?) age. Numerous xenoliths of the sedimentary rocks are found in the intrusive. Aplite, pegmatite, and lamprophyre stringers and dikes are common. Around the edges of the district and resting on the quartz monzonite are Tertiary dacite flows and welded tuffs (Ross, 1953, p. 9–10, 17–18).

Ore deposits are veins in joints in the quartz monzonite and along bedding planes in the quartzite (Ross, 1953, p. 23). Ore minerals are ruby silver minerals and tetrahedrite and varying amounts of pyrite, arsenopyrite, galena, sphalerite, chalcopyrite, stibnite, covellite, chalcocite. Two or three varieties of quartz make up the gangue.

LINCOLN COUNTY

The total recorded gold output of Lincoln County through 1959 was 556,800 ounces. The only major gold districts in the county are the Delamar, the largest gold producer, and the Pioche, which yielded considerable gold from silver-copper-lead-zinc ores from 1935 through 1959.

DELAMAR DISTRICT

The Delamar district is in south-central Lincoln County on the west slope of the Meadow Valley Range, 29 miles southwest of Caliente.

Callaghan's (1937) report of the district is the chief reference for the summary of the history and geology that follows:

The first gold discovery was in 1891, and the district was organized the following year. The Delamar mine soon became the major mine in the district. Statewide, it outproduced all but a few mines at Goldfield and Tonopah. Despite primitive and costly means of transportation and lack of water in its early years, the district developed steadily until 1909, when the Delamar mine was closed. Only a few ounces of gold was produced in the ensuing two decades. In 1931, exploration at the Magnolia mine, the Jumbo claim, and several other leased properties was successful, and significant production began again in 1932.

Before 1902, district production of precious metals was reported in dollar values instead of ounces, but it may be assumed that most of this early production was in gold. According to Callaghan (1937, p. 38–40) the gross yield of the major mines from 1894 through 1901 was $9,407,555. From 1902 through 1957 the district produced 217,240 ounces of gold, all from lode mines.

A thick section of tilted and faulted Cambrian sedimentary rocks is exposed in the district. These rocks are overlain by Tertiary latites, andesites, tuff, and rhyolite that are also faulted but are less tilted than the Cambrian rocks. Small bodies of diorite and dikes and sills of basalt and rhyolite cut the sedimentary rocks. The rhyolite dikes are related to the flows. The mineral deposits were emplaced some time during the period of volcanic activity, as indicated by the fact that some dikes are older and some are younger than the ores.

The major deposits of the district were in the oldest rock, the Prospect Mountain Quartzite of Early Cambrian age. The deposits are of three types: (1) quartzite breccia, cemented and partly replaced by vuggy fine-grained quartz containing comb quartz and sulfides in the vugs, (2) small veins of fine-grained quartz containing free gold and sulfides, and (3) bedded quartzite with gold deposited in small fractures and along bedding planes. Other deposits are in volcanic breccia, intruded by rhyolite dikes, as at the Magnolia mine and in several of the limestone units where scattered prospect pits have revealed small amounts of silver.

PIOCHE DISTRICT

The Pioche district is 19 miles west of the Utah-Nevada State line; the town of Pioche is the county seat of Lincoln County.

This is primarily a silver-lead-zinc copper district; gold is produced as a byproduct. Production began in 1869 but did not reach bonanza proportions until about 1870. Hostile Indians and poor transportation facilities prevented large-scale operations for the first few years. Westgate (in Westgate and Knopf, 1932, p. 5) reported two periods of accelerated production: from 1869 to 1875, and from 1911 through 1958. In the early days two companies—the Meadow Valley Co. and Raymond & Ely—dominated mining in the district, but they were mostly inactive after 1875. The second period of activity was accelerated by the entrance of Combined Metals Reduction Co. into the district in 1915.

Gold production was not recorded before 1906, but in view of the fact that $17 million in metals was produced in 6 years in the early days (Young, 1950, p. 111), considerable gold must have been produced before 1906. From 1906 to 1959, a total of 104,583 ounces of gold was mined in the district.

A thickness of 17,000 to 18,000 feet of Paleozoic sedimentary rocks is exposed in the Pioche district. These are, according to Westgate (in Westgate and Knopf, 1932, p. 6–7), in ascending order: the Prospect Mountain Quartzite and Pioche Shale (Lower Cambrian); Lyndon Limestone, Chisholm Shale, and Highland Peak Limestone (Middle Cambrian); the Mendha Limestone (Upper Cambrian); Yellow Hill Limestone and Tank Hill Limestone (Lower Ordovician); Eureka Quartzite (Middle Ordovician); Ely Springs Dolomite (Upper Ordovician); dolomite of Silurian age; Silverhorn and West Range Dolomites (Devonian), Bristol Pass Limestone; Peers Spring Formation, Scotty Wash Quartzite (Mississippian); and Bailey Spring Limestone (Mississippian and Pennsylvanian). Unconformably overlying the sedimentary rocks is a thick series of Tertiary or late Mesozoic lava flows consisting of dacite, latite, andesite, and a little rhyolite and basalt. Tuffs are interbedded with the flows. Locally, stocks and dikes of quartz monzonite cut the sedimentary rocks and lava flows which have been metamorphosed by the intrusions. The Paleozoic formations have been gently folded and the Paleozoic and pre-Pliocene(?) rocks have been shattered by block faults and thrusts.

Ore deposits, according to Knopf (in Westgate and Knopf, 1932, p. 45), are of three types: (1) silver-bearing fissure veins in Lower Cambrian quartzite, (2) argentiferous lenses and pods in granite porphyry dikes, and (3) replacement deposits of sulfides in limestone and dolomite units in the Pioche Shale, Lyndon Limestone, Mendha Limestone, and the Highland Peak Limestone. The deposit of the Combined Metals mine is in a limestone unit of the Pioche Shale. The deposits all seem to have been contemporaneous, having been formed between two periods of Tertiary dike injection (Knopf, in Westgate and Knopf, 1932, p. 51). The bonanza output of the initial years came from the fissure veins in the quartzite; more recently, interest has focused on the sulfide replacement ores. Minerals of the fissure veins are argentite, cerargyrite, cerussite, and galena in quartz gangue. The podlike deposits in porphyry dikes contain the same minerals as the fissure veins. The replacement deposits are masses of argentiferous pyrite, sphalerite, and galena (Knopf, in Westgate and Knopf, 1932, p. 48–50).

LYON COUNTY

The first gold discovery in Nevada was in Lyon County in 1849 in Gold Canyon in the Silver City district. This discovery sparked the discovery of the Comstock Lode, in Storey County, 10 years later.

Lyon County is on the west edge of the Great Basin; the Sierra Nevada is immediately to the west. Mining districts are in the narrow, north-trending mountain ranges, typical of the Great Basin province. The most important gold districts are Silver City, Como, and Wilson. The major copper district of Yerington has not produced significant quantities of gold and is therefore not included in this report.

Total gold production for the county from 1903 through 1959 was 254,722 ounces.

COMO DISTRICT

The Como (Palmyra, Indian Springs) district is 10 miles southeast of Dayton. Quartz veins were discovered in the early 1860's and, with the Comstock fever still raging, people flocked to this new area, and a town was built before the deposits were properly evaluated (Stoddard and Carpenter, 1950, p. 76). For the next 50 years there was no significant production from the district. Several attempts were made in 1916, 1929, and in more recent years to mine the low-grade ores, but none could be considered an unqualified success.

The Como mines produced ore valued at $212,698 through 1936 (Stoddard and Carpenter, 1950, p. 77). The Hully and Logan mine produced a total of $76,995 worth of ore from 1900 to 1940, and the Star of the West mine produced $1,118 in 1939. These data are admittedly incomplete. Though gold was the principal commodity, the amount of gold included in these totals is not known; however, 10,000 to 15,000 ounces seems to be a reasonable assumption.

The rocks of the district are Tertiary volcanics, primarily andesite, several thousands of feet thick (Stoddard and Carpenter, 1950, p. 76). Quartz veins, striking east, contain gold, silver, and small amounts of copper in a quartz gangue.

SILVER CITY DISTRICT

The Silver City district is in the western tip of Lyon County, in T. 16 N., R. 21 E.

The lode mines of this district are in the southern extension of the mineralized area of the Comstock Lode district. In addition to the lode mining of the district, there have been numerous placer operations which date back to the original discoveries.

The history of the Silver City district is intimately intertwined with that of the Comstock Lode district and is a vivid and brawling episode in the development of the West. In 1849 gold was first found in Nevada in what was later to be the Silver City district by a party of California-bound Mormons who happened to pan the gravels in Gold Canyon. For the next 10 years the placers were worked, and as they were worked out, the miners searched the hills for gold-bearing veins. These searches led to the discoveries near Silver City and later to the main Comstock Lode itself at Gold Hill and Ophir Ravine.

The Silver City district was always in the shadow of the great Comstock Lode, and although it was a steady producer, it never achieved the status of its neighbor. Gianella (1936, p. 18) stated that the total production of the district is indeterminable because so much has been included with the Comstock data. Couch and Carpenter (1943, p. 93–94) recorded a total mineral production from 1871 through 1940 of $12,740,785, but the amount of this apportioned to gold is not known. Placer production data for more recent years is available. Vanderburg (1936a, p. 112) listed a production of 14,625 ounces of placer gold from 1920 to 1923. The largest reported placer production for the district was from 1941 to 1943 when $1,115,752 in bullion was mined (Stoddard and Carpenter, 1950, p. 81). In this operation, the largest dragline and floating washer plant on record was used. Total recorded gold production for the district through 1959 was about 190,000 ounces.

The oldest rocks in the district are limestone, shale, and schist of possible Triassic age. These rocks have been folded and deformed and are unconformably overlain by Triassic metavolcanics about 1,000 feet thick. Quartz monzonite, similar to that in the Sierra Nevada, intruded the Triassic rocks in Late Jurassic time. A thick series of volcanic rocks—andesite, rhyolite, basalt, breccia, and tuff—of early Tertiary age overlies the older rocks. During late Miocene time or post-Miocene time, the Tertiary rocks were faulted and mineralized (Gianella, 1936, p. 32–35). The early Tertiary rocks are overlain by a series of Pliocene(?) and Pleistocene lavas, breccias, and agglomerates. Later movement occurred along the early faults, some of it in comparatively recent time.

The important veins of the district are in fissures and faults. The principal vein, the Silver City vein, occupies a fault closely parallel to Gold Canyon and is a southern branch of the Comstock Lode (Gianella, 1936, p. 88–89). The gangue of the Silver City vein is quartz and calcite. The ore minerals are pyrite, gold, silver, electrum, argentite, and minor chalcopyrite. The sulfides make up only 1 or 2 percent of the veinfillings (Gianella, 1936, p. 92).

WILSON DISTRICT

The Wilson (Pine Grove, Rockland, Cambridge) district is in south-central Lyon County in parts of Tps. 9 and 10 N., Rs. 25 and 26 E. This district was in Mineral County until 1933, when a boundary change put it in Lyon County.

Gold was discovered in some outcrops in this area in 1866, and soon afterward the Wilson and the Wheeler mines were producing. The district produced steadily to 1893, and to that time the Wilson mine had produced ore valued at $5 million, and the Wheeler, $3 million (Hill, 1915, p. 136). Hill reported a production from 1902 to 1911 of $142,524 (about 7,000 ounces) in gold from the district. The Rockland mine produced $263,071 worth of ore during 1915–16 (Stoddard and Carpenter, 1950, p. 96). From 1917 through 1959 the district was idle except for a brief period of small-scale activity in the late 1930's and early 1940's. Total gold production through 1959 was about 408,000 ounces.

The district is underlain by quartz monzonite, very similar to that in the Sierra Nevada batholith (Hill, 1915, p. 134, 135). The ore deposits are in a sheared zone that crosses the quartz monzonite in a northwesterly direction. The quartz monzonite is also cut by at least one granite porphyry dike and is overlain by a series of pink and gray rhyolite flows.

The ore consists of lenses of quartz and pyrite in the crushed zone of monzonite just south of the major fault. The valuable constituents are gold and silver, and the highest grade ore is in the oxidized zone near the surface.

MINERAL COUNTY

In 1910 this county was created from what was formerly the north part of Esmeralda County. Typical of the Great Basin, Mineral County contains narrow, elongate mountain ranges separated by valleys having interior drainage. Most of the mountain ranges are mineralized; the principal ranges are the Wassuk, Gabbs Valley, Gillis, Pilot, and Excelsior. A great variety of mineral products has been mined in this county; gold has been the most valuable product, but considerable amounts of silver, lead, zinc, copper, tungsten, and mercury have been mined.

Mining began in what is now Mineral County in 1860 at Aurora. Soon afterward discoveries were made at Candelaria, Garfield, Oneota, Sante Fe, and Silver Star. The period of greatest mining activity was before 1900.

Production data for the county go back only to 1910, when the county was founded. Vanderburg (1937b, p. 10) listed 219,435 ounces of lode gold and 1,963 ounces of placer gold for 1910–34. From 1935 through 1959 production was 43,986 ounces of lode gold and 738 ounces of placer gold. Total gold production for Mineral County from 1910 through 1959 was 266,122 ounces.

AURORA DISTRICT

The Aurora district is in western Mineral County, 3 miles east of the Nevada-California State line and 30 miles southwest of Hawthorne.

Gold-silver veins were discovered here in 1860. Almost immediately a town named Esmeralda was built, but less than a year later it was abandoned in favor of a site 1½ miles north that is the present location of the town of Aurora, which by 1864 had a population of about 10,000 (Hill, 1915, p. 141). Despite litigation over claims and uncertainty about the location of the California-Nevada boundary, the district prospered until the mid-1880's when the high-grade ore was depleted. In the 1930's there was only small-scale mining by lessees, and the town of Aurora, though substantially built, was almost in ruins (Vanderburg, 1937b, p. 14).

Data for production in the early days are incomplete. Hill (1915, p. 142) estimated at least $27 million in gold and silver from 1861 to 1869. For the same period, Vanderburg (1937b, p. 14, 15) estimated at least $30 million in precious metals. From 1910 to 1920 the district produced $1,882,861 (about 91,400 ounces) in gold; the total through 1959 was about 93,600 ounces.

The following account of the geology is condensed from Hill (1915, p. 143–150). Nearly all the rocks exposed in the area are of volcanic origin and consist, from oldest to youngest, of biotite-quartz latite, andesite, rhyolite, and basalt. After each of the periods of extrusion of andesite, rhyolite, and basalt were periods of erosion. The oldest flow was extruded on a granitic basement rock.

The ore deposits are in veins that cut the biotite-quartz latite and andesite. Most of the veins strike about N. 45° E. and dip moderately southeast. Most of the veins are 1½ to 4 feet thick, but some are as much as 80 feet thick. The veins send off numerous branches which become, in many places, an interlacing network of veinlets. Fine-grained quartz that is usually banded makes up the bulk of the veins; small cavities lined with tiny quartz crystals are common. The ore consists of quartz, adularia, argentiferous tetrahedrite, pyrite, chalcopyrite, and a soft blue-gray material containing gold and possibly silver with selenium. Free gold is present in the richest ores. The occurrence of selenium without tellurium in these ores is unusual and has been noted in only a few mining camps.

BELL DISTRICT

The Bell (Cedar Mountain) district is in the Cedar Mountain Range in eastern Mineral County near the Nye County border.

The silver-lead deposit at the Simon mine was discovered in 1879, but the gold deposits in this area were not found until later. Gold was discovered at the Copper Contact mine in 1902 and at the Olympic (or Omco) mine in 1915 (Vanderburg, 1937b, p. 19).

Before 1919 the Olympic mine yielded $700,000 (about 32,000 ounces of gold) in ore that contained gold with a fineness of 500 (Knopf, 1921a, p. 381). Total gold production of the district through 1959 was about 34,000 ounces.

The gold deposits are associated with Tertiary volcanic rocks—rhyolites and andesites—that underlie lake beds of the Esmeralda Formation (Knopf, 1921a, p. 377–380). At the Olympic mine, the vein is in the upper of two rhyolite flows that have a trachyte flow between them. The vein consists of white sugary quartz containing gold that is not readily visible and is faulted in several places. At the Golden Mile and Clay Peters mines, gold-bearing quartz veins occur in the Luning Formation of Triassic age (Ross, 1961, table 6.1).

CANDELARIA DISTRICT

Silver veins were discovered in the Candelaria district, which is 22 miles south of Mina in the Candelaria Mountains, in 1863 by a party of Spaniards. The town of Columbus was founded, but the district developed slowly because of the complex mineralogy of the oxidized ores. In the 1870's, the Northern Belle mine was successfully developed. The town of Candelaria was soon constructed near the mine, rail connections were made, and the district became one of the leading silver camps in the State. In 1884 the Northern Belle mine was involved in litigation and was sold. About this time the Mount Diablo mine became an important producer, and this mine and the Argentum (the consolidated Holmes and Northern Belle) kept the district booming until the bonanza ores were exhausted in the early 1890's (Knopf, 1923, p. 4–5). The camp declined until 1919, when a brief revival took place under the sponsorship of the Candelaria Mines Co. (Vanderburg, 1937b, p. 25). No important activity has been recorded since, although small-scale operations were reported as recently as 1955 (Page, 1959, p. 9).

The Candelaria has been a silver-producing district, and only relatively insignificant quantities of gold have been recovered. The early production data gave no figures on gold. Knopf (1923, p. 5) mentioned a minimum of $20 million worth of silver to about 1920. From 1903 through 1958, a total of 13,024 ounces of gold was produced.

The oldest rock unit of the district is the Palmetto Formation, composed of chert, dolomite, and shale of Ordovician age (Page, 1959, p. 15–44). This is unconformably overlain by sandstone of the Diablo Formation of Permian age. Overlying the Diablo is the Candelaria Formation, which is composed of sandstone, shale, and a few limestone beds and is of Early Triassic age. A large west-trending mass of serpentine containing fragments of Candelaria shale is exposed in the east-central part of the district. Numerous basic dikes, older than the serpentine and acidic dikes and younger than the serpentine, occur throughout the district. In the vicinity of the Northern Belle mine a rock is exposed which is a complex of sheared and brecciated metasedimentary rocks and metadolerite. All the foregoing rocks are unconformably overlain by Tertiary and Quaternary volcanic rocks, consisting of basalt, dacitic tuffs and flows, rhyolite, and andesitic breccia.

The pre-Tertiary rocks were complexly folded and faulted, perhaps during several episodes, before deposition of the Candelaria Formation. Folding on an east-west axis occurred during post-Triassic, pre-Tertiary time and was accompanied by shearing, faulting, intrusion of peridotite and dikes, and finally by deposition of metalliferous lodes. Additional faulting began in early Pleistocene time and culminated in the fault blocks which characterize the present physiography.

Several types of veins are found in the Candelaria district, but only one type is of economic importance—mineralized fault zones recognizable on the surface by limonite-stained outcrops of fault breccia. Primary ore consists mainly of pyrite and sphalerite and minor galena, chalcopyrite, and arsenopyrite in a gangue of altered country rock, quartz, and dolomite. Oxidized ore, most of which was mined in the early days, is composed predominantly of limonite and manganese oxide with small amounts of bindheimite, anglesite, smithsonite, and cerussite (Page, 1959, p. 47–58).

GARFIELD DISTRICT

The Garfield district is 10 miles northwest of Mina and 25 miles southeast of Hawthorne, just north of a line connecting Hawthorne and Mina.

Silver-gold ore was discovered here in 1882, and in the early days several millions of dollars worth of ore was produced from the principal mine, the Garfield. In later years, the Mabel mine has been an important producer.

Early production of the district is estimated at several million dollars in combined metals (Vanderburg, 1937b, p. 33). Production of gold from 1903 through 1957 was 4,933 ounces. Total gold production of the district through 1959 was probably between 10,000 and 50,000 ounces.

The ore deposits are in quartz veins(?) in volcanic rocks of the Excelsior Formation of Triassic and possible Permian ages and limestone of the Luning Formation of Triassic age (Ross, 1961, p. 82).

GOLD RANGE DISTRICT

The Gold Range (Silver Star, Camp Douglas) district is in the Excelsior Mountains in southern Mineral County, about 7 miles northeast of Mina.

In 1893 veins containing gold and silver were discovered and about $500,000 was produced in the first 10 years (Vanderburg, 1937b, p. 71). Small-scale production continued to 1934, when the increased price of gold caused a noticeable spurt in activity. In 1910 tungsten was discovered in the district.

Total gold production for the district through 1959 was about 97,000 ounces. No activity was reported from the district from 1948 through 1959.

The deposits of the Gold Range district are in veins that branch out from two major faults with a horst between them (Ferguson and others, 1954). Veins on the north fault produced only gold and a little scheelite; veins of the south fault, the Silver Dyke system, were rich in silver and carried only small amounts of gold, and scheelite was encountered at depth. The veins are probably of Pliocene age. Most of the veins are in the Excelsior Formation (Triassic) and the Dunlap Formation (Jurassic); a few cut some Tertiary rhyolite, The major constituents of the auriferous veins are free gold and pyrite with comb quartz and some adularia.

HAWTHORNE DISTRICT

The Hawthorne district, near the town of Hawthorne at the south end of Walker Lake, is predominantly a silver district, but it has produced considerable gold as a byproduct.

Mining began at least as early as the 1880's at the Pamlico and LaPanta mines, which are 10 miles east-southeast of the town of Hawthorne but are included in the Hawthorne district. Hill (1915, p. 157) reported an estimated $200,000 worth of production from the LaPanta and about $500,000 from the Pamlico. The amount of gold represented in his production was not given. Vanderburg (1937b, p. 38) reported $300,000 production, mostly in gold, from the LaPanta. In 1906 the Lucky Boy mine was discovered and became the chief producer for a few years, but production from the entire district decreased in recent years.

Vanderburg (1937b, p. 36) listed yearly production from 1904 through 1935—a total of 155 ounces of placer gold and 4,700 ounces of byproduct gold was produced. From 1936 through 1959, a total of 5,067 ounces of gold was mined in the district.

Hill (1915, p. 151–155) described the geology in the vicinity of the Lucky Boy mine. Cherty limestones, shales, and sandstones of probable Mesozoic age were faulted and intruded by a granodiorite mass which was later cut by aplitic and basic dikes. Near the intrusion the limestones were metamorphosed, producing a skarn of garnet, tremolite, diopside, quartz, and calcite. The vein at the Lucky Boy is in a fracture that cuts the limestone and granodiorite. The average width of the vein is 2 to 3½ feet. Ore consists of fine-grained galena and tetrahedrite and a little pyrite. High-grade ore carries 2,000 to 3,000 ounces of silver per ton, and medium-grade ore carries 50 to 400 ounces of silver to the ton.

MOUNT MONTGOMERY AND ONEOTA DISTRICTS

The Mount Montgomery and Oneota districts are combined here because they adjoin and are geologically similar. They are at the north end of the White Mountain Range, about 4 miles east of Queen, in the southern tip of Mineral County.

The Oneota district was organized in 1862, but no mining was attempted until after 1870 (Vanderburg, 1937b, p. 49). The Indian Queen and the Poorman mines were its major producers. In the Mount Montgomery district, gold, silver, mercury, and fluorspar have been mined. The chief gold mines are the Tip Top and Golden Gate (Vanderburg, 1937b, p. 47, 48).

About $150,000 in gold and silver was produced from the Mount Montgomery district, and about $1 million in gold and silver was produced from the Oneota district up to 1935 (Vanderburg, 1937b, p. 47–49). The amount of gold represented in these totals is not known, but at least 10,000 ounces is assumed. Production of gold from 1935 through 1959 was only 161 ounces; therefore, this combined district is not included in table 10.

Country rock consists of Cretaceous(?) granitic rocks intruded into schists of possible Precambrian age. In the northern part of the district these rocks are overlain by Tertiary felsic volcanic rocks, younger than the Esmeralda Formation. Quartz veins containing gold and silver occur in the volcanic rocks (Ross, 1961, p. 65, 80, pl. 2).

RAWHIDE DISTRICT

The Rawhide (Regent) district, at the south end of the Sand Springs Range in northeastern Mineral County, is 29 miles east of Schurz and 50 miles southeast of Fallon.

The summary of this district is abstracted from Vanderburg's reports (1936a, p. 120–121; 1937b, p. 58–64).

The initial discoveries were made in 1906. Less than 2 years later the town of Rawhide had been built and was populated by about 4,000 people, but in September 1908 a large part of the town was detroyed by fire. This is predominantly a gold camp, and most production has come from numerous small mines rather than a few large ones. From 1908 through 1935, a total of 1,818 ounces of placer gold and 49,034 ounces of lode gold was produced. Total production from 1908 through 1959 was 2,065 ounces of placer and 50,707 ounces of lode gold.

Although most of the gold came from the lode mines, there was considerable working of placer deposits. The most productive placers were in an area ½ mile wide and 1 mile long on the southeast slope of Hooligan Hill. Vanderburg (1936a, p. 120) reported $250,000 total placer production. This conflicts sharply with the $39,953 total compiled by C. W. Merrill (in Vanderburg, 1937b, p. 60).

The lode deposits are in a network of veinlets that cut the country rocks—rhyolite, dacite, and andesite. Kaolinized rhyolite seems to be most strongly mineralized. Ore minerals are electrum, argentite, and cerargyrite.

NYE COUNTY

Nye County, founded in 1864, comprises more than 17,000 square miles in south-central Nevada and is studded with north-trending mountain ranges. The intermontane valleys are not drained, and streams terminate in sinks or salt-encrusted flats.

Sedimentary rocks of Paleozoic and Mesozoic ages are exposed in the mountains in the north; in the western ranges only Mesozoic formations are exposed. In the eastern and central parts of the county, the mountains are composed chiefly of Paleozoic rocks. Masses of granitic rocks of Jurassic and Cretaceous ages have intruded the older rocks and are exposed over large areas. Tertiary lava flows and intrusive rocks are abundant in the southern part of the county.

The most important mineral commodities of the county have been the precious metals. Some of the more successful gold districts are Bullfrog, Tonopah, Round Mountain, and Tybo, where gold- and silver-bearing veins occur in Tertiary rocks. Another highly productive district is the Manhattan, where the highest yields were from veins in Paleozoic rocks.

Gold production for the county from 1903 through 1959 was 2,975,034 ounces—298,593 ounces was from placers and 2,676,441 ounces was from lode mines.

BRUNER DISTRICT

The Bruner (Phomolite) district is in northwestern Nye County at lat 39°05′ N. and long 117°46′ E.

The district was founded in 1906 when small production was reported from the Paymaster mine. In 1936 the Penelas mine, the main producer of the district, was discovered (Kral, 1951, p. 26).

Production of gold from the district from 1936 through 1959 was 17,213 ounces. Earlier production could not be ascertained.

Tertiary rhyolite and andesites cover the area (Kral, 1951, p. 26). Metavolcanic rocks probably underlie the extrusives. The ore deposits are in quartz veins in the younger volcanic rocks with free gold associated with silver.

BULLFROG DISTRICT

The Bullfrog district is in southern Nye County, 60 miles south-southeast of Goldfield. The principal town is Beatty.

The original claims were located in 1904; the customary rush ensued during which the settlements of Bullfrog, Bonanza, Beatty, and Rhyolite mushroomed and competed with one another for new settlers. Competition became so intense that three railroads served the area. The peak period was 1907–10 when $1,687,792 in gold and silver was produced (Kral, 1951, p. 29), mostly from the Montgomery-Shoshone mine. In more recent years activity declined to sporadic small-scale mining. Gold production from 1905 to 1959 was 120,401 ounces, and considerable silver has also been produced.

Ransome, Emmons, and Garrey (1910) described the geology and ore deposits in considerable detail. The oldest rocks in the district are contorted quartzites and mica schists of Ordovician age or older, and they are overlain locally by limestone, shale, and quartzite of Silurian age. Overlying the Paleozoic rocks is a sequence of Tertiary flows and tuffs, 6,000 feet thick, composed of 16 rhyolite units, five flows of basalt, one flow of quartz latite, and one flow of quartz-bearing basalt that caps the sequence. The entire area has been broken by normal faults that trend north to northwest, and the resulting fault blocks are tilted eastward. A late set of faults trends northeast. Ore deposits are mineralized faults or fault zones in the rhyolites. Many of the veins are simple but there are many zones of stringers or veinlets with ill-defined boundaries. The vein material consists of quartz and calcite and finely divided auriferous pyrite. The quartz is crustified and has a porcelaneous texture. Oxidized ore contains gold in limonite; the calcite is partly dissolved, and manganese oxide has been introduced. Varying amounts of silver may be alloyed with the gold.

ELLENDALE DISTRICT

The Ellendale district is a few miles east of Tonopah, in T. 2 N., R. 43 E. High-grade gold ore was discovered in 1909, and for the next few years the district flourished but by 1916 was deserted (Ferguson, 1917, p. 122). According to Kral (1951, p. 56), the only later activity was in 1938–39, when dump material valued at $7,215 was shipped from the Ellendale mine, the only mine of any importance in the district. Total recorded production of gold to 1948 was $166,015 (about 8,060 ounces), but estimates put the total production at between $½ and $1 million (Kral, 1951, p. 55). Because much production by lessees was not reported, the true production of the district must be in excess of 8,000 ounces.

Ferguson (1917, p. 123) noted that most of the deposits are in rhyolite near its contact with andesite porphyry. The ore bodies are in irregular veins filled with iron-stained quartz.

GOLD HILL DISTRICT

The Gold Hill district is 6 miles north of Round Mountain, in the southern Toquima Range, in T. 11 N., R. 44 E. It is mentioned only briefly in the published literature. Ferguson and Cathcart (1954) noted that the major production of the district was in 1931–32, when 24,725 ounces of gold was mined. The district was dormant from 1933 through 1959. According to Couch and Carpenter (1943, p. 120), the total value of production of the district was $902,152, but how much of this was in gold is not known.

The major production came from a single quartz vein in rhyolite (Ferguson and Cathcart, 1954). The veinfilling is fine-grained banded quartz that contains some calcite, small particles of free gold, auriferous pyrite, and argentite.

JACKSON DISTRICT

The Jackson (Gold Park) district is on the west slope of the Shoshone Mountains in northwestern Nye County (lat 39°7′ W., long 117°33′ E.). Originally called the North Union district, the name was changed in 1878 to Jackson. Early production data are fragmentary, but Kral (1951, p. 76) estimated an output of $½ to $1 million, principally in gold. There has been little activity in the area since 1911.

The oldest rock in the area is meta-andesite of Carboniferous(?) age which is overlain by Tertiary rhyolite tuff (Kral, 1951, p. 76). Ore occurs in quartz veins that cut the meta-andesite. Variable amounts of galena and pyrite and small amounts of chalcopyrite are present.

JEFFERSON CANYON DISTRICT

The Jefferson Canyon district is 6 miles northeast of Round Mountain (lat 38°43′ N., long 117° E.) on the west slope of the Toquima Range.

Gold and silver were discovered here in 1866, but no activity was reported until 1871. The principal mines were the Jefferson and the Prussian. Lincoln (1923, p. 171) reported the early production of combined silver and gold at $1 million; the amount of gold represented by this figure is not given. In the past several decades there has been only sporadic activity in this district. Only 3 ounces of gold was produced from 1932 through 1959.

The country rock consists of Ordovician limestone, Cretaceous granite, and Tertiary rhyolite porphyry (Kral, 1951, p. 80–81). The Prussian vein, the principal vein in the district, is along the contact of the limestone and porphyry. Silver minerals—sulfides, sulfantimonides, and chlorides—are the most valuable constituents of the Prussian vein; however, gold is the important component in many other veins.

JOHNNIE DISTRICT

The Johnnie district is in the extreme southeast part of Nye County (lat 36°26′ N., long 116°04′ E.).

Organized in 1890, the district had a recorded production of $382,681 by 1913, although Kral (1951, p. 86) estimated that more than $1 million in ore was produced from 1910 through 1913. Nolan (1936b, p. 69) estimated $500,000 worth of gold was produced before 1904, and 24,653 ounces of gold was produced during 1908–32. Total gold production through 1959 was about 40,000 ounces, mostly from the Johnnie mine.

The bedrock is the Prospect Mountain Quartzite of Cambrian age (Kral, 1951, p. 86–87). The beds are predominantly quartzite, but some conglomerate, shale, and limestone units are also present. Well-defined gold-bearing quartz veins cut these sedimentary rocks. Gold and galena are the chief economic minerals.

LODI DISTRICT

The Lodi (Granite, Marble, Quartz Mountains) district is in northwest Nye County (T. 13 W., R. 36 E.). In 1863 the area was part of the original Mammoth district, but in 1874, the Lodi district was formed from the part of the Mammoth that included the Lodi Hills.

Gold is a byproduct of silver and lead ores which have been the mainstay of the district. Tungsten and some talc also have been produced. The most important mines in the district are the Illinois and the San Rafael (Kral, 1951, p. 94–96).

Available production data are not complete and give combined output only; therefore, the amount of gold represented can only be inferred. Couch and Carpenter (1943, p. 113) reported a total of $809,905 in silver, gold, lead, and copper from 1866 through 1940. The total for 1932 through 1959 was 1,079 ounces of gold (U.S. Bureau of Mines, 1933–66).

Kral (1951, p. 93–94) briefly summarized the geology of the district. The rocks of the district are deformed limestone and dolomite of Triassic age intruded by granodiorite of Jurassic or Cretaceous age. The major ore deposits of lead and silver were deposited in the deformed and ruptured limestone and dolomite during the closing stages of the intrusion. In Tertiary time, lava flows covered the area. These were succeeded by andesite intrusions after which considerable faulting took place. A second period of mineralization filled the fault fissures.

MANHATTAN DISTRICT

Manhattan, at the south end of the Toquima Range about 35 miles north of Tonopah, is a gold district, silver being produced as a byproduct. Although mining had been done in the Toquima Range since 1865, it was not until 1905 that gold was found in the Manhattan area in sufficient quantity and grade to precipitate a rush. By 1906 there were 3,000 people in the general area (Ferguson, 1924, p. 8). The next few years were marked by numerous fraudulent promotion schemes that gave the district widespread notoriety and seriously delayed its development. But placer mining flourished and reached its peak by 1912, after which there was a steady annual decline (Ferguson, 1924, p. 8–9). Lode mining became important after 1908.

From 1906 through 1921 the district produced 136,514 ounces of lode gold and 58,686 ounces of placer gold (Ferguson, 1924, p. 9); through 1959, the total was 280,022 ounces of lode gold and 206,340 ounces of placer gold.

The bedrock of the district is composed of quartzite, limestone, and schist of the Gold Hill Formation of Cambrian age and chert, slate, quartzite, and limestone of the Palmetto Formation of Ordovician age (Ferguson and Cathcart, 1954). Small patches of granite, of Jurassic age, are exposed locally. Tertiary lavas, tuffs, and intrusive bodies comprise the bedrock in the northern part of the district. The Gold Hill Formation is thrust over the Palmetto Formation, and the productive deposits are in the hanging wall of this thrust fault, in limestones and quartzose schist of the Gold Hill Formation. The ore bodies in the limestone show a complex assemblage of metals, including pyrite, stibnite, realgar, orpiment, cinnabar, and free gold in a gangue of calcite, quartz, fluorite, sericite, leverrierite, and sparse adularia. Ore bodies in the quartzose schist have been more productive and consist of networks of small quartz-adularia veins, carrying pyrite and free gold.

The placer gold has come from deep gravels in Manhattan Gulch.

NORTHUMBERLAND DISTRICT

The Northumberland district on on the east side of Toquima Range, 25 miles north of Belmont and 76 miles northeast of Tonopah. It is primarily a silver-producing district and was founded in 1866. By 1891 activity had ceased, and the district was dormant until 1936 when large deposits of low-grade gold ore, amenable to open-pit mining, were discovered (Kral, 1951, p. 135–136). During 1939–42, gold totaling 32,756 ounces was mined. The War Production Board Order L–208 of 1942 caused operations to be recessed until after World War II. Total gold production from 1936 through 1959 was 35,353 ounces.

The rocks consist of dolomitic limestone and carbonaceous and calcareous shale (Kral, 1951, p. 136). A mass of monzonite and a younger porphyritic rhyolite or quartz latite intruded the sediments. The gold deposits occur in a carbonaceous shale bed, 60 to 70 feet thick, in the vicinity of the roof of the monzonite intrusion.

ROUND MOUNTAIN DISTRICT

The Round Mountain district is on the west flank of the Toquima Range, 45 miles north of Tonopah and about 8 miles north of Manhattan.

Rich gold ore was discovered in 1906, but no production was recorded until 1907. Both placer and lode mines were worked from the beginning. The lodes were worked until 1935, but the placers were still being worked, on a fairly large scale, in the early 1950's by the Round Mountain Gold Dredging Corp. Their operations were suspended during 1953–57, but were resumed in 1958; in 1958–59 this company was the largest gold producer in Nevada.

Ferguson and Cathcart (1954) estimated the total gold production of the district to be worth $8 million, of which about 15 or 20 percent was from placers and the remainder was from lodes. This would amount to about 329,000 ounces of lode gold and 58,200 ounces of placer gold. Most of the district's production during 1950–59 was combined with reports from other districts, but it was probably about 150,000 ounces. Total gold production for the district through 1959 was about 537,000 ounces.

The oldest rocks in the area are lower Paleozoic limestone, jasper, and dark slaty schist (Ferguson, 1922, p. 386–398). These rocks are intensely folded and were intruded during Cretaceous time by bodies of granitic magma. Tertiary rocks, chiefly porphyritic rhyolite (Oddie Rhyolite) and lake beds of the Siebert Formation, overlie the folded Paleozoic rocks.

There were two periods of mineralization. The first occurred just after the granitic intrusions and is characterized by huebnerite-bearing veins in the granite. The second period of mineralization is of Tertiary age and resulted in the formation of epithermal gold-bearing quartz veins in the rhyolite. The mineralogy of these veins is relatively simple and consists of gold, auriferous pyrite, and sparse realgar in a gangue of drusy and comb quartz, adularia, and alunite. After the primary gold mineralization, additional fissures were formed in which iron and manganese oxides and gold were deposited by supergene solutions. The gold in these later fractures was probably derived from the primary auriferous pyrite.

TONOPAH DISTRICT

This district is in the southern San Antonio Mountains near Tonopah, the county seat of Nye County and the largest town in the county.

Tonopah was predominantly a silver district, but it also yielded large amounts of gold. The first claims were staked in 1900, and by 1901 there was vigorous activity which lasted until the late 1940's; thereafter, production declined. The principal companies were the Tonopah Mining, the Tonopah Belmont Development, and the Tonopah Extension (Kral, 1951, p. 171).

Lincoln (1923, p. 186) listed the gold production of Tonopah from 1901 through 1921 as $30,360,903 (about 1,473,830 ounces). From 1901 through 1959, a total of 1,880,000 ounces of gold was produced.

The rocks exposed in the Tonopah district are all of Tertiary age and consist of a series of lava flows, volcanic breccias, tuffs, and intrusives that have been somewhat displaced from their original attitudes by extensive faulting. Seven formations recognized in the district (Nolan, 1935b, p. 13) are, from oldest to youngest: the Tonopah Formation (volcanic tuffs, breccias, flows), Sandgrass Andesite (dark lavas interlayered with the Tonopah Formation), Mizpah Trachyte (2,000-foot-thick flows and breccias overlying the Tonopah), Extension Breccia (tabular intrusive mass in west half of district), West End Rhyolite (sills as much as 600 feet thick that intrude the older formations), Fraction Breccia Member of Esmeralda Formation (volcanic breccia unconformably overlying ore bodies), and postore rhyolite (dikes and lenticular bodies that intrude the older rocks). Numerous faults cut the Tertiary rocks, and Nolan (1935b, p. 28–39) divided them into three general groups: the Halifax fault zone which strikes generally northward; the Tonopah, a compound fault that in cross section has a trace that is convex upward; and the youngest group which includes a fault which strikes northwest, another which strikes northeast, and a third which strikes north and dips west.

The ore bodies are replacement veins in faults or fractures (Nolan, 1935b, p. 40–49). The Tonopah fault is believed to have exerted a major control on the movement of mineralizing solutions. Ore bodies are found in all three groups of faults, but the Tonopah and Halifax seem to be more heavily mineralized. Hypogene ore contains electrum, argentite, polybasite, and pyrargyrite in a gangue of quartz, pink carbonate, barite, and altered wallrocks. There has been some supergene enrichment locally, but the hypogene ore has been most important.

TYBO DISTRICT

The Tybo (Hot Creek, Keystone, Empire) district is in northeastern Nye County, in the Hot Creek Range, 65 miles northeast of Tonopah and about 100 miles southwest of Ely (lat 38°23′ N., long 116°23′ E.). In the district, gold is a byproduct of ores mined primarily for their lead and silver content. The first mineral discoveries were made in 1865, and the town of Hot Creek was the population center during the early days (Kral, 1951, p. 189). The district prospered from the rich near-surface silver ores until 1888. The principal mine during this period was the Tybo mine. Despite several attempts at renewing operations, the district remained dormant from 1888 until 1929, when a concentrator was built that successfully separated the galena from sphalerite (Ferguson, 1933, p. 43–44). Gold production from 1872 to 1888 was 20,360 ounces (Ferguson, 1933, p. 43); from 1929 to 1958 it was 6,923 ounces.

The geology of the area was described by Ferguson (1933, p. 13–42). The rocks consist of Paleozoic sedimentary rocks and Tertiary fresh-water sediments, dikes, and flows. The Paleozoic rocks include Cambrian, Ordovician, and Silurian formations. These rocks were tightly folded and faulted; then Tertiary sediments and lavas were deposited. Dikes and masses of Tertiary quartz latite porphyry cut all the older rocks. The Esmeralda Formation, consisting of water-deposited tuffs of late Miocene age, overlies the latite masses, and it in turn is overlain by a series of dacite and andesite flows. There were several periods of faulting that began before Tertiary time and ended after extrusion of the post-Esmeralda lavas.

The ore bodies were deposited after the intrusion of the quartz latite porphyry. They are tabular replacement bodies along the 2–G fault, the oldest major fault in the area. The primary minerals consist of pyrite, sphalerite, argentiferous galena, chalcopyrite, pyrrhotite, and arsenopyrite. Quartz and calcite accompany the sulfides. The ores first mined were oxidized deposits within 300 feet of the surface.

UNION DISTRICT

The Union district, in northwestern Nye County in the Shoshone Range (lat 38°55′ N., long 117°35′ E.), was organized in 1863, and the town of Ione was soon built. After a few brief flurries of activity which yielded about $1 million in gold and silver by 1880 (Lincoln, 1923, p. 196), the district became almost dormant. The discovery of cinnabar in 1907 revived activity somewhat, and since then production of mercury has been fairly consistent; however, gold production from 1903 through 1959 was only 748 ounces. Total gold production cannot be ascertained, but it is assumed that at least 10,000 ounces was produced before 1903.

The oldest rocks in the district are meta-andesites of Carboniferous age (Kral, 1951, p. 196). These are overlain by Triassic slates, limestones, and conglomerates. A small granodiorite stock cuts the sedimentary rocks. The youngest rocks in the area are Tertiary rhyolite and andesite. The mercury and gold deposits are associated with the Tertiary rocks; however, the ore at the Berlin mine, the largest mine in the district, consists of lead-copper-zinc-antimony sulfides in quartz veins in the Carboniferous meta-andesites (Kral, 1951, p. 199–200).

PERSHING COUNTY

Pershing County, created in 1919, is the youngest of the 17 counties of Nevada.

The topography of the county, although less rugged than in most of the State, is typical of that of the Great Basin and consists of north-trending mountain ranges separated by dry valleys.

Pershing County has a wide variety of mineral resources, but silver, gold, tungsten, and mercury have been the mainstays. Mining activity in the area now embraced by Pershing County began in 1860 in the Humboldt district. Soon afterward the Star and Buena Vista districts were discovered, and the town of Unionville became the center of mining activity in the county. The first successful smelter in the State was built at Oreana to treat the base-metal ores. Gold placer deposits were discovered in 1881 in American Canyon, Spring Valley, and Dry Gulch, and these were worked successfully for about 10 years. Discoveries at Seven Troughs and Rochester highlight the mining in the county after 1900 (Vanderburg, 1936b, p. 6).

Production from Pershing County is recorded from 1919, when the county was created. Production of individual districts, in the descriptions that follow, includes the years before Pershing County existed, thus there is a considerable discrepancy between district and county totals.

From 1919 through 1958 Pershing County produced 16,233 ounces of placer gold and 162,109 ounces of lode gold, a total of 178,342 ounces.

HUMBOLDT DISTRICT

The Humboldt (Imlay, Eldorado) district, on the north end and west flank of the Humboldt Range, was organized in 1860 as the first district in the area now included in Pershing County. By 1863, Humboldt City had been founded and had a population of 500. The principal mine was the Imlay, from which a considerable but unknown amount of silver ore was shipped. The Star Peak mine yielded $130,000 in silver and gold up to 1935 (Vanderburg, 1936b, p. 17). Early production data for the entire district are lacking, but from 1932 through 1959 the district produced 35,483 ounces of gold.

The deposit at the Imlay mine consists of a gold- and silver-bearing quartz vein that contains a little lead and copper (Vanderburg, 1936b, p. 16). The country rock is shale, quartzite, and limestone, probably Triassic in age. Ransome (1909a, p. 46) stated that the ores of the northern Humboldt Range, called the Star Peak Range, have several common characteristics—they occur in Triassic rocks; they seem to have a common age, probably Early Cretaceous; and they contain antimony, more silver than gold, and very little lead or zinc.

ROCHESTER DISTRICT

In the Rochester district, in the central Humboldt Range 9 miles east of Oreana, activity began in the 1860's during the intensive search for silver in the Star Peak Range. The placers in nearby Limerick and American Canyons yielded $11 million in gold (Ransome, 1909a, p. 12). There was no great lode production until 1912, when the rich silver-gold ores on Nenzel Hill were discovered. For the ensuing 16 years, production remained at a high level. In 1929, the Rochester Silver Corp., the principal operator, closed down, and activity remained at a low level through 1959.

The following summary of the geology and ore deposits of the Rochester district is from a more detailed account by Knopf (1924, p. 9–58).

The oldest rocks in the district are felsitic trachytes and keratophyres 5,000 feet thick, composing the Rochester Trachyte, of Triassic age. Overlying this is a sequence of rhyolite flows also of Triassic age. Downfaulted limestone beds of Triassic age are found in the western part of the district. Intrusive into the Triassic rocks are large masses of aplite of probable Late Jurassic age. Coarse, angular detritus of possible Pliocene age, capped by basalt of late Pliocene age, occurs locally on the flanks of the Humboldt Range. At the end of Jurassic time, the Triassic rocks were folded into a broad north-trending anticline. This was accompanied by reverse faulting. A later period of faulting occurred at the end of the Pliocene.

Mineralization occurred in Late Jurassic time and was associated with the intrusion of the igneous masses. All ore deposits are in the Triassic rocks; they consist of silver-bearing quartz veins, silver-bearing stockworks, and gold veins (of minor importance). The silver veins, enriched by supergene argentite, have been the most productive deposits.

RYE PATCH DISTRICT

The Rye Patch (Echo) district is on the west flank of the Humboldt Range in central Pershing County, 4 miles east of Rye Patch.

Mining in the district began in 1864 in the principal mine, the Rye Patch. To 1874, this mine produced about $1 million chiefly in silver (Vanderburg, 1936b, p. 33). Presumably no gold was produced in the early days, but in 1935 intensive development was in progress at the Gold Standard property to test the possibility of mining large tonnages of low-grade gold ore. The development apparently was moderately successful because during 1935–59, a total of 9,453 ounces of gold was produced.

The deposit at the Rye Patch mine is in black limestone, the basal unit of the Star Peak Formation, of Middle Triassic age (Lincoln, 1923, p. 204). Several irregular fissures filled with brecciated wallrock, quartz, and calcite cut the limestone. The ore minerals, which are associated with the quartz in these fissures, consist of argentiferous tetrahedrite, galena, sphalerite, and small amounts of gold.

SEVEN TROUGHS DISTRICT

Located on the west slope of the Seven Troughs Range 30 miles west of Lovelock, the Seven Troughs district is primarily a gold-producing district, but the ores also contain considerable silver. Its first acclaim came in 1907 when the Mazuma Hills mine was opened. Although the district never achieved a bonanza output, it maintained a small, but fairly steady gold production which from 1908 through 1959 totaled 160,182 ounces.

The following summary of the geology is based on Ransome (1909a, p. 16–25). The oldest rocks in the area are Jurassic(?) slates which were intruded by a mass of granodiorite. Overlying the slates are mica andesite, basalt, and rhyolite of Tertiary age. The ore deposits are in breccia zones or fissures in the extrusive rocks. Veins are narrow and contain friable quartz and shattered country rock. Gold, in small particles or clusters of grains, is the valuable constituent. Some silver is alloyed with the gold.

SIERRA DISTRICT

The Sierra (Dun Glen, Chafey) district, at the north end of the East Range in the northeast part of T. 33 N., R. 36 E., was founded in 1863 when lode gold and placer gold were discovered in the area. Some of the important lode mines were the Tallulah, Auld Lang Syne, Munroe, Mayflower, and Auburn (Vanderburg, 1936b, p. 39).

The placers were very productive during the early days. Vanderburg (1936a, p. 156) estimated that $4 million worth of placer gold was mined during the 1880's and 1890's from Auburn, Barber, Wright, and Rock Hill Canyons. Most of this output was by Chinese operators, who habitually neglected to report any production; therefore, the estimate probably is not very accurate. Placer mining in recent years has been on a small scale.

Vanderburg (1936b, p. 39) estimated $1 million, mostly in gold, as total lode production for the district. Most of this was mined between 1862 and 1880. From 1908 to 1921 gold production was valued at $314,441. In recent years, however, activity slackened considerably. Total gold production through 1959, including the early placer output, was about 241,000 ounces.

The rocks in the Sierra district dip steeply and consist of the Star Peak Formation of Triassic age, dark slates of Jurassic age, and a thick series of andesitic flows and flow breccias (Ransome, 1909a, p. 50–51). Diabase dikes cut the sedimentary and the extrusive rocks. Ore deposits are in veins, many of which follow the diabase dikes in the volcanics. Vein minerals are quartz, galena, pyrite, sphalerite, and native gold.

SPRING VALLEY DISTRICT

The Spring Valley district is on the east slope of the Humboldt Range, 14 miles east of Oreana.

The gold production has come chiefly from placer deposits. The only productive lode mine was the Bonanza King located in 1868 (Vanderburg, 1936b, p. 42). It produced at most only a few thousand ounces of gold. The placer deposits in American and Limerick Canyons and in Spring Valley were the most productive in the State. Before 1900, a total of $11 million in gold was extracted from these gravels, mostly by the Chinese who operated the placers after the Americans skimmed off the more accessible deposits (Ransome, 1909a, p. 12). Periodically through the later years there was small-scale activity, but only 255 ounces was produced from 1932 through 1959.

STOREY COUNTY

Storey County, in western Nevada, is one of the smallest counties in the State and encompasses only about 200 square miles; yet, it was by far the most important mining county. Its metal output consisted chiefly of silver and gold.

The mining history of this county is essentially the history of the Comstock Lode which began producing in 1859 and continues to be a vital factor in the present mineral industry of Nevada. The Flowery district, on a separate mountain range a few miles east of the Comstock Lode, is the only other precious-metal district in the county. As the production of the Flowery district is often combined with that of the Comstock Lode, in this report they will be combined under the Comstock Lode district.

Production of gold in Storey County from 1859 through 1959 was about 8,560,000 ounces.

COMSTOCK LODE DISTRICT

The Comstock Lode district is in southern Storey County (lat 39°16′ to 39°20′ W., long 119°37′ to 119°40′ E.).

In the turbulent mining history of the west, there are a few names that stand out in bold relief—one of these is the Comstock Lode, the richest mining camp in Nevada. Its fabulous bonanza ores influenced politics as well as the mining industry. National interest centered on the production of the Comstock Lode mines when money was needed to conduct the Civil War, and the early entry of Nevada into the Union was due in large part to this contribution. The discoveries at Comstock also brightened the hopes of discouraged prospectors who were swarming over the crowded California goldfields. Nevada was a new El Dorado, and over the Sierra snows came thousands of Californians to mine the ores at Comstock and to make new discoveries at Peavine, Jumbo, Galena, and elsewhere throughout western Nevada.

Placer gold was mined in Gold Canyon as early as 1852, but it was not until 1859 that the rich silver-gold lode deposits were discovered on Gold Hill by placer miners (Smith, 1943, p. 3). In the beginning the claims were worked as placers, but shortly the diggings revealed vein deposits beneath the overburden. At first the discovery did not generate any particular excitement because the deposits were worked for gold values only, and the black material, rich in silver sulfides, was regarded as a nuisance. In June 1859, an analysis of some of the black sulfides showed that it was worth as much as $3,876 per ton in silver and gold (Smith, 1943, p. 9). News of this spread, and a horde of prospectors and miners from the overcrowded goldfields of California poured into this new silver camp.

The period 1860–80 was one of intermittent bonanza production that made the Comstock Lode the most important and productive camp in the world (Smith, 1943, p. 19). The initial rush in 1860 was followed by a larger one in 1863, when the Ophir and the Gould and Curry mines yielded a record $12,400,000 in gold and silver (Smith, 1943, p. 27). In 1862 the "Washoe process" was developed to treat the Comstock Lode ores. This was a rapid technique of crushing, grinding, and amalgamating the gold and silver from the pulp by steam heating

(Smith, 1943, p. 41–45). The near-surface bonanzas were exhausted by 1869, but the discovery of the deeper Crown Point-Belcher ore body in 1871 revived the district (Lincoln, 1923, p. 223). The later discovery and development of the "Big Bonanza" by the Bonanza Kings—Mackay, Fair, O'Brien, and Flood—brought the district its greatest period of prosperity, 1875–80. By 1881 the large ore bodies of the Consolidated Virginia, Yellow Jacket, and other mines were nearly depleted and in the following decade the existing mines were explored to greater depths—more than 3,000 feet. Heat that was almost unbearable, soft ground, and enormous volumes of hot water were encountered. There were no significant discoveries of ore at these greater depths, and for some time most of the production came from low-grade ore that had been overlooked in the early days. In 1894 the first cyanide plant in Nevada was built on the Comstock Lode, and it enabled profitable extraction of gold from low-grade ores and tailings (Stoddard and Carpenter, 1950, p. 22).

After 1900, consolidation made it possible to dewater many of the old workings and to do more extensive development work. The most productive mines during this period were the old Ophir, the Mexican, and the Consolidated Virginia (Stoddard and Carpenter, 1950, p. 23–25). In the mid-1920's the Consolidated Gold Fields of South Africa entered the Comstock Lode, and, after merging and consolidating several properties in the central part of the district, became the chief operator for a few years (Stoddard and Carpenter, 1950, p. 30). A significant spurt in activity marked the increase in the price of gold in 1934, and the district enjoyed a mild prosperity until the imposition of Order L–208 of the War Production Board, which closed nearly all gold and silver mines. After World War II, the Comstock Lode district slowly reawakened, but annual output in the 1950's was meager compared to that of the early years.

From 1859 through 1921, $164,023,917 (about 7,935,360 ounces) in gold was mined (Lincoln, 1923, p. 225–226). Total gold production through 1959 was about 8,560,000 ounces.

The geology of the Comstock Lode was described first by Richthofen (1866), a German geologist employed by the Sutro Tunnel Co. His report was reproduced almost entirely by Becker (1882). Others who have reported on the geology of the district are King (1870), Lincoln (1923), Gianella (1936), and F. C. Calkins (unpub. data, 1944). Stoddard and Carpenter (1950, p. 55–73) briefly reviewed the reports of the earlier workers and summarized the geology of the district.

The oldest rocks of the district are folded and faulted limestone, shale, schist, quartzite, and metavolcanic rocks of Triassic(?) age. These are intruded by quartz monzonite of Late Jurassic age and are covered by a series of Tertiary volcanic rocks consisting of the Hartford Hill Rhyolite of Eocene age, Alta Andesite of Miocene age, Kate Peak Andesite and Knickerbocker Andesite of Pliocene age, and American Flat Basalt of Quaternary age. The Hartford Hill Rhyolite and Alta Andesite are cut by the Davidson Diorite of late Miocene age. This intrusion was followed by normal faulting, and veins, including the Comstock Lode, were deposited along the faults. Later movement in late Pliocene or early Pleistocene time produced new faults and additional displacement along the older ones.

The lode is a complex shear zone—Y-shaped in cross section, about 13,000 feet long, and several hundred feet wide. Many large blocks of country rock were found in the dominantly quartz gangue in the upper part of the vein system. Calcite is a minor component of the gangue. The ore minerals are argentite, stephanite, and native gold. Coats (1936, p. 532) reported the silver sulfoselenide, aguilarite, associated with silver and argentite in the ores. Sphalerite, galena, pyrite, and chalcopyrite are usually present but not necessarily abundant. Within a few hundred feet of the surface, oxidized ores contained native silver, gold, polybasite, argentite, covellite, chalcocite, anglesite, and wulfenite. Widespread propylitized and sericitized wallrock is characteristic of the Comstock Lode.

WASHOE COUNTY

Located in the northwest corner of Nevada, Washoe County does not have the basin-and-range topography so characteristic of most of Nevada. Instead, it contains a series of valleys—former lakes—separated by low divides. Many lakes still fill the valleys in the northern part of the county, and Pyramid and Winnemucca Lakes in the central part are the largest natural bodies of water in the State. The Virginia Mountains extend northwestward across the central part of the county. South of Reno, the Sierra Nevada is the dominant feature of the western part of the county. The northern part of the county is underlain by lavas, tuffs, and lake beds that, for the most part, contain no economic mineral deposits, but several mining districts in the southern part of the county have produced considerable amounts of gold and silver (Overton, 1947, p. 46–47). Prominent among these are Olinghouse, Leadville, Wedekind and Pyramid. Considerable placer mining was done in the early days at Little Valley, Peavine, and Olinghouse, but there are no reliable production data on these operations (Vanderburg, 1936a, p. 163–166).

The prospectors who flooded into Comstock soon overflowed into adjacent southern Washoe County and discovered mineral deposits in the Jumbo, Galena, and Peavine districts.

Production of gold in the county from 1902 through 1959 was 46,107 ounces.

Although small amounts of gold have been produced from most of the districts in the county, only the Olinghouse may be considered primarily a gold district; it alone has produced more than 10,000 ounces.

OLINGHOUSE DISTRICT

The Olinghouse (White Horse) district is in southeast Washoe County (lat 39°40′ N., long 119°25′ E.), about 12 miles south of Pyramid Lake.

The district was prospected first in 1860, but very little work was done until 1901–3, the period of greatest activity (Hill, 1910a, p. 103). In the mid-1930's there was a brief revival of activity; during the 1940's and 1950's there was only small-scale production by lessees (Overton, 1947, p. 71–72). Production from 1902 through 1921 was $509,530 (about 24,700 ounces) in gold (Lincoln, 1923, p. 240). Total gold production through 1959 was about 36,000 ounces.

The dominant country rock is an older andesite of Tertiary age (Hill, 1910a, p. 104–105) intruded by dikes and sills of porphyritic rhyolite and later andesite. The ore deposits are in the older andesite and consist of zones of altered country rock adjacent to the intrusives. The ore minerals are free gold and small amounts of silver chloride. Minor amounts of chalcopyrite, pyrite, calcite, and quartz are present (Overton, 1947, p. 71).

Vanderburg (1936a, p. 164–166) reported some small-scale placer mining in this district throughout its history, but he gave no production data.

WHITE PINE COUNTY

Prospectors attracted by the silver strikes at Reese River used the town of Austin as a supply point and headquarters from which they explored most of eastern Nevada. Rich silver ore soon was discovered at Battle Mountain, Egan Canyon, White Pine, and Pioche. Indeed, it was probably the rich silver strike at White Pine that influenced the formation of White Pine County from part of Lander County in 1869.

The mines of the county have been noted chiefly for their high-grade silver, copper, and lead ores, but considerable quantities of gold have been produced from the Cherry Creek, Ely, and Osceola districts. Gold production of the county from 1903 through 1959 was 2,049,895 ounces.

CHERRY CREEK DISTRICT

The Cherry Creek (Egan Canyon, Gold Canyon) district is in the Egan Range, 50 miles north of Ely.

Gold was discovered here in 1861 by a group of soldiers, and the district was organized in 1863 (Lincoln, 1923, p. 243). Ores rich in silver, gold, and lead were mined on a fairly large scale from 1872 to 1883. The principal mines during this early period were the Teacup, Star, Exchequer, and Cherry Creek. In the late 1880's a decline began, culminating in a virtual shutdown in 1893. By 1895, however, the district had revived and the mines continued to produce on a small scale (Schrader, 1931, p. 29). Estimates of the early production range from $6 to $20 million in combined metals, but the amount of gold has not been determined. From 1902 through 1959 the district produced 36,197 ounces of gold. From 1952 through 1959 it produced considerable tungsten from scheelite deposits.

The rocks exposed in the Cherry Creek district are chiefly quartzite, shale, and limestone of Cambrian age intruded by small masses of quartz monzonite and diabase (Hill, 1916, p. 160–163). The ore deposits are veins in the quartzite. Ore minerals are galena, sphalerite, pyrite, stromeyerite, copper carbonates, scheelite, and gold (R. M. Smith, written commun., 1962).

ELY DISTRICT

The Ely (Robinson) district is slightly south of the center of White Pine County, 50 miles west of the Utah-Nevada boundary.

As a result of silver-lead-gold ore discoveries in the area, the district was organized in 1868 and was named the Robinson district after a member of the original party that entered the area. The first settlement in the district was Mineral City which by 1873 had a population of 600 (Spencer, 1917, p. 93). The early years were characterized by desultory activity, and interest shifted to the Ward, Osceola, and Taylor districts. In 1886 the county seat was moved from Hamilton to Ely, an event that seemed to coincide with revived activity in the district. At this time silver and gold were the chief metals mined. During 1906–7 there was much activity: ore bodies were developed, mills were constructed, and new companies were formed. Copper was first produced from porphyry ores in 1908, an event that marked the beginning of sustained significant production from the district.

Before 1902 accurate records of production were not kept. Spencer (1917, p. 98) estimated the production before that date at $500,000 to $600,000 in combined metals. From 1902 through 1959, a total of 1,959,659 ounces of gold was extracted from the copper ores of the district.

Spencer's (1917, p. 23–130) classic report on the Ely district is the principal reference for the following outline of the geology and ore deposits. Most of the area is underlain by limestone, quartzite, and shale aggregating 9,000 feet in thickness and ranging in age from Ordovician to Pennsylvanian. These have been extensively faulted and somewhat folded and then invaded by bodies of monzonite porphyry of probable immediate post-Jurassic age. A long period of erosion followed; then in late Tertiary time the area was covered with tuff, agglomerate, and rhyolite flows. Recent erosion has stripped away most of this volcanic cover. Both the invaded sediments and monzonite porphyry were extensively altered, causing development of garnet, jasperoid, and marble in the limestone, pyritization of the shale, and development of sericite and deposition of chalcocite in the porphyry.

Ore deposits occur in an east-trending zone, 9 miles long and ½ to 1½ miles wide. The most important ore bodies are blanketlike masses of supergene-enriched pyritized monzonite porphyry, the chief ore mineral being chalcocite. Small amounts of gold, silver, and other metals are recovered. Small bodies of copper ore are also found in the sedimentary rocks near the monzonite contact, and bodies of silver-lead ore occur farther from the monzonite.

OSCEOLA DISTRICT

The Osceola district is on the west slope of the Snake Range, 35 miles east of Ely. Work began in 1877 on the gold placers of Dry Gulch and continued to 1900 (Weeks, 1908, p. 122–123); there was also small-scale production from lodes during the early days. To 1907, the placers had produced gold worth about $1,800,000, and the lodes, about $200,000 (Weeks, 1908, p. 123). After 1900, the district has had a lethargic development with only brief productive intervals. Total gold production through 1959 was 131,700 ounces—91,555 ounces was from placers, and 40,145 ounces was from lodes.

The following is summarized from Weeks (1908, p. 119–127). The oldest rocks, exposed near the crest of the Snake Range a short distance south of the district, are granite and schist of Precambrian age. These are overlain by a thick section of Cambrian formations consisting of conglomerate, argillite, quartzite, shale, and dark-blue and gray limestone. Locally, granite porphyry of post-Carboniferous age has invaded the sedimentary rocks. Ore deposits are of two types: (1) sheeted zones, and (2) shattered masses in quartzite adjacent to deposits of the first type. All deposits dip steeply and are confined to well-defined zones in the quartzite. Gold is the only economic constituent; quartz is abundant and pyrite is sparsely disseminated in the veins.

NEW MEXICO

The gold-producing districts of New Mexico are distributed in a northeastward-trending mineral belt of variable width that extends diagonally across the State, from Hidalgo County in the southwest corner to Colfax County along the north-central border. From 1848 through 1965 New Mexico is credited with a gold production of about 2,267,000 ounces; however, several million dollars worth of placer gold was mined prior to 1848.

Mining in New Mexico began long before discoveries were made in any of the other Western States (Lindgren and others, 1910, p. 17–19; Jones, 1904, p. 8–20). The copper disposits at Santa Rita were known and mined late in the 18th century, and placer gold mining began as early as 1828 in the Ortiz Mountains south of Santa Fe. In 1839 placer deposits were discovered farther south along the foot of the San Pedro Mountains. The earliest lode mining, except the work at Santa Rita, dates back to 1833 when a gold-quartz vein was worked in the Ortiz Mountains.

New Mexico was incorporated as a Territory of the United States at the close of the Mexican War in 1846, but, because of its isolation, the general lack of knowledge of the region, and the hostility of the Apache Indians, it was not until about 1860 that prospectors and miners were attracted to the region. All mining in the Territory was suspended during the Confederate invasion in 1861–62, and later mining was frequently interrupted by Indian raids (Lindgren and others, 1910, p. 18).

New ore discoveries in the middle and late 1860's and in the 1870's stimulated mining in the Territory. In 1865 placers and, soon afterward, quartz lodes were found in the White Mountains in Lincoln County; in 1866 placer deposits were discovered at Elizabethtown in Colfax County, and silver-lead deposits were discovered in the Magdalena Range in

Socorro County. In 1877 placers and gold-quartz veins were found at Hillsboro, and in 1878 phenomenally rich silver ore was found at Lake Valley in Sierra County. Extension of the Southern Pacific and the Atchison, Topeka and Santa Fe railroads through the southern and central parts of New Mexico frcm 1879 through 1882 was a great stimulus to mining. Rich silver ores were discovered in the 1870's and 1880's, and silver mining flourished until the shallow rich ores were depleted. The drop in the price of silver in 1893 further discouraged silver mining.

At the beginning of the 20th century base-metal mining in New Mexico was resumed, but gold and silver mining was not. In 1912 large-scale copper mining began in the Central district in Grant County and since then most of the State's gold output has come as a byproduct from copper and other base-metal ores (fig. 18).

The mineral belt of New Mexico is in moun-

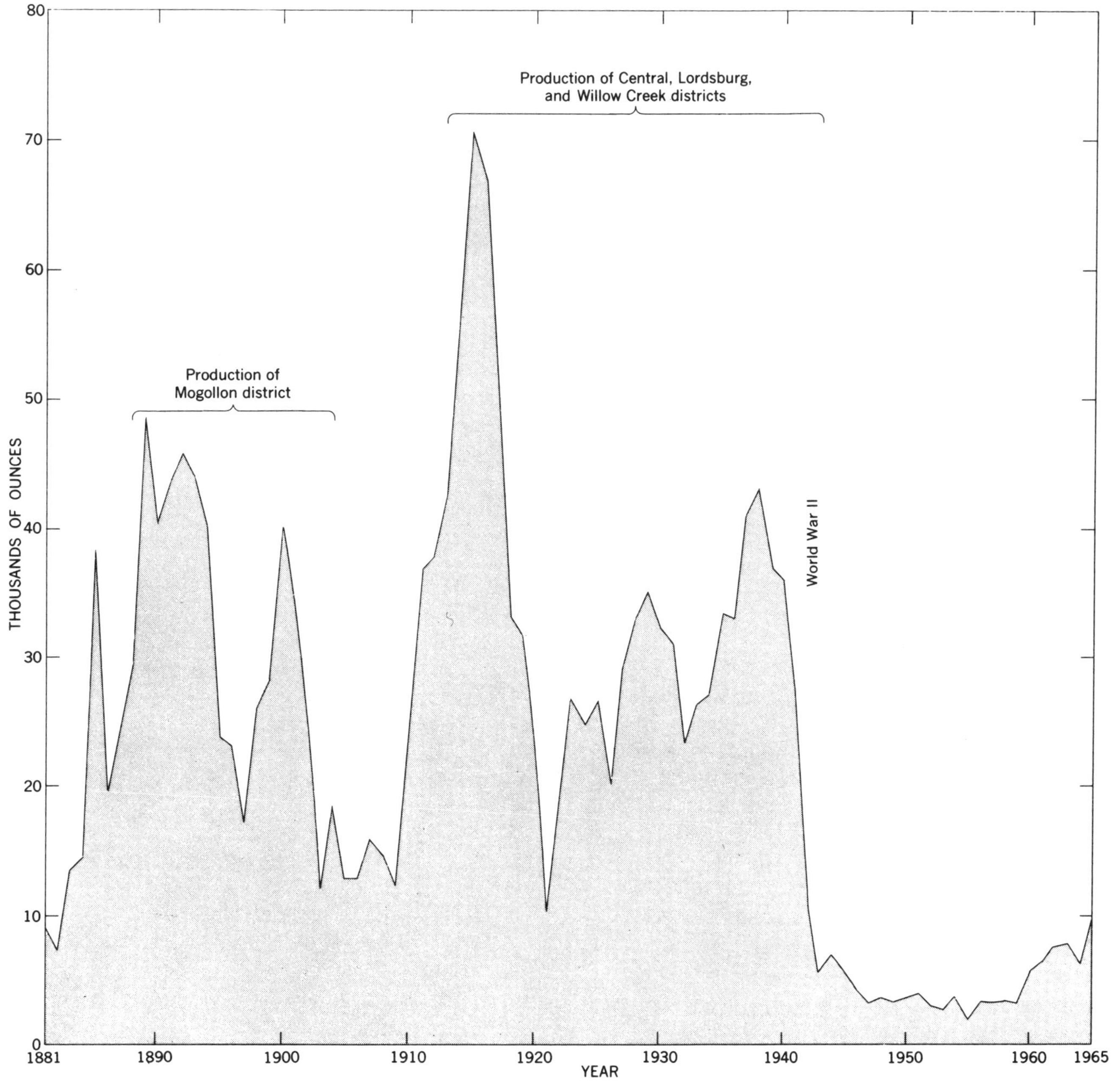

FIGURE 18.—Annual gold production of New Mexico, 1881–1965. Sources of data: U.S. Geological Survey (1883–1924); U.S. Bureau of Mines (1925–34; 1933–66). Production reported in dollar value was converted to ounces at prevailing price per ounce.

tainous terrain that lies between the Colorado Plateau on the northwest and the Great Plains on the east. It is a zone of crustal disturbance in which the rocks were folded and faulted and intruded by stocks, dikes, and laccoliths of monzonitic rocks. Deposits of copper, lead, zinc, gold, and silver occur locally throughout this belt. Some deposits of copper and gold are Precambrian in age (Lindgren and others, 1910, p. 47–51), but most of the ore deposits are associated with Upper Cretaceous or Tertiary intrusive rocks. The gold placers were probably derived from the weathering of these deposits. In later Tertiary time lavas spread out over wide areas of the State, and fissures within these rocks were later mineralized (Lindgren and others, 1910, p. 67–74). These fissure veins are rich in gold and silver, but in most places they are relatively poor in base metals.

In New Mexico, 17 districts in 13 counties yielded more than 10,000 ounces of gold each through 1957 (fig. 19).

BERNALILLO COUNTY

Bernalillo County is along the Rio Grande in north-central New Mexico. Mining has been of slight economic importance in the county, and gold production has come only from the Tijeras Canyon district, between the Sandia and Manzano Ranges.

TIJERAS CANYON DISTRICT

Information on the discovery and production of gold in the Tijeras Canyon district is meager. Total gold production was about 34,488 ounces (Martin, 1953, p. 645), most of which was mined from 1882 through 1903. In 1959 the Tijeras Canyon district was included in the Sandia military base and was made inaccessible to prospectors or miners.

The ore occurs in a north-trending system of fissures and faults in Precambrian granite and metamorphic rocks and along the contact of the Precambrian rocks with the overlying limestone of Pennsylvanian age. The ore chiefly contains lead and silver and smaller amounts of copper and gold. Fluorspar is a common gangue. Apparently most of the ore was mined from the oxidized zone (Ellis, 1922, p. 40–42).

CATRON COUNTY

Catron County, which was separated from Socorro County in 1921, lies along the western border of the State, and ranks second, next to Grant County, in the production of gold in the State. Through 1959 it had yielded about 362,225 ounces of gold, of which 362,132 ounces was produced through 1950 (Martin, 1953, p. 645). During 1904–42 about 40 percent of all the silver and 25 percent of all the gold produced in New Mexico came from this county. Except for small shipments of tin concentrates during 1940–43, the entire metal output of the county came from lodes in the Mogollon (Cooney) district in the southwest corner of the county, about 85 miles northwest of Silver City, the nearest railhead (Anderson, 1957, p. 31–32).

MOGOLLON DISTRICT

A sergeant named James C. Cooney, who was stationed at Fort Bayard, staked the first claims in the Mogollon (Cooney) district in 1875, but hostile Apache Indians prevented the shipment of ore until 1879. Intermittent Indian raids continued to harass the miners until the defeat of Geronimo in 1885. The mines were then developed rapidly; by 1905 the district had produced $5 million worth of copper, silver, and gold (Ferguson, 1927, p. 34). By 1924 many of the original mines, including the Cooney, were closed because of depletion of the surface ores. Exploitation of the lower grade sulfide ores at depth demanded large-scale mining methods, and as a result, most properties were consolidated under the Mogollon Mines Co. The district was moderately active through 1946, but it was virtually idle from 1947 through 1959. The entire gold production of Catron County through 1959 came from the Mogollon district.

The Mogollon Range, in which the ore deposits are found, is composed of a section more than 8,000 feet thick of Tertiary lavas and pyroclastic rocks interbedded with subordinate amounts of sandstone and conglomerate. The ubiquitous Gila Conglomerate of Pliocene or Pleistocene age unconformably overlies the older Tertiary rocks. The rocks are cut by a network of normal faults of several ages (Ferguson, 1927, p. 5–25).

The ore deposits are in silver- and gold-bearing quartz veins along faults. The composition of the wallrock apparently exerted little influence on the content of the veins; however, the fracturing characteristics of the wallrock controlled the size and altitude of the ore bodies (Ferguson, 1927, p. 44–45). Calcite, quartz, and fluorite are the principal gangue minerals; adularia is present, but it is rare. The primary metallic minerals in the veins are pyrite, chalcopyrite, bornite, chalcocite, sphalerite, galena, stromeyerite, and probably tetrahedrite. Silver in the form of argentite is the valuable component in most veins. The upper parts of the veins are oxidized to irregular depths and contain limonite, malachite, azurite, chrysocolla, cerargyrite, and

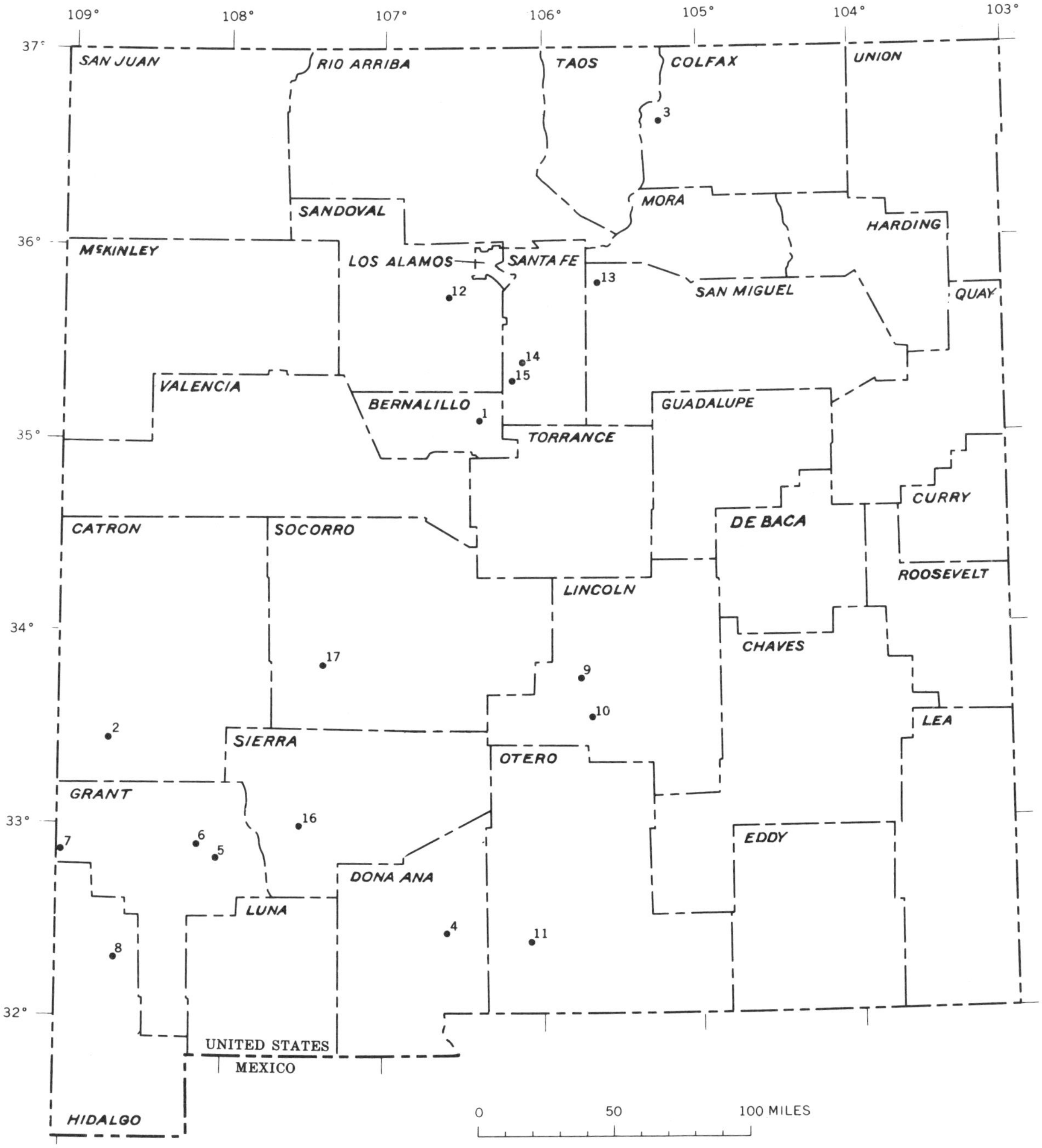

FIGURE 19.—Gold-mining districts of New Mexico.

Bernalillo County:
1, Tijeras Canyon.
Catron County:
2, Mogollon.
Colfax County:
3, Elizabethtown-Baldy.
Dona Ana County:
4, Organ.
Grant County:
5, Central; 6, Pinos Altos; 7, Steeple Rock.
Hidalgo County:
8, Lordsburg.
Lincoln County:
9, White Oaks; 10, Nogal.
Otero County:
11, Jarilla.
Sandoval County:
12, Cochiti.
San Miguel County:
13, Willow Creek.
Santa Fe County:
14, Old Placer; 15, New Placer.
Sierra County:
16, Hillsboro.
Socorro County:
17, Rosedale.

sparse native silver and native gold (Ferguson, 1927, p. 38–50).

COLFAX COUNTY

Colfax County, which lies just south of the New Mexico-Colorado border, has been an important source of lode and placer gold. Small quantities of silver, copper, and lead have also been mined. The metal mining districts in Colfax County are centered in the Cimarron Range which is along the western edge of the county. Martin (1953, p. 645) reported a total gold production for Colfax County through 1952 of 282,717 ounces. This may be too low; the amount credited to the two principal districts in this report totals about 358,000 ounces through 1959.

The most productive placer deposits are in the Moreno Creek valley near Elizabethtown on the west side of the Cimarron Range, and the most productive lode deposits are in the Baldy (Ute Creek) area on the east side of the range, east of the Elizabethtown district.

ELIZABETHTOWN-BALDY DISTRICT

Copper float, found by an Indian on the upper slope of Baldy Peak, was exhibited at Fort Union early in the 1860's (Graton, in Lindgren and others, 1910, p. 92–93). This was the first mineral discovery in the Elizabethtown-Baldy district, and some of the men stationed at the fort located claims where the float had been found. In the fall of 1866, men sent by the owners to do assessment work did some panning along Willow Creek and discovered rich placer deposits; a boom followed in the spring of 1867. Although some locations were made on lodes, including the famous Aztec lode, most were on placers. To provide sufficient water for placering, a ditch about 41 miles long was dug from the headwaters of the Red River and was completed in 1868.

The placer deposits along Grouse and Humbug Gulches, tributaries of Moreno Creek, each yielded more than $1 million in placer gold and silver. Another $2 million worth of placer gold and silver was recovered from the valleys of Moreno and Willow Creeks (Anderson, 1957, p. 38–39), and some gold also came from the gravels along Ute Creek. Graton (in Lindgren and others, 1910, p. 93) estimated the placer production of the Elizabethtown-Baldy district prior to 1904 at $2.5 million, and C. W. Henderson (in U. S. Bureau of Mines, 1929, pt. 1, p. 740) estimated the production through 1929 at about $3 million (145,138 ounces). The total placer production through 1959 was about 146,980 ounces.

Most of the lode gold of Colfax County has come from the Baldy area. Graton (in Lindgren and others, 1910, p. 93, 97) estimated production at about $2 million (96,760 ounces) through 1903. The Aztec mine, discovered in 1868 and one of the oldest and richest gold mines in the State, accounted for more than half of the early output. The lode mines were virtually idle from 1941 through 1959. Through 1959, total lode production was about 221,400 ounces, and total lode and placer production was 368,380 ounces.

The Cimarron Range consists of eastward-tilted and faulted sedimentary rocks—the Pierre Shale of Cretaceous age and the Raton Formation of early Tertiary age. These two formations are separated by an unconformity and both are intruded by dikes and sills of quartz monzonite porphyry (Lee, 1916, p. 327–329).

The principal ore bodies are in pockets and stringers in the basal conglomeratic sandstone of the Raton Formation along the unconformity. Much ore is in the underlying Pierre Shale, as much as 5 feet below its contact with the Raton Formation. Minute fissures filled with ore minerals interlace the shale and extend upward into the conglomerate. The gangue is mainly calcite, and ore minerals are pyrite, chalcopyrite, sphalerite, and possibly galena. Native gold is present as wire gold and irregularly shaped masses (Lee, 1916, p. 329–330). Most of the deposits are associated with the porphyry intrusive bodies. Chase and Muir (1923, p. 272) noted that some ore bodies are in contact metamorphic deposits in calcareous rocks adjacent to quartz monzonite porphyry. These are few in number and have been less productive than the veins.

DONA ANA COUNTY

Dona Ana County is in the center of the southernmost tier of counties in New Mexico. The total gold production of the county through 1959 was about 13,500 ounces; almost all production has come from the Organ district, which includes the north end of the Organ Mountains and the extreme south end of the San Andres Mountains.

ORGAN DISTRICT

Ore was discovered in the Organ district in 1849 (Dunham, 1935, p. 185–191), and, from the time of discovery to 1952, the district produced copper, lead, silver, zinc, and gold valued at about $2½ million (Anderson, 1957, p. 40). Of this total, gold amounts to about $242,227 or 11,435 ounces. Most of the gold output was before 1906; the district was inactive from 1951 through 1959.

The Organ Mountains consist chiefly of quartz monzonite intruded into Paleozoic sedimentary rocks. At the north end of the district the bedrock consists of westward-tilted Paleozoic formations overlying Precambrian granite and metamorphic rocks (Lindgren and others, 1910, p. 205–213; Dunham, 1935, p. 26–89).

The ore deposits in the Organ district occur in or near the quartz monzonite batholith. The principal ore deposits contain mixed sulfides of copper, lead, silver, and zinc with smaller amounts of gold. Locally the values are principally in gold. The lode ore deposits comprise (1) veins, both in the Precambrian rocks and in the intrusive quartz monzonite, (2) deposits along the Torpedo-Bennett fault, a major fault zone, which extends along the west side of the Organ Mountains, and (3) replacement deposits in the sedimentary rocks (Dunham, 1935, p. 111–136).

Most of the gold has been recovered from veins. Veins in the Precambrian rocks are valuable chiefly for gold, and gold has also been recovered from ores along the Torpedo-Bennett fault. A few veins that cut the quartz monzonite are valuable for gold, but most of them are mined for silver.

The ore deposits vary considerably in mineral composition. The veins in the Precambrian rocks consist mainly of pyrite and chalcopyrite in quartz; sphalerite and galena are less common. The fact that the gold content is related to the copper content suggests that the gold is most commonly associated with chalcopyrite; some gold was found as inclusions in pyrite.

Other common ore minerals in other deposits in the district include tetrahedrite, argentite, enargite, and tetradymite (bismuth telluride). The most common gangue minerals in addition to quartz are green fluorite, siderite, and local barite.

In parts of the district there is a crude zonal arrangement of ore with respect to the quartz monzonite (Dunham, 1935, p. 136–140). The ore bodies nearest the quartz monzonite contain copper and are succeeded outward by zinc deposits, which in turn grade into lead deposits. Gold is found chiefly in the copper and zinc zones.

GRANT COUNTY

Grant County, in southwestern New Mexico, contains several highly productive mining districts and ranks first in the State in the production of mineral wealth. The ore deposits are diverse and have yielded copper, lead, zinc, silver, gold, iron, manganese, and molybdenum.

Total gold production of the county through 1959 was about 501,000 ounces. Before 1900 placers and oxidized ores were the chief sources of the gold, but from 1912 through 1959 much gold has been a byproduct of base-metal mining. The major districts are the Central, Pinos Altos, and Steeple Rock.

CENTRAL DISTRICT

The Central district, which includes Santa Rita, Hanover, Fierro, and Bayard, is in eastern Grant County and has produced copper, zinc, iron, lead, and small amounts of gold and silver. From 1904 through 1959 the entire district produced about 140,000 ounces of gold, mostly as a byproduct from base-metal ores. Gold production before 1904 is not known but presumedly was negligible.

Copper ores at Santa Rita were probably known to the Indians at an early date and to the Mexicans before the American occupation. Small amounts of copper were produced in this district intermittently for a century beginning in 1804, and large-scale copper mining began in 1911 (Spencer and Paige, 1935, p. 5–9; Lasky, 1936, p. 102–105; Graton, in Lindgren and others, 1910, p. 306).

In 1906 a detailed study was undertaken to determine the feasibility of open-pit mining of the copper deposits of the Santa Rita basin in the Central district. In September 1910 stripping began and by 1912 copper was being produced in large quantities (Spencer and Paige, 1935, p. 8–9). Silver-bearing lead carbonate ores were mined in the Bayard area as early as 1870, and lead-zinc deposits in the Hanover area were developed on a large scale by 1912. The district continued to be a significant producer of copper, lead, and zinc through 1959. Gold and silver were byproducts.

The following summary of the geology and ore deposits is from Spencer and Paige (1935) and Lasky (1936).

The Central district is underlain by a relatively complete section of Paleozoic sedimentary rocks, in which every system of the Paleozoic Era is represented. These rocks are unconformably overlain by Cretaceous sedimentary rocks. Folding and faulting related to igneous activity took place in Cretaceous and Tertiary time. The igneous rocks include sills, stocks, and dikes of quartz diorite and granodiorite and also include younger quartz latite tuffs and andesitic basalt flows. Locally, the sedimentary and intrusive rocks are intensely altered. Additional faulting occurred after the latest igneous activity.

Ore deposits are of three principal types: contact metamorphic deposits, veins, and disseminated copper deposits in granodiorite porphyry. The contact metamorphic deposits are in certain limestone beds adjacent to the Hanover-Fierro stock. Some deposits are commercially valuable magnetite bodies with subordinate amounts of pyrite, chalcopyrite, and chalmersite. Others are masses of sphalerite, galena, hedenbergite, ilvaite, and manganese-bearing calcite, which are valuable for their zinc content. The veins are mineralized fractures related to the quartz diorite and granodiorite intrusions. Sphalerite, pyrite, chalcopyrite, and galena are the chief sulfide constituents of these deposits. Quartz and sericite are common gangue minerals. The disseminated copper deposit at Santa Rita is in the upper highly fractured part of a granodiorite stock and in the invaded sedimentary rocks near the contact. Primary pyrite and chalcopyrite were converted to rich deposits of chalcocite by supergene enrichment processes. The chalcocite is overlain by a blanket of malachite, azurite, chrysocolla, cuprite, and native copper (Spencer and Paige, 1935, p. 64–75). The gold content of all the primary ore is very low; however, the enriched and oxidized parts of the veins and disseminated copper deposits yield considerable amounts of gold as a byproduct.

PINOS ALTOS DISTRICT

The Pinos Altos district is about 8 miles northeast of Silver City in the Pinos Altos Mountains. Both placer and lode gold were discovered in 1860, and within 2 years about 30 lode mines were being worked. The Civil War and the postwar depredations of Apache Indians brought about almost complete abandonment of the camp for several years (Lindgren and others, 1910, p. 297). In 1867, operations were resumed and they continued with brief interruptions until the late 1950's. Gold was the principal product in the early years. Silver, copper, and lead later gained significance, and after 1912, zinc was of major importance.

Gold production in ounces is summarized in the following table:

	Lode	*Placer*
1860–1904 [1]	69,445	36,690
1905–29 [1]	25,380	3,949
1930–59	10,150	2,008
Total	104,975	42,647

[1] Wells and Wootton (1940, p. 11) and Lasky and Wootton (1933, p. 59–60).

The most productive placer deposits were found along Bear Creek Gulch, Rich Gulch, Whiskey Gulch, and unnamed gulches near the old Gillette shaft. The principal lode mines are on the east side of the Pinos Altos Mountains; a few are on the upper western slope.

The Pinos Altos Mountains consist of eastward-tilted and faulted limestone of Pennsylvanian age, Cretaceous quartzite, shale, and andesite breccia. These rocks are intruded by hundreds of mafic dikes, and by masses of diorite and granodiorite of Late Cretaceous or early Tertiary age. North of the Pinos Altos district the sedimentary and intrusive rocks are covered by younger Tertiary tuff (Paige, 1911, p. 109–125).

The lode deposits are of two types: veins in igneous rocks and replacement deposits in the limestone.

The veins range in length from a few hundred feet to nearly a mile and have an average width of 2½ feet. The ore minerals are pyrite, sphalerite, galena, and chalcopyrite. Quartz is the principal gangue, but calcite, barite, and rhodochrosite are locally present. Gold and silver are present in all the veins.

The replacement deposits occur at two distinct horizons in the limestone, 4 to 15 feet apart. The ore consists of intimately intergrown sphalerite, chalcopyrite, pyrite, quartz, and carbonate minerals. Zinc, copper, silver, and small amounts of gold are recovered from these ores (Paige, 1911, p. 113–125).

STEEPLE ROCK DISTRICT

The Steeple Rock district is in western Grant County, about 4 miles from the New Mexico-Arizona boundary. Shortly after the initial discoveries in 1880, the Carlisle mine was developed and by 1897 its production was valued at about $3 million in gold and silver (Graton, in Lindgren and others, 1910, p. 327). Production figures from 1897 through 1931 are not available, and although ore was shipped, the total production is believed to have been small (Anderson, 1957, p. 76). A fairly prosperous interval began in 1932 and lasted through 1955. During this period 34,050 ounces of gold, in addition to considerable silver, copper, lead, and zinc, was produced. The district was idle from 1956 through 1959.

The rocks in the district are lavas of Tertiary age and range in composition from soda rhyolite to diorite. Quartz, accompanied by small amounts of calcite, is the predominant gangue mineral. Pyrite, sphalerite, chalcopyrite, and galena are the ore minerals.

HIDALGO COUNTY

Hidalgo County, in the southwest corner of the State, was part of Grant County until 1920. Its chief mineral products are copper, gold, silver, and lead; through 1952 it is credited with a gold production of about 227,000 ounces. More than nine-tenths of this production has come from the Lordsburg district, which has yielded gold as a byproduct of base-metal ores.

LORDSBURG DISTRICT

The Lordsburg district is 3 to 8 miles south-southwest of the town of Lordsburg at the north end of the Pyramid Mountains. It includes the Pyramid camp on the south end of the district and the Virginia (Shakespeare) camp on the north end. Copper has been the most important metal mined, and gold and silver have been valuable byproducts.

Recorded gold production of the Lordsburg district from 1904 through 1959 was about 223,750 ounces, of which about 189,000 ounces was produced before 1933. Prior to 1904 the total production of silver, copper, lead, and gold from the district had a value of about $500,000 (Lasky and Wootton, 1933, p. 72), but the amount of gold has not been ascertained.

Prospecting for silver began about 1870; however, the major early interest in the area was generated after it had been salted with diamonds. The ensuing stampede resulted in discovery of a few silver deposits, but development lagged until the copper potential of the area was considered. After several years of sporadic exploration, the Emerald vein was developed in the early 1900's, and by 1932 workings on this vein were the deepest in the State. The Emerald vein yielded nine-tenths of the ore mined in the district (Lasky, 1938, p. 25–27). Activity continued at a moderate rate through 1959.

Rocks of the Lordsburg district consist mainly of basalt, intrusive rhyolite breccia, and rhyolite volcanic necks of early Cretaceous age and a stock of granodiorite of Late Cretaceous or early Tertiary age. Numerous dikes of quartz latite and felsite cut the granodiorite and older rocks (Lasky, 1938, p. 9–11).

The ore deposits in the district are characterized by abundant tourmaline and chalcopyrite. The ore occurs in veins along faults that were repeatedly reopened during mineral deposition. Six stages of mineral deposition are recognized, but only the second stage yielded exploitable ore deposits (Lasky, 1938, p. 31–33). The important ore minerals are chalcopyrite, pyrite, specularite, sphalerite, and galena; the most common gangue minerals are quartz, calcite, tourmaline, barite, and manganosiderite. The Emerald vein (Lasky, 1938, p. 28) has been traced on the surface for more than 6,000 feet, mined to a vertical depth in the Eighty-five mine of 1,900 feet, and explored to a depth of 2,250 feet. Lasky (1938, p. 34) pointed out that the grade of ore mined and the ratio between the different metals are remarkably uniform and that the roots of the main shoot in the Emerald vein are almost identical in grade with the average grade of the last 850,000 tons of ore mined.

LINCOLN COUNTY

Gold lodes are the most important deposits in Lincoln County. The total gold production of Lincoln County through 1959 was about 163,647 ounces; however, mining virtually ceased from 1943 through 1959. Although production has come from a number of districts (Graton, in Lindgren and others, 1910, p. 175–184), only the White Oaks and Nogal districts have produced more than 10,000 ounces of gold.

NOGAL DISTRICT

The Nogal district, in the Sierra Blanca Range about 6 miles southwest of the town of Nogal, has produced minor amounts of placer and lode gold, mostly before 1908. Gold placers were found in Dry Gulch, northeast of Nogal Peak, in 1865, and lode deposits were found at the site of the American Lode mine in 1868. Mining did not begin, however, until this region was withdrawn from the Mescalero Indian Reservation in 1882. By 1910 ore worth about $250,000 had been mined, but operations declined thereafter (Anderson, 1957, p. 92). The district was mostly idle from 1936 through 1959. Total gold production was about 12,850 ounces; most of it was from lode mines.

Bedrock in the Nogal district is predominantly monzonite porphyry which has intruded Cretaceous sedimentary rocks that are exposed east, west, and north of the Sierra Blanca Range. The monzonite porphyry is cut by dikes of diorite porphyry. Scattered patches of andesite flows and tuffs, of probable Tertiary age, are found near Nogal Peak, but their relations with the other rocks are not clear (Graton, in Lindgren and others, 1910, p. 176–177).

The ore deposits are in stringers of quartz and dolomite in the monzonite porphyry and quartz-calcite veins in andesite. The ore minerals are gold, pyrite, sphalerite, galena, and chalcopyrite. A mass of bleached, kaolinized, and brecciated porphyry, located about 1 mile southeast of Nogal Peak, has also yielded gold and a little silver (Graton, in Lindgren and others, 1910, p. 178).

WHITE OAKS DISTRICT

The White Oaks district has produced about seven-eighths of the gold in Lincoln County. It is about 12 miles northeast of Carrizozo in the White Oaks Mountains, which form the northern continuation of the Sierra Blanca Range. A small amount of placer gold was produced intermittently in the 1850's and 1860's in Baxter Gulch (Graton, in Lindgren and others, 1910, p. 179). The gold-bearing vein deposits were not discovered until 1879 in what is now known as the Homestake mine. The Old Abe mine was the most productive in the district and reached a depth of 1,375 feet (Jones, 1904, p. 172–173). The total production of the district through 1903 was $2,860,000 (Jones, 1904, p. 175). From 1903 to 1926 a small amount of gold was produced in most years, and through 1925 the total production was about $3 million; most of it was lode gold (Lasky and Wootton, 1933, p. 78). Only small-scale activity was reported through the 1930's, and the district was practically idle from 1941 through 1959. The total gold production of the district through 1959 was about 146,500 ounces; most of it was from lodes.

The rocks in the White Oaks district (Graton, in Lindgren and others, 1910, p. 179–180) are Cretaceous shale and post-Cretaceous fine-grained monzonite. Both are cut by lamprophyre dikes.

The ore deposits are in veins that cut the monzonite, lamprophyre dikes, and the shale. Most of the veins are narrow stringers, but where the intervening wallrock is impregnated with ore minerals, the deposits are irregular shoots. Gold, auriferous pyrite, and huebnerite are the common ore minerals. Quartz, albite, fluorite, and tourmaline are associated vein minerals.

OTERO COUNTY

Otero County, in southern New Mexico along the Texas border, is relatively poor in mineral deposits, yet a few small mines in the Jarilla district produced a total of about 16,500 ounces of gold through 1959.

JARILLA DISTRICT

The Jarilla (Orogrande) district is in the Jarilla Mountains about 50 miles north-northeast of El Paso in the southwest corner of Otero County. The first prospecting was done in 1879, but little interest was generated until turquoise was discovered about 20 years later (Jones, 1904, p. 194). Gold and copper lodes were mined on a small scale, and a little gold was recovered from dry placer operations. The most active period was 1905–18; the district was dormant from 1948 through 1959.

The Jarilla Mountains are underlain by Carboniferous limestone intruded and domed by an irregular mass of fine-grained monzonite porphyry. Near the contact, the limestone is metamorphosed to a skarn of garnet, diopside, epidote, quartz, and tremolite. The ore deposits are in fracture zones and along bedding planes in the metamorphosed limestone. Specularite and gold- and silver-bearing pyrite and chalcopyrite are the chief primary ore minerals; oxidized ore contains much limonite, malachite, and chrysocolla (Graton, in Lindgren and others, 1910, p. 185–186). The placer ground that has been worked is on the southeastern slope of the Jarilla Mountains. Most of the placer gold has been recovered with some form of dry washer. Black sand constitutes approximately 1 percent of the gravel and is reported to run about $40 per ton in gold, which is equivalent to about 40 cents in gold per ton of gravel. The black sand also carries magnetite, ilmenite, hematite, and zircon (Wells and Wootton, 1940, p. 14).

SANDOVAL COUNTY

Sandoval County, in northwestern New Mexico, is mostly west of the Rio Grande. Small amounts of gold and silver were produced from veins in the county, and copper has been produced from sandstone deposits. The gold and silver came from the Cochiti district in the foothills of the Valles Mountains, about 30 miles west of Santa Fe.

COCHITI DISTRICT

The Cochiti district was prospected in the 1870's or 1880's, but boundary disputes with Mexico dampened any early enthusiasm to locate claims. By 1889 much exploration was underway, resulting in the discovery of the Albemarle deposit in 1894. During a period of feverish activity from 1894 through 1904 more than $1 million in gold and silver was mined (Lindgren and others, 1910, p. 150). In 1905 mining ceased and was never resumed except for brief flurries in 1914–16 and 1932–40. The district was mostly idle from 1941 through 1959. The total gold production through 1959 was about 41,500 ounces.

The country rock of the Cochiti district consists of sandstone of probable Cretaceous age which has been intruded and domed by monzonite and related porphyries, also probably of Cretaceous age. Overlying these rocks is rhyolite 500 to 800 feet thick of probable Miocene age (Lindgren and others, 1910, p. 151). The ore bodies consist of quartz lodes as much as 150 feet wide in shattered and brecciated zones in the monzonite. Ore minerals extend into the wallrock, but nowhere do the veins extend into the overlying rhyolite (Lindgren and others, 1910, p. 153–162). Sphalerite, pyrite, and chalcopyrite are the most abundant sulfides, but argentite is probably the principal ore mineral. Galena occurs sparingly. Gold may be associated with the pyrite. None of the base-metal sulfides was sufficiently abundant to be of economic importance. The deepest ore known in the district pinched out at a depth of about 600 feet.

SAN MIGUEL COUNTY

San Miguel County, in northeastern New Mexico, adjoins Santa Fe County on the east. Deposits of gold, silver, copper, lead, and zinc are found in the mountainous northwest corner of the county in the Willow Creek district. The total gold production of the county through 1959 was 178,961 ounces.

WILLOW CREEK DISTRICT

Almost the entire production of the Willow Creek (Pecos) district came from the Pecos mine, formerly known as the Hamilton or Cowles mine. Discovered in 1881, the deposit was developed slowly, and in the early 1900's, it was developed primarily as a copper mine. Intensive exploration that began in 1916 later revealed large reserves of lead-zinc ore at depth. From 1926 through 1939, under the ownership of American Metal Co., the mine produced $36 million in gold, silver, copper, lead and zinc. Aside from minor activity in 1943–44, the district was dormant from 1940 through 1959. Total gold production for the district through 1959 was roughly 178,300 ounces.

Precambrian diabase, granite, and schist are exposed in the deeper canyons of the district where they are unconformably overlain by the Magdalena Formation of Pennsylvanian age. The unconformity and overlying sedimentary rocks dip 7°–12° SW. (Krieger, 1932, p. 351–352).

The ore deposits are in a mineralized shear zone in the Precambrian schist. Both the shear zone and ore are believed to be of Precambrian age, for neither extends into the overlying Pennsylvanian rocks. Pyrite and sphalerite are the most abundant ore minerals; chalcopyrite and galena are less abundant, and pyrrhotite, bornite, argentite, and proustite are sparse (Krieger, 1932, p. 462, 463). Harley (1940, p. 84) reported minor roscoelite, and Lasky (in Lasky and Wootton, 1933, p. 93) reported sparse tetrahedrite. The gangue minerals are quartz, chlorite, actinolite, sericite, and tourmaline. The gold is associated with quartz and chalcopyrite (Harley, 1940, p. 84).

SANTA FE COUNTY

Santa Fe County is in north-central New Mexico, along the western edge of the Great Plains physiographic province.

Gold has been mined from placers and lodes along the western boundary of the county in the Cerrillos Hills, Ortiz Mountains, and San Pedro Mountains. These ranges are circular in outline and were formed by doming of Carboniferous and Cretaceous sedimentary rocks by laccolithic sheets of Tertiary monzonite porphyry (Lindgren, in Lindgren and others, 1910, p. 163–165).

Gold placers were mined as early as the 1830's; therefore, the early production can only be estimated. The principal gold districts are the Old Placer and the New Placer; each produced an estimated $2 million in gold (Lindgren, in Lindgren and others, 1910, p. 75, 168). Total county gold production through 1959 probably was between 150,000 and 200,000 ounces.

NEW PLACER DISTRICT

The New Placer (San Pedro) district is on the west side of the San Pedro Mountains between the towns of San Pedro and Golden. Most of the gold production came from placers that were mined before 1880, but after 1904 there was also an appreciable output of lode gold. The placer deposits were discovered in 1839 (Lindgren, in Lindgren and others, 1910, p. 174), 11 years after those of the Old Placer district were discovered. The placers are in Lazarus Gulch and in branches of Tuerto Creek near Golden on the west side of the mountains.

It has been estimated that the New Placer district produced about $2 million (96,759 ounces) from beginning of production to 1904 (Lindgren and others, 1910, p. 75). This figure represents chiefly placer gold but it may also include some lode gold; figures on lode production before 1904 are not available. From 1904 through 1957 the district produced 2,931 ounces placer gold and about 16,000 ounces of lode gold. Total gold production was about 115,700 ounces. There was no recorded production from 1957 through 1959.

The San Pedro Mountains consist of Carboniferous formations at least 700 feet thick intruded by a laccolith, sheets, and dikes of monzonite and related porphyries probably of Late Cretaceous or early Tertiary age (Lindgren and others, 1910, p. 170–175). Numerous small gold-bearing veins, containing quartz, calcite, pyrite, and free gold, occur both in the porphyry and in the sedimentary rocks. In the lower part of the laccolithic roof are found small copper-bearing contact metamorphic deposits, and in limestone farther away from the igneous contact are found replacement deposits rich in galena.

The placer gold is found in alluvial fans along the mountain front and in the gravels of streams that have reworked the alluvial fans.

OLD PLACER DISTRICT

The Old Placer (Ortiz, Dolores, Cerrillos) district is on the east side of the Ortiz Mountains. Placer deposits were found in the Old Placer district in 1828—probably the first gold discoveries in New Mexico. Gold-quartz veins were discovered in the district 5 years later. The richest placers were found at the mouth of Cunningham Gulch near the old town of Dolores where the gravels form a mesa, a remnant of the upper part of an alluvial fan. Lower grade placers were mined in Dolores Gulch, west of Cunningham Gulch, and on the south side of the Ortiz Mountains. Unrecorded but probably small amounts of gold were mined from lodes which were known as early as 1833 (Lindgren and others, 1910, p. 168–169). Total gold output of the district is about 99,300 ounces, most of which was mined from placers before 1900.

The Ortiz Mountains and Cerrillos Hills were formed from laccolithic masses of monzonitic rock intruded into sedimentary rocks, chiefly shale, of Cretaceous age (Lindgren, in Lindgren and others, 1910, p. 164–170). The monzonite is laced with numerous small veins, some of which cut across the contact into the surrounding shales. Rich shoots containing free gold were found in the oxidized zone, and below it the gold is probably contained in the sulfides, which include pyrite, chalcopyrite, sphalerite, silver-bearing galena, some arsenopyrite, and locally molybdenite. The veins also contain specularite and magnetite. Gangue minerals are quartz and calcite. The contact-metamorphic ores are found in garnetized limestone which contains grains of gold-bearing chalcopyrite.

SIERRA COUNTY

Located in the southwestern part of the State, Sierra County contains many mining districts, which in earlier years made the county one of the foremost mining centers in New Mexico. Gold has been produced from numerous districts, but only the Hillsboro district has yielded more than 10,000 ounces. Total gold production of the county through 1959 was about 183,900 ounces.

HILLSBORO DISTRICT

The Hillsboro (Las Animas) district is about 25 miles southwest of Truth Or Consequences. Both lodes and placers were discovered in 1877 and were worked intensively from 1884 through 1905 (Harley, 1934, p. 139–140). Mining was resumed from 1931 through 1942, but was spasmodic from the end of World War II through 1959. Harley (1934, p. 140–141) estimated gold production from 1877 through 1931 at $2,200,000 (106,400 ounces) from placers and $4,700,000 worth of combined metals from lode mines. Total gold production through 1959 was probably about 149,000 ounces, roughly two-thirds of which was from placers.

The gold placer deposits of the district cover an area of about 18 square miles of dissected alluvial fans east of the Animas Hills, about 6 miles northeast of the town of Hillsboro (Harley, 1934, p. 125, 137–138, 166–169). The most productive deposits were the Luxemburg placers at the apex of the fan now drained by Grayback, Hunkidori, and Greenhorn Gulches.

The most productive lode mines are in the southwest part of a mineralized area in the Animas Hills, north of the Rio Percha. Bedrock is predominantly extrusive andesite and latite, intruded by two small monzonite masses and related dikes. Drill holes about 1,150 feet deep have penetrated lower Paleozoic limestone beneath the volcanic rocks (Harley, 1934, p. 131). Most of the lode gold has come from quartz veins, 2 to 8 feet wide, that are along dikes of latite in the andesite (Harley, 1934, p. 133–139). The ore minerals are chalcopyrite, bornite, and pyrite, accompanied by gold and silver. Molybdenite is an accessory ore mineral and tetradymite is found locally.

SOCORRO COUNTY

Socorro County, in the west-central part of the State along the Rio Grande, contains a variety of mineral deposits valued mainly for copper, lead, zinc, and, to a lesser extent, gold and silver. In 1921 Catron County was formed from part of Socorro County, and much of the early gold output attributed to Socorro County came from the Mogollon district now in Catron County. Total gold production through 1959, excluding the Mogollon district, was about 32,000 ounces, mostly from the Rosedale district. Though the Magdalena district is the most important camp in the county, its ores are rich in lead and zinc and have yielded less than 4,000 ounces of gold.

ROSEDALE DISTRICT

The Rosedale district is in the northern San Mateo Mountains in the southwest corner of Socorro County, about 25 miles southwest of Magdalena.

Gold was discovered in the district about 1882. Development work was delayed by frequent Indian attacks, but operations began in the 1890's and production was maintained until 1916 (Wells and Wootton, 1940, p. 19). The Rosedale mine, the most productive in the district, was active from 1934 through 1937. No detailed early production figures have been found, but Wells and Wootton (1940, p. 19) reported that the district produced about $500,000 (24,190 ounces) in gold through 1916. There was no placer production. No production was recorded from 1941 through 1959. The total gold production of the district through 1959 was about 27,750 ounces.

The San Mateo Mountains consist of rhyolite, tuffs and breccias (Gordon, in Lindgren and others, 1910, p. 259–260). The veins are in well-defined mineralized shear zones in rhyolite and rhyolite porphyry. Most of the ore is oxidized and consists of free-milling gold in a gangue of bluish-white quartz and small amounts of iron and manganese oxides. Sulfides appear below water level at a depth of about 725 feet. The higher grade ore is said to be associated with manganese oxide (Lasky, 1932, p. 95).

NORTH CAROLINA

North Carolina, which has produced more gold than any of the other Southeastern States, has many gold mines arranged in zones within two physiographic provinces—the Piedmont and the Blue Ridge. Most of the deposits and the most productive mines are in the Piedmont province in Mecklenburg, Rowan, Cabarrus, and Davidson Counties (fig. 20). Deposits in the Blue Ridge province are in Burke and Transylvania Counties.

Much of the bedrock in the gold-producing areas is granite, mica schist, and gneiss and hornblende gneiss of Precambrian, Precambrian(?) and Paleozoic(?) age. All these rocks were intruded by granite, diorite, and monzonite of Paleozoic age (Stuckey and Conrad, 1958, p. 12–26). Also syenite, pyroxenite, and dunite of Paleozoic age form small intrusive masses in both physiographic provinces.

The first information on gold production in North Carolina was the mint returns for the State in 1793, but no information is available as to source (Bryson, 1936, p. 7). The first record of discovery of gold in North Carolina was in 1799, when a 17-pound nugget was found on the Reed plantation in Cabarrus County. This discovery and others on the Reed property stimulated interest in gold mining in the Southeastern States, and by 1825 mining was in full swing. During the period 1829–55, the most productive in the State's history, 393,119 ounces of gold was produced (Broadhurst, 1955, p. 18).

An interesting sidelight, pointing out the importance of North Carolina as a gold producer, was the private coinage of gold by Christian Bechtler and his son, jewelers, who coined gold in $1.00, $2.50, and $5.00 denominations with the consent of the Federal Government (Bryson, 1936, p. 10–11) from 1831 to 1857. No record of gold coined was maintained for these 26 years; therefore, total gold production for the pre-Civil War years is very difficult to estimate.

The first production in North Carolina was from placers and saprolite; by 1850 several important lode mines were opened, namely the Reed, Gold Hill, Kings Mountain, Rudisil, Conrad Hill, and Phoenix. These mines were closed during the Civil War, but most of them were reactivated after the war. The periods that stand out as especially productive in the post-Civil War history of North Carolina are 1882–91, 1902–6, and 1912–15 (Bryson, 1936, p. 12). From 1954 through 1960 a few thousand ounces of gold was produced from the Ore Knob mine in Ashe County and the Hammee mine in Vance County as a byproduct in the mining of copper and tungsten.

Total gold production of North Carolina from 1799 through 1960 is estimated at 1,168,000 ounces.

BURKE COUNTY

In Burke County the Mills property (Brindletown placers), 13 miles southwest of Morganton in the South Mountain region, was worked as early as 1828, and by 1916, this property had produced an estimated $1 million (50,000 ounces) in gold (Pardee and Park, 1948, p. 65). A few small quartz veins were worked for a time, but the placers were the more productive. The only activity in this area in recent years was an unsuccessful attempt in 1953–54 to mine placer monazite with byproduct gold on the upper part of the First Broad River about 8 miles southeast of Brindletown at the southern end of Richland Mountain. Apparently little, if any, gold was produced (W. C. Overstreet, written commun., 1962).

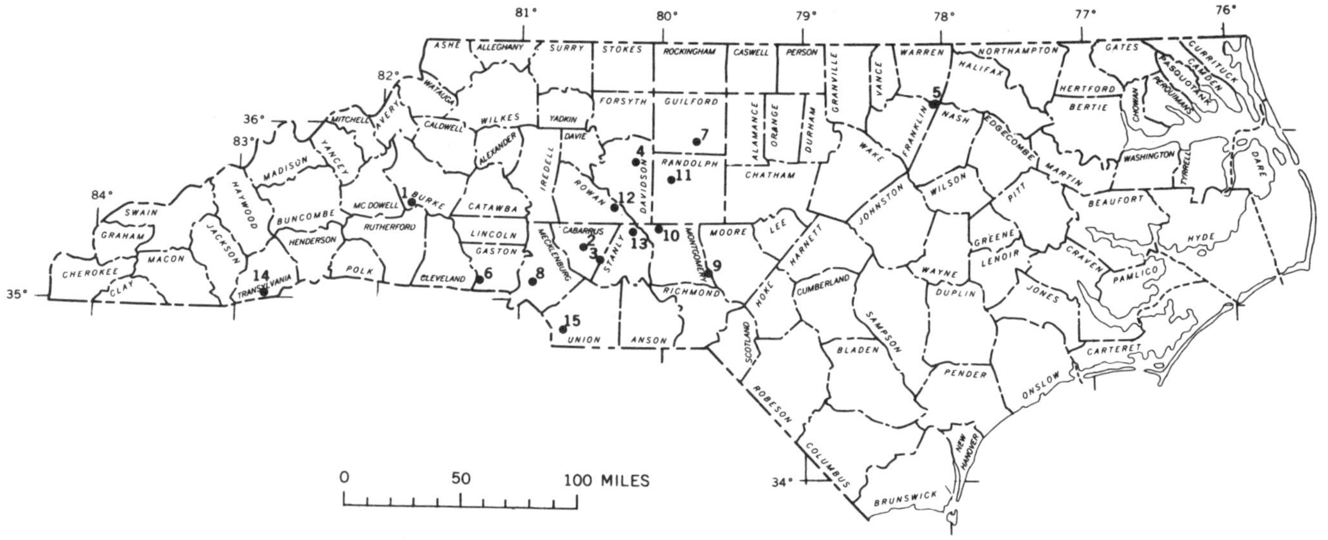

FIGURE 20.—Gold-mining localities of North Carolina. 1, Mills property; 2, Phoenix mine; 3, Reed mine; 4, Cid district; 5, Portis placers; 6, Kings Mountain mine; 7, Gardner Hill, Lindsey, North States, Jacks Hill mines; 8, Rudisil and St. Catherine mines; 9, Iola and Uwarra mines; 10, Russell and Steel mines; 11, Hoover Hill mine; 12, Gold Hill district; 13, Parker mine; 14, Fairfield Valley placers; 15, Howie mine.

The South Mountains are composed of mica and hornblende schists and gneisses, which are locally garnetiferous, and are cut by dikes of granite, pegmatite, diorite, and gabbro (Bryson, 1936, p. 133–134). Weathering has progressed to great depths, and most of the outcrops are saprolite. The schists and gneisses are cut by small quartz veins consisting of milky quartz and decomposed sulfides and small amounts of gold.

CABARRUS COUNTY

PHOENIX MINE

In Cabarrus County, the Phoenix mine, 6 miles southeast of the town of Concord, was discovered some time before 1856 and was worked for short intervals until 1906 (Pardee and Park, 1948, p. 67). There is no record of more recent activity. The total gold production was about $400,000 (about 19,400 ounces).

Although the mine is in a mass of diabase, Nitze and Hanna (1896, p. 121) and Bryson (1936, p. 89) considered the country rock near the mine to be schist, but Pardee and Park (1948, p. 67) considered it to be fine-grained diorite, partly altered to epidote-chlorite schist. The principal vein of the deposit is the Phoenix, a quartz vein ranging in thickness from about 1 to 4 feet and containing pyrite, chalcopyrite, gold, and galena in a gangue of quartz, barite, and calcite-ankerite-siderite.

REED MINE

The Reed (Reid) mine is 2½ miles south of the town of Georgeville in Cabarrus County.

This mine was the site of the first authenticated discovery of gold in North Carolina. In 1799, Conrad Reed, a 12-year-old boy, found a nugget of gold weighing 17 pounds in the gravels of a creek on his father's plantation (Bryson, 1936, p. 7–8). Between 1803 and 1835 additional nuggets, weighing an aggregate 115 pounds, were found on the property. In 1831 lode deposits were discovered and were worked profitably for a few years, but for a long time the mine was idle pending the settlement of the Reed Estate. There were brief periods of activity in the 1880's and 1890's; the most recent work in the area consisted of some small-scale placer operations in the mid-1930's. Production of the mines is estimated at somewhat in excess of $1 million (about 50,000 ounces) in gold (Pardee and Park, 1948, p. 69).

Country rock in the vicinity of the mine is chiefly fine-grained volcanic tuff which is intruded by a greenstone sill (Pardee and Park, 1948, p. 70). The volcanic rocks are Paleozoic(?) in age and are part of the Carolina slate belt sequence (Stuckey, 1958). The fresh bedrock is covered with a thick mantle of saprolite which locally has yielded gold. The lodes are in the greenstone sill, which is interlaced with gold-bearing quartz fissure veins.

DAVIDSON COUNTY

The Cid district is an area of about 125 square miles in southern Davidson County that extends from the Yadkin River on the southwest to about a mile beyond the village of Cid on the northeast.

The earliest record of activity in this district is in 1832 at which time the Conrad Hill mine was already producing (Pardee and Park, 1948, p. 72). The Silver Hill mine began operation a few years later. Other important mines in the district were the Cid and the Emmons. Except for the Civil War period when the mines were closed, most of the activity of the Cid district occurred before 1885 (Pogue, 1910, p. 96). The last brief flurry was in 1906–7 (Pardee and Park, 1948, p. 73). In 1959 the mines were inaccessible and the buildings were in ruins.

Production for this district is difficult to determine because of fragmentary early records. Pardee and Park (1948, p. 72–73) estimated the total yield to be $75,000 to $250,000 in gold from the Conrad Hill mine and $1 million or more in lead, silver, zinc, and a little gold from the Silver Hill mine. Total gold production from all mines probably did not exceed 20,000 ounces.

Bedrock in the Cid district was described by Pogue (1910, p. 26–38). In general it consists of bands of volcanic rocks—tuff, breccia, dacite, rhyolite—that trend northeast to north and have been metamorphosed to slates and schists, compressed into large folds, and intruded by dikes of gabbro and diabase. The ore deposits at the Conrad Hill mine are quartz-chalcopyrite-ankerite veins oxidized to depths of 50 feet. The veins of the Silver Hill mine contain argentiferous cerussite extending from the surface to a depth of 60 feet, and below 60 feet they consist of manganese oxide, galena, and sphalerite (Pardee and Park, 1948, p. 73).

FRANKLIN COUNTY

In Franklin County the only important gold production has come from the Portis placers in the northeast corner of the county, just east of the Wood Post Office.

From 1840 to 1935, placer mining was sporadic in this area. Both alluvial placers and saprolite deposits were worked, but scarcity of water for hydraulic mining was a great obstacle to any large-scale operations (Nitze and Hanna, 1896, p. 26). Total gold production is unknown, but estimates of value range from several hundred thousand to more than one million dollars (Pardee and Park, 1948, p. 73).

Bedrock is mostly sericite schist and a schistose diorite weathered at the surface to a thick layer of saprolite. These rocks are intruded by several dikes and sills of a granitic rock which, where decomposed, consists of a mixture of quartz and kaolin, known locally as the "white belt." Gold was released and concentrated by the weathering of quartz veinlets that crisscross the "white belt" (Pardee and Park, 1948, p. 74).

GASTON AND CLEVELAND COUNTIES

The Kings Mountain mine is about 2 miles south of the town of Kings Mountain, near the Gaston-Cleveland County line.

The lode deposit at Kings Mountain was worked intermittently from 1834 to about 1895 and produced an estimated $750,000 to $1 million in gold (Keith and Sterrett, 1931, p. 8). Most of the gold came from quartz veins, but some came from placers in the streams below the mine and some came from saprolite.

The ore deposits are found in a belt of chloritic mica schist within which are enclosed layers of dolomitic marble and graphite schist. Bordering the chloritic mica schist on the northwest is a layer of black sericite schist. The rocks occur in various stages of metamorphism, are intruded on the southeast by gneissic granite, and are much faulted (W. C. Overstreet, written commun., 1962). Also, the rocks are compressed into a series of northeast-trending folds whose limbs dip at high angles. The ore deposits are in veins in the dolomitic marble. The veins are predominantly siliceous dolomite, quartz, and pyrite and carry small amounts of pyrrhotite, fluorite, tetrahedrite, galena, sphalerite, chalcopyrite, and gold.

GUILFORD COUNTY

Most of the gold production of Guilford County came from the Gardner Hill, Lindsay, North States, and Jacks Hill mines, which are grouped in the southern part of the county, 8 to 12 miles southwest of Greensboro.

The mines were opened in the early 1850's, but by 1860 most of them were closed, and after a brief revival in the 1880's, they remained closed. No production records were found for the mines, but the value of their output was estimated to be $225,000 including an undetermined amount in copper (Pardee and Park, 1948, p. 75–76).

Granite is the bedrock in this area. The gold, which was associated with the sulfides, was deposited in quartz veins containing pyrite, chalcopyrite, and siderite. At depth these veins were rich in copper, which became the principal commodity as mining progressed (Pardee and Park, 1948, p. 75–76).

MECKLENBURG COUNTY

The St. Catherine and Rudisil mines, the principal gold producers in Mecklenburg County, are in the city of Charlotte about half a mile apart on opposite ends of the same vein.

The St. Catherine mine was opened in 1826. Its early history is obscure, and after the Civil War it was worked by the operators of the Rudisil mine (Pardee and Park, 1948, p. 80).

The Rudisil mine, discovered in 1829, produced $30,000 in gold during 1 month in 1830; thereafter, ownership of the property changed several times. The mine operated from 1840 until the outbreak of the Civil War, from 1880 to 1887, and from 1905 to 1908 (Pardee and Park, 1948, p. 78). In 1934 the mine was dewatered, reopened, and was productive through 1937. It was idle again from 1937 through 1959. Total gold production from these two mines was probably not less than 60,000 ounces.

The country rock at the Rudisil mine is granite and schist (Pardee and Park, 1948, p. 79). The ore is in pockets in two quartz veins known as the "back vein" and the "front vein" (Bryson, 1936, p. 111). These veins follow approximately the granite-schist contact and are cut by several diabase dikes. The ore bodies consist chiefly of intensely fractured pyrite and quartz and are located at places where the veins flatten (Pardee and Park, 1948, p. 79).

MONTGOMERY COUNTY

The Iola and Uwarra mines, in eastern Montgomery County 2 miles west of the town of Candor, exploited the same vein. They were discovered in 1900 and are among the more recent gold discoveries in the Piedmont. By 1915, the Iola had produced $900,000 (about 45,000 ounces) and the Uwarra, $100,000 (about 5,000 ounces) in gold (Pardee and Park, 1948, p. 82). Operations were suspended in 1916, and the properties remained idle through 1959.

Ore deposits are along the contact of the Cretaceous Coastal Plain sediments with the metamorphosed tuffs, flows, and breccias of the Paleozoic(?) volcanic rocks of the Carolina slate belt (Stuckey, 1958). The deposits are in narrow veins, in siliceous pyritic zones in schist, and in groups of stringer veins (Hafer, 1914, p. 27). Most of the ore came from the Iola vein, which was worked for 2,000 feet along its strike. The ore contained very few sulfides and was free milling.

RUSSELL AND STEEL MINES

The Russell and Steel mines are in northwestern Montgomery County along the Uwharrie River, 2 to 3 miles west of Ophir.

The early history of these two lode mines is obscure. Gold was discovered at the Steel mine about 1832, but no information concerning time of its discovery at the Russell site could be found (Pardee and Park, 1948, p. 83). Both mines have been idle for a long time; the buildings were in ruins and the workings were inaccessible at the time they were visited by Pardee and Park before 1948. Production data are fragmentary and are based on estimates. Total production of the Russell mine is estimated at about $300,000 (about 15,000 ounces) in gold. Production data of the Steel mines is available only for 1887, when $150,000 (about 7,500 ounces) in gold was produced (Pardee and Park, 1948, p. 83).

According to Nitze and Hanna (1896, p. 74, 77) country rock in the vicinity of the mines is argillaceous slate, but according to Pardee and Park (1948, p. 83, 84) it is silicified schist. At the Russell mine the ore occurs in silicified and pyritized zones in the country rock; at least six such zones have been worked successfully by open cuts. At the Steel mine ore consists of thin seams of free gold, galena, sphalerite, chalcopyrite, and pyrite (Nitze and Hanna, 1896, p. 77). These seams are conformable with the slaty cleavage or schistosity.

RANDOLPH COUNTY

The Hoover Hill mine, the principal gold producer in Randolph County, is about 12 miles west-northwest of Asheboro, on the east side of the Uwharrie River. The lode deposit was discovered in 1848 and was worked for several years by lessees, a practice which inhibited its efficient development. In 1881, the Hoover Hill Gold Mining Co., Ltd., of London, England, gained control of the mine, and in the following 14 years a total of $300,000 in gold was extracted (Pardee and Park, 1948, p. 86). The mine was inactive from 1895 to 1914. Small-scale activity was reported in 1914 and again in 1917, after which the property was closed and remained so through 1959. Total gold production was about $350,000 (about 17,000 ounces).

The deposit is in a dark-gray rhyolite and flow breccia of Paleozoic(?) age in the sequence of sedimentary and pyroclastic rocks in the slate belt (Pardee and Park, 1948, p. 16, 85). The ore bodies occur in sheared northeastward-trending zones interlaced with quartz seams which contain free gold and a very small amount of sulfide. The ore is free milling (Pardee and Park, 1948, p. 86).

ROWAN COUNTY

GOLD HILL DISTRICT

The Gold Hill district is a strip about 18 miles long and 8 miles wide in southeastern Rowan

County and northeastern Cabarrus County and extends from the Yadkin River on the north to near the town of Mount Pleasant on the south. The settlement of Gold Hill is near the center of the district.

The search for gold in this part of North Carolina was stimulated by the discoveries of the large nuggets on the Reed plantation in 1799. Gold was first found in the Gold Hill district at the Barringer mine before 1824, and by 1842 the principal veins of the district had been located (Laney, 1910, p. 78). The district developed fairly rapidly and produced an estimated $3 million in gold before the Civil War (Laney, 1910, p. 79). The mines were reopened after the war and were active until they were closed in 1915. The principal mines of the district were the Randolph, Barnhardt and Old Field, the Honeycutt, the Troutman, the Union Copper, and the Whitney. Their combined production was about $3,300,000 or about 160,000 ounces, in gold (Pardee and Park, 1948, p. 89). The shaft of the Randolph mine was 820 feet deep and was one of the deepest in the Piedmont (Laney, 1910, p. 98).

The Gold Hill district is underlain by two general types of bedrock: (1) rocks of the volcanic series consisting of slates, tuffs, breccias, and flows and (2) intrusive greenstone, granite, and diorite (Laney, 1910, p. 115–118). These are separated by a fault, known as the Gold Hill fault; the greenstone, granite, and diorite occur in the northwest half of the district and the volcanic rocks, in the southeast half. The volcanic rocks have been tightly folded near their contact with the intrusives. Of intrusive rocks, the granite is the youngest, the greenstone, the oldest. Most of the veins of the district are in volcanic rocks in a zone of minor faulting just southeast of the Gold Hill fault. Veins are of two types: quartz veins in extensively silicified wallrock, and stringers of ore minerals along foliation planes in schistose volcanic rocks. The quartz veins and the adjacent silicified wallrock contain the important gold deposits of the district. The stringers contain copper and small amounts of gold. The ore minerals common to both types of veins are auriferous pyrite, chalcopyrite, galena, and sphalerite.

STANLY COUNTY

PARKER MINE

The Parker mine, located at the town of New London in northern Stanly County, was one of the first mines to be worked in North Carolina and was very productive in the years before the Civil War. Most of the gold was mined from colluvial placers, although veins were worked in later years. In the 1890's considerable underground exploration was done with favorable results, but apparently there was no sustained production (Pardee and Park, 1948, p. 94). In 1935, there was brief activity at the Parker mine when a rich pocket in a quartz vein yielded several hundred ounces of gold (Pardee and Park, 1948, p. 94). The property was inactive from 1935 through 1959. Total gold production from the Parker mine was somewhat in excess of the 10,000 ounces estimated from the early placer operations (Pardee and Park, 1948, p. 93).

The country rock near the mine consists of argillaceous, sericitic, and chloritic slates and schists of volcanic origin, which are typical of sequences observed elsewhere in the slate belt (Bryson, 1936, p. 64–79). The country rock is intruded by dikes and sills of greenstone porphyry and other basic intrusives. The lode deposits consist of groups of quartz stringers that interlace the country rock in many directions. The placers were derived from the deep saprolite that blankets most of the area. Gold was mechanically concentrated in colluvial deposits wherein the upper part of the saprolite moved downhill in response to frost action and gravity. These placers were worked by hydraulic methods.

TRANSYLVANIA COUNTY

FAIRFIELD VALLEY PLACERS

The Fairfield Valley placers are in southern Transylvania County between lat 35°03′ and 35°08′ N. and long 82°50′ and 83°00′ W., in the northern drainage area of the Toxaway River.

This area has been only briefly discussed in the published literature. Most of the production was in the 1800's; deposits have been idle for many years.

According to Nitze and Hanna (1896, p. 191–192), the gravels along Georgetown Creek, one of the tributaries of the Toxaway, yielded between $200,000 and $300,000 in gold (about 10,000 to 15,000 ounces). They reported that considerable reserves of auriferous gravels remained in the area.

UNION COUNTY

HOWIE MINE

The Howie mine, which is 3 miles northwest of Waxhaw, was the largest in Union County. It was developed some time before 1840 as a consequence of placer mining in the vicinity. The lodes were quickly exploited, yielding an estimated $250,000 in 1854 (Pardee and Park, 1948, p. 98). After a period of idleness brought on by the Civil War, the mine was again opened in 1885 and remained active on a small scale at intervals until 1934. No activity was reported from 1934 through 1959. Estimated production of the mine was about 50,000 ounces of gold (Pardee and Park, 1948, p. 98).

The deposit is in a fine-grained sericite schist, which has the texture of a fine-grained tuff and is part of the sequence of rocks in the slate belt (Pardee and Park, 1948, p. 16; Bryson, 1936, p. 64). These rocks strike northeast and dip steeply northwest. They are cut by many diabase dikes. The upper 50 feet or more of bedrock is weathered to saprolite in which original textures and structures have been preserved. The ore bodies are concentrations of gold-bearing stringers in schist that has been impregnated with fine-grained quartz, pyrite, pyrrhotite, and a little gold (Pardee and Park, 1948, p. 98). This zone is conformable in general with the schistosity of the country rock.

OREGON

Oregon had been rather heavily traversed by settlers on their way to the more populous coastal communities long before gold was discovered in the State. Fear of hostile Indians no doubt discouraged many from prospecting the promising-looking mountain ranges and stream channels at any distance from the main immigration routes. It was not until 1852 that gold placers were worked at Rich Gulch in Jackson County and Josephine Creek in Josephine County (Raymond, 1870, p. 214, 217). The more widely publicized discoveries of placer gold at Griffin Gulch in Baker County in 1861 (Wagner, 1959, p. 21) and at John Day and Canyon Creek in Grant County slightly later (Rand, 1959, p. 44) triggered an avalanche of prospectors and miners of sufficient magnitude to eventually establish the gold mining industry in the State (fig. 21). Other early placer operations were in the Willow Creek country in Malheur County, where several districts were organized (Browne, 1868, p. 591).

After the initial period of high production during which the richer placers were exhausted, discoveries of auriferous quartz veins helped stabilize the mining economy. Lode mining began as early as 1859 on the Gold Hill vein in Jackson County (Raymond, 1870, p. 214–232); gold-bearing quartz veins were also worked in the 1860's in the Canyon Creek district, the Eagle Creek district, the Mormon Basin district, and the Baker district.

The first boom in Oregon expired about 1870, but it had been strong enough to attract people with diversified talents so that other industries such as farming and cattle raising cushioned the shock. In addition, the gold rush was responsible for the early entry of railroads into the State, and this hastened the growth of cities and provided a more stable economy.

Although mining of gold in Oregon was at an alltime low in 1965 (fig. 22), mining of nickel, uranium, mercury, and a host of nonmetals was flourishing as one of the important industries in the State.

Total production of gold in Oregon from 1852 through 1965 was 5,796,680 ounces. This total includes estimates of Lindgren (1901, p. 569–571) for production before 1900 and data from the U.S. Geological Survey (1904–24) and the U.S. Bureau of Mines (1925–66) for the years 1902–65. Production data for districts are fragmentary, especially where production of several districts was combined in the reports, thus the totals for districts are minima.

BAKER COUNTY

Gold was first discovered in eastern Oregon in 1861 in Griffin Gulch in the Baker district, Baker County. The town of Auburn was soon established as the first settlement and base for exploration. By about 1870 the richest placers were exhausted, but quartz lodes were discovered and developed, although slowly, and by 1900 were substantially productive in the Cracker Creek, Cornucopia, and Sumpter districts. As placer production decreased, Auburn declined, and Baker became the most important town in the county.

Production data for Baker County before 1880 were not found. From 1880 to 1899, the county produced $8,958,073 (about 434,850 ounces) in gold (Lindgren, 1901, p. 573). From 1904 through 1957, it produced 747,548 ounces of lode gold, 402,490 ounces of placer gold, and 11,626 ounces unidentified as to source. Total recorded gold production through 1959 was about 1,596,500 ounces; from 1954 through 1959 only a few hundred ounces was produced.

Placer mining revived after 1912, and after World War II it was more productive than lode mining. Most of the county's gold production in recent years was from the Sumpter district placer mines, which were closed in 1955.

Lode deposits of Baker County generally are fissure veins that are related to intrusions of granitic, dioritic, and gabbroic rocks (Lindgren, 1901, p. 614). The deposits most commonly are found near contacts of these intrusive rocks with sedimentary or metasedimentary rocks.

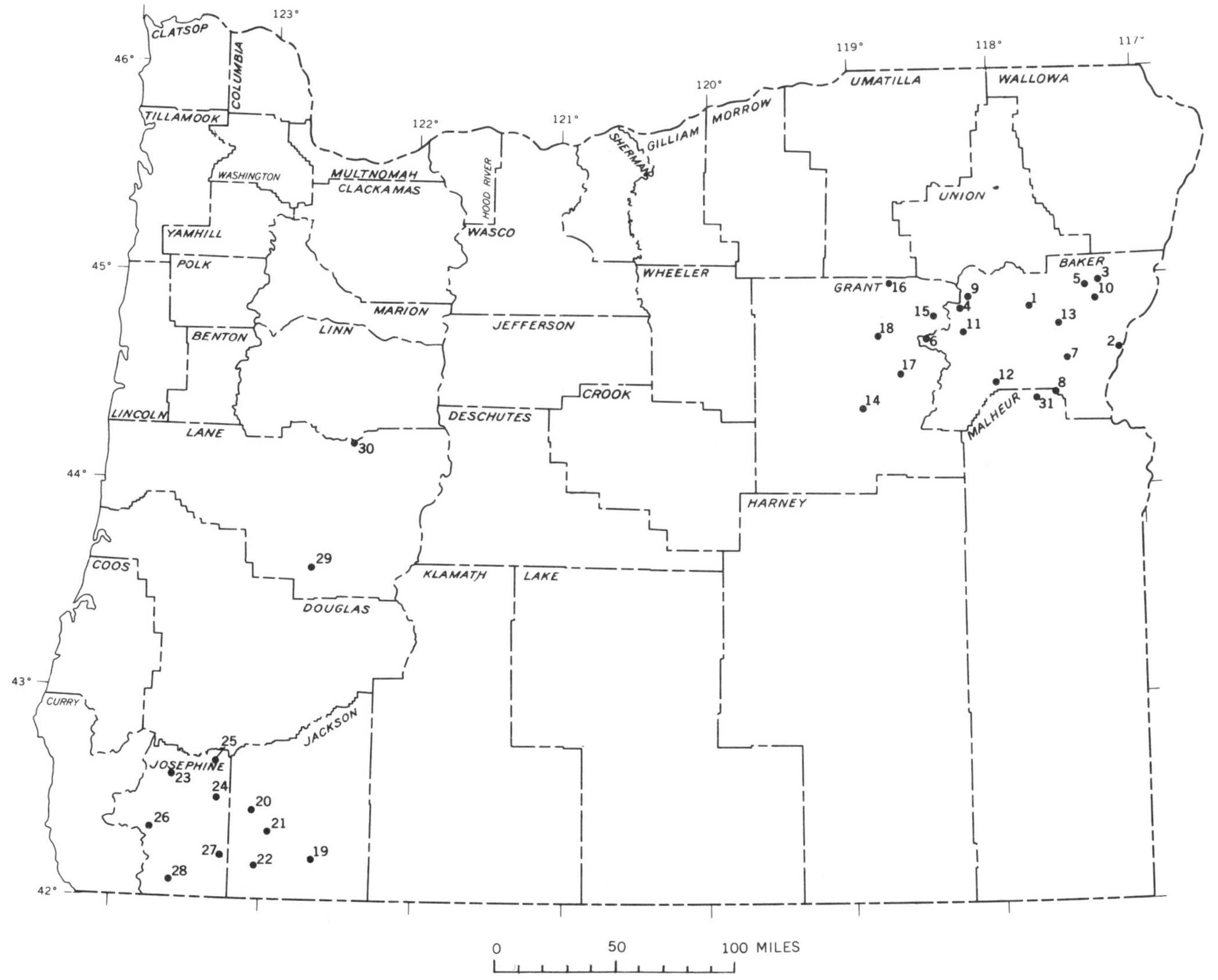

FIGURE 21.—Gold-mining districts of Oregon.

Baker County:
1, Baker; 2, Connor Creek; 3, Cornucopia; 4, Cracker Creek; 5, Eagle Creek; 6, Greenhorn; 7, Lower Burnt River valley; 8, Mormon Basin; 9, Rock Creek; 10, Sparta; 11, Sumpter; 12, Upper Burnt River; 13, Virtue.

Grant County:
14, Canyon Creek; 15, Granite; 16, North Fork; 17, Quartzburg; 18, Susanville.

Jackson County:
19, Ashland; 20, Gold Hill; 21, Jacksonville; 22, Upper Applegate.

Josephine County:
23, Galice; 24, Grants Pass; 25, Greenback; 26, Illinois River; 27, Lower Applegate; 28, Waldo.

Lane County:
29, Bohemia; 30, Blue River.

Malheur County:
31, Malheur.

BAKER DISTRICT

Production in the Baker district has been chiefly from the placers in Griffin Gulch but this was in the early years and was unrecorded. After 1900 more than half of the gold produced in the district came from lode mines. Production of gold from 1906 through 1959 was 19,825 ounces from lode mines, 10,890 ounces from placers, and 5,437 ounces undifferentiated—a total of 36,152 ounces.

The oldest rocks of the district are greenstone, phyllite, quartz schist, and limestone composing the Burnt River Schist of probable pre-Carboniferous age (Gilluly, 1937, p. 9–13) and the Elkhorn Ridge Argillite, composed of argillite, tuff, lava, chert, and

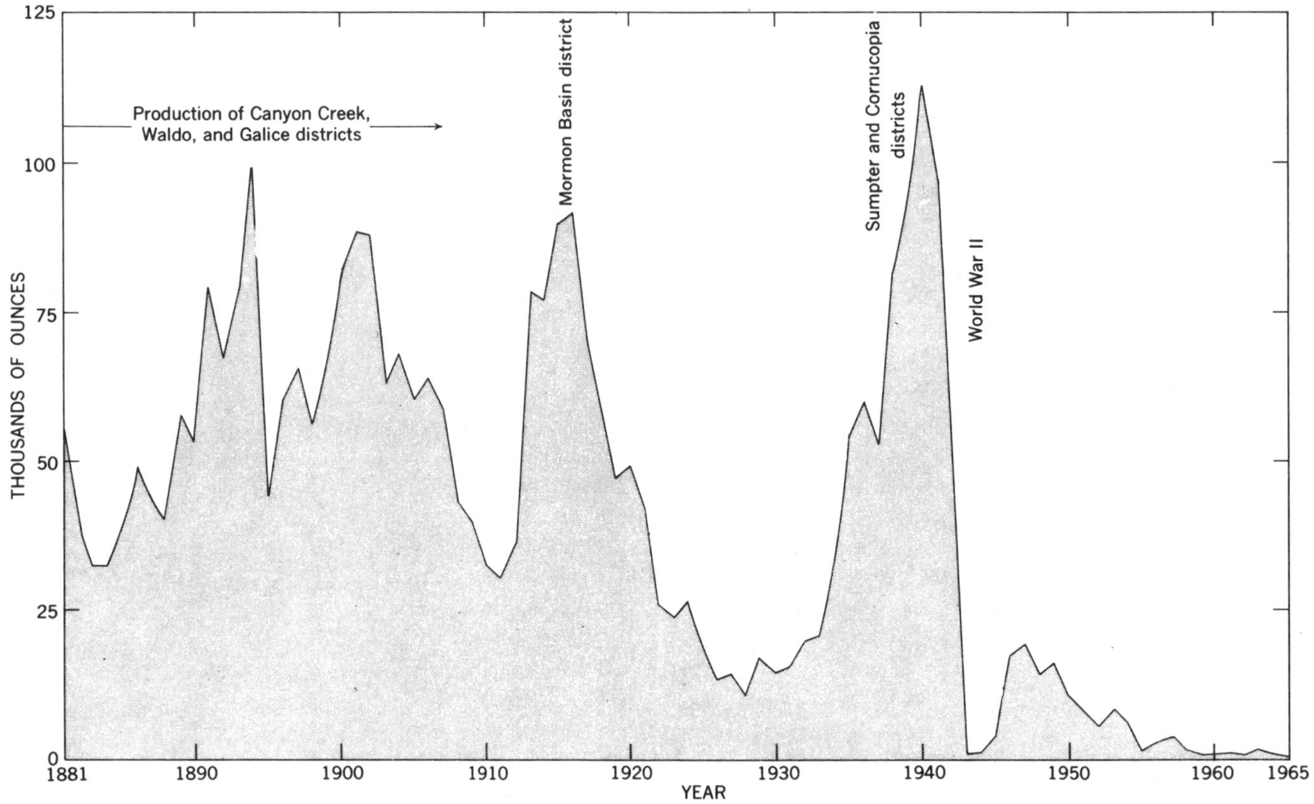

FIGURE 22.—Annual gold production of Oregon, 1881–1965. Sources of data: 1881–1923 from U.S. Geological Survey (1883–1924); 1924–65 from U.S. Bureau of Mines (1925–34, 1933–66). Production reported in dollar value was converted to ounces at the prevailing price per ounce.

greenstone, of Permian and Triassic age (Bostwick and Koch, 1962). An unconformity separates these rocks from the superjacent Tertiary andesite and basalt flows. The pre-Tertiary rocks are thrown into strong folds that strike west, but the Tertiary rocks are only gently warped (Gilluly, 1937, p. 8).

The lode deposits are fissure and replacement veins in the pre-Tertiary rocks (Gilluly, 1937, p. 92). Gold, pyrite, chalcopyrite, sphalerite, and locally stibnite and galena occur in a gangue of quartz, sericite, carbonate, and a little clay and scheelite.

Placers have been worked in nearly all the gulches on the south end of Elkhorn Ridge, on Marble Creek, and on Salmon Creek. The most important placers were in Blue Canyon near Auburn, where some of the early discoveries were made.

CONNOR CREEK DISTRICT

The Connor Creek district is along the west drainage of the Snake River between lat 44°21′ and 44°44′ N. and long 117°03′ and 117°18′ W.

Placer mining began in this district in the 1860's along Connor Creek, and in 1871 lode gold was discovered at Connor Creek mine. After an estimated maximum production of $2 million in gold (Lindgren, 1901, p. 757), the mine was closed in 1910 and was reopened only briefly in 1915–18 (Gilluly and others, 1933, p. 50). Small amounts of placer gold were produced from the district until 1942. From that time through 1959 there was virtually no production. The district produced about 97,000 ounces of lode gold and about 6,100 ounces of placer gold through 1959.

The following summary of the geology of the district is from Gilluly, Reed, and Park (1933, p. 50).

The country rock is dominantly black carbonaceous slate and quartz phyllite and contains small amounts of greenstone, chlorite schist, and limestone. These rocks are of possible Triassic and Jurassic age. The beds dip steeply to the northwest and strike N. 20°–45° E. Granitic rocks have intruded the metasediments west of the district. The gold deposits are in northwest-trending quartz veins that dip steeply southwest. Free gold occurs in the Connor mine with some argentite and pyrite.

CORNUCOPIA DISTRICT

The Cornucopia district, between lat 44°57′ and 45°05′ N. and long 117°00′ and 117°15′ W., reported very little activity until 1880–85 (Lindgren, 1901, p. 742). Its gold production to 1903 was valued at $1,008,000 (Oregon Department of Geology and Mineral Industries, 1939, p. 25). Production was fairly steady from 1903 through 1941, but it was only a few ounces from 1942 through 1959. Recorded production from 1907 through 1959 was 255,698 ounces of lode gold, 2,441 ounces of placer gold, and 5,800 ounces undifferentiated as to origin.

The oldest rocks in the area are metavolcanics and clastics of the Clover Creek Greenstone, of Permian age (Ross, 1938, p. 21). Other metasedimentary rocks that overlie the Clover Creek Greenstone have obscure stratigraphic relations with one another and are classed as Carboniferous and Triassic. Overlying the Paleozoic rocks are the Martin Bridge Formation and a thick section of younger sediments, all of Late Triassic age. At the close of the Jurassic the rocks were folded and metamorphosed, and in mid-Cretaceous time a granodiorite batholith intruded the series (T. P. Thayer, written commun., 1962). During the closing stages of this igneous activity, the veins were formed, uplift and dissection followed, then the basalt flows of the Columbia River Basalt were poured out on this erosion surface.

The veins occupy shear zones in both the metamorphic and granitic rocks. The larger veins strike N. 40° E. and dip 40° W.; many are offset en echelon. Vein minerals consist of pyrite, sphalerite, chalcopyrite, galena, tetrahedrite, tellurides, and native gold, with quartz as gangue (Goodspeed, 1941, p. 185). Successive stages of microbrecciation and turbid quartz are not noticeable features of these veins.

CRACKER CREEK DISTRICT

The Cracker Creek district is between lat 44°48′ and 44°54′ N. and long 118°03′ and 118°17′ W., north of Sumpter.

The most important lode in this district and in Oregon, the North Pole-Columbia, was discovered in 1887, and it produced about $9 million in gold (Oregon Dept. Geology and Mineral Industries, 1939, p. 34). From 1907 through 1959 a total of 189,389 ounces of gold was recorded from the district.

The country rock in the district is the Elkhorn Ridge Argillite, which probably is of Permian and Late Triassic age. Cutting this argillite is the North Pole-Columbia lode, a vein system that trends northwest to east and continues unbroken for a distance of 5 miles (Lindgren, 1901, p. 658). The vein material consists of quartz, arsenopyrite, pyrite, and some chalcopyrite. Most of the gold occurs in the fine arsenopyrite (Parks and Swartley, 1916, p. 61). Comb structure is common, and some of the earlier minerals are crushed and shattered indicating some movement along the fissure system during deposition.

EAGLE CREEK DISTRICT

The Eagle Creek district is between lat 44°49′ and 45°05′ N. and long 117°00′ and 117°45′ W., in the southern end of the Wallowa Mountains. The boundaries of this district overlap those of the Cornucopia district, and rightly so, for the gold-bearing gravels of the Eagle Creek district were derived from the Cornucopia stock.

Mining began in this district in the early 1860's when placers along Eagle Creek were worked. Those along Paddy Creek were worked also, but most of the gold production was from lodes and some was a byproduct of copper ore. The Sanger mine, the largest producer in the district, yielded an estimated $1½ million in gold from auriferous quartz veins (Lindgren, 1901, p. 738). The total early production of the district was estimated at $1,687,400 (about 82,000 ounces) in gold (Lindgren, 1901, p. 738–739). Total recorded production from 1931 through 1951 was 5,782 ounces of lode gold and 69 ounces of placer gold; from 1952 through 1959, no production was recorded.

The country rock of the area is chiefly Triassic greenstone and limestone cut by granitic and diabasic dikes (Gilluly and others, 1933, p. 63). The veins contain pyrite, chalcopyrite, sphalerite, galena, and free gold in a gangue of quartz and some calcite.

GREENHORN DISTRICT

The Greenhorn district is between lat 44°33′ and 44°44′ N. and long 118°25′ and 118°32′ W. in Baker and Grant Counties.

Both silver and gold veins were mined in the district before 1910. The Bonanza, the chief mine, produced $1¾ million in gold before 1904; it operated only sporadically from 1904 through 1916 (Parks and Swartley, 1916, p. 39). After 1930 the bulk of production was from placers. The total gold production of the district through 1959 was 89,200 ounces from lodes and 10,382 ounces from placers.

The following summary of the geology of the district is taken from "Oregon Metal Mines Handbook" (Oregon Department of Geology and Mineral Industries, 1939, p. 52–53). The district, which is on the eastern lower slopes of Vinegar Hill, is underlain by greenstone, argillite, serpentine, and granodiorite, and is surrounded by younger lava flows of Tertiary age. The granodiorite was intruded into the greenstone and argillite, and the ore deposits probably were emplaced during the closing stages of the intrusion. The deposits in the Bonanza mine and its vicinity are in argillite; those near the town of Greenhorn are in greenstone. The ores contain mostly gold and silver, but varying amounts of copper and lead are locally present.

Placers near Winterville, Parkerville, and McNamee Gulch were successfully worked. The value of boulders of silicified *Tempskya* (Cretaceous) "fern wood" in Eocene(?) gravels exceeded the value of the gold (T. P. Thayer, written commun., 1962).

LOWER BURNT RIVER VALLEY DISTRICT

The Lower Burnt River valley district, which includes Weatherby, Gold Hill, Durkee, Chicken Creek, and Pleasant Valley, is between lat 44°17′ and 44°43′ N. and long 117°10′ and 117°41′ W., along Burnt River in southern Baker County.

The lode mines in this district were worked in the early 1880's, and the placers probably were worked earlier. Small production from the Weatherby area was maintained until 1955; however, most of the production was in early days, when no accurate records were kept. Some of the major lode mines were the Gold Ridge, Gleason, Little Bonanza, and Little Hill. Estimates of early lode production total $928,000 in gold (about 45,000 ounces) (Lindgren, 1901, p. 765; Oregon Department of Geology and Mineral Industries, 1939, p. 67–71). Total production for the district through 1959 was at least 50,000 ounces of lode gold and 3,500 ounces of placer gold. Production data for placers are reliable only for the period since 1932.

Slates, schists, and limestones of possible Triassic age (Lindgren, 1901, pl. 64) are cut by a mass of granodiorite, diorite, and quartz diorite. The sedimentary rocks strike N. 70°–80° E. and dip steeply to the north (Lindgren, 1901, p. 763). Associated with the intrusive masses are discontinuous small quartz veins that are rich in gold.

Nearly all the gulches and streams that drain into the Burnt River in this district contain auriferous placers.

MORMON BASIN DISTRICT

The Mormon Basin (Dixie Creek, Rye Valley, Malheur) district is between lat 44°22′ and 44°31′ N. and long 117°23′ and 117°40′ W. in southern Baker County and northern Malheur County.

As early as 1863 placers were mined in the Rye Valley area and were credited with a production of $1 million in gold (Swartley, 1914, p. 228). Although quartz veins were known in the district in the early days, their gold production was not significant until after 1900; it was valued at about $2¼ million for the period 1906 to 1916 (Oregon Department of Geology and Mineral Industries, 1939, p. 76). About half of this was from the Rainbow, the largest gold mine in the district, and, from 1913 to 1915, the most productive in the State (Gilluly and others, 1933, p. 38). The district reported only small production from 1915 through 1948, and it was idle from 1949 through 1959. Total gold production through 1959 was about 177,500 ounces from lode mines and 56,200 ounces from placer workings.

Gilluly, Reed, and Park (1933, p. 31–49) discussed in some detail the geology and mines of the Mormon Basin area. The oldest rocks exposed are quartzite, quartz schist, slate, greenstone, and chlorite schist of unknown age. These were intruded by masses of gabbro, dunite, pyroxenite, and harzburgite altered for the most part to greenstone, amphibolite, serpentine, and talc. These igneous rocks have been highly sheared and are foliated. A large mass of quartz diorite makes up Pedro Mountain, a prominent landmark, and there are smaller bodies of this same rock throughout the district. The lower parts of the basin are covered by Tertiary stream deposits interbedded with dacite and andesite flows. The gold deposits are in veins in pre-Tertiary rocks near the quartz diorite masses. Vein minerals are quartz, ankerite, and fuchsite as gangue and pyrite, arsenopyrite, galena, sphalerite, polybasite, hessite, tetrahedrite as ore minerals.

ROCK CREEK DISTRICT

The Rock Creek district is between lat 44°49′ and 45°03′ N. and long 118°00′ and 118°15′ W., 10–15 miles northwest of Baker.

The district, discovered in the late 1880's, was a steady gold producer until 1914, after which activity declined; it was idle in 1959. The principal mine, the Baisley-Elkhorn, produced an estimated $950,000, chiefly in gold (Oregon Department of Geology and Mineral Industries, 1939, p. 85).

Estimated early production of the district was $1 million, mostly in gold (Lindgren, 1901, p. 646). Production from 1934 through 1959 totaled 3,282 ounces of lode gold and 193 ounces of placer gold.

A conservative total for the district would be about 51,000 ounces of gold.

The following is summarized from Lindgren's (1901, p. 645–647) description of the geology of the district. The north end of Elkhorn Ridge is composed of granodiorite, the south part is dominantly argillite, and the Rock Creek district is along the contact between them. Diorite dikes cut the argillite near the contact. Near its borders the intrusive is dioritic, becoming granodioritic toward the interior. Most of the veins are discontinuous but form a zone in the diorite approximately parallel to the argillite-diorite contact. Gangue is quartz with some calcite. Gold occurs in pyrite or as an intergrowth with sphalerite. Other sulfides are galena, chalcopyrite, and locally ruby silver.

SPARTA DISTRICT

The Sparta district is between lat 44°36′ and 44°57′ N. and long 117°02′ and 117°23′ W.

Although placer deposits were known in the area at an early date, it was not until 1873, when the Sparta ditch was completed, that enough water was available to exploit the gravel-filled gulches which yielded about $157,000 in gold before 1900 (Lindgren, 1901, p. 737). Quartz veins were discovered a few years after the discovery of the placers, and from 1889 to 1892 they yielded $677,000 in gold (Lindgren, 1901, p. 736). Shortly thereafter the district declined rapidly, and from 1952 through 1959 it was idle. Total production from the district through 1959 was about 35,200 ounces of lode gold and about 7,700 ounces of placer gold.

The district is underlain by quartz diorite and albite granite of presumable Mesozoic age (Gillully and others, 1933, p. 57–58). These rocks intruded Permian greenstone, only remnants of which remain in the area. Columbia River Basalt unconformably overlies the older rocks. The ore deposits are gold-bearing quartz veins in the diorite and granite. Most of the veins are narrow and cannot be followed for any great distance.

SUMPTER DISTRICT

The Sumpter district, between lat 44°37′ and 44°48′ N. and long 118°00′ and 118°18′ W., is predominantly a placer district, but there has been a small gold production from quartz veins that cut argillite. Placer deposits were discovered here in 1862, and production was almost continuous until 1955.

Records of production before 1932 have not been found, but from 1932 through 1955 the district produced 129,004 ounces of placer gold and 2,206 ounces of lode gold. No production was reported from 1955 through 1959.

Terrace gravels along the Powder River and gravels in its tributary gulches, above the town of Sumpter, contain varying amounts of gold. Damming of the Powder River by lavas of the Columbia River Basalt resulted in thick accumulations of gold-bearing gravels in the Sumpter Valley (Lindgren, 1901, p. 655–656). As the river cut through the barrier, lower terraces were created, and these also were worked extensively.

UPPER BURNT RIVER DISTRICT

The Upper Burnt River district, which includes Bridgeport, Bull Run, Unity, and Hereford, is in southern Baker County, between lat 44°15′ and 44°36′ N. and long 117°35′ and 118°20′ W. It is a large district and includes many localities that have produced small amounts of both placer and lode gold. Early production data are scant, but apparently some placers were worked before 1900. Total gold production through 1959 was about 9,300 ounces from all sources.

According to the Oregon Department of Geology and Mineral Industries (1939, p. 97–98), the eastern part of the district is predominantly argillite and contains some limestone and lava flows, and the western part is covered by more recent flows. Auriferous gravels along the Burnt River have been mined.

VIRTUE DISTRICT

The Virtue district is between lat 44°43′ and 44°57′ N. and long 117°22′ and 117°45′ W.

This is predominantly a lode district; placer operations consisted of small-scale diggings in some of the gulches below the veins. The Virtue mine, discovered in 1862, was one of the largest gold producers in eastern Oregon (Lindgren, 1901, p. 722). Other mines in the district that have produced significant quantities of gold are the Brazos, Flagstaff, Hidden Treasure, and White Swan. The latest production reported from the district was in 1956.

Early production of the district was about $2,500,000 in gold (about 121,000 ounces); about $2,200,000 came from the Virtue mine, which had its best years before 1900 (Gilluly, 1937, p. 73). Yearly production data for the district go back only to 1935. The total for the period 1935 through 1957 was 4,837 ounces from lode mines and 288 ounces from placers. Total gold production for the district through 1959 was about 126,000 ounces.

In the northern part of the district a strongly sheared diorite is the predominant country rock, whereas the southern part is underlain by argillite that strikes east-west (Lindgren, 1901, p. 721–722). Most of the more prominent veins strike northwest, and they occur in both the diorite and argillite. Gilluly (1937, p. 94) noted that the veins consist of quartz, calcite, scheelite, and a little sericite. Small amounts of native gold, pyrite, and chalcopyrite are present.

GRANT COUNTY

Grant County covers much of the southwestern part of the Blue Mountain region of northeastern Oregon where pre-Tertiary gold-bearing rocks are exposed.

The geology of the county, as summarized by the Oregon Department of Geology and Mineral Industries (1941, p. 14–15), includes rocks that range in age from Paleozoic to Tertiary. The oldest rocks are greenstone, argillite, and chert containing small lenses of Permian limestone. Several tens of thousands of feet of Upper Triassic and Jurassic rocks, mostly tuffaceous sandstone, shale, and some limestone, are exposed in the southwest part of the county. The Paleozoic rocks were intruded by peridotite, gabbro, and diorite, and all, including the Mesozoic rocks, were intruded by granodiorite. Tertiary rocks cover much of the county. These are the Clarno and John Day Formations (tuff, lava, and agglomerate of Eocene age), the Columbia River Basalt (Miocene age), Mascall Formation (tuffs that overlie the Columbia River Basalt), and Rattlesnake Formation (tuffs and lavas of Pliocene age).

Soon after the initial discoveries of placer gold at Griffin Gulch in 1861, discoveries were made at Sumpter and Canyon Creek, and by 1864 nearly all the mining districts of the Blue Mountains area were known (Lindgren, 1901, p. 563–564). The important gold-producing districts in Grant County were the Canyon Creek, Granite, Greenhorn (partly in Baker County), North Fork, Quartzburg, and Susanville.

From 1880 to 1899, Grant County produced $3,022,564 (about 146,000 ounces) in gold (Lindgren, 1901, p. 573). From 1904 through 1957 it produced 77,840 ounces of lode gold, 226,835 ounces of placer gold, and 19,967 ounces undifferentiated as to source. Approximate total gold production through 1959 was 470,600 ounces.

CANYON CREEK DISTRICT

The Canyon Creek district, which is between lat 44°11′ and 44°30′ N. and long 118°45′ and 119°33′ W. and includes most of the drainage area of the John Day River in Grant County, is noted chiefly for its gold placers along the river. Lindgren (1901, p. 717) estimated that the early production from these placers was about $15 million in gold (about 725,000 ounces). Hydraulic operations were conducted in the 1880's, and dredges were in operation sporadically after 1900.

Recorded gold production for the district from 1904 through 1959 was 899 ounces from lode mines, 91,711 ounces from placers, and 504 ounces from undifferentiated sources. Total production, including Lindgren's estimate of early production, was about 818,000 ounces.

Quartz veinlets containing rich pockets of native gold occur in carbonatized gabbro, serpentine, and greenstone in the vicinity of Little Canyon Mountain. Although these deposits were spectacular, they were small, and their production was not sustained.

GRANITE DISTRICT

The Granite district is between lat 44°45′ and 44°54′ N. and long 118°18′ and 118°33′ W., in eastern Grant County.

As early as 1862 placer gold was mined from the gravels of Granite Creek, Clear Creek, and Bull Run; in 1874 lode mining became commercially important when the Monumental and La Belleview mines, the most productive lode mines in the district, were discovered. Much of the early placer mining was done by the Chinese, who at one time outnumbered the Americans (Lindgren, 1901, p. 686). From World War II through 1959 the district was virtually idle with the exception of the Buffalo mine which supplied nearly all the lode gold mined in eastern Oregon during that period (Koch, 1959, p. 1).

Bedrock in the Granite district consists predominantly of a group of bedded metasedimentary rocks that were originally shales and small amounts of limestone, sandstone, and interbedded lava flows (Koch, 1959, p. 3–5). In the eastern part of the district a large granodiorite intrusion cuts the metasedimentary rocks. The layered rocks were thrown into east-trending isoclinal folds. Unconformably overlying these rocks are less severely folded and somewhat faulted Tertiary auriferous gravels, andesite tuff-breccias, and lava flows (Koch, 1959, p. 3–5).

The lode deposits are in veins in the pre-Tertiary metasedimentary rocks near or in the granodiorite. The veins are of two types: (1) open-space fillings characterized by quartz and calcite gangue and fragments of unreplaced wallrock, and (2) dike material, gouge, crushed country rock, and sparse quartz and calcite. In veins of the first type, the major metallic constituents are pyrite, chalcopyrite, tetrahedrite, arsenopyrite, sphalerite, and galena. In veins of the second type, pyrite is predominant, and in many veins it is the sole metallic mineral (Koch, 1959, p. 9–11).

Koch (1959, p. 38) estimated the total lode production of the Granite district to be $1,800,000, most of which was in gold and in small amounts of silver. This would represent, conservatively, about 75,000 ounces of gold. Recorded lode production for the district from 1904 through 1959 was 37,250 ounces. Placers yielded $1,033,000 in gold through 1914 (Oregon Dept. Geology and Mineral Resources, 1941, p. 40). Recorded placer production from 1904 through 1959 was 34,080 ounces and total gold production for the district was about 160,000 ounces.

GREENHORN DISTRICT

The Greenhorn district straddles the Baker-Grant County line. The western part of the district, in Grant County between lat 44°33′ and 44°45′ N. and long 118°18′ and 118°43′ W., will be discussed here.

The mines in the Greenhorn district reached their peak of productivity between 1895 and 1910 (Allen, 1951, p. 398). From 1910 until 1942 there was only sporadic activity, and from 1942 through 1959, almost none. Only fragmentary records of early production are available. A total of the estimates of early production of individual mines is $346,000 (about 16,800 ounces) in gold (Oregon Department of Geology and Mineral Industries, 1941, p. 66–97). Recorded production from 1932 through 1959 was 4,829 ounces from lode mines, 4,612 ounces from placers, and 425 ounces undifferentiated as to source.

The following summary of the geology of the district is from T. P. Thayer (written commun., 1962). Paleozoic meta-argillites and greenstones were intruded by lower Mesozoic ultramafic rocks, by diorite, and by related dikes of probable mid-Cretaceous age. These rocks are folded and faulted. Tertiary flows and tuffs overlap the older rocks on the south and east. The ore deposits are mostly fissure fillings within or near dikes that were emplaced in fractures in pre-Tertiary rocks. Quartz, pyrite, arsenopyrite, pyrrhotite, sphalerite, chalcopyrite, and tetrahedrite were deposited during the first of two stages of mineralization. A second stage included the preceding minerals and galena, calcite, specular hematite, and gold.

NORTH FORK DISTRICT

The North Fork district includes the drainage area of the North Fork of the John Day River and Desolation Creek between lat 44°45′ and 45°00′ N. and long 118°15′ and 118°55′ W.

This is a placer district that dates back to the early 1860's. Pardee and Hewett (1914, p. 10) estimated the total minimum production to 1914 at $893,000 in gold (about 43,000 ounces); since then, only 1,336 ounces have been reported from the district. The principal mines were the French Diggings and the North Fork. At the French Diggings both moraine and stream gravels were mined, and at the North Fork a gold-bearing terminal moraine was mined (Parks and Swartley, 1916, p. 97, 164).

QUARTZBURG DISTRICT

The Quartzburg district is in eastern Grant County between lat 44°28′ and 44°36′ N. and long 118°35′ and 118°47′ W.

In 1862, placers at Dixie Creek were discovered, and shortly afterward lode mines were producing in the district. After the initial boom of placer mining, in which estimated production ranged from $600,000 to $6 million (Swartley, 1914, p. 198), the district slowed down to sporadic small-scale activity. Lindgren (1901, p. 710) stated the production from lode mines to 1900 did not exceed $100,000. From 1904 through 1959, the recorded gold production from the district was 954 ounces from lodes, 8,534 ounces from placers, and 624 ounces undifferentiated as to source. Total production through 1959, using the $600,000 figure for the early placer production, was about 45,100 ounces.

The dominant rocks exposed in the Quartzburg district (Gilluly and others, 1933, p. 86–88) are meta-andesite, metadiabase, other volcanics, and small amounts of argillite, of possible Carboniferous age. Diorite, gabbro, and serpentine bodies and their associated porphyritic dikes cut the metavolcanics and sediments. A mid-Cretaceous series of more acid intrusives—quartz diorite and granodiorite—is exposed in the Dixie Creek valley and near the head of Ruby Creek. The Columbia River Basalt once covered the entire area, but it has been eroded from the mineralized area. Gold and small amounts of copper and cobalt occur in fissure veins in the pre-Tertiary rocks. These veins probably are related to the quartz diorite intrusions. Quartz, dolomite, and calcite compose the gangue, and pyrite, arsenopyrite, glaucodot, cobaltite, bismuth, bismuthinite, tetrahedrite, pyrrhotite, chalcopyrite, sphalerite, and galena are the chief metallic minerals. Much gold came from oxidized parts of these veins in the early days (Lindgren, 1901, p. 710).

SUSANVILLE DISTRICT

The Susanville district is between lat 44°41′ and 44°47′ N. and long 118°41′ and 118°52′ W.. in eastern Grant County.

Most of the production from this district was from placer mining before 1900. The placers were discovered in 1864, and those along Elk Creek and along the north side of the Middle Fork of the John Day River yielded $600,000 in gold (Swartley, 1914, p. 169). These placers were inactive in 1930 (Gilluly and others, 1933, p. 117). The Badger mine, discovered in the late 1860's, was the most important lode property in the district (Swartley, 1914, p. 170), but after several years of successful operation it was closed in 1905, reopened briefly in 1922, and closed again (Gilluly and others, 1933, p. 111). Most of the recent production from the district was from dredging operations. From 1932 through 1959 the district produced 937 ounces of lode gold and 17,809 ounces of placer gold. Total production through 1959, including the estimated earlv placer production, was about 48,750 ounces.

Gilluly, Reed, and Park (1933, p. 106–111) described the geology and ore deposits in some detail. The country rock throughout most of the Susanville district is schist of unknown age. This was intruded by bodies of gabbro and peridotite which are now mostly altered to serpentine. A large quartz diorite mass borders the district on the north and aplitic dikes from this intrusion cut the schist and ultrabasic rocks. Higher areas in the district are capped by Columbia River Basalt. Ore deposits are fissure veins parallel to the schistosity in the country rocks. Many veins seem to be related to the aplite dikes. Quartz is the dominant gangue mineral; metallic minerals include pyrite, marcasite, arsenopyrite, chalcopyrite, pyrrhotite, sphalerite, galena, stibnite, tetrahedrite-tennantite, and chalcocite. Gold occurs in the sulfides and also as free gold.

JACKSON COUNTY

The first gold mining in the State was in Jackson County. In 1852, placers along Jackson Creek were worked. Soon afterward placers were discovered along other creeks in the vicinity, and mining of these deposits became a major industry in the county (Oregon Department of Geology and Mineral Industries, 1943, p. 11). Lode deposits were discovered as early as 1859, but the chief gold production has come from the placers. The major districts in the county are Ashland, Gold Hill, Jacksonville, and Upper Applegate.

Much of the gold production from the county was before 1880, when there were no reliable records of the output; however, Winchell (1914b, p. 29), combining estimates and recorded data, reported gold production worth $7,110,333 from 1852 through 1912. From 1904 through 1959 the county produced 35,067 ounces of lode gold, 136,030 ounces of placer gold, and 16,787 ounces undifferentiated as to source. Total gold production from 1852 through 1959, including Winchell's estimates, was about 495,000 ounces.

The geology of Jackson County is given in "Oregon Metal Mines Handbook" (Oregon Department of Geology and Mineral Industries, 1943, p. 13–19). Schists of pre-Mesozoic age underlie the southwest part of the county, and Triassic greenstones and metasedimentary rocks, named the Applegate Group by Wells (1956), underlie its western part. In the northwest part of the county is a small patch of black slate, conglomerate, and tuffaceous sandstone of the Galice Formation, of Jurassic age. The schists, greenstones, and Galice sedimentary rocks were intruded first by masses of peridotite, now altered to serpentine, and later by granitic rocks. In the central part of the county, in Bear Creek and Cottonwood Creek valleys, remnants of the marine Hornbrook Formation of Cretaceous age are present (Wells, 1956). A narrow band of sandstones of the Tertiary Umpqua Formation underline Bear Creek valley, which crosses the county in a northwest direction. Lavas, breccias, and tuffs of Miocene and Pliocene age cover the central one-third of the county; these were intruded by small bodies of basalt and diorite. Pliocene and Pleistocene lavas and cinder cones—the High Cascade Series—cover much of the eastern part of the county. The gold deposits are concentrated in the western part of the county and are found in rocks of the Applegate Group and in the granitic and dioritic intrusives.

ASHLAND DISTRICT

The Ashland district is between lat 42°01′ and 42°11′ N. and long 122°31′ and 122°48′ W., in south-central Jackson County.

Mining began here in 1858 (Winchell, 1914b, p. 77) when placers were discovered at Forty-nine Diggings. These were highly productive for about 20 years. Lode deposits were worked as early as 1890, and the chief producer was the Ashland mine which yielded about $150,000 in gold from 1892 to 1899 (Winchell, 1914b, p. 77). The total production of this mine was estimated to be worth $1,300,000 (Oregon Department of Geology and Mineral Industries, 1943, p. 25). There was sporadic activity in the district up to 1942, but only a few ounces have been reported since that time. Production of the district from 1933 through 1959 was 1,764 ounces of lode gold and 163 ounces of placer gold. Total production through 1959, including estimates of early production, was about 66,400 ounces of gold.

At Forty-nine Diggings, the major placer mine in the district, Quaternary gravels were originally mined, but productive channels were also found later in conglomerates of the Cretaceous Hornbrook Formation (Anderson, 1914, p. 90–93). Other placers were in the Quaternary gravels along Bear Creek and its tributaries.

GOLD HILL DISTRICT

The Gold Hill district is between lat 42°23′ and 42°43′ N. and long 122°47′ and 123°15′ W., in northwestern Jackson County, and includes the Foots Creek area.

Placers were worked in the district as early as 1853, but the big strike occurred in 1859 when lode gold was discovered; an estimated $400,000 was mined from the Gold Hill pocket in the first year (Winchell, 1914b, p. 154). The chief lode mines in the district were the Braden, Sylvanite, and Whitney. The lode deposits were important in the early days, but, with the exception of the Sylvanite mine, they were small though rich and were quickly mined out. The placers on Foots, Sam, Galls, Sardine, Evans, and Pleasant Creeks were worked on a fairly large scale for many years. Dredges and hydraulic methods were in use from the early days until as late as the early 1940's (Oregon Department of Geology and Mineral Industries, 1943, p. 42). The district was active on a small scale as recently as 1957.

Complete early production data could not be found. Parks and Swartley (1916, p. 109, 193) reported that total production from the Gold Hill pocket was at least $700,000 in gold, and the Revenue pocket is said to have produced $100,000 in gold. From 1908 through 1959, scattered production data totaled 2,847 ounces of lode gold and 35,021 ounces of placer gold. Total gold production through 1959, including the estimated early production from the Gold Hill pocket, was a minimum of 80,000 ounces.

Metavolcanic rocks of Triassic age are the most abundant country rock in the Gold Hill district (Wells and others, 1940). These were intruded by masses of peridotite and granite, and considerable folding and thrusting accompanied the intrusions. Conglomerates and arkoses of Cretaceous age cover parts of the area, and Tertiary sediments occur in the central part of the district. The veins are genetically related to the granitic intrusive and occur in it or in the surrounding Triassic sediments.

The veins consist of quartz lenses in fractures a few hundred feet long (Wells, 1956). In many veins, crushed rock fills the fractures between quartz lenses. The ore zones consist of mineralized quartz or crushed rock, commonly accompanied by seams and masses of chloritic material. Most of the gold is free and unassociated with sulfides, but in some veins pyrite, pyrrhotite, and minor galena and sphalerite may constitute as much as 3 percent of the ore.

JACKSONVILLE DISTRICT

The Jacksonville district is between lat 42°11′ and 42°23′ N. and long 122°45′ and 123°03′ W., in the Bear Creek valley. Medford is the chief town in the district.

The initial gold discoveries in Oregon were made in this district in 1851 on Jackson Creek, and mining began the following year. The placers were profitable until about 1870, after which the Chinese worked the lower grade gravels that remained (Winchell, 1914b, p. 138). In the 1930's the old placer workings were dredged (Oregon Department of Geology and Mineral Industries, 1943, p. 132). Quartz veins were discovered in the 1860's; the chief mines were the Town and the Opp. The lode deposits of this district are similar to those of the Gold Hill district in that they are extremely rich pockets of auriferous quartz which can be mined out in a short time. With this type of activity it is difficult to keep production records; consequently, estimates must be accepted in lieu of factual data.

Early placer production from the Jacksonville district is also unrecorded. J. T. Pardee (in Shenon, 1933a, p. 37) credited the Town pocket with a production of at least $100,000 in gold, and Winchell (1914b, p. 149) credited the Opp mine with production of at least $100,000. The district was fairly active up to 1942; thereafter, production decreased and remained very low through 1959.

Production of the district from 1904 through 1959 was 7,090 ounces of lode gold and 9,172 ounces of placer gold. The district probably yielded a minimum of 26,000 ounces, including the early estimates of the Opp and Town mines, and possibly twice that much, if the early unknown placer production is included.

Wells (1956) mapped and described the geology

of the district. Its southern and western parts are underlain by altered basic flows, breccias, and pyroclastics interlayered with sedimentary rocks, known as the Applegate Group of Late Triassic(?) age. These rocks were intruded by a diorite mass, part of which crops out in the northwest corner of the district. Rocks of the Hornbrook Formation (of Late Cretaceous age) are exposed in a band along the west edge of the Bear Creek valley. From Medford eastward, the district is underlain by the Umpqua Formation, a succession of sandstones, shales, and conglomerates of Tertiary age. A wide strip of alluvium in the central part of the district fills the valley of Bear Creek. The lode deposits are gold-quartz veins containing minor amounts of sulfides. The veins cut rocks of the Applegate Group and may be related to the diorite intrusive.

UPPER APPLEGATE DISTRICT

The Upper Applegate district is in southwestern Jackson County between lat 42°01′ and 42°20′ N. and long 123°00′ and 123°15′ W.

This was predominantly a placer district. Placers first were discovered along Forest Creek, and the district was organized in 1853 (Winchell, 1914b, p. 125). The original discoveries were soon worked out, but other rich placers were found along Ferris Gulch, and Althouse, Humbug, Keeler, and Sterling Creeks. Hydraulic methods were introduced in the early 1880's; the Sterling mine, with an estimated early production of $3 million (Diller and Kay, 1909, p. 69), was one of the most successful of the hydraulic mines. Other large producers were the Layton, Pearce, Spaulding, and Old Sturgis mines. More recently draglines were used in this district.

Only one lode mine, the Steamboat, was commercially important; before 1869 it produced $350,000 in gold from gold-quartz veins in altered andesite (Winchell, 1914b, p. 136).

Early production data are fragmentary, but the estimates from Winchell (1914b) and from the Oregon Department of Geology and Mineral Industries (1943) give a minimum of 165,000 ounces of gold before 1905. From 1904 through 1959 the district produced 2,135 ounces from lodes, 45,900 ounces from placers, and 779 ounces undifferentiated as to source. Total production through 1959 was about 210,000 ounces.

JOSEPHINE COUNTY

Josephine County has been one of the leading producers of gold in Oregon and has yielded significant amounts of the State's chrome and copper output. Gold was found on Josephine Creek as early as 1852, and the following year additional discoveries on Althouse Creek precipitated a rush during which prospectors spread throughout southwestern Oregon. Hydraulic methods were introduced as early as 1856 to mine the placers.

As in many other mining camps, the depletion of the placers in Josephine County led to the search for lode deposits. By the early 1860's quartz mines were active in the Grants Pass district, and somewhat later, in the Galice, Greenback, and Waldo districts.

Diller (1914b, p. 47) estimated that from 1852 to 1900 the annual production of gold in the county exceeded $450,000, or a total of about $21,600,000 (about 1,048,000 ounces) for those years. From 1901 through 1959 the county produced 187,913 ounces of gold. Total gold production from 1852 through 1959, including Diller's estimate, was about 1,235,000 ounces.

The geology of Josephine County is summarized by R. C. Treasher (in Oregon Department of Geology and Mineral Industries, 1942, p. 11–15). The oldest rock is greenstone of Triassic(?) age which underlies much of the southern part of the county, extends north-northeastward, and crops out in the northeast corner. Quartz veins containing iron, copper, zinc sulfides, and gold are common in this rock. The western part of the county is underlain by interbedded sedimentary and volcanic rocks of Jurassic age that strike parallel to the Triassic greenstone. The sedimentary rocks, the Galice and Dothan Formations, are predominantly black slates that contain varying amounts of sandstone, conglomerate, and tuff. Interbedded with these two formations is a greenstone unit. Peridotite and serpentine occupy belts several miles wide within the Jurassic sequence and strike concordantly with the regional north-northeast trend. Sulfide and gold-bearing quartz veins fill fractures in the Jurassic sediments and greenstone.

Masses of igneous rock of Jurassic or Cretaceous age that range in composition from granite to diorite are exposed in the southeast, northeast, and northwest parts of the county. A small patch of Horsetown(?) Formation, of Cretaceous age, is exposed in the Takilma area in the southwest part of the county.

At numerous localities throughout the county, channels, which were eroded into rocks of Cretaceous age and older, were filled with gold-bearing conglomerates of Tertiary age (Shenon, 1933b, p. 152–154). Gold placers also occur in high terraces of Pleistocene age along the Rogue River.

The major gold-producing districts in Josephine County are the Galice, Grants Pass, Greenback, Illinois River, Lower Applegate, and Waldo.

GALICE DISTRICT

The Galice district is between lat 42°28′ and 42°44′ N. and long 123°28′ and 123°54′ W., in the northwest corner of Josephine County, and includes the Mount Reuben district in this report.

Placer mining began in this district along Galice Creek in 1854. By the 1880's the richer deposits were mined out and Chinese took over many of the operations (Oregon Department of Geology and Mineral Industries, 1942, p. 16). The Old Channel and the Benton mines were among the important gold producers in southwestern Oregon. The Old Channel mine, about 1 mile west of Galice, was first worked in 1860 and was one of the largest, if not the largest, hydraulic mine in Oregon (Oregon Department of Geology and Mineral Industries, 1942, p. 48–59). The workings were in a gravel terrace about 600 feet above the Rogue River. The Benton, a lode mine in the Mount Reuben area, was located in 1893 and was worked until 1905. It was reopened in 1936 and closed again from 1942 through 1959. During 1940 and 1941 the Benton was the largest underground mine in southern Oregon (Oregon Department of Geology and Mineral Industries, 1942, p. 17). Other important mines in the Galice district were the Almeda, Gold Bug, Oriole, Black Bear, and Robertson. The periods of greatest production from the quartz mines were from 1900 to 1910 and from 1939 to 1942. The district was practically inactive from 1951 through 1959.

The Galice district produced about $5 million in gold to 1913 (Diller, 1914b, p. 47). From 1914 through 1959, gold production included 16,600 ounces from lode mines, 7,258 ounces from placers, and 1,941 ounces undifferentiated as to source. Total production, including estimates of early production, was about 268,000 ounces.

The following description of the geology of the Galice district has been summarized from Wells and Walker (1953). Steeply dipping sedimentary, volcanic, and metamorphic rocks of Late Jurassic age cross the district in a northeastward-trending belt. From oldest to youngest these consist of sandstone, shale, and siltstone of the Dothan Formation, altered lava flows, tuffs, breccias, and agglomerates of the Rogue Formation, and mudstone, sandstone, tuff, and agglomerate of the Galice Formation. These rocks were intruded by sheets and dikes of peridotite, gabbroic amphibolite, quartz diorite, and dacite porphyry, all ranging in age from Late Jurassic to Early Cretaceous. The rocks were compressed into isoclinal folds that trend northeastward and were later torn by faults, the most prominent of which are high-angle reverse faults that strike concordantly with the strike of the rocks. There are a few northwest-trending normal faults in the area.

Gold is the chief commodity of the Galice district, but considerable copper, silver, and a little lead, in addition to gold, have been produced at the Almeda mine (Shenon, 1933c, p. 24).

The veins of the Galice district fill fractures in many of the Jurassic igneous rocks—the gabbroic amphibolite, diorite, and dacite bodies. Veins also occur in the Rogue Formation and its metamorphosed equivalent; however, there are no mineralized fractures in the Dothan or Galice Formations. The veins dip steeply and most of them strike north or north-northeast. In most deposits the gold is free and is associated with pyrite, pyrrhotite, and some chalcopyrite in a quartz gangue.

At the Almeda mine a second period of mineralization is recognized. It is characterized by abundant chalcopyrite and a little sphalerite and galena in a gangue of barite (Wells and Walker, 1953).

GRANTS PASS DISTRICT

The Grants Pass district is in east-central Josephine County between lat 42°24′ and 42°35′ N. and long 123°15′ and 123°35′ W. Included within this district are the Jumpoff Joe Creek, Rogue River, Winona, and Merlin camps.

The earliest mining was along Picket and Jumpoff Joe Creeks several years after the discoveries along Josephine Creek in 1852. Although records are scanty, apparently this district was not important until lode quartz mining began in the 1890's (Winchell, 1914b, p. 215). The major lode mine was the Daisy or Hammersley. Some of the important placer mines were along Jumpoff Joe Creek, the Rogue River, and the Dry Digging at the town of Grants Pass. The district was sporadically active through the 1930's, but only a few mines were in operation in 1942 (Oregon Department of Geology and Mineral Industries, 1942, p. 66). From 1951 through 1959 only a few ounces was reported from the district. Estimates of early lode production credit the Granite Hill mine with $65,000 in gold (Diller and Kay, 1909, p. 58), the Daisy with $200,000, and the Baby with $20,000 (Winchell, 1914b, p. 225, 228). Incomplete production data for the district from 1904 to 1932 total 5,218 ounces. From 1932 through 1957 the district produced 540 ounces of lode gold and 6,087 ounces of placer gold.

Total production through 1959, including the estimates of early production, was about 22,000 ounces.

The predominant country rock in the Grants Pass district consists of northeast-trending bands of serpentine, greenstone, and Galice sedimentary rocks, all of Jurassic age (Diller and Kay, 1924, p. 2–7). A dioritic intrusive of Late Jurassic or Early Cretaceous age transects the other rocks. The lode deposits are in small quartz veinlets and stringers in greenstone and in the diorite intrusive. The veinfilling is mainly quartz with small amounts of pyrite, arsenopyrite, chalcopyrite, galena, and local pyrrhotite. Most of the gold occurs in the free state with quartz, but some of the sulfides carry varying amounts of gold.

GREENBACK DISTRICT

The Greenback district, which includes Graves, Wolf, and Coyote Creeks, is in the northeast corner of Josephine County, between lat 42°37′ and 42°43′ N. and long 123°16′ and 123°28′ W.

The date of gold discovery in this district is unknown, but placers along Graves and Wolf Creeks probably were discovered in 1860 (Winchell, 1914b, p. 182) and were productive through the 1940's. In the late 1890's and early 1900's, lode mines such as the Greenback, Dorothea, and Livingston were discovered, and they exceeded the placers in production. For some time in the early 1900's the Greenback mine was regarded as the largest producer in southwest Oregon (Diller, 1914b, p. 31). After the 1930's, however, production from placers was much greater than that from the lode mines. From World War II through 1959 the Greenback district produced only 100 to 200 ounces of gold annually.

Records of early production in the Greenback district do not exist and estimates are fragmentary. The Dorothea mine produced $50,000 in gold, and the Livingston, $20,000 (Oregon Department of Geology and Mineral Industries, 1942, p. 101, 110). Winchell (1914b, p. 184) reported early production of $400,000 from placers along Graves Creek. Total recorded production for the district from 1904 through 1959 was 37,062 ounces—2,001 ounces from lode mines, 28,853 ounces from placers, and 6,208 ounces undifferentiated. Total gold production through 1959, including Winchell's estimate of early placer production from Grave Creek, must have been at least 55,000 ounces.

The geology of the Greenback district is very similar to that of the Grants Pass district. Alternating bands of greenstone, serpentine, and sediments of the Galice Formation cross the district in a northeasterly direction (Diller and Kay, 1924). Most of the lode mines are in greenstone near the contact with serpentine bodies. The deposits are in small veins and stringers. Veinfilling is mainly quartz and small amounts of pyrite, arsenopyrite, chalcopyrite, galena, and local pyrrhotite. Gold occurs chiefly in the free state: some is associated with the sulfides.

ILLINOIS RIVER DISTRICT

The Illinois River district is along the west boundary of Josephine County between lat 42°13′ and 42°29′ N. and long 123°38′ and 124°05′ W.

Placer mining was reported as early as 1852 in the gravels of Josephine Creek, a tributary of the Illinois River (Raymond, 1870, p. 217–218), but records of early production are so fragmentary that the early output from the district is uncertain (Wells and others, 1949, p. 21). Scattered data attribute 2,006 ounces to the district from 1904 to 1932 (U.S. Geological Survey, 1904–24; U.S. Bureau of Mines, 1925–32). From 1932 through 1959 the district produced 327 ounces of lode gold and 3,670 ounces of placer gold. Total recorded production through 1953 was 6,003 ounces, but the unrecorded early production must have been at least 5,000 to 10,000 ounces. There was no recorded production from 1954 through 1959.

The geology of the Illinois River district was described by Wells, Hotz, and Cater (1949, p. 2–21). The country rock is chiefly tuffs, agglomerates, and flows of the volcanic member of the Galice Formation of Jurassic age. These rocks strike northeast and dip fairly steeply to the southeast. Discontinuous bodies of serpentine and larger masses of peridotite are also present. An elongate mass of hornblende diorite occupies the northwestern part of the district and borders the serpentine and peridotite. Lode gold deposits are of two types—small tabular quartz bodies or pockets containing free gold and sulfides, and auriferous gossans from which the sulfides have been leached. Both occur in noncarbonaceous rocks of the Galice Formation at a considerable distance from the hornblende diorite. The most productive placers have been those along the Illinois River.

LOWER APPLEGATE DISTRICT

The Lower Applegate district is in southeastern Josephine County between lat 42°07′ N. and long 123°15′ and 123°36′ W.

The recorded production of this district from 1904 through 1959 was only 4,180 ounces and does not warrant its inclusion in this report; however, as placers were mined along Williams Creek soon after 1852 and through the 1870's (Winchell, 1914b, p. 229), it seems logical to assume a total production of well over 10,000 ounces. Most of the production was from placers, but lode mines were discovered as early as 1860 (Winchell, 1914b, p. 229) and were active on a small scale until 1950. The major lode mines were the Humdinger, Oregon Bonanza, and Porcupine. The most productive placers were along Williams, Slate, and Oscar Creeks and Missouri Flat.

The Lower Applegate district is underlain by Triassic(?) greenstone that is intruded by diorite and serpentine. Galice sedimentary rocks of Jurassic age are exposed in the western part of the district. The gold deposits are in quartz veins in the greenstone, diorite, and sedimentary rocks. Shenon (1933a, p. 50–51) postulated that the ores are related to the acidic intrusives and were formed at shallow depths and at moderate temperatures. Quartz, calcite, pyrite, galena, arsenopyrite, and native gold are the vein constituents. Shenon (1933a, p. 50) noted apophyllite as gangue in the Humdinger mine.

WALDO DISTRICT

The Waldo district is in southern Josephine County between lat 42°00′ and 42°10′ N. and long 123°30′ and 123°50′ W.

Placers have been the mainstay of this district; however, there are a few lode mines, and some gold is produced as a byproduct from some of the copper mines. Placers were discovered along Althouse Creek in 1853 (Shenon, 1933b, p. 178–179) and were developed mainly by a group of sailors who constructed a long ditch to carry sufficient water to work the placers. By 1901 production declined, but the district was rejuvenated shortly afterward when hydraulic mining enabled substantial economical production from lower grade gravels. The district was active until 1942, but from then until 1959 it was virtually idle. Shenon (1933b, p. 179) estimated a total minimum placer gold production of $4 million (about 194,000 ounces) up to 1932. From 1932 through 1959 the district produced 1,228 ounces from lode mines and 18,614 ounces from placers. Total production through 1959 was about 213,800 ounces. The principal placer mines were the Llano de Oro, Deep Gravel, and Platerica mines. The Queen of Bronze copper mine, whose total production was valued at more than $1,350,000, yielded ore containing from 0.04 to 0.44 percent gold and 5.16 to 16.33 percent copper (Shenon, 1933b, p. 163).

The geology of the Waldo district was described in considerable detail by Shenon (1933b, p. 148–161). Triassic metamorphosed conglomerate, limestone, chert, argillite, and sandstone crop out in a narrow band trending north-south through the central part of the district. The Galice Formation of Jurassic age underlies the southwest corner of the district, and conglomerate and sandstone of the Cretaceous Horsetown(?) Formation underlie much of the northwestern part. Patches of Tertiary conglomerate, which is gold bearing, occur along the East Fork of the Illinois River in the central part of the district. Quaternary gravels, among them the auriferous Llando de Oro Formation, fill the valley of the East Fork of the Illinois River and its tributary streams and gulches. Metabasalt, metagabbro, and serpentine underlie most of the southeastern part of the district. The serpentine is believed to be of Jurassic or Early Cretaceous age, but the age of the metagabbro and metabasalt is unknown. Near the greenstone-serpentine contacts copper sulfides were deposited as irregular lenses in fractures. These deposits are in both the greenstone and serpentine. Small irregular deposits of chromite in the serpentine also have been mined.

LANE COUNTY

Lane County has been a relatively small gold producer even though mining of the precious metals began as early as 1858 and continued in a desultory fashion through the 1940's. Most of the gold has come from veins in the Bohemia and Blue River districts.

Total recorded gold production of Lane County from 1880 through 1959 was slightly more than 46,000 ounces. Considering that mining began in 1858, it seems reasonable to assume that at least 50,000 ounces of gold was produced. The rocks exposed in the county are sedimentary and igneous and range in age from Eocene to Recent (Smith and Ruff, 1938, p. 11–22). The oldest rocks are sandstones, shales, and volcanics composing the Umpqua Formation of Eocene age. This is overlain by the Calapooya Formation, also of Eocene age, consisting dominantly of pyroclastics. The uppermost Eocene formation is the Tyee Sandstone. Oligocene sediments are the Fisher Formation (tuffs and breccias) and the Eugene Formation (tuffaceous sandstone and shale). The Eocene and Oligocene sediments are present in the western half of the county, generally west of the Willamette River valley. A thick section of Miocene, Pliocene, and Pleistocene basalt and andesite lava flows, associated tuffs and agglomerates, and some dioritic intrusives younger than the Miocene lavas compose most of the bedrock of the eastern part of the county, including the Cascade Range. Some of the volcanic activity extended into Pleistocene and Recent time.

The gold deposits are in oxidized-sulfide veins of Eocene or younger age.

BLUE RIVER DISTRICT

The Blue River district is in Lane and Linn Counties, between lat 44°10′ and 44°20′ N. and long 122°10′ and 122°25′ W.

The Lucky Boy mine, the only large producer in the district, was discovered in 1887. Gold production from the district was estimated to be worth $50,000 to $100,000 before 1896, and it was 7,728 ounces from 1896 to 1924 (Callaghan and Buddington, 1938, p. 115–116). Only 44 ounces was reported from the district from 1924 through 1959. The total production, using the lower estimate of Callaghan and Buddington, was about 10,200 ounces.

The geology of the district, as described by Callaghan and Buddington (1938, p. 114–117), is characterized by flat-lying andesitic lavas and breccias of probable Miocene age which have been intruded by small plugs and dikes of diorite. The ore deposits are in small quartz veins containing sphalerite, galena, chalcopyrite, pyrite, and local tetrahedrite. Apparently most of the ore bodies are in the oxidized parts of these veins.

BOHEMIA DISTRICT

The Bohemia district is 35 miles southeast of Cottage Grove between lat 43°35′ and 43°45′ N. and long 122°35′ and 122°45′ W. on the divide between the Umpqua and Willamette drainage systems.

The district was described by Callaghan and Buddington (1938, p. 38–81), and the information that follows, unless otherwise noted, was abstracted from their report.

The district was discovered in 1858, and some ore was mined until 1877, when the mill closed and the district became inactive (Diller, 1900, p. 7). In 1891 there was a revival of activity that continued until about 1912. Since then, activity has been somewhat sporadic. There was no recorded production from 1952 through 1959.

The entire gold production of 14,591 ounces in Lane County from 1880 to 1900 is credited to the Bohemia district. From 1902 through 1930 the district produced 13,695 ounces, and from 1931 through 1959 it produced 10,270 ounces of lode gold and 81 ounces of placer gold. Total recorded gold production through 1959 from the district is 38,637 ounces.

Most of the district is underlain by bedded Miocene(?) volcanic rocks with an aggregate thickness of 6,500 feet. These rocks are composed of approximately equal amounts of tuffs, andesite lavas, and volcanic breccias. Several small dioritic plugs, dikes, and a stock intrude the volcanics, and the gold deposits seem to be arranged around the intrusives. The deposits are oxidized sulfide veins containing in the unweathered state drusy quartz, galena, chalcopyrite, sphalerite, and specularite.

MALHEUR COUNTY

Considerable gold has been produced from the Malheur district, in northern Malheur County, and from the Mormon Basin district which extends into Baker County and has been described on page 220. As might be expected, early production from such border-straddling districts was reported with little consideration for geography; however, it is fairly certain that the bulk of the Mormon Basin output was from the part of the district in Baker County.

Gold production data for Malheur County are complete from 1904, but data on district production before 1932 are fragmentary. From 1904 through 1959 Malheur County produced 13,522 ounces of lode gold and 13,860 ounces of placer gold. More than one-third of this came from the Mormon Basin district.

MALHEUR DISTRICT

The Malheur district is about 10 miles west-southwest of the Mormon Basin district in northern Malheur County.

Information on this district is fragmentary. The district's greatest production was in 1875, just after the completion of the Eldorado ditch which provided sufficient water to mine the gulch gravels on a fairly large scale. Production for that year was $150,000 in gold (Lindgren, 1901, p. 772–773). Lindgren (1901, p. 773) also reported some quartz mines in the district, but apparently these never proved to be of any importance. No further mining was reported until the late 1930's and early 1940's. From 1932 through 1942, the district produced 36 ounces of lode gold and 2,277 ounces of placer gold. From 1942 through 1959 no production was reported. The minimum total production for the district through 1959, including Lindgren's report of $150,000 for 1875, was about 9,600 ounces of gold.

MORMON BASIN DISTRICT

The Malheur County part of the Mormon Basin district produced 4,133 ounces of lode gold and 5,199 ounces of placer gold between 1904 and 1959, but before 1932 not all the annual production was reported. From 1952 through 1959, no gold production was reported from the district.

The geology and history of this district have been described under Baker County (p. 216–218).

PENNSYLVANIA

In Pennsylvania, gold has been produced in significant quantities only at the Cornwall iron mine, about 5 miles south of Lebanon in the southern part of Lebanon County.

Mining of the Cornwall deposit began in 1742 (Hickok, 1933, p. 194) and was still active in 1959. Iron has been the chief commodity, but small amounts of copper, gold, and silver have also been recovered. The first gold production recorded was in 1908, when about 35 ounces was refined from copper concentrates. The total gold output of the Cornwall mine through 1959 was 37,459 ounces, most of which was produced after 1937.

The oldest rocks of the area, according to Geyer and others (1958), are of Cambrian age and consist of five limestone and dolomite members of the Conococheague Formation. These are overlain by four formations of the Beekmantown Group of Ordovician age, and by the Annville, Myerstown, and Hershey Limestones and Martinsburg Formation, also of Ordovician age. In the immediate vicinity of the Cornwall deposit are two rock units of doubtful age: one of these is known as the Mill Hill slate and may be an outlier of Martinsburg Shale; the other is conglomerate or breccia called "blue conglomerate" by the miners. The entire Paleozoic section was folded into a recumbent synclinorium that trends east-northeast. Considerable thrust faulting accompanied the folding.

The Paleozoic rocks are unconformably overlain by shales, sandstones, and conglomerates of the Gettysburg Formation of Triassic age. These rocks are warped into a homocline that dips north. The contact between the two series of rocks trends east and in many places is a fault. Large sills, dikes, and plugs of diabase of Triassic age intrude all the sedimentary rocks, and in part of the area a sill separates the Triassic and Paleozoic rocks.

The Cornwall deposit is a contact metasomatic deposit at the contact of a diabase dike and Cambrian limestone. The dike has an elliptical outcrop pattern but at depth becomes sheetlike, which creates a trough where the ore bodies of replaced limestone are situated. The ore consists chiefly of magnetite and actinolite and lesser amounts of chalcopyrite, pyrite, diopside, phlogopite, chlorite, and serpentine. Small amounts of gold are recovered from copper concentrates, which suggests that it occurs with chalcopyrite.

SOUTH CAROLINA

Gold was discovered in South Carolina in 1827 in placers at the Haile mine, which was to become the largest gold producer in the Southeastern States (Newton and others, 1940, p. 1). Placers were also worked at the site of the Brewer mine before 1830. The first record of gold production in South Carolina was in 1829, when a shipment was sent to the mint (Becker, 1895, p. 256). Another major gold-producing property in South Carolina, the Dorn mine in McCormick County, became productive in 1852. The early period of intense activity was terminated by the Civil War, and though the mines were reopened afterward, the Haile mine was the only property in South Carolina that prospered. But by the early 1900's production at the Haile also declined, and except for a brief revival during World War I, the gold mines of South Carolina were largely dormant from 1900 to 1937. With the rejuvenation of the Haile mine in 1937, South Carolina became the leader in gold production in the Southeast. The War Production Board Order L–208 forced the shutdown of the gold mines, and the State has not produced any gold since 1943. Total gold production of South Carolina through 1959 was 318,801 ounces (fig. 3).

The geology of the gold belt of South Carolina is similar to that of North Carolina. The Haile and Brewer mines are in the schistose rocks of the slate belt (Pardee and Park, 1948, p. 16). The Dorn mine, in rocks of similar character, is in the southwest part of the State, near the Georgia border.

CHESTERFIELD COUNTY

The Brewer mine is about 1½ miles west of Jefferson in northwest Chesterfield County.

Gold placers were discovered in 1828 on this property and were worked even after the vein deposits were discovered. In the 1880's the surficial deposits were mined on a fairly large scale by hydraulic methods; the vein deposits also continued to be worked (Pardee and Park, 1948, p. 106). By 1894 or 1895 the mine was closed and was operated only during brief intervals after that time. The most recent activity was in 1939 when 8 ounces of gold was recovered from placers. Production of the Brewer mine was estimated at about $450,000 in gold (about 21,840 ounces) (Pardee and Park, 1948, p. 106).

The country rock in the Brewer mine is quartz sericite schist, derived from bedded tuffs that are part of the slate belt (Pardee and Park, 1948, p. 106–107). These have been folded into a northeastward-trending syncline. North of the area, a body of granite is exposed, and it is believed that this intrusion is responsible for most of the hydrothermal alteration of the schist in the mine area (Pardee and Park, 1948, p. 107). The ore deposit is an ill-defined mass of silicified schist that contains pyrite and minor amounts of enargite, covellite, cassiterite, and bismuth. Most of the gold occurs with the pyrite, but some free gold is present. An unusual feature of this deposit is the large body of fine-grained topaz that constitutes much of the northwest part of the lode (Pardee and Park, 1948, p. 109). The lode is weathered to depths of 40 to 60 feet, and the weathered material forms a sandy mantle in which native gold is concentrated. This material also comprises the placer deposits.

LANCASTER COUNTY

The Haile mine, in southern Lancaster County and 3½ miles northeast of Kershaw, is the most productive gold mine in the Southeastern States and is probably the oldest mine in South Carolina. In 1827 gold-bearing placers were discovered along one of the creeks on the property. By 1829 the lode deposits were found and were quickly developed; lode mining supplanted the placer activity. The California gold rush and the Civil War curtailed operations, but by 1880 the Haile was again active and remained open until 1918 (Newton and others, 1940, p. 2). During this period pyrite, useful for manufacturing sulfuric acid, was an important product in addition to gold. The mine was opened again in 1935 after the increase in the price of gold, and from 1937 through 1942, it produced a total of 60,013 ounces. During this period the Haile accounted for most of the gold production of the southern Appalachian States. The Haile mine was closed at the end of 1942 and remained idle through 1959. Total gold production of the Haile mine through 1959 was 278,080 ounces.

The host rock of the ore deposits is light-gray sericite schist of the slate belt sequence. The rock was originally a tuff or volcanic ash (Pardee and Park, 1948, p. 114). About 3 miles northeast of the mine the bedrock is granite, but the contact between the schist and granite is concealed by the Cretaceous sandstones that unconformably overlie the older rocks. Several northwest-trending diabase dikes cut across the trend of the schistosity of rocks.

There are two types of ore bodies at the Haile mine: large masses of pyritized schist and quartz-pyrite bodies containing gold. During World War I the pyrite deposits were mined to produce sulfuric acid (Schrader, 1921, p. 332). The gold-bearing quartz and pyrite deposits are replacement bodies in two zones in the schist. These zones trend northeastward and are conformable with the general trend of schistosity (Pardee and Park, 1948, p. 114–115). The mineralized rock consists mostly of fine-grained quartz through which is scattered much fine-grained pyrite and extremely fine-grained gold. Locally, sphalerite and pyrrhotite are present in small amounts.

The mine has more than 6,000 feet of underground workings and at least five open cuts (Schrader, 1921, p. 333).

McCORMICK COUNTY

The Dorn mine is in the town of McCormick, in central McCormick County.

The first record of gold production from this property was for a shipment in 1853 worth $300,000 (Pardee and Park, 1948, p. 119). Although little else could be found concerning its early history, the mine probably was operated for several years before the Civil War. It was idle from 1880 to 1932, at which time some development work was done. No production was reported from this most recent activity; the mine was apparently closed and remained inactive through 1959. Total gold production through 1959 (Sloan, 1908, p. 27) is estimated to be worth $900,000 (43,700 ounces).

The predominant bedrock in the area is sericite schist. This is cut by a basic dike and a light-gray rock containing clusters of quartz and feldspar, locally called "birdseye porphyry" (Pardee and Park, 1948, p. 119). The ore deposits are lenticular bodies and groups of stringers. The lenticular lodes are replacement deposits of quartz and sericite with pyrite and a little covellite, chalcopyrite(?), and manganese minerals (Sloan, 1908, p. 26). Gold probably occurs in association with the sulfides. The stringers consist of galena, sphalerite, and chalcopyrite (Pardee and Park, 1948, p. 119).

SOUTH DAKOTA

The gold deposits of South Dakota are in the Black Hills, in the western part of the State (fig. 23). South Dakota ranks third among the States in total gold production and has been the leading gold producer in recent years. Its total gold production through 1965 was 31,207,892 ounces.

The first documented discovery was made in 1874,

during General George A. Custer's expedition to reconnoiter the Black Hills. The actual discovery is credited to two miners named Ross and McKay, who were attached to the expedition and found gold in gravel bars along French Creek. News of this discovery attracted many prospectors to the area, even though the country then belonged to the Sioux Indians who were not enthusiastic to have their domain overrun. Equally adamant in this respect was the United States Government which was bound by a treaty to keep white men out of the Black Hills. In 1875, another expedition under the direction of W. P. Jenney was sent to the Black Hills to officially report on the potential mineral wealth of the region. The French Creek discoveries were confirmed, and numerous additional occurrences of placer gold were reported (Newton and Jenney, 1880, p. 226–294). In 1876 the Black Hills were ceded to the United States, and prospectors flooded into the area and found gold in Deadwood Gulch, Nigger Hill, and Rockerville. By 1880 from $6 to $8 million worth of placer gold had been mined, about half of which came from Deadwood Gulch (Lincoln, 1937, p. 11–12).

The first lode claims were located in December 1875 in Precambrian rocks in the Lead district; these were later purchased to form the original holdings of the Homestake Mining Co. As the placers became depleted, the Homestake Co., through acquisition of other properties and intelligent development, became the leading operator in the Black Hills and the largest gold producer in the United States (fig. 24). Several smaller companies also developed gold lodes in the Deadwood-Two Bit, Garden, Bald Mountain, Squaw Creek, Hill City, and Keystone districts.

The Black Hills consist of a core of Precambrian rocks surrounded by concentric bands of Paleozoic and Mesozoic rocks that dip gently away from the core. They are intruded by sills, stocks, and dikes of igneous rocks that range in composition from rhyolite and phonolite to quartz monzonite (Darton and Paige, 1925).

The Precambrian rocks are exposed in a northwest-trending oval area about 60 miles long and 25 miles wide, and they form the highest part of the Black Hills. These rocks consist of (1) intensely folded metasedimentary rocks, including schist,

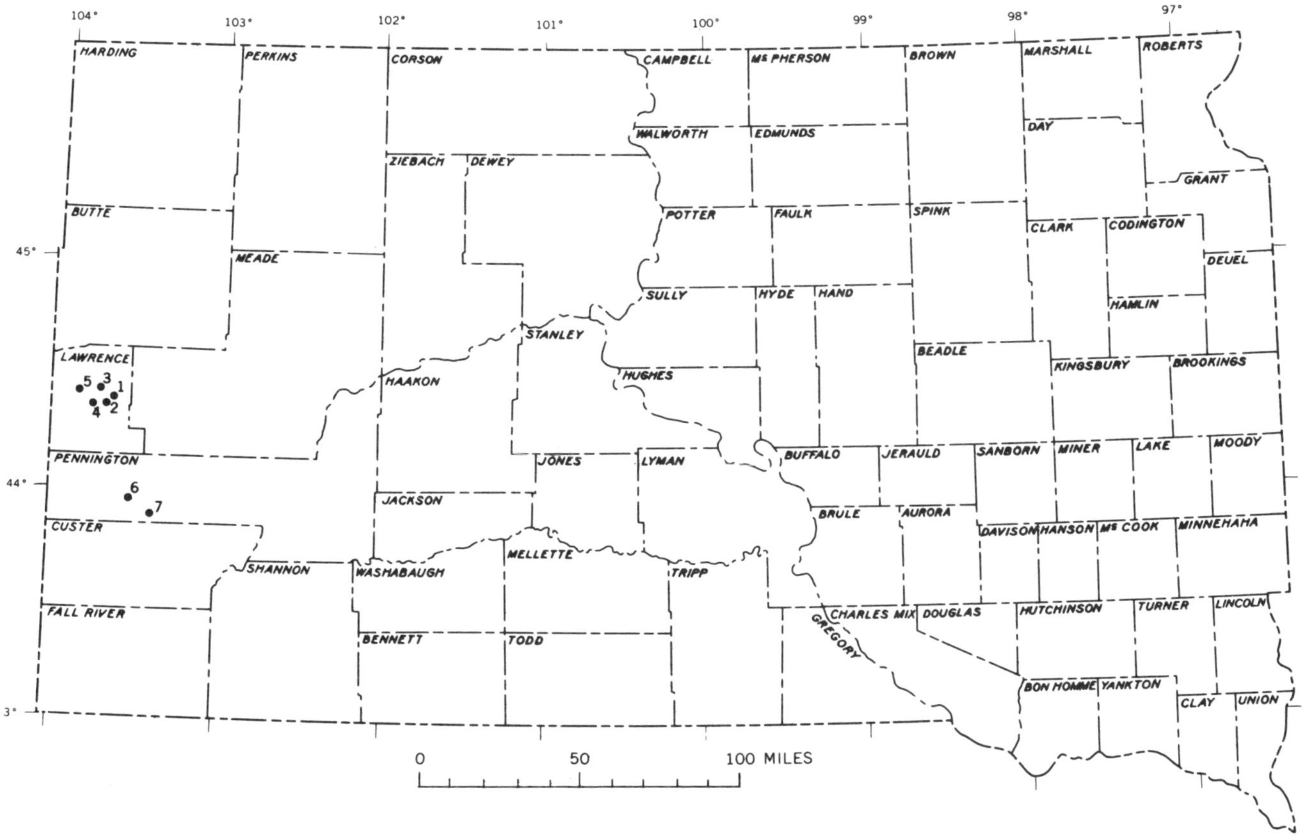

Figure 23.—Gold-mining districts of South Dakota. 1, Deadwood-Two Bit; 2, Lead; 3, Garden; 4, Bald Mountain; 5, Squaw Creek; 6, Hill City; 7, Keystone.

slate, and quartzite, (2) amphibolites that cut the metasedimentary rocks, and (3) granite that intrudes the other two (Noble and Harder, 1948). The famous Homestake ore body occurs in a cummingtonite schist unit, known as the Homestake Formation, which ranges from 200 to 300 feet in thickness and lies stratigraphically about 2,000 feet above the base of the Precambrian rocks exposed in the Lead area.

Encircling the outcrop area of Precambrian rocks is a thick section of Paleozoic sedimentary rocks which are, in ascending order, the Cambrian Deadwood Formation, the Ordovician Whitewood Formation, the Mississippian Englewood and Pahasapa Formations, the Pennsylvanian Minnelusa Formation, and the Permian Opeche Formation and Minnekahta Limestone. The outer rim of the Black Hills is made up of a series of rims and hogbacks of Mesozoic rocks. The main period of deformation that produced the Black Hills dome occurred in post-Cretaceous time, during the Laramide orogeny. The structures seem to be a result of vertical forces, caused probably by magmatic intrusions (Noble, 1952).

The gold deposits of the Black Hills can be grouped into the following classes:

1. Replacement deposits in Precambrian rocks.
2. Deposits that resemble placers in the basal conglomerate of the Cambrian.
3. Replacement deposits of Tertiary age in the Deadwood Formation and Pahasapa Limestone.

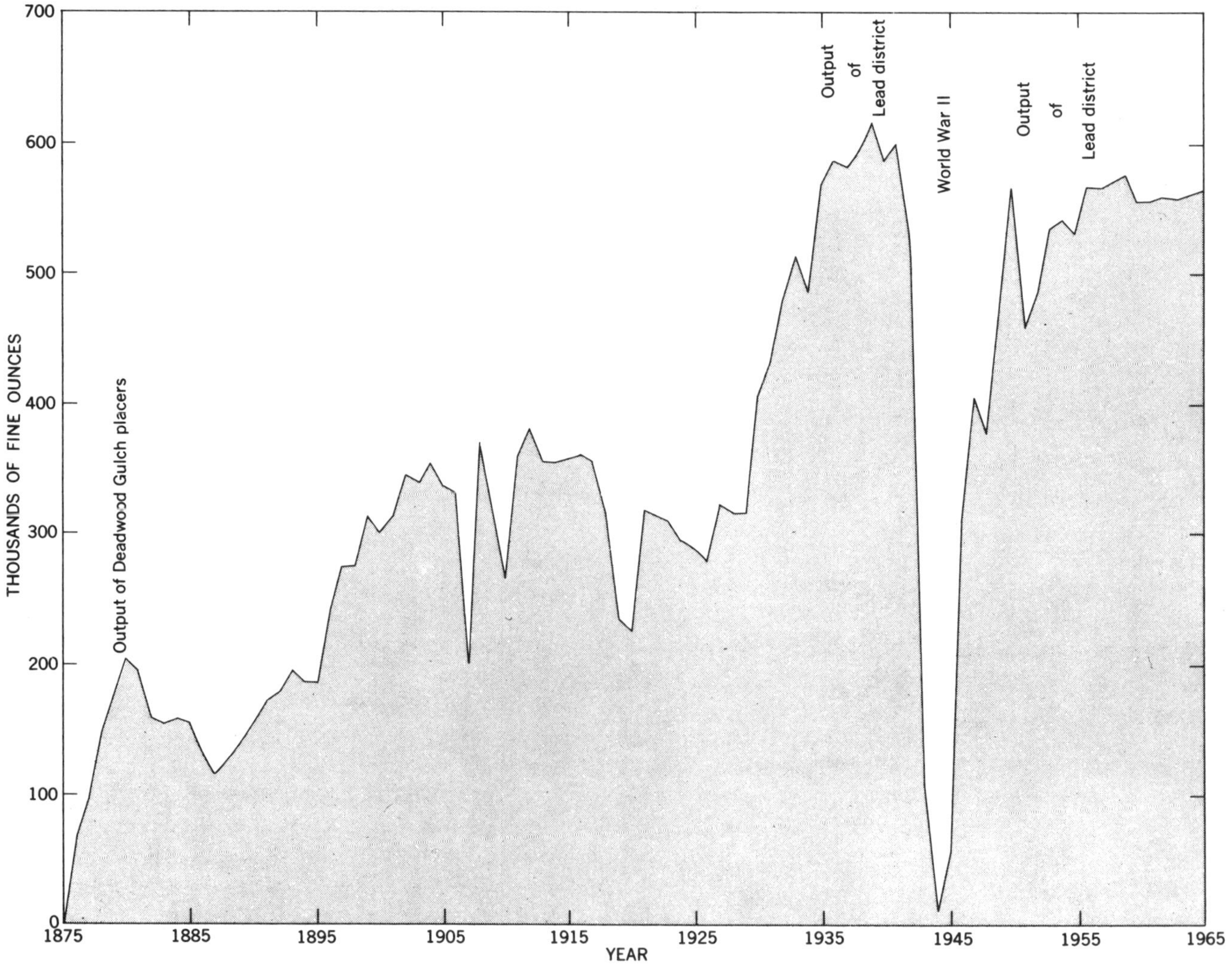

FIGURE 24.—Annual gold production of South Dakota, 1875–1965. Sources of data: 1875–80 and 1894 from O'Harra and Todd (1902, p. 52), 1881–1923 from U.S. Geological Survey (1883–1924, 1896–1900), and 1924–65 from U.S. Bureau of Mines (1925–34, 1933–66). Production reported in dollar value was converted to ounces at the prevailing price per ounce.

4. Deposits in the Tertiary eruptive rocks.
5. Recent placer deposits.

In the early days of mining in the Black Hills substantial amounts of gold, silver, and lead were obtained from deposits in the Paleozoic rocks, but these were soon exhausted and the bulk of the gold has come from the Homestake replacement ore bodies. The main gold-producing area consists of about 100 square miles in the northern Black Hills. Seven districts have produced more than 10,000 ounces of gold; five are in Lawrence County and two, in Pennington County.

LAWRENCE COUNTY

Lawrence County is in western South Dakota along the Wyoming State line. It includes much of the northern part of the Black Hills and most of the mineralized area, including the famous Homestake mine in the Lead district.

Through 1959, Lawrence County produced a total of 26,386,000 ounces of gold, mostly from the Homestake mine in the Lead district. Other gold districts that have yielded more than 10,000 ounces are the Deadwood-Two Bit, Garden, Bald Mountain, and Squaw Creek.

BALD MOUNTAIN DISTRICT

The Bald Mountain district, which includes the Portland area, is 3½ miles southwest of the Lead district.

Claims were located in the Portland area in 1877, but early mining was handicapped by the highly refractory nature of the ore. By 1891 the milling and metallurgical difficulties were overcome by the chlorination process, and in 1892 cyanidation proved successful (Connolly and O'Harra, 1929, p. 143–147). The district entered a period of prosperous development that ended at the close of World War I owing to high costs. The increased price of gold in 1934 caused a pronounced reactivation which lasted until World War II. After the war, mining was resumed on a small scale, but increased operating costs again forced the owners to close in 1959.

About $3 million worth of bullion, mostly in gold, was produced by the Mogul Mining Co. up to 1900 (Allsman, 1940, p. 38). Other companies were also active during this early period. Total gold production of the district through 1959 was roughly 1,400,000 ounces.

Rocks of the district are chiefly southwest-tilted strata of the Cambrian Deadwood Formation, underlain by the Precambrian schist. Numerous sheets, dikes, and irregular bodies of Tertiary phonolite and rhyolite porphyry cut the older rocks (Irving and others, 1904, p. 144–145).

The gold deposits are in replacement bodies in the Deadwood Formation and are the most productive deposits of this type in the Black Hills. Ore bodies are in two zones known locally as the "upper contact" and "lower contact." Deposits in the "lower contact" are in lenticular dolomite beds interbedded with shale within a stratigraphic interval of from 6 to 30 feet above the basal quartzite unit of the Deadwood Formation. The "upper contact" is defined as a sequence of mineralized dolomite beds and shale 12 to 18 feet below the *Scolithus* sandstone, which is the uppermost unit of the Deadwood Formation (Irving and others, 1904, p. 122–123).

Ore deposits occur in vertical shoots, probably mineralized fractures through which the ore solutions moved and from which replacement was started. The distance to which replacement has extended away from the fractures varies with the character of the beds and intensity of the mineralizing action. The widths of the vertical shoots range from thin seams up to 10 feet, and rarely up to 40 feet. Ore bodies of considerable width may be due either to coalescence of several parallel shoots or to the existence of many intersecting fractures (Irving and others, 1904, p. 134–136). The vertical extent of the shoots depends upon the thickness of the dolomitic rocks through which they pass, although some shoots extend into both overlying and underlying sandstone or shale. The maximum length of the shoots is several hundred feet; the longer shoots probably overlap fractures arranged en echelon.

The ore is classified under two types: blue ore which is the primary ore, and red ore which is oxidized ore. The primary ore consists of pyrite and probably arsenopyrite, most of which is very fine grained to microscopic in size. In some ore the gold telluride sylvanite has been found, but most of the gold is believed to be associated with the fine-grained pyrite (Connolly and O'Harra, 1929, p. 162). Small amounts of galena and sphalerite are seen in polished sections of the ore. The gangue is chiefly quartz and some fluorite, gypsum, and barite. Most of the ore mined is the red ore, which consists mainly of gold-bearing limonite and is amenable to cyaniding. Blue ore is highly refractory and is not extensively mined.

DEADWOOD-TWO BIT DISTRICT

The Deadwood-Two Bit district is near the town of Deadwood in east-central Lawrence County. The district includes mining camps on Deadwood, Two Bit, Strawberry, and Elk Creeks. Both placers and lodes have been productive; however, most of the gold has come from placers in Deadwood Gulch. The total minimum gold output through 1959 was about 284,000 ounces.

The Deadwood Gulch placers, discovered in 1875, yielded an estimated $4 million (193,500 ounces) in gold by 1880. Stimulated by the rich placer finds, prospectors combed the area and quickly found a variety of other gold-bearing deposits, including placerlike deposits in the basal conglomerate of the Cambrian Deadwood Formation.

The first quartz mill brought into the Black Hills reached Deadwood in September 1876 and was erected near Gayville in Deadwood Gulch (Connolly and O'Harra, 1929, p. 138). It treated conglomerate ore from the Hidden Treasure mine in Spring Gulch and before the close of the year had produced $20,000 in gold. Additional mills were built, and by the early part of 1878, milling of conglomerate ore was at its height with 20 mills and 500 stamps in operation. After 1878 the richer deposits gradually became exhausted, and by 1881 work upon them had practically ceased. The amount of gold recovered is not known (Allsman, 1940, p. 22–23; Irving and others, 1904, p. 98–111).

In 1878 gold ore was discovered in the Precambrian rocks in the Cloverleaf mine in the southeastern part of the district near Roubaix on Elk Creek about 8 miles southeast of Deadwood. It was worked for only about 10 years, but during this period $400,000 in gold was extracted. Periodic operations continued in later years, but the mine was closed in 1937. Total production of the mine was about 43,885 ounces of gold and about 300 ounces of silver (Allsman, 1940, p. 14, 15).

The earliest record of production from replacement deposits in the Deadwood Formation is in 1892, when the Mascot mine, about 3½ miles east of Deadwood, began shipping ore (Allsman, 1940, p. 50). The discovery of veins in the Tertiary eruptive rocks in Strawberry Gulch, about 3 to 4 miles southeast of Deadwood, dates back at least to 1893 when the Oro Fino property of the Gilt Edge Mines, Inc., was worked (Allsman, 1940, p. 56).

The history of the Deadwood-Two Bit district is characterized by sporadic activity, and there has been no major producer with sustained output. The district was virtually dormant from 1937 through 1959.

The deposit of the Cloverleaf mine is in Precambrian rock composed of mica schist, slate, chlorite schist, quartzite, and amphibolite. The ore consists of galena, sphalerite, pyrite, and native gold in a saddle-shaped mass of quartz on a southeast-plunging anticlinal fold in the mica schist (Connolly and O'Harra, 1929, p. 113).

The so-called placer deposits in the Deadwood Formation consist of a gold-bearing conglomerate overlying the Precambrian rocks. Pebbles and small boulders of quartz, quartzite, and schist are cemented by pyrite or iron oxide where the conglomerate is gold bearing. The barren conglomerate is characterized by a quartzitic or calcareous matrix. Though Irving and Emmons (in Irving and others, 1904, p. 99, 111) did note that some of the gold may have been introduced with the pyrite and some may have been chemically reprecipitated in the conglomerate by ferric sulfate solutions, they postulated that much of it was of detrital origin and was derived from erosion of the gold lodes in the Precambrian rocks nearby. Noble (1950, p. 246), on the other hand, considered it doubtful that any of the gold was of placer origin.

Gold has also been mined from replacement deposits in dolomite beds of the Deadwood Formation. Two zones, known as the "lower contact" and "upper contact," contain the ore bodies. The "lower contact," which ranges from a few feet to 30 feet in thickness, consists of several dolomite beds interlayered with shale beneath an impervious shale and immediately overlying the basal conglomerate unit. The "upper contact" is near the top of the formation and consists of two to six beds of dolomite separated by shale. The ore bodies are lenticular masses parallel to bedding and consist of aggregates of quartz, chalcedony, barite, and fluorite and contain disseminated fine-grained pyrite, arsenopyrite, and local stibnite. Tellurium is present in analyses, and the gold and silver probably occur in fine-grained telluride minerals (Irving and others, 1904, p. 124–143).

A few gold deposits in the Deadwood-Two Bit district, near Strawberry Gulch, occur in Tertiary eruptive rocks and in adjacent brecciated Precambrian and Cambrian rocks. Most of the ore is in the form of auriferous limonite fissure fillings in a large mass of decomposed quartz monzonite porphyry. The limonite gives way at depth to pyrite and a little galena and copper sulfides (Allsman, 1940, p. 57).

GARDEN DISTRICT

The Garden (Maitland) district is 1 to 3 miles northwest of Lead, in Blacktail and Sheeptail Gulches and False Bottom Creek.

The dates of mineral discovery and earliest mining in this district have not been ascertained, but it is probable that some properties were being worked in the 1880's. In 1902 the Maitland mine, which became the principal mine in the district, was put into operation. Activity continued until 1942, when the Maitland was closed. From 1943 through 1959, no production was reported from the district. The total gold output of the district through 1959 was at least 176,000 ounces; the Maitland mine is credited with 137,000 ounces.

The district is in the northeast part of the Precambrian core of the Black Hills dome. Bedrock consists of slate, schist, and quartzite beds of Precambrian age, the Deadwood Formation of Cambrian age, and bodies of intrusive quartz monzonite porphyry and rhyolite of Tertiary age (Darton and Paige, 1925). The ore deposits are replacement bodies in dolomite beds in the lower part of the Deadwood Formation, immediately above the basal conglomerate. Fractures, parallel to the foliation of the Precambrian rocks, extend upward into the Deadwood and provided avenues for the mineralizing solutions. Primary ore consists of finely divided gold and silver in pyrite, but most of the ore mined was oxidized and was probably mostly gold- and silver-bearing limonite (Allsman, 1940, p. 42).

LEAD DISTRICT

The Lead district, which includes Yellow Creek, is in central Lawrence County in the central part of the mineralized area of the Black Hills. The district contains the famous Homestake mine, the leading gold producer in the United States and the only major operation in the district.

Through 1959, the Homestake Mining Co. produced a total of about 24,450,000 ounces of gold and 5,830,000 ounces of silver. Of this amount, about 1,552,665 ounces of gold and 305,600 ounces of silver were mined before 1904 by companies that were later consolidated with the Homestake (data furnished by and published with permission of the Homestake Mining Co.).

The Homestake Mining Co., which was incorporated in 1877, originally held only two fractional claims covering about 14 acres. These claims were purchased from prospectors who had located them in 1876 and had taken out about $5,000 in gold. Other companies—the Father de Smet, Highland, and Deadwood-Terra—were organized and in operation in 1878, but they were gradually assimilated by Homestake (Irving and others, 1904, p. 57). By 1931 the Homestake Co. controlled 654 mining claims covering 5,639 acres (Allen, 1931, p. 290).

The expanding operations are best reflected by production data. From 1881 through 1894, annual gold output ranged from 45,960 ounces to 66,280 ounces. In 1900, about 172,000 ounces was produced, and in 1910, about 225,000 ounces. Production exceeded 500,000 ounces in 1935 and, except for the period 1942–52, it remained above 500,000 ounces per year through 1959.

Rocks in the Lead district are mainly Precambrian in age and consist of six formations with a total thickness of about 20,000 feet. A few erosional remnants of the basal conglomerate of the Cambrian Deadwood Formation cap some of the hills and ridges. Igneous rocks are of two ages: amphibolite bodies derived from Precambrian gabbroic rocks, and small stocks, plugs, and dikes of Tertiary porphyries that range in composition from granite to syenite (Noble and Harder, 1948, p. 942–954).

The Precambrian rocks are dominantly iron-magnesium schistose rocks in the lower part of the sequence and argillaceous phyllites and schists in the upper part. They were isoclinally folded in Precambrian time and deformed further during the time of Tertiary intrusive activity. In the vicinity of the Homestake mine the lower three Precambrian formations—the Poorman, Homestake, and Ellison Formations—are exposed. All the major ore bodies occur in the Homestake Formation, which is a sideroplesite schist containing many bands of recrystallized chert. Where the Precambrian rocks were metamorphosed to the garnet zone of progressive metamorphism, the sideroplesite schist of the Homestake Formation was converted to cummingtonite schist (Noble and Harder, 1948, p. 963–965).

The ore bodies are linear or pipelike replacement deposits in the Homestake Formation. The schist is chloritized and has masses of quartz and crosscutting and conformable veins of quartz, quartz-chlorite-arsenopyrite, pyrrhotite, quartz-ankerite, and calcite-pyrite. Arsenopyrite is also abundant in the chloritized rock near the conformable quartz veins. Four distinct stages of mineralization have been recognized. Gold is associated with arsenopyrite and also occurs in chloritized rock along the walls of quartz veins. Chlorite-pyrrhotite schist which surrounds conformable quartz masses also contains considerable gold (Noble, 1950, p. 231–236).

Noble (1950, p. 224–231) noted that the ore bodies were localized in zones of younger cross folds superimposed on the older isoclinal folds. Dilatancy, or increase of porosity in these zones, permitted a free circulation of mineralizing fluids.

The age of mineralization of the Homestake deposits has been postulated as both Precambrian and Tertiary. After reviewing the evidence and the opinions of earlier workers, Noble (1950, p. 245–

247) concluded that the problem was far from solved.

In addition to those just described, two other types of gold deposits have been mined on a small scale in the district. Auriferous conglomerate in the thin remnants of the Deadwood Formation in the hills just north of the town of Lead supported small gold-mining operations, and replacement deposits in the lower dolomite bed of the Deadwood Formation in the Yellow Creek area yielded about 125,070 ounces of gold to 1920 (Connolly and O'Harra, 1929, p. 137–142; Allsman, 1940, p. 40). The Wasp No. 2 mine was the chief producer in the Yellow Creek area.

SQUAW CREEK DISTRICT

The Squaw Creek district, which includes the Ragged Top, Elk Mountain, and Carbonate areas, is in western Lawrence County west of the Bald Mountain and Garden districts. The recorded gold production of the district through 1959 was about 76,000 ounces, of which about 75,800 ounces came from the Ragged Top Mountain area.

Lead and silver ores were discovered in the Carbonate area in the early 1880's and peak production was from 1885 to 1891. Only small amounts of gold were recovered as a byproduct from this ore (Allsman, 1940, p. 53). In 1896 considerable excitement was caused by the discovery of boulders of silicified limestone containing gold in the Ragged Top Mountain area. Shortly thereafter gold lodes were found west and south of Ragged Top Mountain and in the Squaw Creek and Annie Creek areas. The deposits north of Ragged Top Mountain yielded about $316,000 in gold (15,285 ounces) from 1896 to 1899. The mines west of Ragged Top Mountain were most active from 1899 to 1906 (Allsman, 1940, p. 53). After 1914 the district declined, and only a few ounces of gold from scattered placer activities was reported from 1915 through 1959.

The Squaw Creek district is a plateau 2½ miles wide and 5 miles long on the northwest side of the Black Hills dome. The Mississippian Pahasapa Limestone, which forms the caprock on the plateau, is underlain by the Cambrian sedimentary rocks which are exposed along streams that have cut through the limestone. The sedimentary rocks are intruded by Tertiary porphyry bodies, and in the Ragged Top Mountain area a laccolith of phonolite is intruded at the base of the Carboniferous beds (Irving and others, 1904, p. 172). The ore bodies occur in the flat-lying Pahasapa Limestone adjoining the phonolite mass.

The ore deposits occur in silicified vertical fractures and in irregular masses of silicified limestone in the Pahasapa. The most productive ore bodies, west of Ragged Top Mountain, are flat shoots near the surface, which apparently are lateral extensions from the tops of vertical fissure veins. A thin, relatively impervious capping, which seems to cover most of the deposits, apparently caused the rising mineralizing solutions to spread below the cap, thus forming the flat ore bodies (Allsman, 1940, p. 52).

The ore body consists of light-buff silicified limestone and purple fluorite containing gold, silver, and tellurium. The presence of tellurium indicates that the precious metals probably occur as tellurides in the unaltered ore. In general the veins are shallow and are said to become narrow at depth; in places ore bodies pinch out at depths of 60 feet. The veins have not been explored generally to any great depth (Irving and others, 1904, p. 173–177).

PENNINGTON COUNTY

Pennington County lies just south of Lawrence County and includes part of what is known as the southern Black Hills. From available production records, which are very fragmentary and incomplete, it is estimated that Pennington County had a minimum production through 1959 of about 128,000 ounces of gold; most of it was from lode deposits and small amounts were from placers.

Gold was found in 1875 in the gravels of Spring Creek, Palmer Gulch, Castle Creek, and Rapid Creek by the Jenney expedition (Newton and Jenney, 1880, p. 238–272). Most of the placers were of low grade, and the discouraged prospectors turned northward to the more promising diggings in the Deadwood area and left the southern part of the Black Hills virtually deserted. The new arrivals found that most of the favorable ground around Deadwood had been claimed; accordingly, some of them, prospecting enroute, returned to the southern Black Hills (Hughes, 1924, p. 21–26). In 1876 the Columbia lode in the Keystone district was located; the nearby Bullion lode was found in 1877 (Connolly and O'Harra, 1929, p. 118–119). In the Hill City area, the Gold Metal deposit was explored as early as 1878 (Allsman, 1940, p. 72). Gold mining in the early years was apparently conducted in a desultory fashion, and production probably was small.

In May 1883, tin ore was discovered in what is now known as the Etta spodumene mine, and other discoveries of tin ore in the Harney Park area followed. The tin boom lasted until about 1894, after which gold prospecting was resumed and several significant discoveries were made (Connolly and O'Harra, 1929, p. 115–116). Among these were the Keystone and the Holy Terror lodes which were located in 1892 and in 1894 respectively. In 1898 the Keystone was sold to the Holy Terror Co.; the combined properties have been the largest producers in the southern Black Hills (Allsman, 1940, p. 91–94). After 1903 the most active period was in the early 1940's, when the Keystone mine was reopened briefly. Most of the mines in Pennington County were idle during 1906–27. In 1928 and 1929 some mines were revived in the Keystone district; in 1935 some lode mines and placers in the Hill City district were worked. Gold mining in Pennington County practically ceased from 1943 through 1959. In the county, only the Keystone and Hill City districts have produced more than 10,000 ounces of gold.

HILL CITY DISTRICT

The Hill City district is an area of widely scattered gold deposits in western Pennington County in the vicinity of Hill City, near the headwaters of Spring Creek and around Rochford to the northwest of Hill City. Although production figures are incomplete for the early years, it is estimated that the Hill City district had a minimum total output through 1959 of roughly 35,400 ounces of gold, mostly from lodes. The district was dormant from 1939 through 1959.

The Hill City district lies along the west side of the mass of Precambrian rocks that forms the core of the Black Hills. The Precambrian rocks consist of complexly folded and distorted schist and quartzite. A short distance to the southeast of the district these rocks are intruded by the Precambrian Harney Peak Granite (Darton and Paige, 1925, p. 3–5; Connolly and O'Harra, 1929, p. 129–134).

The lode-gold deposits occur in quartz fissure veins and lenses and mineralized shear zones. The deposits southwest and east of Hill City are chiefly quartz veins that cut the metamorphic rocks (Allsman, 1940, p. 69). The veins range in width from a few inches to 6 feet. Most of them are shallow, although a few have been mined to depths of 700 feet. The veins consist predominantly of quartz in which free gold is irregularly distributed. West of Silver City, a quartz vein in the schist contains masses and streaks of lead-antimony sulfide, arsenopyrite, pyrite, a little sphalerite, and free gold (Paige, in Darton and Paige, 1925, p. 28).

The mineralized shear zones are most common in a belt extending northwest from Hill City (Allsman, 1940, p. 69). These are zones of brecciated schist cemented by granular quartz and arsenopyrite, pyrite, sphalerite, and free gold. Most of these deposits are low grade.

In the Rochford area gold deposits are found in quartz veins and lenses that cut the cummingtonite schist (Connolly and O'Harra, 1929, p. 129–134). The ore minerals are arsenopyrite, pyrite, pyrrhotite, chalcopyrite, a little magnetite, and gold which is associated particularly with the arsenopyrite. The gangue minerals are cummingtonite, quartz, carbonates, biotite, garnet, and chlorite. The general character of the ore and the geologic relations are analogous to those in the Homestake ore body (Noble and Harder, 1948, p. 954–955).

KEYSTONE DISTRICT

The Keystone district is in western Pennington County and extends from about 3½ miles northwest of the town of Keystone to 1½ miles southeast. From available records, it is estimated that the Keystone district had a minimum output through 1959 of about 85,000 ounces of lode gold, of which about 76,000 ounces came from the Keystone-Holy Terror mine (Allsman, 1940, p. 91–94). No figures are available on the amount of placer production, which apparently was small.

The Keystone district is on the northeast side of the Harney Peak batholith near the eastern margin of the core of Precambrian rocks of the Black Hills (Darton and Paige, 1925). Precambrian rocks consisting of schist, quartzite, amphibolite, and many granite and pegmatite dikes, are the predominant rock units of the district. The rocks are tightly folded and are cut by faults and shear zones, some of which are mineralized (Connolly and O'Harra, 1929, p. 120–121).

The ore bodies are in quartz veins or lenticular replacement deposits which trend parallel to the foliation of the enclosing schist. The Holy Terror vein was mined for a maximum distance of 1,200 feet along the strike and to a depth of 1,200 feet, and it ranged from a few inches to 6 feet in width. The gangue consisted of white quartz and the ore mineral was coarse flaky gold (Allsman, 1940, p. 91). Other deposits contained a wider variety of minerals, including arsenopyrite, pyrrhotite, pyrite, chalcopyrite, sphalerite, and native gold as ore minerals and quartz, hornblende, biotite, ankerite, chlorite, graphite, and garnet in the gangue. In some deposits the gold was very fine grained. The ore deposits are believed to be Precambrian in age and genetically related to the Harney Peak Granite (Connolly and O'Harra, 1929, p. 123–129).

TENNESSEE

Almost all Tennessee's gold has come from placer deposits in Monroe County and from the copper ores of the Ducktown district in Polk County, both in the southeast corner of the State.

Gold was discovered on Coker Creek, Monroe County, in 1827, and by 1854 a total of $46,023 worth of gold had been extracted from placers in this area (Ashley, 1911, p. 83–84), where sporadic small-scale operations continued from the close of the Civil War to about 1911. Total production from the Coker Creek area was about 9,000 ounces (R. A. Laurence, written commun., 1962). Fissure veins, high terrace gravels, present stream gravels, and alluvial cones were mined (O. N. Rove, unpub. data, 1926). The vein deposits are too low grade to be of economic value.

The search for gold in the early 1840's led to discoveries of copper ores at Ducktown, and mining of the rich chalcocite deposits began in 1847. By 1879 these ores were exhausted. Though there were large reserves of primary sulfide ore, the status of copper metallurgy and prices at that time made further mining unprofitable (Emmons and Laney, 1926, p. 31). After 1890 new roasting techniques were developed; the mines were reopened and were active through 1959.

Gold ores, as such, were not mined in the Ducktown district, but small amounts of gold and silver were recovered from the sulfide ores after 1904. Although early records are incomplete and inaccurate, the best available data indicate that Tennessee's total gold production from 1831 through 1959 was about 23,800 ounces, of which 14,872 ounces was recovered from the Ducktown ores (R. A. Laurence, written commun., 1962).

The country rocks in the Ducktown district consist of graywacke, conglomerate, mica schist, slate, staurolite schist, and garnet schist, all units of the Great Smoky Group, of late Precambrian age. These are cut by several gabbro dikes. The rocks have been intricately folded, but the major pattern consists of three northeastward-plunging anticlines on which are superimposed numerous drag folds (Emmons and Laney, 1926, p. 14, 24). Three fault systems, some preore and others postore, cut the rocks (Simmons, 1950, p. 68). The ore deposits are tabular or lens-shaped replacement bodies in limestone in the mica schist, which has been complexly folded and faulted (Emmons and Laney, 1926, p. 64). Ross (1935, p. 40–43, 97–101), on the other hand, believed the deposits to be multistage hydrothermal vein deposits. The ore is of three types: surficial gossan, rich in hydrous iron oxides; secondary sulfide ore, just below the water table; and the primary sulfide ore. The primary minerals are pyrrhotite, chalcopyrite, pyrite, sphalerite and minor amounts of galena, bornite, magnetite and arsenopyrite. Gangue minerals in the primary ore are actinolite, tremolite, garnet and some zoisite, quartz, calcite, and dolomite. In the secondary ore, chalcocite is the most abundant ore mineral. Covellite, marcasite, and numerous copper sulfates are sparse, and small amounts of gold and silver occur in the primary and secondary sulfide ores (Emmons and Laney, 1926, p. 41–51, 76).

UTAH

Most of the ore deposits in Utah are found in its western part—in the mountain ranges in and flanking the Great Basin. The most productive districts, principally the Bingham, Tintic, Camp Floyd, and Park City, are south and east of Salt Lake City. Through 1960 Utah produced about 17,765,000 ounces of gold and ranked sixth among the States in total gold production; 13 districts in 9 counties yielded more than 10,000 ounces of gold each through 1957 (fig. 25).

The State's early development was influenced more by religious motives than by the gold fever which drew settlers to the other Cordilleran States. Furthermore, placer deposits, the first incentive to prospecting in the other Western States, were unimportant in Utah.

In 1847, when Utah was still part of Mexico, the Mormons crossed the plains and formed a settlement in the valley of Great Salt Lake. Under the direction of the church, they established other settlements in a few years on nearly all the important streams where irrigation was practicable or where conditions were especially favorable for stock raising. Mining, however, was discouraged (Butler and others, 1920, p. 117–118).

Nevertheless, the presence of metallic deposits in Utah was known to the early Mormon settlers, for small amounts of lead ore were mined in the 1850's for making bullets. Active prospecting, however, was first undertaken in 1862 by members of the California Volunteers, stationed at Camp Douglas near Salt Lake City, many of whom were prospectors and miners from the gold fields of California. Though lead ore was mined earlier from the Rollins mine in Beaver County, the first claim in Utah was located on outcrops of lead carbonate in Bingham Canyon in September 1863. In December of that year the first mining district, the West Mountain,

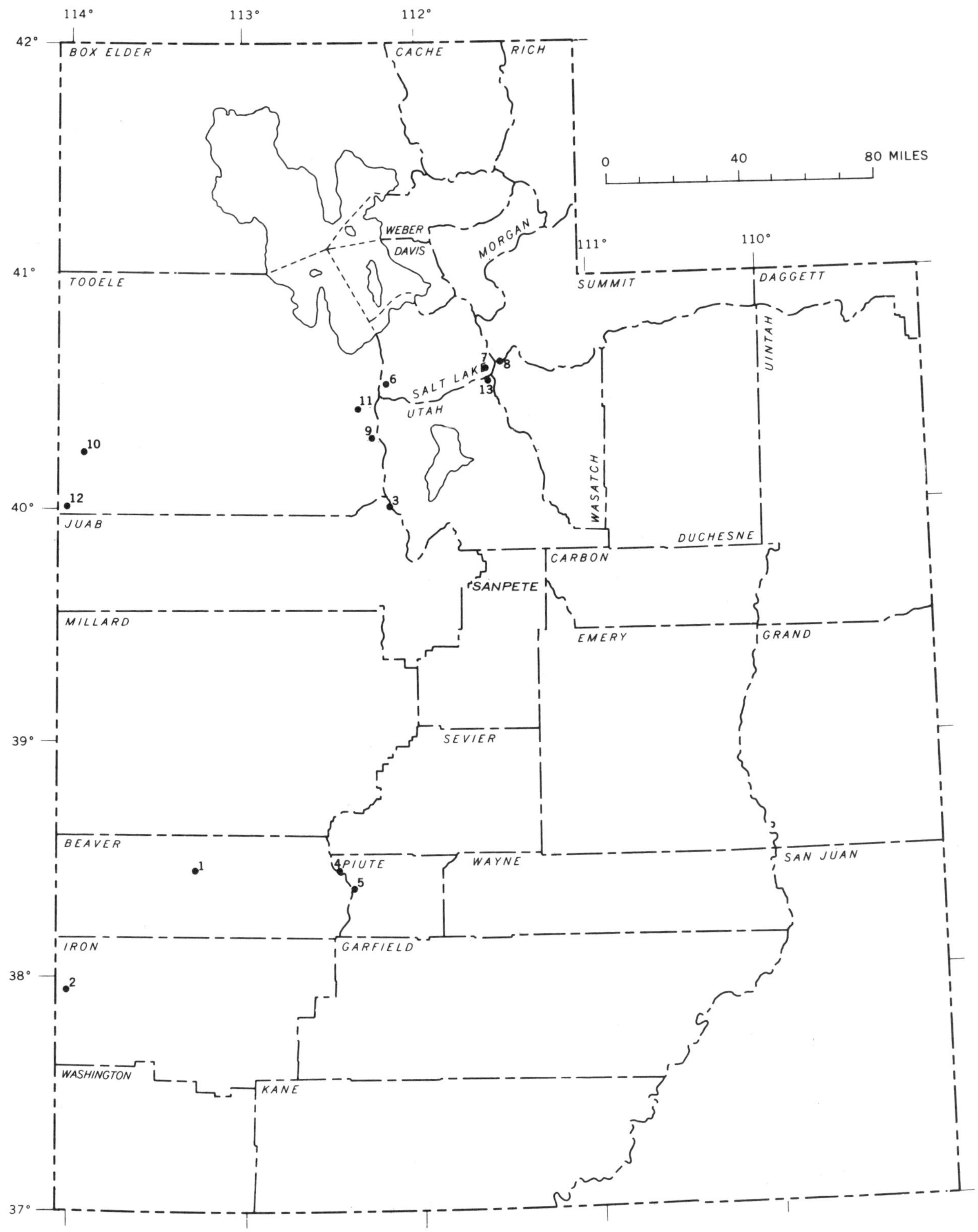

FIGURE 25.—Gold-mining districts of Utah.

Beaver County:
1, San Francisco.
Iron County:
2, Stateline.
Juab County:
3, Tintic.
Piute County:
4, Gold Mountain; 5, Mount Baldy.
Salt Lake County:
6, Cottonwood; 7, Bingham.
Summit and Wasatch Counties:
8, Park City.
Tooele County:
9, Camp Floyd; 10, Ophir-Rush Valley; 11, Clifton; 12, Willow Springs.
Utah County:
13, American Fork.

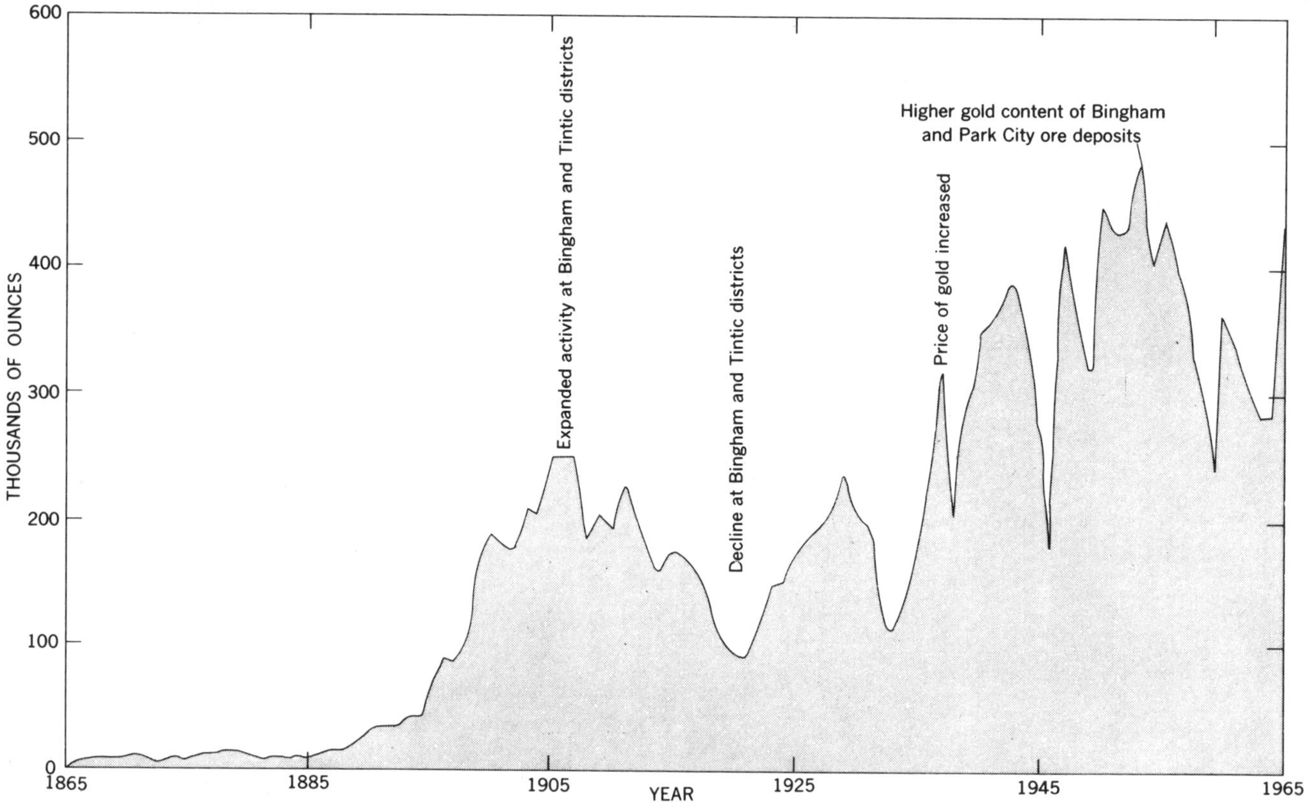

FIGURE 26.—Annual gold production of Utah, 1865–1965. Sources of data: 1865–1917 from Butler, Loughlin, and Heikes (1920, p. 127–128); 1918–23 from U.S. Geological Survey (1919–24); 1924–65 from U.S. Bureau of Mines (1925–34; 1933–66). Production reported in dollar value was converted to ounces at the prevailing price per ounce.

was formed. Gold placers were found in Bingham Canyon in 1864 and were mined the following year. Their total yield was only 91,000–95,000 ounces. By 1870 production from silver-lead lode deposits became important throughout the State (Butler and others, 1920, p. 118).

As in the other Western States, the ore deposits of Utah are closely related to stocks and small batholiths mostly of Tertiary age. Small amounts of gold occur in all the mineral deposits of the State, except the iron and uranium-vanadium deposits. Most of the gold, however, was recovered as a byproduct of base-metal ores (fig. 26). The large porphyry copper deposit at Bingham is the largest producer of byproduct gold in the United States.

BEAVER COUNTY

Beaver County, in southwestern Utah, contains extensive deposits of silver, lead, zinc, copper, and relatively small amounts of gold.

It is credited with the first mineral output in Utah, a few tons of lead ore produced from 1860 to 1863 at the Rollins mine in the Lincoln district (Butler and others, 1920, p. 503). It became important in mining when silver was discovered in the early 1870's in the San Francisco, Star, and Beaver Lake districts and remained important until 1926. Gold production was mainly from 1860 to 1950; total production from 1860 through 1959 was about 55,850 ounces. The San Francisco was the only district that produced more than 10,000 ounces.

SAN FRANCISCO DISTRICT

The San Francisco district, located in the San Francisco Mountains in the central part of Beaver County, has yielded 60 percent of the gold output of the county, mostly as a byproduct of base-metal ores. Records of early production are incomplete, but Butler (in Butler and others, 1920, p. 503) credited the district with a gold output of 21,822 ounces through 1917. Total production through 1959 was about 33,400 ounces.

Ore was discovered in about 1871, but the district was of little importance until the Horn Silver mine became productive in 1876 (D. B. Huntley, quoted by Butler, 1913, p. 111). For about 10 years this mine was one of the most successful in the State. Several other mines in the district also were active intermittently, depending on the fluctuating prices of base metals and silver.

The following description of geology and ore deposits is by D. M. Lemmon (written commun., 1963).

Sedimentary rocks exposed in the San Francisco Mountains are in three thrust plates. The top plate, which makes up Frisco Peak, is composed of upper Precambrian quartzite and argillite; the middle plate is Upper Cambrian and Ordovician dolomite, limestone, shale, and quartzite; and the lower plate is Mississippian and Pennsylvanian dolomite, limestone, and minor sandstone. After thrusting, the older rocks were largely covered by Tertiary volcanic rocks and then intruded by quartz monzonite.

The ore deposits that have yielded much of the byproduct gold are the silver-lead-copper-zinc replacement deposits in volcanic and carbonate rocks at the Horn Silver mine. At the surface, the main ore bodies are along a fault contact between Upper Cambrian carbonate rocks in the footwall and volcanic rocks in the hanging wall; the fault enters silicified carbonate at about 750 feet and remains in the altered sedimentary rocks to the 1,600-foot level. Deepest ore found was on the 1,200-foot level, but principal output was above the 1,000-foot level. The principal primary ore minerals are galena, pyrite, and sphalerite, and the less important ore minerals are chalcopyrite, sulfantimonides, and sulfarsenides. A large suite of secondary minerals is developed through oxidation and through secondary enrichment of sulfides. All the ore contains a small amount of gold, perhaps 0.01 to 0.02 ounce per ton.

The copper ore of the Cactus mine is in breccia pipes in quartz monzonite. The principal primary ore minerals are pyrite and chalcopyrite, and small amounts of tetrahedrite, bornite, and cosalite are present. The important gangue minerals are hematite, sericite, quartz, tourmaline, siderite, anhydrite, and barite. In 1905–12, gold recovery was about 0.008 ounce per ton from 1,230,302 tons of copper ore treated. The ratio of silver to gold recovered was about 22:1.

IRON COUNTY

Iron County is in southwestern Utah, south of Beaver County along the Nevada border. In the central part of the county, the Iron Springs district produced major amounts of iron; in the extreme western part, the Stateline district produced silver, lead, and gold. Most of the 12,760 ounces of gold credited to the county through 1959 came from the Stateline district.

STATELINE DISTRICT

The Stateline (Gold Springs) district is along the Utah-Nevada boundary at about lat 38° N. Though the area was well traveled for many years, the mineralized outcrops that mark the ore deposits were neglected, primarily because gold had not been found in the stream gravels and partly because the limestone containing rich silver and lead deposits elsewhere in the State was not exposed in the Stateline district. Prospecting began in earnest in 1896, and success was almost immediate (Heikes, in Butler and others, 1920, p. 564, 565). The district entered a period of sustained development about 1917, after which decreasing ore reserves and increasing pumping costs forced most mines to close. Some mines were reopened during 1932–42, but all were virtually inactive from 1943 through 1959.

The bedrock of the district consists of extrusive latite, rhyolite, and rhyolite tuff (Butler, in Butler and others, 1920, p. 563–567). In the vicinity of Gold Springs, latite is exposed in the lower areas and is overlain by rhyolite; to the north around Stateline, rhyolite is the prevailing rock. All the formations appear to be horizontal but are extensively fissured.

The ore deposits occur in north-trending veins; in the Gold Springs camp the most productive veins were found in the latite and in the Stateline area some of the best deposits were found in the rhyolite (Butler and others, 1920, p. 565). The veins are crustified and consist chiefly of chalcedonic to fine-grained quartz, adularia (locally known as "yellow quartz"), carbonates, and generally a small amount of fluorite. The ore minerals are pyrite and native gold. Some gold is light colored and probably contains considerable silver. Some rich ore carries abundant tellurium; thus, a telluride of gold and silver may be one of the primary minerals. Oxidized ores contain cerargyrite, molybdite, and native mercury. In general the deposits are relatively shallow, but some in the Ophir mine were explored to a depth of 500 feet. Some veins end at depths of less than 100 feet where they separate into numerous quartz stringers in highly altered rock.

JUAB COUNTY

Juab County, in western Utah along the Nevada boundary, is in the eastern part of the Great Basin. The most important ore deposits are in the Tintic district, in the northeastern corner of the county, where large amounts of silver, gold, lead, copper, and zinc were mined. Several other districts produced gold, but only the Tintic had an output of more than 10,000 ounces. It produced approximately 2,648,000 ounces through 1959; however, this total included production of the East Tintic district, which is contiguous with the main Tintic district but is in Utah County.

TINTIC DISTRICT

The Tintic district, which includes the East Tintic district in Utah County, is about 60 miles south of Salt Lake City in the central part of the East Tintic Mountains. Eureka, the principal town, is near the center of the area.

One of the three most important mining districts in Utah, the Tintic yielded about $428,000,000 worth of silver, lead, gold, copper, and zinc through 1959. Of the 2,648,000 ounces of gold produced through 1959, about 65 percent came from the main Tintic district and about 35 percent from the East Tintic. The principal mines were the Chief, Centennial Eureka, Mammoth, Gemini, Eureka Hill, Iron Blossom, Tintic Standard, North Lilly, and Eureka Lilly.

The first claim was located in December 1869, and the district was organized the following year. In 1870, many deposits of silver-bearing lead-carbonate ore were found but were not developed on a large scale because of poor transportation facilities. The small amounts of rich silver and gold ores that were mined in the early 1870's were shipped to smelters at San Francisco, Calif., Baltimore, Md., and Swansea, Wales. Somewhat later most of the ores were sent to Argo and Pueblo, Colo., and the Salt Lake valley, Utah, for treatment (Lindgren and Loughlin, 1919, p. 105).

Railroad transportation, which became available in the late 1870's and early 1880's, had an immediate impact on the district. In 1879 the output of the district nearly doubled; production for 1885 was valued at $1 million and for 1890, at $5 million (Lindgren and Loughlin, 1919, p. 106).

The success of the district was established by important discoveries of several concealed ore bodies. In 1881 and 1882 the Iron Blossom and Godiva ore bodies were found at depths of a few hundred feet below the surface, and the subsurface extension of the Gemini ore zone was located. In 1909, drifts on the Chief 1 mine intercepted rich silver-lead ore from the northward continuation of the Mammoth ore zone (Cook, 1957, p. 76, 77). In 1916, exploration in the East Tintic area reached its climax when the large silver-lead ore body of the Tintic Standard mine was found at a depth of more than 1,000 feet (M. B. Kildale, in Cook, 1957, p. 104).

The annual gold production in the Tintic district was relatively small through most of the 1880's, but it increased sharply in 1889, and in 1907 reached its peak of 113,000 ounces valued at $2,335,000 (V. C. Heikes, in Lindgren and Loughlin, 1919, p. 108). Except for declines during World Wars I and II, the district was active until 1957. No mining was reported in 1958 and 1959.

According to H. T. Morris (in Cook, 1957, p. 4–26), the East Tintic Mountains are composed of a section of sedimentary rocks more than 32,000 feet thick, which are complexly faulted and folded, intruded by quartz monzonite and monzonite stocks, plugs, and dikes, and covered by quartz latite and latite flows and pyroclastics. The oldest rocks are late Precambrian in age and are phyllitic shales and quartzites tentatively correlated with the Big Cottonwood Formation of the Wasatch Range. Rocks of Cambrian age are the Tintic Quartzite and the superjacent carbonate and shale formations consisting of the Ophir Formation, Teutonic Limestone, Dagmar Limestone, Herkimer Limestone, Bluebird Dolomite, Cole Canyon Dolomite, Opex Formation, and Ajax Limestone. The carbonate lithology is persistent throughout the remainder of the Paleozoic section, which consists of the following formations: Opohonga Limestone and Fish Haven Dolomite of Ordovician age, the Bluebell Dolomite of Late Ordovician, Silurian, and Devonian age, the Victoria Formation of Devonian age, the Pinyon Peak Limestone of Late Devonian and Mississippian(?) age, the Madison Limestone, Deseret Limestone, Humbug Formation, and Great Blue Limestone of Mississippian age, the Manning Canyon Shale of Mississippian and Pennsylvanian age, the Oquirrh Formation of Pennsylvanian age, and the Diamond Creek(?) Sandstone and Park City(?) Formation of Permian age.

This entire sedimentary section was folded into a series of north-trending anticlines and synclines, the most prominent of which are, from west to east, the North Tintic anticline, the Tintic syncline, and the East Tintic anticline. The rocks were also complexly faulted several times and were intruded by quartz monzonite and monzonite porphyry stocks and latite, andesite, and diabase plugs, dikes, and sills. Tertiary extrusive rocks, consisting of the Packard and Fernow Quartz Latites and younger latite and basalt, cover large areas in the southern and eastern part of the East Tintic Mountains (H. T. Morris, in Cook, 1957, p. 30–51).

The ore deposits occur in limestone replacement bodies and in fissure veins, which have a spatial relationship with each other and with the intrusive rocks. Many of the replacement bodies, which were by far the most productive deposits in the district, are on the northward projection of fissure veins. Four principal replacement ore zones are recognized—the Gemini, Chief, Godiva, and Iron Blossom. They are elongate bodies, continuous in strike but discontinuous vertically, occupying a stratigraphic interval of 6,000 feet. The ore zones are continuous across faults; at certain fault intersections, chimneys of ore as much as 2,400 feet in vertical dimension are present (Cook, 1957, p. 63–70).

The common ore minerals of the replacement deposits are galena, sphalerite, argentite, enargite, and tetrahedrite. Oxidation of these deposits extends to depths of 2,000 feet and is marked by accumulations of malachite, azurite, chrysocolla, covellite, anglesite, cerussite, smithsonite, calamine, hydrozincite, cerargyrite, native silver, and plumbojarosite. Ore minerals of the fissure veins are chiefly enargite, argentite, and galena, and minor amounts of sphalerite, chalcopyrite, arsenopyrite, and tetrahedrite are present. Gangue minerals are pyrite, quartz, calcite, and barite (Cook, 1957, p. 70–71).

Both types of ore deposits are associated with bands of hydrothermal alteration. Near fissure veins, the rocks are impregnated with pyrite, jasperoid, barite, and sericite; the replacement deposits are surrounded by zones of jasperoid, clay minerals, dolomite, pyrite, and sericite (F. H. Howd, in Cook, 1957, p. 124–134).

Native gold is a rare constituent of the Tintic ores, though some oxidized ore shoots of the Mammoth mine contained flakes of native gold associated with jasperoid and quartz. Most of the gold is recovered from ore containing abundant enargite (Lindgren and Loughlin, 1919, p. 142).

PIUTE COUNTY

Piute County, one of Utah's smaller counties, is in the south-central part of the State and is immediately east of Beaver County. Gold lodes in the Tushar Range in the western part yielded most of its mineral wealth; through 1959 about 240,000 ounces was produced, mainly from the Gold Mountain and Mount Baldy districts. Silver, lead, and copper were also mined on a smaller scale.

Gold-bearing sand was discovered in about 1868 in Pine Gulch Creek in the Ohio district about 6 miles southwest of Marysvale. Later in the same year gold lodes were found (Butler and others, 1920, p. 541). Discoveries of lodes immediately north of the Ohio district led to the organization of the Mount Baldy district in 1878. Data from these two districts are combined in this report. After the successful introduction of the cyanide process, interest was concentrated on an area north of the Mount Baldy district that contained gold deposits which previously had resisted the amalgamation treatment. These deposits were developed, and by 1889 the Gold Mountain district was organized (Butler and others, 1920, p. 540). Mining flourished in the county until 1941, after which activity decreased; production remained small through 1959.

GOLD MOUNTAIN DISTRICT

The Gold Mountain (Kimberly) district in the northwest part of Piute County is just south of the Sevier County line and about 10 miles west-northwest of Marysvale. Some deposits are in the adjacent part of Sevier County.

After the perfection of the cyanide process for treating complex ores, previously known gold-silver lodes were developed. The Gold Mountain district was organized in 1889, and a mill was built at the Annie Laurie mine which was to become the most productive mine of the area. During the most prosperous period, from 1901 through 1913, a total of 134,744 ounces of gold was mined, chiefly from the Annie Laurie and Sevier mines (Butler and others, 1920, p. 540–541). Activity declined after 1914, and the district was virtually idle from 1918 to 1934. A brief resurgence occurred from 1934 through 1940 which was followed by intermittent small-scale activity through 1959. Total gold production through 1959 was about 159,000 ounces.

Bedrock in the Gold Mountain district consists of a basement of sedimentary rocks of pre-Tertiary age overlain by two groups of volcanic rocks—an earlier Tertiary(?) sequence of andesite, dacite, and quartz latite breccias and tuffs with a few intercalated flows predominantly of quartz latite and a later Tertiary(?) sequence of white rhyolite tuff with a few local interbedded quartz latite flows. The older sequence of volcanic rocks is intruded by masses of quartz monzonite (Callaghan, 1938, p. 98–100).

The ore deposits are silver- and gold-bearing quartz veins 3 to 30 feet thick in the earlier Tertiary(?) volcanic rocks. The ore minerals are gold, finely divided argentite, and pyrite in a gangue of quartz, carbonates, adularia, and barite (Lindgren, 1906a). Locally the veins contain copper stains and quicksilver (Butler and others, 1920, p. 544).

MOUNT BALDY DISTRICT

The Mount Baldy (Ohio) district is on the east side of the Tushar Range about 6 miles southwest of Marysvale. The early records of the district are fragmentary, but the first mineral discoveries in the Ohio camp were made about 1868 and in the Mount Baldy camp about 1878. Though many claims were located in both camps, early production apparently was small; records show an output of 8,000 to 10,000 tons of ore from 1868 to 1903 (Butler and others, 1920, p. 542). Mining was intensified from 1910 through 1940 but was sporadic thereafter. No activity was reported in 1959. Production before 1904 cannot be determined (Butler and others, 1920, p. 542), but from 1904 through 1959 it was 77,500 ounces of gold, most of which came from lead-silver-gold replacement deposits in the Deertrail mine.

The geology is similar to that of the Gold Mountain district. Sedimentary rocks of Carboniferous, Triassic, and Jurassic ages are overlain by volcanic rocks of Tertiary age. The lowermost unit is a bed of quartzite more than 200 feet thick. It is overlain by interbedded dolomite and quartzite about 650 feet thick which contain Permian fossils near the top. A 500-foot-thick interval of Triassic limestone overlies the Permian rocks, and 2,100 feet of nonmarine shales, sandstones, and quartzite overlies the Triassic rocks. Lying upon these nonmarine beds are limestones, shales, and sandstones of Jurassic age (Callaghan, 1938, p. 98–99). The sedimentary rocks are overlain by Tertiary volcanic rocks, which are separated into two units. The lowermost unit, of earlier Tertiary(?) age, consists of volcanic breccia and tuff and a few interbedded flows predominantly of quartz latite. The upper unit, of later Tertiary(?) age, is mainly rhyolite tuff containing a few local flows of porphyritic quartz latite (Callaghan, 1938, p. 99–100).

All the rocks are cut by faults. The steep eastern and western flanks of the Tushar Range are bounded by fault systems, and within the range there are many faults parallel to the ones that bound it (Butler and others, 1920, p. 539–540). Throughout most of the area, the strata, though locally warped, dip toward the west and southwest (Callaghan, 1938, p. 102).

The ore deposits are in replacement bodies and veins. The Deertrail mine, which is the largest producer, is in a limestone replacement body, the only important deposit of this type in the district. Ore consists of oxidized products of galena and pyrite having a high gold and silver content. The gangue is sericite, quartz, and iron oxide. The ore body is a blanket deposit that replaced the upper part of a Jurassic limestone bed and possibly part of the overlying quartzite. At several places the ore is in two zones separated by 20 to 25 feet of unaltered rock (Butler and others, 1920, p. 550).

The vein deposits (Butler and others, 1920, p. 543–545, 555–557) occurred chiefly in the Ohio camp but their yield of gold and silver was small, and the yield of lead, copper, and zinc was smaller. However, some veins contain alunite and were of interest as a source of potash and alumina. The gold-silver veins occur almost exclusively in the volcanic rocks, where they occupy faults and fissures. The typical gangue minerals are quartz, carbonate, and local barite, adularia, and fluorite. The ore minerals are galena, chalcopyrite, tetrahedrite, pyrite, and sphalerite. In the rich oxidized gold ore, the gold is in part free and may be combined with silver as a telluride. Most of the mined ore was oxidized.

SALT LAKE COUNTY

Salt Lake County, in north-central Utah, is bounded on the northwest by the Great Salt Lake, on the east by the Wasatch Mountains, on the south by the Traverse Mountains, and on the west by the northern part of the Oquirrh Range. It is distinguished politically by Salt Lake City, the State capital, and economically by Bingham, the most productive mining district in the State.

Most of the 10,651,000 ounces of gold produced through 1959 came from this district; about 30,000 ounces came from the Cottonwood district.

Soldiers, attached to the California Volunteers under Gen. P. E. Connor, arrived in Utah in 1862 and established Camp Douglas, overlooking Salt Lake City. Many of the men, who were prospectors and had experienced the gold fever in California, began prospecting the ranges near Salt Lake City. The first mineral locations were made in Bingham Canyon in September 1863; other discoveries followed rapidly. Gold placers also were mined in Bingham Canyon in 1865 and within a few years had yielded about $1 million in gold (48,379 ounces). They were the only important placer-gold producers in the State (Butler and others, 1920, p. 118, 340).

Ore deposits were discovered in the Little Cottonwood camp near Alta in 1865 and in the Big Cottonwood camp in 1868 or 1869 (V. C. Heikes, in Calkins and Butler, 1943, p. 71–72, 77).

BINGHAM DISTRICT

The Bingham (West Mountain) district, about 20 miles southwest of Salt Lake City on the east slope of the Oquirrh Range, is the leading mining district in Utah and is one of the major copper districts in the United States. It is also the fourth largest gold producer in the United States; its total production through 1959 was about 10,610,000 ounces. In addition to copper—its chief commodity—and gold, large amounts of lead, zinc, silver, and molybdenum have been produced from the district.

One of the major stimuli to early prospecting in this region was Gen. P. E. Connor, who was in charge of the Third California Infantry stationed at Camp Douglas near Salt Lake City in 1862. Many of the troops had previous mining experience in California and were encouraged by General Connor to search for mineral deposits. By September 1863, they found outcrops of lead carbonate in Bingham Canyon. This was formally located as the West Jordan claim, and in December 1863 the West Mountain district was formed. Handicapped by lack of transportation facilities and suitable reduction plants, the miners made little progress. In 1864, however, placers were found in Bingham Canyon, and these yielded $1 million in gold by 1871 and an additional $500,000 in later years. The completion of rail facilities to Bingham by 1873 removed the major obstacle to exploiting the lodes (Boutwell, 1905, p. 81–85).

Lead and silver were the principal products of the district until the financial depression of 1893, when the price of silver dropped. Interest turned to copper deposits that previously were considered too low-grade to be mined. Experiments for treating low-grade copper ore were undertaken at the Highland Boy mine in 1896, and exploration revealed large pyritic copper ore bodies. Elsewhere in the district several mills were built to treat disseminated copper deposits in monzonite. After several years of experimentation, exploration, and consolidation of properties, large-scale mining of the disseminated copper deposits was begun in 1907 by the Utah Copper Co. (Boutwell, 1935, p. 349). Mining continued at an increased rate. In 1936 the Utah Copper Co. was absorbed by Kennecott Copper Corp., and Kennecott became the major producer in the district. The large-scale exploitation of the disseminated copper deposits, which continued through 1959, is responsible for Bingham's status in the mining industry.

Most of the gold is recovered as a byproduct of the copper ore; thus, the gold output, which was mined from vein and replacement deposits in sedimentary rocks before 1907 and which was less than 10,000 ounces annually, jumped significantly with the inauguration of large-scale copper mining and reached a high of about 450,000 ounces in 1953.

The predominant bedrock in the Bingham district is the Oquirrh Group of Pennsylvanian age, which consists of about 16,000 feet of limestone and sandstone units. Four formations are recognized in the Oquirrh Group. In ascending order they are the Maple Formation, White Pine Formation, Butterfield Formation, and Bingham Mine Formation (J. E. Welsh and A. H. James, in Cook, 1961, p. 7–11). Many limestone and sandstone units within these formations are mappable units; some are formally named, others are not, especially in the mine areas. In the northern part of the district, a considerable area is underlain by the Curry, Clinker, and Park City Formations of Permian age. These rocks are intruded by several granite, granite porphyry, and monzonite stocks of Tertiary age—notably the Bingham and Last Chance stocks—and by sills and dikes of monzonite. Along the eastern edge of the district, the foothills of the Oquirrh Range are capped with volcanic flows, breccias, agglomerates, and ash deposits of Tertiary age (W. H. Smith, in Cook, 1961, p. 101–116).

The structure of the Bingham district is complex and apparently exerted a strong influence on the emplacement of the stocks. A series of large northwest-trending folds known as the Bingham syncline, the Middle Canyon syncline, and the Copperton anticline are cut by several large west- to northwest-trending thrust faults and high-angle normal and reverse faults, and by a system of northeast-trending high-angle reverse faults. The stocks and mineral deposits appear to be controlled by the intersections of northeast faults with the trends of the fold axes and northwest-trending faults (A. H. James and others, in Cook, 1961, p. 49–66).

The major ore deposit of the district is that of the Utah Copper mine, an open pit 1½ square miles in area excavated in the Bingham stock, a body of altered monzonite porphyry. Surrounding the stock is a roughly circular zone that contains most of the lead-zinc veins and replacement deposits (A. H. James and others, in Cook, 1961, p. 81–97).

The disseminated copper ore body is in a vertical cylinder of shattered and altered monzonite. Grains of copper sulfides coat the walls of fissures and are disseminated throughout the monzonite. In addition, the ore body is interlaced with veins and veinlets of quartz and orthoclase containing chalcopyrite, pyrite, molybdenite, galena, and sphalerite. Oxidized ore contains copper in the form of azurite and malachite. The zone of supergene enrichment, which constitutes the largest part of the ore body, contains the copper minerals chalcopyrite, chalcocite, covellite, and bornite. The copper mineral in the primary sulfide ore is chalcopyrite (Boutwell, 1935, p. 355–356).

The replacement deposits, which occur in limestone beds near fissures, are an important source of lead, silver, copper, and zinc. The copper ores contain pyrite, chalcopyrite, and minor amounts of arsenopyrite, bornite, and tetrahedrite and local specularite. Gangue minerals are quartz, carbonate, and garnet.

Fissure veins have been the least productive of the various deposits in the district. They occur in quartzite and limestone beds and also in some of the intrusive rocks. Most of the fissure veins have been mined for lead and silver; a few have yielded gold, copper, and zinc. The common vein minerals are pyrite, galena, sphalerite, and tetrahedrite, and gangue minerals are calcite, quartz, rhodochrosite, and barite (Boutwell, 1905, p. 126–154).

COTTONWOOD DISTRICT

The Cottonwood district, which includes Big and Little Cottonwood camps, is on the western slope of the Wasatch Range in the southeastern corner of Salt Lake County about 20 miles southeast of Salt Lake City; it is immediately north of the American Fork district in Utah County and immediately southwest of the Park City district in Summit and Wasatch Counties.

The Cottonwood, American Fork, and Park City districts are clustered in an irregular area whose center lies at the intersection of the north-south folds and thrusts of the Wasatch Range with the westward projection of the anticlinal axis of the Uinta Mountains (Calkins and Butler, 1943, p. 3–4). At the intersection of these structures, some fairly large intrusive bodies or stocks occur and, other than dikes or sills, are the only intrusive rocks known in the Wasatch Mountains. According to Calkins (Calkins and Butler, 1943, p. 3–4), "This segment also contains the only ore deposits in the Wasatch Range from which any considerable production has been won, the presence of these deposits having doubtless resulted from the combination of intricate structure with large intrusive bodies that are not too deeply eroded."

The total gold production of the Cottonwood district through 1959 was about 30,275 ounces, of which approximately 16,650 ounces was produced before 1900 (V. C. Heikes, in Calkins and Butler, 1943, p. 81). The chief metals recovered from the ores are, in order of value, silver, lead, copper, gold, and zinc.

The earliest recorded mining claims in the district were located in August 1865 in the Little Cottonwood camp, and in 1866 several veins of argentiferous galena were found (V. C. Heikes, in Calkins and Butler, 1943, p. 72–73). The discovery in 1868 of the Emma ore body, one of the most productive in the district, greatly stimulated prospecting in the region. The earliest locations in the Big Cottonwood camp probably were made in 1868 and 1869, but little development work was done until 1871. By the end of 1880 more than 1,000 locations were made but most of them were relinquished; most of the remaining were productive only on a small scale (V. C. Heikes, in Calkins and Butler, 1943, p. 77). Very few properties have produced any ore in recent years.

The growth of the Emma mine into a major producer stimulated mining throughout Utah. Several rich ore bodies were discovered in rapid succession in the Little Cottonwood area in the early 1870's, and the following decade proved to be the most productive in its history (V. C. Heikes, in Calkins and Butler, 1943, p. 77–82). The Cottonwood district was active from 1867 through 1954, but production was relatively small after 1927.

The rocks of the Cottonwood district are dominantly sedimentary, ranging in age from Precambrian to Jurassic and having an aggregate thickness of about 12,000 feet. They are cut by intrusive stocks and dikes of probable Late Cretaceous or Tertiary age. The Precambrian rocks consist of several thousand feet of quartzite and shale overlain by tillite, formerly regarded as Cambrian in age but now thought to be Precambrian (M. D. Crittenden and others, in Marsell, 1952, p. 4–6). These are overlain by rocks of Cambrian age, consisting of the Tintic Quartzite, Ophir Shale, and Maxfield Limestone. An unconformity separates the Maxfield Limestone from the overlying unnamed basal Mississippian dolomite (M. D. Crittenden and others, in Marsell, 1952, p. 9). Above this formation are Mississippian, Pennsylvanian, and Permian strata, which, in ascending order, are the Madison Limestone, Deseret Limestone, Humbug Formation, Morgan(?) Formation, Weber Quartzite, and Park City Formation. Triassic rocks are represented by the Woodside, Thaynes, and Ankareh Formations. The Nugget Formation, of Jurassic age, is the youngest sedimentary formation exposed in the district (Calkins and Butler, 1943, p. 7–33).

In Late Cretaceous and early Tertiary time the rocks were folded and dislocated by thrusts and high-angle normal and reverse faults. The thrusts have very low angles; many are along bedding planes in the sedimentary rocks. Stocks and dikes of porphyritic quartz monzonite, granodiorite, and diorite cut the sedimentary rocks and are apparently younger than the thrust faults, though some high-angle faults are younger than the intrusives (Calkins and Butler, 1943, p. 52, 61).

The most important ore deposits of the district are replacements of limestone beds adjacent to fissures and deposits in brecciated limestone along thrust faults. Other deposits, less productive, are contact metamorphic deposits and fissure veins in quartzite and siliceous shale of Precambrian and Cambrian age. The replacement and breccia deposits are similar in mineralogy. Pyrite is most abundant and is accompanied by chalcopyrite, bornite, tetrahedrite, enargite, galena, and sphalerite. Tungstenite occurs in the Old Emma mine, and bismuthinite, in the Sells mine. Variable amounts of quartz, barite, and iron and manganese carbonates make up the gangue. The fissure-vein deposits contain pyrite and tetrahedrite and some galena, in a quartz gangue. The contact metamorphic deposits were mined chiefly for magnetite. They contain mainly lime silicate minerals, magnetite, ludwigite, chalcocite, bornite, chalcopyrite, periclase, and spinel (Calkins and Butler, 1943, p. 91–95).

SUMMIT AND WASATCH COUNTIES

Discussions of these two counties, which adjoin each other along the east slope of the Wasatch Range, are combined because the major mining district in the area, the Park City district, straddles the boundary. Gold production data for the counties were not found, but as the Park City district is the only mining center of any consequence in either county, the district's production of approximately 790,000 ounces through 1959 is assumed to be equivalent to that of both counties.

PARK CITY DISTRICT

The Park City district, about 25 miles southeast of Salt Lake City, encompasses the Uinta district in the southwest corner of Summit County and the Snake Creek and Blue Ledge districts in the northwest corner of Wasatch County.

Though silver and lead are the chief commodities, considerable gold, copper, and zinc are also mined. The 790,000 ounces of gold produced through 1959 makes Park City the fourth largest gold district in Utah.

After the discovery of ore in the middle 1860's in the Little Cottonwood and other districts on the west slope of the Wasatch Range, prospectors crossed to the east slope of the range and discovered lead-silver ore in the Park City district in about 1869. The first shipment of ore was made in 1870 or 1871 (Boutwell, 1912, p. 19). Important discoveries of lead-silver ore were made in rapid succession and resulted in the organization of the Uinta district in Summit County in 1869 and in the Snake Creek and Blue Ledge districts in Wasatch County in 1870. In 1872, about 2 years after the first locations were made, the famous Ontario vein was discovered. Its bonanza ore bodies stimulated interest in the new area and gave Park City early prominence in the turbulent mining industry. Prospecting in the western part of the district led to discovery of rich lead-silver replacement deposits on Treasure Hill and, in 1892, to the opening of extensive replacement deposits at the Silver King site.

Because of the high content of the ores, the prosperity of the district fluctuated with the price of silver; the decline in price in the 1890's, especially in 1893, caused temporary intermittent production or closure in some mines. However, the lower prices in 1893 stimulated development of more economical methods of mining and reduction and more effective recovery methods, and large concentrating mills were erected to treat larger volumes of low-grade ores. In 1901 new discoveries of rich smelting ore were made and Park City production increased abruptly. After 1905 zinc became an important product. Recent activity in the district is toward the consolidation of the older properties and deeper exploration for bedded replacement ore bodies; the rich oxidized surface ores have long been depleted. The two major operators in the area are United Park City Mining Co. and New Park Mining Co. (C. L. Wilson, in Williams, 1959, p. 182).

Predominant bedrock in the district is a section of sedimentary formations that are folded, faulted, and intruded by igneous rocks and are covered locally by volcanic rocks.

The oldest rock unit is the Mineral Fork Tillite of Precambrian age. It is overlain by the Tintic Quartzite of Cambrian age, the lowermost formation of a thick interval of Paleozoic rocks, which includes the Ophir Shale and Maxfield Limestone of Cambrian age, the basal Mississippian dolomite, the Gardison Limestone, Deseret Limestone, Humbug Formation, and Doughnut Formation of Mississippian age, the Round Valley Limestone and Weber Quartzite of Pennsylvanian age, and the Park City Formation of Permian age. Mesozoic sedimentary rocks are represented by the Woodside

Shale, Thaynes Formation, and Ankareh Shale of Triassic age and the Nugget Sandstone of Jurassic age. During Tertiary time, folding and faulting preceded and accompanied igneous intrusions of granite, quartz monzonite, diorite, and diorite porphyry. Faulting also occurred as recently as Pliocene or Pleistocene time. The main structural feature is the north-plunging Park City anticline on which are superimposed smaller east-trending folds which only slightly modify the Park City anticline (C. L. Wilson, in Williams, 1959, p. 183).

The ore deposits are in fissure veins in both sedimentary and igneous rocks and are in bedded replacement deposits mostly in limestones near fissures. Veins mined in the early years were found in the Weber Quartzite and younger rocks; in recent years ore bodies have been found in veins in diorite porphyry, Humbug Formation, and Deseret Limestone. Replacement deposits were first found in the Park City and Thaynes Formations; they have recently been found in the Humbug Formation and Deseret Limestone (C. L. Wilson, in Williams, 1959, p. 186–188).

Oxidized lead-silver ores containing cerussite, anglesite, iron oxides, argentite, smithsonite, azurite, malachite, and chrysocolla were the bonanza ores of early operations. Lead-silver sulfide ores of somewhat lower grade were mined later. These ores contain galena, tetrahedrite-tennantite, pyrite, some sphalerite, and rarely bournonite. Some deposits contain argentite, famatinite, and ruby silver minerals. Lead-zinc sulfide ores contain galena and sphalerite with pyrite and some tetrahedrite. Nearly all types of ore in the district contain small amounts of gold, and in the New Park mine, some calcite-quartz veins are rich in gold (C. L. Wilson, in Williams, 1959, p. 188).

TOOELE COUNTY

Tooele County, which is in northwestern Utah, contains a variety of mineral deposits. Gold is the chief mineral commodity; through 1959 a total of about 1,257,000 ounces was produced from the four major districts of Camp Floyd, Ophir-Rush Valley, Clifton, and Willow Springs. Lead, silver, arsenic, and tungsten are also mined.

CAMP FLOYD DISTRICT

The Camp Floyd (Mercur) district, in the southern part of the Oquirrh Mountains about 55 miles southwest of Salt Lake City, is unlike the other major mining districts of Utah. It is primarily a gold district and silver and mercury are byproducts. The district is the third largest gold producer in the State; total output through 1959 was about 1,115,000 ounces.

The first mineral location in the area was a gold placer claim, and the district was organized in 1870. Placer mining, however, was unsuccessful because of the low grade and lack of water. Early discoveries of rich silver lodes also proved to be disappointing (Gilluly, 1932, p. 123). Interest in the area declined to the extent that the town of Lewiston, which had a population of 1,500 in the 1870's, became largely deserted. The Mercur lode, at first unsuccessfully worked as a mercury deposit, had a high content of gold, but the gold could not be recovered by the amalgamation treatment commonly used at that time. In 1890 attempts to treat the Mercur ore by the newly developed cyanide process were successful. As a result, prospectors again swarmed into the district, the town of Mercur was built on the old site of Lewiston, and new mines were developed rapidly. This period of prosperity lasted from 1890 to 1917, during which time the Mercur, Delamar, Geyser-Marion, Sacramento, Sunshine, Overland, Daisy, and La Cigale mines were the chief producers (Gilluly, 1932, p. 123–124). Mines were closed from 1917 through 1931, but in 1932 some were reactivated, and in 1933 a 500-ton cyanide plant was constructed to treat old tailings. Enthusiasm generated by increased prices in 1934 caused a significant resurgence of activity that lasted until 1945, when the mines again were closed. No production was reported from 1949 through 1959.

The Oquirrh Mountains consist of Paleozoic sedimentary formations, totaling more than 22,000 feet in thickness; the formations are deformed into northwest-trending open folds, are intruded by various igneous rocks, and are cut by numerous normal faults. In the Camp Floyd district, which is along the west flank of the mountains, Mississippian formations, consisting of the Deseret Limestone, Humbug Formation, Great Blue Limestone, and Manning Canyon Shale, are folded into the Ophir anticline (Gilluly, 1932, pl. 12). Two small stocks and several sills of Eagle Hill rhyolite, of Tertiary age, cut the sedimentary rocks just south of the town of Mercur (Gilluly, 1932, p. 58).

The major ore deposits of the district are bedded replacement deposits of gold and gold-mercury in the Great Blue Limestone. Silver and silver-lead replacement deposits and gold and gold-mercury fissure veins are of subordinate importance. The principal minerals of the gold-bearing replacement deposits are pyrite, realgar, orpiment, and cinnabar. The gangue is mostly jasperoid but contains small amounts of barite and calcite. The gold is too fine grained to be seen and its mode of occurrence is not known, although analyses have shown a relationship between it and carbon (Butler and others, 1920, p. 394).

CLIFTON DISTRICT

The Clifton (Gold Hill) district is in the Clifton Hills near the Utah-Nevada boundary. Its ore deposits are varied and contain a wide range of valuable metal constituents. Besides gold, the deposits have yielded significant amounts of copper, lead, silver, and smaller amounts of tungsten, bismuth, molybdenum, and arsenic (Nolan, 1935a, p. 119).

The first mineral discoveries were made in 1858, but hostile Indians discouraged any mining in the area until 1869. In 1871 a smelter was built, and small amounts of silver, lead, and gold were produced for a few years. Interest was renewed in the area in 1892 when a mill was constructed to treat ores from the Cane Springs, Alvarado, and Gold Hill mines; total gold production from these mines from 1892 through 1895 was worth $207,896 (V. C. Heikes, in Butler and others, 1920, p. 475). Intermittent activity continued to 1917, when the completion of rail facilities enabled the deposits to be exploited on a larger scale. Much activity was maintained through 1934, after which production again dropped. The district was virtually idle from 1945 through 1959. Total recorded gold production from 1892 through 1959 was about 26,000 ounces.

The rocks of the Clifton district consist of a thick section of Paleozoic sedimentary rocks, chiefly dolomite and limestone, that range in age from Early Cambrian through Permian. These rocks are intruded by a stock of quartz monzonite and dikes of porphyry and aplite of Tertiary age. Five cycles of folding and faulting, beginning in Late Cretaceous or Eocene time and continuing to the time of the quartz monzonite intrusion, created a complex structural terrain that was further modified by normal faults of more recent age (Nolan, 1935a, p. 4–64).

The ore deposits of the district are of several diverse mineralogical and genetic types. Nolan (1935a, p. 97–103) classified them as:

1. Pipelike deposits locally containing tungsten and molybdenum.
2. Veins:
   - (a) Veins characterized by silicate minerals in the gangue.
   - (b) Veins containing chiefly quartz and metallic sulfides.
   - (c) Veins containing chiefly carbonate minerals with or without quartz.
3. Replacement bodies:
   - (a) Arsenic minerals dominant.
   - (b) Copper-lead-silver minerals dominant.

The replacement bodies yielded most of the mineral wealth of the district; however, most of the gold came from veins in limestone beds near their contact with the quartz monzonite stock. These veins are characterized by abundant wollastonite and small amounts of zoisite, vesuvianite, garnet, and diopside. Chalcopyrite is the most abundant sulfide and is accompanied by pyrite, bornite, arsenopyrite, and galena. Quartz and calcite are locally abundant, and native gold is present in small quantities.

OPHIR-RUSH VALLEY DISTRICT

The Ophir-Rush Valley (Stockton) district, in the central part of the west flank of the Oquirrh Mountains between the Camp Floyd district to the south and the Bingham district to the north, is known chiefly for lead, silver, copper, and zinc. Gold was recovered chiefly as a byproduct of the base-metal ores; total production through 1959 was about 104,000 ounces.

Silver deposits were found in 1864 in Rush Valley by soldiers of the California Volunteers stationed at a nearby military post known as "Camp Relief." Efforts at smelting the ore at first met with small success and the mines were abandoned by the end of 1865. After the Civil War the original claim owners, who were soldiers, were discharged and returned to their homes; however, mining laws were amended to make their claims permanently valid. This action retarded development of the district for several years (Gilluly, 1932, p. 117–118). Lead deposits were found in the Ophir area in 1865, but very little work was done on claims until 1870. Additional discoveries of silver-lead ores in the early 1870's in the Ophir and Rush Valley areas caused a brief period of prosperity that lasted until about 1880 at Ophir and until 1890 at Rush Valley (V. C. Heikes, in Butler and others, 1920, p. 363–366).

Beginning in 1904, production increased sharply. Zinc was first recovered from ores in the Ophir area in 1911 and from the Rush Valley mines in 1913. Activity has continued, with periodic fluctuations, through 1959.

Most of the exposed rock in the district consists of sedimentary formations that range in age from Cambrian to Pennsylvanian. The Cambrian rocks, about 2,500 feet thick, consist of the Tintic Quartzite at the base, the Ophir Formation, Hartmann Limestone, Bowman Limestone, and Lynch Dolomite. The Devonian System is represented by about 185 feet of Jefferson(?) Dolomite. Rocks of Mississippian age are the Deseret Limestone, Humbug Formation, and Great Blue Limestone. The Manning Canyon Shale is of Mississippian and Pennsylvanian age and is overlain by the Oquirrh Formation of Pennsylvanian age (Gilluly, 1932, p. 6–38). The rocks are folded into a northwest-trending anticline, the Ophir anticline, and are broken by fissures and faults, especially in the vicinity of Ophir Canyon, where a northeast-trending zone of faults has offset the axis of the Ophir anticline and the sedimentary beds about 2,000 feet. Northwest-trending normal faults are parallel to the west front of the Oquirrh Mountains (Gilluly, 1932, p. 69–74). Small intrusive stocks, dikes, plugs, and sills of monzonite, rhyolite, andesite, lamprophyre, and nepheline basalt cut the sedimentary formations.

The most important ore deposits are in the Honorine mine, just east of the town of Stockton. The ore bodies are in bedded replacement deposits in limestone beds of the Oquirrh Formation where these beds intersect faults or fissures. Primary ore consists of pyrite, galena, sphalerite, chalcopyrite, and arsenopyrite in a gangue of quartz and lime silicate minerals. Oxidized ore contains cerussite, plumbojarosite, jarosite, malachite, smithsonite, aurichalcite, pyromorphite, and limonite (Gilluly, 1932, p. 160–162). In the Ophir area, the chief deposits are in replacement bodies in Mississippian limestones, especially the Great Blue Limestone. A few deposits occur in the Ophir Formation and the Jefferson(?) Dolomite. With local exceptions, these deposits contain the same minerals as the replacement deposits in the vicinity of Stockton. Fissure veins occur throughout the district, but they are of little economic importance (Gilluly, 1932, p. 136–137).

WILLOW SPRINGS DISTRICT

The Willow Springs district is in the southern part of the Deep Creek Range in the southwestern corner of Tooele County. Through 1959 it produced about 11,650 ounces of gold, lead, silver, and some copper.

The district was organized in 1891, but for many years it made only a few small shipments of silver ore (Nolan, 1935a, p. 167). Its period of greatest activity was that of recorded production, 1934–50. The ore shipped during this period consisted of high-grade lead-silver and gold ores. The district was virtually idle from 1951 through 1959.

Metamorphic rocks of Precambrian age are the oldest exposed rocks. They are nonconformably overlain by the Goshute Canyon Formation of Precambrian or Cambrian age. Completing the Cambrian sequence are the Prospect Mountain Quartzite, Pioche Shale, Abercrombie Formation, Young Peak Dolomite, Trippe Limestone, Lamb Dolomite, Hicks Formation, and lower part of the Chokecherry Dolomite. The upper part of the Chokecherry Dolomite and the Fish Haven Dolomite represent the Ordovician System, and the Laketown Dolomite, the Silurian. Devonian formations exposed in the district are the Sevy Dolomite, Simonson Dolomite, and Guilmette Formation. In the northern part of the district, younger rocks, including the Woodman Formation, Ochre Mountain Limestone, Manning Canyon Formation of Mississippian age, and the Oquirrh Formation of Pennsylvanian age, are faulted against the lower Paleozoic units (Nolan, 1935a, pl. 1; Bick, 1959, p. 1065–1068). All the sedimentary formations are cut by faults that trend west or northwest and are deformed into a westward-tilted block by north-trending normal faults.

The ore deposits are in replacement veins and in bedded replacement deposits. The ores were probably completely oxidized at the surface and were rich in silver. Some of the vein ore examined by Nolan (1935a, p. 167–168) contained quartz, tetrahedrite, and galena.

UTAH COUNTY

Utah County, in north-central Utah, is bounded on the east by the crest of the Wasatch Range, on the north by the Traverse Mountains, on the northwest by the Oquirrh Mountains, and on the southwest by the East Tintic Mountains.

Several mining districts were organized in the county, but only the American Fork and East Tintic districts yielded substantial amounts of gold. The East Tintic district, which is geologically contiguous with the Tintic district in Juab County, was described in the discussion of Juab County. The total gold production of Utah County cannot be determined, because much of the output of East Tintic was combined with that of the Tintic.

AMERICAN FORK DISTRICT

The American Fork district, in the northeastern part of Utah County in the Wasatch Range, is about 5 miles southeast of the Cottonwood district.

After the major discoveries at Bingham Canyon, miners prospected in the Wasatch Range and found silver-lead lodes in Cottonwood Canyon and in the American Fork area. The district was organized in 1870, and the Miller mine soon became its chief producer. By 1880, however, most of the mines were idle. Production remained small until 1904, when a large new ore body in the Miller mine was found; this ore body was mined until 1908 (V. C. Heikes, in Calkins and Butler, 1943, p. 80–85). From 1923 until 1935 the district experienced considerable activity, but from 1936 through 1959 its was largely dormant. Total gold production of the district through 1959 was about 45,000 ounces.

The geology of the American Fork district is similar to that of the Cottonwood district discussed under "Salt Lake County." In general, the rocks consist of a thick section of sedimentary units ranging in age from Precambrian to Mississippian. These rocks were folded along north-trending axes, cut by thrusts and high-angle faults, and intruded by the Little Cottonwood stock, a mass of quartz monzonite of Late Cretaceous or Tertiary age (Calkins and Butler, 1943, p. 38–71).

The major ore deposits of the district are replacement bodies in limestones adjacent to faults and fissures. A few deposits occur in fissure veins in quartzite beds of Precambrian and Cambrian age. The most common ore minerals of the replacement deposits are galena, pyrite, tetrahedrite, bornite, enargite, and sphalerite; chalcopyrite is locally present, and jamesonite occurs rarely. Gangue minerals are quartz, barite, and dolomite (Calkins and Butler, 1943, p. 94–95). The replacement deposit at the Miller mine, the largest producer in the district, is in shattered beds of the Maxfield Limestone. The ore was oxidized and contained silver-rich galena, cerussite, gold, and hydrous iron oxides. Some ore contained as much as 2.45 ounces of gold per ton, but more commonly the gold content ranged from 0.1 to 0.5 ounce per ton (Butler and others, 1920, p. 279–280).

VIRGINIA

The gold-bearing areas of Virginia are east of the Blue Ridge Mountains in a belt 15 to 25 miles wide and 200 miles long (Watson, 1907, p. 549–550). Fauquier, Fluvanna, Goochland, Orange, and Spotsylvania Counties contain the most important deposits.

The earliest reference to gold in the southern Piedmont was made by Thomas Jefferson, who described a piece of ore containing 17 pennyweights of gold found in 1782 along the Rappahannock River in Virginia (Pardee and Park, 1948, p. 27). The first gold-mining company incorporated in the State was the Virginia Mining Co. of New York, which operated the Grasty tract in Orange County from 1831 to 1834 (Watson, 1907, p. 549). Mint records show that $2,500 in gold was produced in Virginia in 1829 (Taber, 1913, p. 6), probably from placers in Goochland County. Other deposits along the gold belt were discovered in the early 1830's, and the years before the Civil War were the most productive in the State's history. The Civil War halted development of gold mining in Virginia, and after the war, despite attempts at revival, the gold mines did not regain their former level of productivity. When the price of gold was increased in 1934, there was a short-lived flurry. Several mines reopened and operations in the Virgilina district yielded some gold. Production declined after 1938 and after 1945 it stopped. Total gold production of the State through 1959 was 167,558 ounces (fig. 3).

The ore deposits are in northeast-trending schists and gneisses of sedimentary and igneous origin. These are cut by auriferous quartz-pyrite veins that in general are concordant with the strike and dip of the host rocks.

FAUQUIER COUNTY

The Franklin mine is in southern Fauquier County about 3 miles south of Morrisville. Although it is the largest in Fauquier County, its history is incomplete. Watson (1907, p. 553) reported activity at the mine in 1901 and 1902, at which time tailings were being cyanided. Pardee and Park (1948, p. 54) reported some development work on the property in 1934 and 1935 but no production during these years. Production data on this mine could not be found, but there is a strong likelihood, especially in view of the fact that a 20-stamp mill was built on the property, that it produced about 10,000 ounces of gold (Watson, 1907, p. 553).

Country rock in the vicinity of the mine is altered and sheared diorite or quartz diorite. There are two major veins—the Franklin and House—and the rock adjacent to them is sericitized and silicified (Pardee and Park, 1948, p. 54–55). Massive white quartz is the principal constituent; considerable sericite and small quantities of ankerite and calcite complete the gangue assemblage. The dominant metallic mineral is pyrite, which occurs in large crystals, lenses, nodules, and layers in both the veins and wallrock. Gold is in the pyrite. Other sulfides present in small amounts are chalcopyrite and chalcocite.

FLUVANNA AND GOOCHLAND COUNTIES

The Tellurium, Moss, and Busby mines are along the Fluvanna-Goochland County line within a mile of each other.

In 1829 or 1830 gold placers were worked along

Busby Branch, and soon afterward the Busby lode was discovered. The Busby deposits showed great promise in the early years of the mine's operation (Taber, 1913, p. 154) but were worked for only a few years. The property was in ruins by 1865. The Tellurium lode, which was one of the first vein deposits to be mined in Virginia, was discovered about 1832 and was worked before placers were found in its immediate vicinity (Taber, 1913, p. 153). Of the three mines, in the early years of production the most sustained production came from the Tellurium; gold valued at a minium of $200,000 (10,000 ounces) was mined before the Civil War. There was sporadic activity at the Tellurium property in the 1880's, in 1909–10, and most recently in 1935, but there was no significant production. The Moss lode mine became active in 1835, but it closed in 1838. It was reopened in 1891 and was in operation in the early 1900's (Taber, 1913, p. 145). In 1931, cleanup operations were conducted and a small amount of underground exploration was done (Pardee and Park, 1948, p. 56).

Total production from these three mines could not be determined. Watson (1907, p. 559) estimated an output valued at $1 million for the Tellurium mine, but Taber (1913, p. 154) regarded about $200,000 as being more nearly correct for the early production. No data could be found on the production of the Moss and Busby mines.

Country rock in the vicinity of these mines is a series of quartz-mica schists interbedded with quartzite. A body of granite is exposed northeast of the mines (Taber, 1913, p. 155–156). The major deposit at the Tellurium mine is in a quartzite bed that is interlaced with stringers of quartz and feldspar containing small amounts of pyrite, native gold, sphalerite, tetradymite, and tellurium(?). Another type of deposit at the Tellurium mine consists of a vein composed of a series of interconnected quartz lenses in the schistose country rock. These lenses are conformable with the foliation and contain free gold (Taber, 1913, p. 157–168). The geology of the Moss and Busby mines is very similar to that of the Tellurium; all three mines probably are on the same vein system.

ORANGE COUNTY

The Vaucluse mine, in northeastern Orange County, is 18 miles west of Fredericksburg and 2 miles north of the Wilderness Post Office.

Placers on this property were first worked in 1832; the lode deposits were discovered several years afterward. From 1844 to the outbreak of the Civil War the property was worked extensively by an English mining company, and Bass (1940, p. 80) estimated that the Vaucluse mine could have yielded most of the prewar gold production of Virginia, which amounted to 50,000 to 70,000 ounces. The mine was idle from 1860 until 1934. From 1935 through 1938, it produced most of the 5,901 ounces of gold that was produced in the State. It was again idle from 1938 through 1959. Total minimum production probably was about 50,000 ounces.

The bedrock at the mine consists of quartz-sericite-chlorite schist (Bass, 1940, p. 82, 84). The ore deposits are in a northeast-trending shear zone which is concordant with the foliation of the schist. The ore shoots are found in this shear zone and are pod-shaped lenses of quartz that carry concentrations of pyrite with which the gold is associated. Small amounts of galena and chalcopyrite usually accompany the pyrite. Gangue minerals in addition to quartz are sericite, ankerite, chlorite, and calcite (Bass, 1940, p. 82–87).

SPOTSYLVANIA COUNTY

The Whitehall mine is in west-central Spotsylvania County. Little detailed description of this property was found in the literature. Silliman (1837, p. 101) mentioned some rich placers in existence in 1836 near the Whitehall mine. Watson (1907, p. 555) noted that gold was found at the site of the Whitehall mine in 1806 and that the mine was worked from 1848 until just before the Civil War. He noted that the mine was reopened after the war and was active in the 1880's, and he estimated $1,800,000 as the total value of gold production for the mine to 1881. No record could be found of further activity nor of information pertaining to the geology of the area.

WASHINGTON

Washington has not been a major gold-producing State; nevertheless, its annual output of gold has been steady, and contrary to the present nationwide trend of the industry, its production in recent years has increased (fig. 27). This paradox is exemplified by the Knob Hill mine in the Republic district, which ranks third among the leading lode-gold-producing mines in the United States, and the Gold King mine in the Wenatchee district, which ranks tenth (U.S. Bureau of Mines, 1960, v. 1, p. 509).

Gold was first discovered in the State in 1853 in the Yakima River valley by a party under the command of Capt. George McClelland exploring for a possible railroad route (Huntting, 1955, p. 28). By

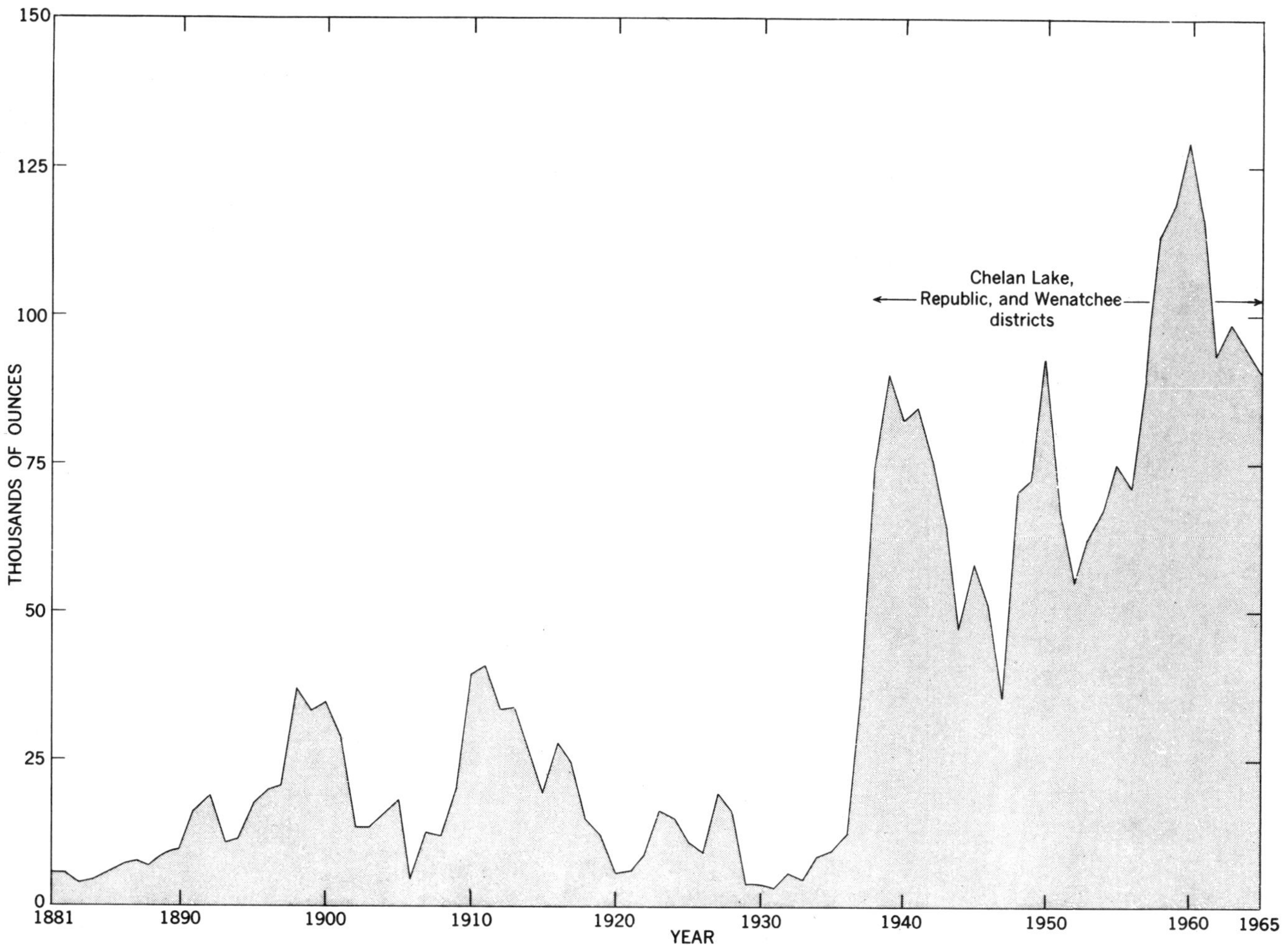

FIGURE 27.—Annual gold production of Washington, 1881–1965. Sources of data: 1881–1923 from U.S. Geological Survey (1883–1924); 1924–65 from U.S. Bureau of Mines (1925–34, 1933–66). Production for 1957–65 includes some from Pennsylvania. Production reported in dollar value was converted to ounces at prevailing price per ounce.

1855, prospectors were active in the Colville district although the first discoveries were not made until 1883. In 1855, small placers were found along the Columbia and Pend Oreille Rivers. From the 1850's through the 1880's, placers were worked along streams in Okanogan, Whatcom, Chelan, and Kittitas Counties and along the major streams of the State—the Columbia and Snake Rivers. By 1900, however, most of the placer deposits were exhausted.

Important lode discoveries were made in the early 1870's and as the placers were mined out, the lode mines became the chief producers. The Republic district in Ferry County is the major lode gold district in the State (fig. 28). Other important lode districts are the Wenatchee, Blewett, Mount Baker, Monte Cristo, Slate Creek, and Oroville-Nighthawk. A significant contributor to the gold output in recent years was the Holden mine in the Chelan Lake district, Chelan County, where gold was produced as a byproduct from copper ores. This mine, however, was closed, probably permanently, in 1957 (A. E. Weissenborn, written commun., 1962).

Total gold production for the State from 1860 through 1956 was 2,844,331 ounces (U.S. Bureau of Mines, 1956, p. 1204). Production figures for the period 1957–65 include some production from Pennsylvania and therefore are too high by an uncertain amount, probably a few thousand ounces. In the data presented in the succeeding pages, a total gold production of only about 2,300,000 ounces is indicated. The reason for the discrepancy is in the different estimates by various authors for unrecorded production before 1900, especially for the period 1860–66, during which the State produced $9 million in gold (Huntting, 1955, p. 33). Most of the gold produced before 1900 was from placers, but only 2 percent of the total from 1900 to 1952 was from them (Huntting, 1955, p. 32).

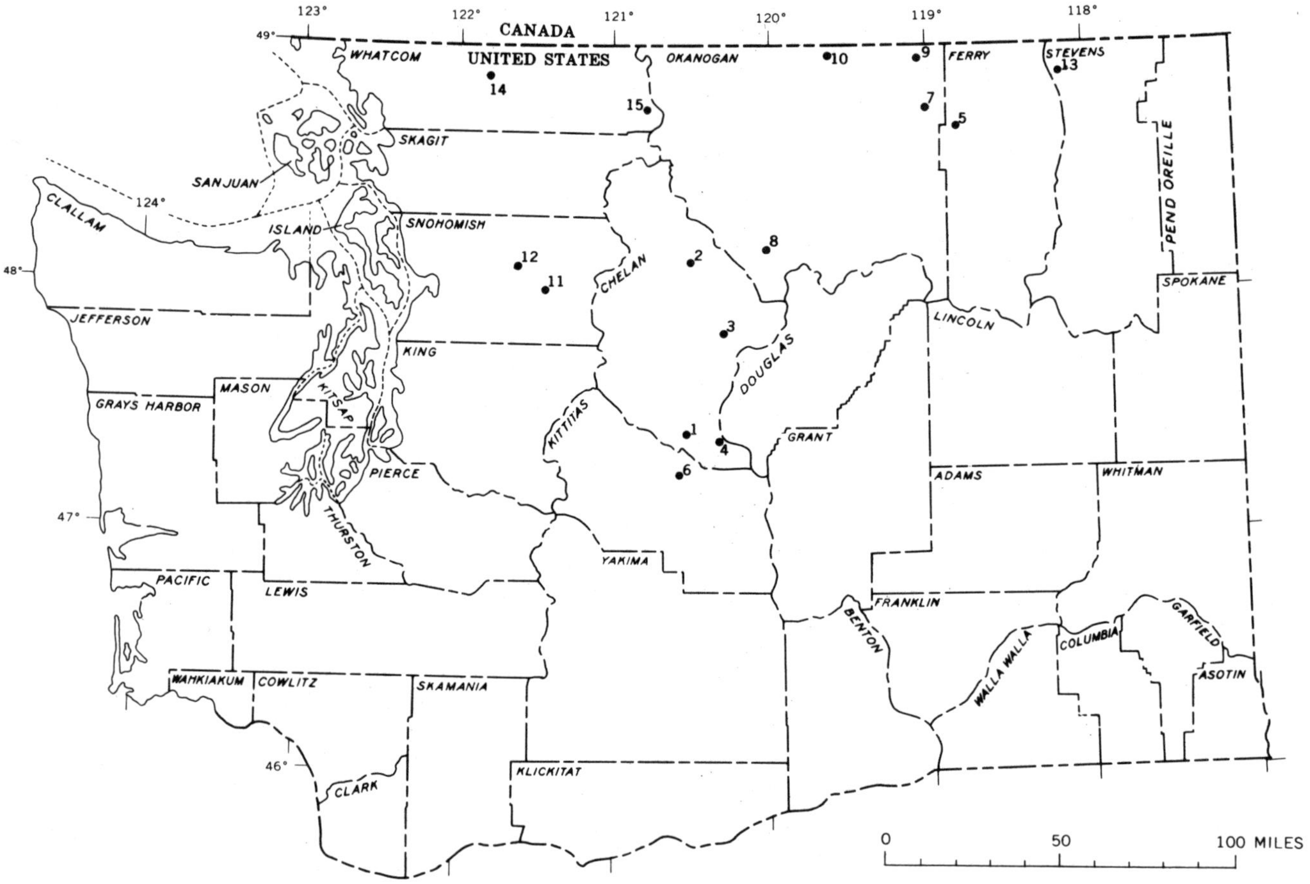

FIGURE 28.—Gold-mining districts of Washington.

Chelan County:
1, Blewett; 2, Entiat; 3, Chelan Lake; 4, Wenatchee.
Ferry County:
5, Republic.
Kittitas County:
6, Swauk.
Okanogan County:
7, Cascade; 8, Methow; 9, Myers Creek; 10, Oroville-Nighthawk.
Snohomish County:
11, Monte Cristo; 12, Silverton.
Stevens County:
13, Orient.
Whatcom County:
14, Mount Baker; 15, Slate Creek.

CHELAN COUNTY

In 1860 placers were discovered in the Blewett (Peshastin) district, in what is now Chelan County; at that time this area was part of Kittitas County. The first lode discoveries were made in the same district in 1874.

The largest gold-producing district of the State is the Chelan Lake whose output from 1938 through 1956 boosted Chelan County to the lead in production for the State. This district, however, was inactive from 1957 to 1959. Other important gold districts are the Wenatchee and Entiat.

Production of the county from 1903 through 1959 was 666,198 ounces of lode and byproduct gold and 581 ounces of placer gold. Production data for the years 1952–55 were combined with those of Ferry and King Counties (U.S. Bureau of Mines, 1952–55); consequently, separate figures for Chelan County are not available. Production data before 1903 also are not available, but Weaver (1911, p. 71) estimated the value of placer and lode gold from the Blewett district between 1870 and 1901 at $1½ million (about 72,000 ounces).

BLEWETT DISTRICT

The Blewett (Peshastin) district is in south-central Chelan County, at lat 47°25′ N. and long 120°40′ W.

Rich gold placers were discovered on Peshastin Creek in 1860 and were worked intermittently for several years. In 1874 vein deposits were found in Culver Gulch. For many years only the oxidized parts of the veins were mined, but in the late 1890's extensive development revealed new and rich ore bodies and for a while the district prospered. After 1910, however, there was only small-scale activity. Total production from 1870 to 1959 was approximately 850,900 ounces.

The oldest rocks in the area are of Carboniferous age and consist of the "contact" schist, the Peshastin Formation, composed of black slates and quartzites, and the Hawkins Formation, composed of a series of breccias, tuffs, and flows (Weaver, 1911, p. 26–56). Intruding these formations are large masses of peridotite, extensively altered to serpentine. Small irregular masses and stringers of Mesozoic granodiorite intrude the peridotite. Unconformably overlying the older rocks are sandstone, conglomerate, and shale that compose the Swauk Formation of Eocene age. Cutting all these rocks are diabase dikes and small masses of gabbro.

The ore bodies occupy fissure veins in the serpentine. Vein material consists of quartz, calcite, and talc. Native gold and iron oxide occur in the oxidized zone and arsenopyrite and pyrite occur at depth. Gold placers along Peshastin and Negro Creeks are of two types: older channel and bench gravels and younger gravels along the present stream courses (Weaver, 1911, p. 82, 83).

CHELAN LAKE DISTRICT

The Chelan Lake (Holden, Railroad Creek) district is in northwest Chelan County on the east slope of the Cascade Range between lat 48°07′ and 48°19′ N. and long 120°30′ and 120°45′ W. Chelan Lake forms the northeast boundary of the district.

Activity in this area began at least as early as 1892, when first claims were staked by J. H. Holden. Other prospects were located in the 1890's; among these was the Crown Point mine which began producing molybdenum ore in 1897. Little else of the early history of the district was recorded. In 1938, after years of options and changes of owners, the Holden mine was taken over by a subsidiary of the Howe Sound Co. It then became the largest gold, silver, and copper producer in the State, and remained so until 1956, when increased costs and complex mining problems made operation marginal. The mine was closed in 1957.

Production of the district (in large part, that of the Holden mine) from 1938 through 1951 was 514,525 ounces of gold. Its production data from 1952 through 1956 were combined with data of other districts and could not be determined separately.

The country rock in the vicinity of the Holden mine consists of hornblende and biotite-bearing schist and gneiss, quartzite, and marble of probable pre-Devonian age (F. W. Cater, oral commun., 1962). These rocks were isoclinally folded and sheared, then were intruded by peridotite and quartz-ornblende diorite bodies, and later, by dikes, sills, and small offshoots of the Cretaceous Chelan batholith, which is well exposed east of the district. Plugs and dikes of the Cloudy Pass granogabbro, of Tertiary age, intrude the older rocks. The ore deposits are replacements of a breccia zone in the metamorphic rocks. The ores are Tertiary in age and are related to the Cloudy Pass intrusive. Prominent ore minerals are magnetite, quartz, pyrite, pyrrhotite, sphalerite, and chalcopyrite, and galena and gold occur in minor amounts.

ENTIAT DISTRICT

The Entiat district, in east-central Chelan County, is the largest district in the State and occupies 790 square miles between lat 47°40′ and 48°00′ N. and long 120°10′ and 120°45′ W.

Huntting's report (1943, p. 24–26) constitutes most of the published information on the history and ore deposits of this district. The largest mine in the area is the Rex (or Rogers) mine, which produced $170,000 (about 8,250 ounces) in gold by 1930 (Huntting, 1955, p. 48). The Rex was in existence as early as 1906, so the Entiat district dates back to that time and perhaps earlier. Small platinum and gold placers along the Entiat River were worked also, but production from them was small.

The 8,250 ounces of gold produced from the Rex mine between 1906 and 1930 is the only recorded production from the Entiat district. Huntting (1943, p. 25), however, listed two other lode mines that produced unknown amounts. Estimated minimum total production for the Entiat district is 10,000 ounces.

Huntting (1943, p. 24–25) summarized the geology of the district, part of which was studied in detail by Waters (1932). The oldest rock is the Swakane Gneiss, believed to be pre-Ordovician in age, which is intruded by the Chelan Granodiorite. Locally along Lake Chelan are small patches of other Paleozoic metasedimentary rocks and scattered through the area are remnants of Tertiary lake deposits and basalt.

Free gold, the chief ore mineral, occurs with quartz in veins cutting the Swakane Gneiss. Native silver, cinnabar, ilmenite, and nickel-rich pyrrhotite occur in the ores in varying amounts. The relation of ore deposits to any of the nearby intrusives has not been determined.

WENATCHEE DISTRICT

The Wenatchee district is in the southeastern corner of Chelan County at about lat 47°22′ N. and long 120°20′ W.

The Gold King mine, the chief mine of the district, was located in 1885, but very little mining was done until 1894, when about $1,600 in bullion was produced. Sporadic activity continued until 1911 and again from 1934 to 1949. When the Lovitt Mining Co. acquired the property in 1949, production began on a large scale. Lovitt and McDowall (1954, p. 38) reported a total of 102,376 ounces of gold produced from 1949 through 1953; this high output continued, and in 1960 the Gold King was the tenth largest producer of lode gold in the United States. Total gold production of the Wenatchee district through 1959 was about 190,000 ounces (A. E. Weissenborn, written commun., 1962).

Bedrock in the vicinity of the Gold King mine consists of steeply dipping beds of the Swauk Sandstone of Eocene age. The ore deposits are in a silicified dikelike body that is cut by innumerable small quartz veins. The ore minerals are gold, silver, and minor amounts of pyrite; however, there seems to be no relationship between the valuable minerals and the pyrite. The gold is very finely divided in the quartz (Lovitt and McDowall, 1954, p. 38–39).

FERRY COUNTY

From 1904, when systematic compilation of production data was begun, to 1938, Ferry County was the leading gold producer in Washington. After 1938, the productive Holden mine boosted Chelan County to the lead, but in the late 1950's accelerated activity in the Republic district of Ferry County probably restored this county to its former status.

From 1896 to 1958 a minimum of 839,000 ounces of gold was mined in Ferry County. More than 99 percent of it was from the Republic district, and the remainder—a recorded aggregate of 6,000 ounces—was from the Danville district and the Columbia River placers.

REPUBLIC DISTRICT

The Republic (Eureka) district is in western Ferry County near the town of Republic, about 25 miles south of the international boundary.

The Republic district has had the most consistent record of large gold production of any district in the State. Prospecting began in this area when the northern part of the Colville Indian Reservation was opened in 1896. Deposits assaying high gold content were soon found, and many shipments were made until 1901 when the district closed. By 1903 railroads linked the district with large smelters on the Pacific coast, and small-scale activity was resumed. In 1909 the discovery of substantial amounts of high-grade ore at the Republic mine and of new ore bodies on other properties resulted in a revival of the district; later large-scale production from the Lone Pine and Knob Hill mines sustained activity through 1928. Mining fluctuated from 1928 until after World War II, when the Knob Hill mine emerged as the largest and most consistent producer. In 1960 it was the third most productive lode-gold mine in the United States.

The estimated minimum total production of gold from the Republic district from 1896 through 1959 was 836,393 ounces; all production was from lode mines except for a few hundred ounces from placers.

The dominant geologic feature of the area is the Republic graben, which is 4 to 10 miles wide and at least 52 miles long. It is bounded on the northwest by the Scatter Creek and Bacon Creek fault zones and on the southeast by the Sherman and other faults (Calkins and others, 1959; Muessig and Quinlan, 1959; Staatz, 1960, p. B304). Within the graben, mostly near the margins, are narrow belts of greenstone and other rocks of Permian and Triassic ages. Most of the graben is filled with Tertiary lavas and bedded rocks consisting of, from oldest to youngest, the O'Brien Creek Formation, Sanpoil Volcanics, and the Klondike Mountain Formation (Muessig and Quinlan, 1959). Granodiorite of Cretaceous age underlies the area northwest of the Scatter Creek and Bacon Creek fault zones, and quartz monzonite of Tertiary and Cretaceous age is exposed on the southeast side of the Sherman fault. Other intrusive rocks, of Tertiary age, exposed in the Republic graben consist mostly of plugs, dikes, and sills of diorite, rhyodacite, quartz latite porphyry, trachyandesite, andesite porphyry, rhyolite, and basalt and stocks of quartz monzonite and granodiorite (R. L. Parker, written commun., 1960).

The Republic graben was formed in early Tertiary time, and later faulting, possibly as late as early Miocene, disrupted rocks in it. The ore deposits are along the Republic fault, a high-angle fault that trends north within the graben. Throughout most of the Republic district, ore occurs as fissure fillings along one to four veins; most veins are in altered flows of the Sanpoil Volcanics. At the Republic mine, the lower part of the Klondike Mountain Formation forms the hanging wall of the vein. The vein minerals consist of fine-grained to chalcedonic quartz with stringers of very fine grained pyrite, chalcopyrite, stephanite, naumannite, native silver, and electrum. Adularia is common, and laumontite, marcasite, and fluorite are present in small amounts (S. J. Muessig, written commun., 1960).

KITTITAS COUNTY

The only gold deposits in Kittitas County that have yielded 10,000 ounces or more are those of the Swauk district. In the early days the Peshastin district, now part of Chelan County (p. 256), was included in Kittitas County and accounted for much of its early production. Recorded county production from 1903 through 1959, all of which was attributed to the Swauk district, was 7,141 ounces, of which 4,972 ounces was placer gold. Production before 1903 is unrecorded, but there is an 11-year record from 1884 to 1895 (Smith, 1903, p. 76) which credited the county with $764,163 worth of gold (37,095 ounces). Landes, Thyng, Lyon, and Roberts (1902, p. 88–89), referring to the early production of the Swauk placers, stated, "It is not possible to form even an estimate of the total output of these placers. The early workers did not keep any accurate record of their output, and the present operators are keeping their information to themselves."

SWAUK DISTRICT

The Swauk district is between lat 47°14′ and 47°16′ N. and long 120°28′ and 120°42′ W.

Placers were discovered in this area in 1868 and auriferous veins, in 1881 (Smith, 1903, p. 76). Most of the placers contain fine gold, but some deposits are characterized by coarse nuggets and wire and leaf gold. The limited area of the drainage basin and the lack of rounding of the gold particles make it seem likely that the gold was derived from the quartz veins in the vicinity.

The vein deposits are narrow fissure veins in sandstone and shale of the Swauk Formation of Eocene age. A peculiar type of breccia known as birds-eye quartz constitutes much of the vein material in several mines (Smith, 1903, p. 79–80). This consists of fragments of black shale enclosed in quartz and calcite. Gold occurs in fine grains in the quartz and as incrustations on the surface of quartz.

OKANOGAN COUNTY

Okanogan County, one of the largest counties in the State, has several gold-producing districts—Cascade, Oroville-Nighthawk, Myers Creek, and Methow.

Mining in the county began in 1859 in the gravels along the Similkameen River. In 1871, lode deposits were discovered near Conconully (Patty, 1921, p. 20). Production data on gold before 1903 are not available, but from that date through 1959 the county produced 34,000 ounces of lode gold and 1,775 ounces of placer gold. Total gold production for the county from 1859 through 1959 was probably between 85,000 and 90,000 ounces.

Metamorphic rocks and local patches of sedimentary rocks compose the bedrock of the county. These have been extensively intruded by granite and other igneous rocks.

CASCADE DISTRICT

The Cascade (Wauconda) district, near the east boundary of Okanogan County, is about 20 miles south of the Canadian boundary and 12 miles northwest of Republic, at the headwaters of Granite Creek.

Production data for the district are available only for 1935 to 1957, when 7,886 ounces of lode gold was produced, primarily from the Bodie mine. Although the discovery date of gold for the district is not known, activity was reported as early as 1901 (Landes and others, 1902, p. 25). It can be assumed that in the ensuing 34 years at least a few thousand ounces of gold was produced and that an estimated total production of 10,000 to 15,000 ounces is reasonable. The principal properties are the Wauconda (Landes and others, 1902, p. 25–26) and the Bodie (Huntting, 1955, p. 69).

The bedrock of the district consists of gneiss, schist, and metasedimentary rocks that have been intruded by masses of granite (Landes and others, 1902, p. 24). These rocks are cut by porphyritic andesite intrusives and are covered by basaltic lavas. The ore bodies are in fissure veins in the metamorphic rocks. The vein material is largely quartz and calcite, and finely divided native gold is the ore mineral.

METHOW DISTRICT

The Methow (Squaw Creek) district is along Squaw Creek—a tributary of the Methow River—and is 9 miles above the mouth of the Methow River, 53 miles north of Mansfield, and 73 miles north-northeast of Wenatchee.

Lode deposits were discovered in 1887; the Red Shirt mine was the first producer (Hodges, 1897, p. 85). The major properties are the Hidden Treasure, Friday, Bolinger, and Highland Light. Production data before 1932 are incomplete, but from 1932 through 1959 output of 16,473 ounces of lode gold and 9 ounces of placer gold is recorded.

The deposits are in east-trending fissure veins in gneiss and granite. Quartz and calcite compose the bulk of the veinfilling, and gold and silver are the valuable components (Landes and others, 1902, p. 37).

MYERS CREEK DISTRICT

The Myers Creek (Chewsaw, Mary Ann Creek) district is in the northeast corner of Okanogan County near the town of Chewsaw.

Placer gold was discovered in this district in 1888 along Mary Ann Creek (Landes and others, 1902, p. 27), but the area was not developed to any extent until the early 1900's. Most of the production was from lode deposits. Including estimates by Umpleby (1911a, p. 28), the total gold production of the district through 1959 was a minimum of about 9,500 ounces.

The area is underlain by a thick series of Paleozoic sedimentary rocks, lava, and porphyry that were intruded by granitic masses of Mesozoic age (Umpleby, 1911a, p. 29–32). The Paleozoic igneous rocks are andesite and basalt; the Mesozoic batholithic masses are syenites and granites. Quartzite is the most abundant rock in the sedimentary section; however, slate, schist, and limestone are also present.

Copper, gold, and silver ore deposits are of two types—contact metamorphic replacement deposits in limestone near the contact of the intrusives and invaded rock, and fissure veins (Umpleby, 1911a, p. 32–39). In the replacement deposits chalcopyrite is the chief ore mineral; gold is a subordinate constituent in the chalcopyrite and pyrite. In the fissure veins, which occur in all rock types in the district, free gold, chalcopyrite, pyrite, galena, sphalerite, and arsenopyrite are found in a gangue of quartz and calcite. Gold is more abundant in the vein deposits.

OROVILLE-NIGHTHAWK DISTRICT

The Oroville-Nighthawk (Palmer Mountain) district, in northern Okanogan County, is just south of the international boundary between lat 48°50′ and 49°00′ N. and long 119°28′ and 119°42′ W.

As early as 1859 placers were worked on the Similkameen River (Umpleby, 1911b, p. 75–76), but this activity ended when the area was set aside as an Indian reservation. The district was reopened in the late 1890's, at which time lode deposits were developed. Most of the production was before 1900. Umpleby (1911b, p. 76) estimated a maximum output before 1900 of $1 million in gold—half placer and half lode. Data from 1903 through 1959 show a total output of 450 ounces of placer gold and 740 ounces of lode gold. Total production from the district through 1959 may be estimated as 49,000 to 50,000 ounces—half placer gold and half lode gold.

The oldest rocks in the area are clay slate, siliceous schist, limestone, and interbedded andesite and basalt believed to be of Paleozoic, possibly Carboniferous, age. The Similkameen batholith, a granitic mass of Late Cretaceous or early Tertiary age, intruded the metasedimentary rocks. Tertiary lake beds, locally deformed, cover considerable areas near the Similkameen River; these lake beds are unconformably overlain by scattered patches of andesite flows (Umpleby, 1911b, p. 64–84; Patty, 1921, p. 222–228).

Ore deposits are of two types: disseminated deposits rich in copper, and vein deposits carrying considerable gold, silver, lead, and copper. The disseminated deposits are related to the Similkameen batholith (Patty, 1921, p. 224), and the veins are distributed along the granite-sedimentary rock contact. Veins show varied mineralogy; they range from simple quartz veins to others showing successive movement and overlapping deposition of sulfides. Gold, which is the chief commodity in some veins, occurs as native gold and also in pyrite, chalcopyrite, and galena. Silver occurs in various silver minerals, argentiferous galena, and cerargyrite. The disseminated copper deposits have not been developed to any great extent.

SNOHOMISH COUNTY

In south-central Snohomish County gold was produced from several districts in the western part of the Cascade Range. These districts—Monte Cristo, Index, Silverton, Silver Creek and Sultan—are more or less contiguous and occupy an area about 10 miles wide and 20 miles long extending from about the center of the county south to the King County boundary.

The Monte Cristo and Silverton districts produced most of the gold in the county. Patty (1921, p. 282) estimated that the combined early production of all metals, but mostly gold, from these districts was worth $7 million. From 1903 through 1956, production was 9,595 ounces of lode gold and 535 ounces of placer gold.

MONTE CRISTO DISTRICT

The Monte Cristo district, on the west slope of the Cascade Range, is about 40 miles east of Everett, along the Everett and Monte Cristo Railroad.

Overlying an older granitic terrane is a thick sequence of arkose beds that Spurr (1901, p. 791) correlated with the Swauk Sandstone of Eocene age. Andesite of Miocene age overlies the arkose, and several masses of tonalite, of later Miocene age, cut the andesite and produced considerable contact metamorphism. Basaltic dikes cut both the arkose and andesite. Pleistocene volcanic activity was fairly intense in this area. Flat-lying andesite, tuff, and breccia of Pleistocene age unconformably overlie all older rocks.

Spurr (1901, p. 804–805) believed that ore deposition began in late Pliocene or early Pleistocene time and continued to the Recent. The most important deposits are mineralized joints within or near the tonalite masses. Ore minerals are galena, sphalerite, chalcopyrite, pyrite, and arsenopyrite. An upper zone, which is nearest the surface, contains galena, sphalerite, and chalcopyrite and is richer in gold and silver than ore at depth (Spurr, 1901, p. 864).

There is no record of activity in the Monte Cristo district from 1918 through 1959, and the only production data for the district are estimates of early combined production from the Monte Cristo and Silverton districts of $7 million in gold (Patty, 1921, p. 282). The Monte Cristo district probably produced roughly half of this amount.

SILVERTON DISTRICT

The Silverton district is about 12 miles northwest of Monte Cristo along the Stilaguamish River.

Copper-gold-silver ore was discovered in this district in 1891 (Thyng, in Landes and others, 1902, p. 66). The district became dormant about 1910 and remained inactive through 1959.

The dominant bedrock in the district is granite overlain by sedimentary rocks (Thyng, in Landes and others, 1902, p. 64). The ore bodies occur in fissure veins at the contacts of granite and diorite bodies. Chalcopyrite, the chief metal-bearing mineral, contains the gold. Argentiferous galena is abundant, as are pyrite, arsenopyrite, pyrrhotite, and sphalerite. Pyrargyrite occurs in small quantities (Thyng, in Landes and others, 1902, p. 65).

STEVENS COUNTY

The first mineral discoveries in Stevens County were made in 1883 in the Colville district (Weaver, 1920, p. 134). Shortly afterward additional discoveries were made in the Deer Trail and Chewelah districts. A major factor in attracting prospectors to this part of the State was the opening of the Colville Indian Reservation to mineral exploration in 1896. Rich gold ores were soon discovered on the reservation and across the Columbia River in adjacent parts of Stevens County. Those in Stevens County were quickly mined out, and gold mining in the county virtually ceased in the following years. Subsequent gold production was obtained almost entirely as a byproduct from the mining of base-metal ores.

Total gold production from 1902 through 1959 was 52,145 ounces, mostly from lode mines.

The major gold-producing district in the county is the Orient. The Chewelah district is second in importance, but its total recorded production, byproduct gold from copper-silver ores, is slightly less than 5,000 ounces. Much of Stevens County is underlain by metamorphosed sedimentary rocks of unknown age (Weaver, 1920, p. 44). Locally, these have been intruded by masses of granite and diorite and they are overlain by tuffs, flows, and volcanic breccias with interbedded sediments. Long irregular tongues of basalt flows of probable Tertiary age overlie the metamorphic and igneous rocks in the southern part of the county where they fill depressions on an earlier Tertiary erosion surface. A few small patches of tuffs, breccias, and lavas of late Tertiary age occur in the west-central and north-central parts of the county.

ORIENT DISTRICT

The Orient (Pierre Lake) district is in northwest Stevens County between lat 48°50′ and 48°57′ N. and long 118°05′ and 118°10′ W.

This district was formed in 1902 as a result of significant discoveries at the First Thought and Napoleon mines (Fulkerson and Kingston, 1958, p. 4). The First Thought was the major gold producer in the county during 1900–20 (Fulkerson and Kingston, 1958, p. 1).

Recorded gold production for the district through 1942 was 45,057 ounces; all was presumably from lode mines. From 1942, when the First Thought mine was closed, through 1959 no production was reported from the district.

The predominant rocks exposed in the district are andesite and latite flows of the Rossland Formation of Mesozoic or Tertiary age (Weaver, 1920, p. 257–258). These flows overlie various older rocks —shale, limestone, quartzite, and schist, which are typical of the metasedimentary Stevens Series of Weaver (1920, p. 50–51).

Ore deposits occur in the latite in fractured and brecciated zones that are cemented by silica and carbonate. Gold is the chief ore mineral and occurs with finely disseminated pyrite. Bancroft (1914, p. 69) believed that the ore deposits were related to bodies of rhyolite and monzonite porphyry that were emplaced during Mesozoic or Tertiary time.

WHATCOM COUNTY

Mineralized areas in Whatcom County are in the Cascade Range, and the ore deposits are related to the intrusions of granodiorite along the axis of the range.

Most of the gold mined in Whatcom County came from the Mount Baker and Slate Creek districts, which produced about equal amounts. From 1903 through 1953, the county produced 89,156 ounces of lode gold and 2,425 ounces of placer gold, about half of which was mined in the late 1930's. No production was recorded from 1953 to 1959.

MOUNT BAKER DISTRICT

The Mount Baker district is in north-central Whatcom County between lat 48°50′ and 49°00′ N. and long 122°25′ and 122°35′ W.

Early discoveries of placer gold along Ruby Creek focused attention on this district, but no important deposits were found there until 1897 (Patty, 1921, p. 21). The most important lode gold mines were the Boundary Red Mountain and the Lone Jack. District production of lode gold through 1948 was estimated at a minimum of 55,000 ounces; no production was reported from 1948 through 1959. Huntting (1955, p. 132, 133) reported some placers in the district, but production from them was probably negligible.

The country rock in the district is slate (Lyon, in Landes and others, 1902, p. 42). The ore deposits are in quartz veins or in sulfide-rich veins of calcareous material. Gold is present as native gold, as a telluride, and in association with sulfides.

SLATE CREEK DISTRICT

The Slate Creek district is in the extreme eastern part of Whatcom County, in the heart of the Cascade Range, within lat 48°45′ and 48°50′ N. and long 120°45′ and 121°00′ W.

Gold discoveries were made as early as 1893 at the Gold Ridge, Eureka, and Mammoth properties (Lyon, in Landes and others, 1902, p. 48), but production data were not found for the years before 1933. Total production from 1933 through 1953 was 29,172 ounces; no production was reported from 1953 through 1959.

The country rock consists of shale, limestone, and sandstone of the Similkameen Formation of Cretaceous age (Lyon, in Landes and others, 1902, p. 46, 47). These sediments are compressed into steep north-trending folds. Numerous vertical dikes of porphyry cut the sedimentary rocks and strike parallel to the fold axes. The ore deposits are gold-quartz veins in east-trending fissures. Gold occurs in sulfides, in tellurides, and as native gold.

WYOMING

Gold was first found in Wyoming in placers along the Sweetwater River in 1842, in what was to become the Atlantic City-South Pass district. The original discoverer, however, died or was killed before he reached his home; as a result, the news was not widely spread. Despite privations and Indian raids, small groups of prospectors attempted gold mining along the Sweetwater River at intervals through the 1850's and early 1860's. The first great rush occurred after the discovery of the Cariso lode in 1867 (Raymond, 1870, p. 327–328). Placers were found far to the southeast in the Douglas Creek district in 1868.

Small amounts of gold were mined in Wyoming almost every year from 1867 through 1938, but only the South Pass-Atlantic City and Douglas Creek districts yielded more than 10,000 ounces each. From 1938 through 1959, the gold mining industry of the State steadily declined. The total gold output through 1959 was about 82,000 ounces.

ALBANY COUNTY

The Douglas Creek district, in southwestern Albany County, is the only district in the county that produced more than 10,000 ounces of gold through 1959.

Placers were found in Moore's Gulch in 1868, and during that year they yielded about $8,000 in gold (Osterwald and Osterwald, 1952, p. 64–66). Though small placer operations continued, they were overshadowed by the more productive gold-bearing quartz and silver-copper-gold veins found later. Henderson (1916, p. 251) reported $40,000 worth of placer gold and $189,000 worth of lode gold from Albany County between 1869 and 1893. Except for a small flurry of mining from 1934 to 1940, the district was virtually idle from 1900 through 1959. Total gold production through 1959 was probably 10,000 to 11,000 ounces.

The gold placers were along Douglas Creek and its tributaries in an area about 15 miles long and 10 miles wide. Lode deposits occur in veins in Precambrian schist. A gold-quartz vein 2 to 6 feet wide in the Keystone mine probably yielded most of the gold of the district. Veins containing pyrrkotite, chalcopyrite, and gold were worked for copper, silver, and gold (Osterwald and Osterwald, 1952, p. 64–66).

FREMONT COUNTY

The Atlantic City-South Pass district is in southern Fremont County at the southeast end of the Wind River Range, about 23 miles south of Lander. Most of the gold produced in Wyoming came from this district. The estimates of the gold output of the district vary considerably. Spencer (1916, p. 27–28) estimated the output to 1915 at about $1 million (72,500 ounces). Armstrong (1948, p. 37), using Spencer's figures, estimated the total gold production of the district to May 1947 at about $2 million (about 86,000 ounces), but Martin (1954, p. 1618) credited all Wyoming through 1951 with only 80,040 ounces. Considering the output from other areas in Wyoming, the gold production of the Atlantic City-South Pass district through 1959 probably was not more than 70,000 ounces.

Though placer gold was discovered as early as 1842, important mining operations did not begin until after the Cariso lode was found in 1867 (W. C. Knight, quoted by Trumbull, 1914, p. 76–82). Through 1874 the district produced about $735,000 in gold (Henderson, 1916, p. 248), but production declined sharply thereafter, because of the exhaustion of the rich oxidized ores near the surface. Intermittent exploration in more recent years resulted in only minor production (Armstrong, 1948, p. 35–37).

The bedrock of the Atlantic City-South Pass district consists chiefly of isoclinally folded and faulted schists, gneisses, granulite, amphibolite, diorite, and granodiorite, all of Precambrian age (Armstrong, 1948, p. 11–34). Gold-bearing veins have been found in fault zones in all varieties of the country rock (Armstrong, 1948, p. 37–42). They occur in an en echelon pattern in zones as much as 1,000 feet long. The ore-bearing veins are mostly 2 to 6 feet wide, but they may be as much as 12 feet wide and 50 feet long. The unoxidized ore minerals consist of pyrite, arsenopyrite, and local chalcopyrite and galena (Spencer, 1916, p. 28–34).

SELECTED BIBLIOGRAPHY

Adams, G. I., 1930, Gold deposits of Alabama and occurrences of copper, pyrite, arsenic, and tin: Alabama Geol. Survey Bull. 40, 91 p.

Adams, G. I., Butts, Charles, Stephenson, L. W., and Cooke, Wythe, 1926, Geology of Alabama: Alabama Geol. Survey Spec. Rept. 14, 312 p.

Allen, A. W., ed., 1931, Gold mining and milling at Lead, South Dakota, 1876–1931: Eng. Mining Jour., v. 132, no. 7, p. 287–342.

Allen, R. C., 1912, Gold in Michigan, *in* Mineral resources of Michigan: Michigan Geol. and Biol. Survey Pub. 8, Geol. Ser. 6, p. 355–366.

Allen, R. M., Jr., 1951, Structural control of some gold-base metal veins in eastern Grant County, Oregon: Econ. Geology, v. 46, no. 4, p. 398–403.

Allsman, P. T., 1940, Reconnaissance of gold-mining districts in the Black Hills, South Dakota: U.S. Bur. Mines Bull. 427, 146 p.

Anderson, A. L., 1934, Geology of the Pearl-Horseshoe Bend gold belt, Idaho: Idaho Bur. Mines and Geology Pamph. 41, 36 p.

——— 1943, Geology of the gold-bearing lodes of the Rocky Bar district, Elmore County, Idaho: Idaho Bur. Mines and Geology Pamph. 65, 39 p.

——— 1947, Geology and ore deposits of Boise Basin, Idaho: U.S. Geol. Survey Bull. 944–C, p. 119–319.

——— 1949, Silver-gold deposits of the Yankee Fork district, Custer County, Idaho: Idaho Bur. Mines and Geology Pamph. 83, 37 p.

——— 1953, Gold-copper-lead deposits of the Yellowjacket district, Lemhi County, Idaho: Idaho Bur. Mines and Geology Pamph. 94, 41 p.

——— 1956, Geology and mineral deposits of the Salmon quadrangle, Lemhi County, Idaho: Idaho Bur. Mines and Geology Pamph. 106, 102 p.

Anderson, A. L., and Wagner, W. R., 1946, A geological reconnaissance of the Hailey gold belt (Camas district), Blaine County, Idaho: Idaho Bur. Mines and Geology Pamph. 76, 26 p.

Anderson, C. A., and Creasey, S. C., 1958, Geology and ore deposits of the Jerome area, Yavapai County, Arizona: U.S. Geol. Survey Prof. Paper 308, 195 p.

Anderson, C. A., Scholz, E. A., and Strobell, J. D., Jr., 1956, Geology and ore deposits of the Bagdad area, Yavapai County, Arizona: U.S. Geol. Survey Prof. Paper 278, 103 p.

Anderson, E. C., 1957, The metal resources of New Mexico and their economic features through 1954: New Mexico Bur. Mines and Mineral Resources Bull. 39, 183 p.

Anderson, F. M., 1914, The Forty-nine mines of the Ashland region, Oregon, *in* Diller, J. S., Mineral resources of southwestern Oregon: U.S. Geol. Survey Bull. 546, p. 90–93.

Arizona Bureau of Mines, 1938, Some Arizona ore deposits: Arizona Bur. Mines Bull. 145, Geol. Ser. 12, 136 p.

——— 1958, Geologic map of Yavapai County, Arizona: Tucson, scale 1:375,000.

Armstrong, F. C., 1948, Preliminary report on the geology of the Atlantic City-South Pass mining district, Wyoming: U.S. Geol. Survey open-file rept., 65 p.

Ashley, G. H., 1911, The gold fields of Coker Creek, Monroe County, Tennessee: Tennessee Geol. Survey, Resources of Tennessee, v. 1, no. 3, p. 78–107.

Averill, C. V., 1931, Preliminary report on economic geology of the Shasta quadrangle: California Jour. Mines and Geology, v. 27, no. 1, p. 3–65.

——— 1935, Mines and mineral resources of Siskiyou County: California Jour. Mines and Geology, v. 31, no. 3, p. 255–338.

Averill, C. V., 1936, Mineral resources of Modoc County: California Jour. Mines and Geology, v. 32, no. 4, p. 445–457.

——— 1937, Mineral resources of Plumas County: California Jour. Mines and Geology, v. 33, no. 2, p. 79–143.

——— 1939, Mineral resources of Shasta County: California Jour. Mines and Geology, v. 35, no. 2, p. 108–191.

——— 1941a, Mineral resources of Trinity County: California Jour. Mines and Geology, v. 37, no. 1, p. 8–89.

——— 1941b, Mineral resources of Humboldt County: California Jour. Mines and Geology, v. 37, no. 4, p. 499–528.

——— 1942, Mines and mineral resources of Sierra County: California Jour. Mines and Geology, v. 38, no. 1, p. 7–67.

Averill, C. V., and Erwin, H. D., 1936, Mineral resources of Lassen County: California Jour. Mines and Geology, v. 32, no. 4, p. 405–444.

Averill, C. V., King, C. R., Symons, H. H., and Davis, F. F., 1948, California mineral production for 1946: California Div. Mines Bull. 139, 176 p.

Ball, S. H., 1906, Notes on some ore deposits of southwestern Nevada and eastern California: U.S. Geol. Survey Bull. 285–A, p. 53–73.

Ballard, S. M., 1924, Geology and gold resources of Boise Basin, Boise County, Idaho: Idaho Bur. Mines and Geology Bull. 9, 103 p.

——— 1928, Geology and ore deposits of the Rocky Bar quadrangle: Idaho Bur. Mines and Geology Pamph. 26, 41 p.

Bancroft, Howland, 1911, Reconnaissance of the ore deposits in northern Yuma County, Arizona: U.S. Geol. Survey Bull. 451, 130 p.

——— 1914, Ore deposits of northeastern Washington: U.S. Geol. Survey Bull. 550, 215 p.

Barnes, F. F., and Cobb, E. H., 1959, Geology and coal resources of the Homer district, Kenai coal field, Alaska: U.S. Geol. Survey Bull. 1058–F, p. 217–260.

Barrell, Joseph, 1907, Geology of the Marysville mining district, Montana, a study of igneous intrusion and contact metamorphism: U.S. Geol. Survey Prof. Paper 57, 178 p.

Bass, C. E., 1940, The Vaucluse gold mine, Orange County, Virginia: Econ. Geology, v. 35, no. 1, p. 79–91.

Bastin, E. S., and Hill, J. M., 1917, Economic geology of Gilpin County and adjacent parts of Clear Creek and Boulder Counties, Colorado: U.S. Geol. Survey Prof. Paper 94, 379 p.

Bateman, P. C., 1956, Economic geology of the Bishop tungsten district, California: California Div. Mines Spec. Rept. 47, 87 p.

Becker, G. F., 1882, Geology of the Comstock Lode and the Washoe district: U.S. Geol. Survey Mon. 3, 422 p.

——— 1895, Reconnaissance of the gold fields of the southern Appalachians: U.S. Geol. Survey 16th Ann. Rept., pt. 3, p. 251–331.

——— 1898, Reconnaissance of the gold fields of southern Alaska, with some notes on general geology: U.S. Geol. Survey 18th Ann. Rept., pt. 3, p. 1–86.

Behre, C. H., Jr., 1953, Geology and ore deposits of the west slope of the Mosquito Range: U.S. Geol. Survey Prof. Paper 235, 176 p.

Bick, K. F., 1959, Stratigraphy of Deep Creek Mountains, Utah: Am. Assoc. Petroleum Geologists Bull., v. 43, no. 5, p. 1064–1069.

Billingsley, Paul, and Grimes, J. A., 1918, Ore deposits of the Boulder batholith of Montana: Am. Inst. Mining Engineers Trans., v. 58, p. 284–361.

Blixt, J. E., 1933, Geology and gold deposits of the North Moccasin Mountains, Fergus County, Montana: Montana Bur. Mines and Geology Mem. 8, 25 p.

Bostwick, D. A., and Koch, G. S., Jr., 1962, Permian and Triassic rocks of northeastern Oregon: Geol. Soc. America Bull., v. 73, no. 3, p. 419–421.

Boutwell, J. M., 1905, Economic geology of the Bingham mining district, Utah, with a section on areal geology, by Arthur Keith, and an introduction on general geology, by S. F. Emmons: U.S. Geol. Survey Prof. Paper 38, 413 p.

——— 1912, Geology and ore deposits of the Park City district, Utah: U.S. Geol. Survey Prof. Paper 77, 231 p.

——— 1935, Copper deposits at Bingham, Utah, *in* Copper resources of the world: Internat. Geol. Cong., 16th, Washington, D.C., 1933, v. 1, p. 347–359.

Bowen, O. E., Jr., and Gray, C. H., Jr., 1957, Mines and mineral deposits of Mariposa County, California: California Jour. Mines and Geology, v. 53, nos. 1–2, p. 35–343.

Brewer, W. M., 1896, A preliminary report on the upper gold belt of Alabama, in the counties of Cleburne, Randolph, Clay, Talladega, Elmore, Coosa, and Tallapoosa: Alabama Geol. Survey Bull. 5, p. 1–105.

Broadhurst, S. D., 1955, The mining industry in North Carolina from 1946 through 1953: North Carolina Dept. Conserv. and Devel., Div. Mineral Resources, Econ. Paper 66, 99 p.

Brooks, A. H., 1902, Preliminary report on the Ketchikan mining district, Alaska, with an introductory sketch of the geology of southeastern Alaska: U.S. Geol. Survey Prof. Paper 1, 120 p.

——— 1916, Preliminary report on the Tolovana district [Alaska]: U.S. Geol. Survey Bull. 642–G, p. 201–209.

Brooks, A. H., and Capps, S. R., 1924, The Alaskan mining industry in 1922: U.S. Geol. Survey Bull. 755–A, p. 1–56.

Brown, J. S., 1926, The Nixon Fork country: U.S. Geol. Survey Bull. 783, p. 97–144.

Brown, R. G., 1908, The vein system of the Standard mine, Bodie, California: Am. Inst. Mining Engineers Trans., v. 38, p. 343–357.

Browne, J. R., 1868, Report on the mineral resources of the States and territories west of the Rocky Mountains: Washington, U.S. Treasury Dept., 674 p.

Browne, J. R., and Taylor, J. W., 1867, Reports upon the mineral resources of the United States: Washington, U.S. Treasury Dept., 360 p.

Bryson, H. J., 1936, Gold deposits in North Carolina: North Carolina Dept. Conserv. and Devel. Bull. 38, 157 p.

Buddington, A. F., 1929, Geology of Hyder and vicinity, southeastern Alaska, with a reconnaissance of Chickamin River: U.S. Geol. Survey Bull. 807, 124 p.

Buddington, A. F., and Chapin, Theodore, 1929, Geology and mineral deposits of southeastern Alaska: U.S. Geol. Survey Bull. 800, 398 p.

Burbank, W. S., 1932, Geology and ore deposits of the Bonanza mining district, Colorado: U.S. Geol. Survey Prof. Paper 169, 166 p.

Burbank, W. S., 1933, Vein systems of the Arrastre Basin and regional geologic structure in the Silverton and Telluride quadrangles, Colorado: Colorado Sci. Soc. Proc., v. 13, no. 5, p. 135–214.

——— 1941, Structural control of ore deposition in the Red Mountains, Sneffels, and Telluride districts of the San Juan Mountains, Colorado: Colorado Sci. Soc. Proc., v. 14, no. 5, p. 141–261.

Burgess, J. A., 1909, The geology of the producing part of the Tonopah mining district: Econ. Geology, v. 4, p. 681–712.

——— 1917, The halogen salts of silver at Wonder, Nevada: Econ. Geology, v. 12, no. 7, p. 589–593.

Butler, B. S., 1913, Geology and ore deposits of the San Francisco and adjacent districts, Utah: U.S. Geol. Survey Prof. Paper 80, 212 p.

Butler, B. S., Loughlin, G. F., and Heikes, V. C., and others, 1920, The ore deposits of Utah: U.S. Geol. Survey Prof. Paper 111, 672 p.

Butler, B. S., Wilson, E. D., and Rasor, C. A., 1938, Geology and ore deposits of the Tombstone district, Arizona: Arizona Bur. Mines Bull. 143, Geol. Ser. 10, 114 p.

Cady, W. M., Wallace, R. E., Hoare, J. M., and Webber, E. J., 1955, The central Kuskokwim region, Alaska: U.S. Geol. Survey Prof. Paper 268, 132 p.

Calkins, F. C., 1938, Gold deposits of Slumbering Hills, Nevada: Nevada Univ. Bull., v. 32, no. 3, 26 p.

Calkins, F. C., and Butler, B. S., 1943, Geology and ore deposits of the Cottonwood-American Fork area, Utah: U.S. Geol. Survey Prof. Paper 201, 152 p.

Calkins, J. A., Parker, R. L., and Disbrow, A. E., 1959, Geologic map of the Curlew quadrangle, Ferry County, Washington: U.S. Geol. Survey open-file rept.

Callaghan, Eugene, 1937, Geology of the Delamar district, Lincoln County, Nevada: Nevada Univ. Bull., v. 31, no. 5, 69 p., 8 pls., 9 figs.

——— 1938, Preliminary report on the alunite deposits of the Marysvale region, Utah: U.S. Geol. Survey Bull. 886–D, p. 91–134.

——— 1939, Geology of the Searchlight district, Clark County, Nevada: U.S. Geol. Survey Bull. 906–D, p. 135–188.

Callaghan, Eugene, and Buddington, A. F., 1938, Metalliferous mineral deposits of the Cascade Range in Oregon: U.S. Geol. Survey Bull. 893, 141 p.

Capps, S. R., 1912, The Bonnifield region, Alaska: U.S. Geol. Survey Bull. 501, 64 p.

——— 1913, The Yentna district, Alaska: U.S. Geol. Survey Bull. 534, 75 p.

——— 1916, The Chisana-White River district, Alaska: U.S. Geol. Survey Bull. 630, 130 p.

——— 1919, The Kantishna region, Alaska: U.S. Geol. Survey Bull. 687, 116 p.

——— 1925, An early Tertiary placer deposit in the Yentna district [Alaska]: U.S. Geol. Survey Bull. 773–A, p. 53–61.

Carlson, D. W., 1955, Mines and mineral resources of Sacramento County, California: California Jour. Mines and Geology, v. 51, no. 2, p. 117–199.

Carlson, D. W., and Clark, W. B., 1954, Mines and mineral deposits of Amador County, California: California Jour. Mines and Geology, v. 50, no. 1, p. 149–285.

Chapin, Theodore, 1918, The Nelchina-Susitna region, Alaska: U.S. Geol. Survey Bull. 668, 67 p.

Charles, Abbot, 1947, Mines and mineral resources of Stanislaus County, California: California Jour. Mines and Geology, v. 43, no. 2, p. 85–100.

Chase, C. A., and Muir, Douglas, 1923, The Aztec mine, Baldy, New Mexico: Am. Inst. Mining and Metall. Engineers Trans., v. 68, p. 270–281.

Clark, W. B., 1955, Mines and mineral resources of San Joaquin County, California: California Jour. Mines and Geology, v. 51, no. 1, p. 21–95.

——— 1957, Gold, *in* Wright, L. A., ed., Mineral commodities of California: California Div. Mines Bull. 176, p. 215–226.

Clark, W. B., and Carlson, D. W., 1956, Mines and mineral resources of El Dorado County, California: California Jour. Mines and Geology, v. 52, no. 4, p. 369–591.

Coats, R. R., 1936, Aguilarite from the Comstock Lode, Virginia City, Nevada: Am. Mineralogist, v. 21, no. 8, p. 532–534.

Cobb, E. H., 1962, Lode gold and silver occurrences in Alaska: U.S. Geol. Survey Mineral Inv. Resource Map MR–32.

Collier, A. J., Hess, F. L., Smith, P. S., and Brooks, A. H., 1908, The gold placers of parts of Seward Peninsula, Alaska, including the Nome, Council, Kougarok, Port Clarence, and Goodhope precincts: U.S. Geol. Survey Bull. 328, 343 p.

Connolly, J. P., and O'Harra, C. C., 1929, The mineral wealth of the Black Hills: South Dakota School Mines Bull. 16, 418 p.

Cook, D. R., ed., 1957, Geology of the East Tintic Mountains and ore deposits of the Tintic mining districts: Utah Geol. Soc. Guidebook to the geology of Utah, no. 12, 183 p.

——— 1961, Geology of the Bingham mining district and northern Oquirrh Mountains: Utah Geol. Soc. Guidebook to the geology of Utah, no. 16, 145 p.

Cooper, C. L., 1940, Mining and milling methods and costs at Knob Hill mine, Republic, Washington: U.S. Bur. Mines Inf. Circ. 7123, 29 p.

Cooper, J. R., 1951, Geology of the tungsten, antimony and gold deposits near Stibnite, Idaho: U.S. Geol. Survey Bull. 969–F, p. 151–197.

Cooper, J. R., and others, 1959, Geologic map of Cochise County, Arizona: Arizona Bur. Mines.

Corry, A. V., 1933, Some gold deposits of Broadwater, Beaverhead, Phillips, and Fergus Counties, Montana: Montana Bur. Mines and Geology Mem. 10, 45 p.

Couch, B. F., and Carpenter, J. A., 1943, Nevada's metal and mineral production (1859–1940 inclusive): Nevada Univ. Bull., v. 37, no. 4, Geology and Mining Ser. 38, 159 p.

Crawford, R. D., 1913, Geology and ore deposits of the Monarch and Tomichi districts, Colorado: Colorado Geol. Survey Bull. 4, 317 p.

Crawford, R. D., and Gibson, Russell, 1925, Geology and ore deposits of the Red Cliff district, Colorado: Colorado Geol. Survey Bull. 30, 89 p.

Crawford, R. D., and Worcester, P. G., 1916, Geology and ore deposits of the Gold Brick district, Colorado: Colorado Geol. Survey Bull. 10, 116 p.

Cross, Whitman, 1896, Geology of Silver Cliff and the Rosita Hills, Colorado: U.S. Geol. Survey 17th Ann. Rept., pt. 2, p. 263–403.

Cross, Whitman, and Purington, C. W., 1899, Description of the Telluride quadrangle [Colorado]: U.S. Geol. Survey Geol. Atlas, Folio 57.

Cross, Whitman, and Ransome, F. L., 1905, Description of the Rico quadrangle [Colorado]: U.S. Geol. Survey Geol. Atlas, Folio 130.

Currier, L. W., 1935, A preliminary report on the geology and ore deposits of the eastern part of the Yellow Pine district, Idaho: Idaho Bur. Mines and Geology Pamph. 43, 27 p.

Curtis, G. H., Evernden, J. F., and Lipson, J. I., 1958, Age determination of some granitic rocks in California by the potassium-argon method: California Div. Mines Spec. Rept. 54, 16 p.

Darton, N. H., 1925, A résumé of Arizona geology: Arizona Bur. Mines Bull. 119, Geol. Ser. 3, 298 p.

Darton, N. H., and Paige, Sidney, 1925, Description of the central Black Hills [South Dakota]: U.S. Geol. Survey Geol. Atlas, Folio 219.

Davis, F. F., 1948, Mines and mineral resources of Napa County, California: California Jour. Mines and Geology, v. 44, no. 2, p. 159–188.

Davis, F. F., and Carlson, D. W., 1952, Mines and mineral resources of Merced County: California Jour. Mines and Geology, v. 48, no. 3, p. 207–251.

Davis, L. E., and Ashizawa, R. Y., 1960, The mineral industry of California: U.S. Bur. Mines Minerals Yearbook, 1959, v. 3, p. 147–204.

Diller, J. S., 1898, Description of the Roseburg quadrangle [Oregon]: U.S. Geol. Survey Geol. Atlas, Folio 49.

——— 1900, The Bohemia mining region of western Oregon, with notes on the Blue River mining region and on the structure and age of the Cascade Range, accompanied by a report on the fossil plants associated with the lavas of the Cascade Range, by F. H. Knowlton: U.S. Geol. Survey 20th Ann. Rept., pt. 3, p. 7–36.

——— 1901, Description of the Coos Bay quadrangle [Oregon]: U.S. Geol. Survey Geol. Atlas, Folio 73.

——— 1903, Description of the Port Orford quadrangle [Oregon]: U.S. Geol. Survey Geol. Atlas, Folio 89.

——— 1914a, Auriferous gravels in the Weaverville quadrangle, California: U.S. Geol. Survey Bull. 540–A, p. 11–21.

——— 1914b, Mineral resources of southwestern Oregon: U.S. Geol. Survey Bull. 546, 147 p.

Diller, J. S., and Kay, G. F., 1909, Mineral resources of the Grants Pass quadrangle and bordering districts, Oregon: U.S. Geol. Survey Bull. 380–A, p. 48–79.

——— 1924, Description of the Riddle quadrangle [Oregon]: U.S. Geol. Survey Geol. Atlas, Folio 218.

Dings, M. G., 1951, The Wallapai mining district, Cerbat Mountains, Mohave County, Arizona: U.S. Geol. Survey Bull. 978–E, p. 123–163.

Dings, M. G., and Robinson, C. S., 1957, Geology and ore deposits of the Garfield quadrangle, Colorado: U.S. Geol. Survey Prof. Paper 289, 110 p.

Donnelly, Maurice, 1934, Geology and mineral deposits of the Julian district, San Diego County, California: California Jour. Mines and Geology, v. 30, no. 4, p. 331–370.

Dunham, K. C., 1935, The geology of the Organ Mountains, with an account of the geology and mineral resources of Dona Ana County, New Mexico: New Mexico Bur. Mines and Mineral Resources Bull. 11, 272 p.

Dunn, R. L., 1894, Auriferous conglomerate in California: California State Mineralogist, 12th Ann. Rept., p. 459–471.

Eakin, H. M., 1913, Gold placers of the Innoko-Iditarod region [Alaska]: U.S. Geol. Survey Bull. 542–G, p. 293–303.

——— 1915, Mining in the Hot Springs district [Alaska]: U.S. Geol. Survey Bull. 622–G, p. 239–245.

——— 1918a, Lode mining in the Juneau gold belt [Alaska]: U.S. Geol. Survey Bull. 662–B, p. 77–92.

——— 1918b, Gold mining in the Porcupine district [Alaska]: U.S. Geol. Survey Bull. 662–B, p. 93–100.

——— 1919, The Porcupine gold placer district, Alaska: U.S. Geol. Survey Bull. 699, 29 p.

Eckel, E. B., 1949, Geology and ore deposits of the La Plata district, Colorado: U.S. Geol. Survey Prof. Paper 219, 179 p. [1950].

Eckel, E. C., 1903, Gold and pyrite deposits of the Dahlonega district, Georgia: U.S. Geol. Survey Bull. 213, p. 57–63.

Ellis, R. W., 1922, Geology of the Sandia Mountains: New Mexico State Univ. Bull. 4, Geol. Ser. 3, 45 p.

Elsing, M. J., and Heineman, R. E. S., 1936, Arizona metal production: Arizona Bur. Mines Bull. 140, Econ. Ser. 19, 112 p.

Emmons, S. F., 1896, The mines of Custer County, Colorado: U.S. Geol. Survey 17th Ann. Rept., pt. 2, p. 405–472.

——— 1898, Tenmile district special, Colorado: U.S. Geol. Survey Geol. Atlas, Folio 48.

Emmons, S. F., Irving, J. E., and Loughlin, G. F., 1927, Geology and ore deposits of the Leadville mining district, Colorado: U.S. Geol. Survey Prof. Paper 148, 368 p.

Emmons, W. H., 1907, The Granite-Bimetallic and Cable mines, Philipsburg quadrangle, Montana: U.S. Geol. Survey Bull. 315–A, p. 31–55.

——— 1908, Gold deposits of the Little Rocky Mountains, Montana: U.S. Geol. Survey Bull. 340–A, p. 96–116.

——— 1910, A reconnaissance of some mining camps in Elko, Lander, and Eureka Counties, Nevada: U.S. Geol. Survey Bull. 408, 130 p.

——— 1937, Gold deposits of the world: New York, McGraw-Hill Book Co., 562 p.

Emmons, W. H., and Calkins, F. C., 1913, Geology and ore deposits of the Philipsburg quadrangle, Montana: U.S. Geol. Survey Prof. Paper 78, 271 p.

Emmons, W. H., and Laney, F. B., 1926, Geology and ore deposits of the Ducktown mining district, Tennessee: U.S. Geol. Survey Prof. Paper 139, 114 p.

Emmons, W. H., and Larsen, E. S., 1923, Geology and ore deposits of the Creede district, Colorado: U.S. Geol. Survey Bull. 718, 198 p.

Ferguson, H. G., 1914, Gold lodes of Weaverville quadrangle, California: U.S. Geol. Survey Bull. 540–A, p. 22–79.

——— 1917, The Golden Arrow, Clifford, and Ellendale districts, Nye County, Nevada: U.S. Geol. Survey Bull. 640–F, p. 113–123.

——— 1922, The Round Mountain district, Nevada: U.S. Geol. Survey Bull. 725–I, p. 383–406.

——— 1924, Geology and ore deposits of the Manhattan district, Nevada: U.S. Geol. Survey Bull. 723, 162 p.

——— 1927, Geology and ore deposits of the Mogollon mining district, New Mexico: U.S. Geol. Survey Bull. 787, 100 p.

Ferguson, H. G., 1933, Geology of the Tybo district, Nevada: Nevada Univ. Bull., v. 27, no. 3, 61 p.
——— 1944, The mining districts of Nevada: Nevada Univ. Bull., v. 38, no. 4, p. 77–108.
Ferguson, H. G., and Cathcart, S. H., 1954, Geology of the Round Mountain quadrangle, Nevada: U.S. Geol. Survey Geol. Quad. Map GQ–40.
Ferguson, H. G., and Gannett, R. W., 1932, Gold-quartz veins of the Alleghany district, California: U.S. Geol. Survey Prof. Paper 172, 139 p.
Ferguson, H. G., Muller, S. W., and Cathcart, S. H., 1954, Geology of the Mina quadrangle, Nevada: U.S. Geol. Survey Geol. Quad. Map GQ–45.
Ferguson, H. G., Muller, S. W., and Roberts, R. J., 1951, Geology of the Winnemucca quadrangle, Nevada: U.S. Geol. Survey Geol. Quad. Map GQ–11.
Finch, J. W., chm., and others, 1933, Ore deposits of the Western States [Lindgren volume]: New York, Am. Inst. Mining Metall. Engineers, 797 p.
Fischer, R. P., and others, 1946, Metallic mineral deposits of Colorado: U.S. Geol. Survey Missouri Basin Studies 8, maps with text and tables.
Franke, H. A., 1935, Mines and mineral resources of San Luis Obispo County: California Jour. Mines and Geology, v. 31, no. 4, p. 402–464.
Fulkerson, F. B., and Kingston, G. A., 1958, Mine production of gold, silver, copper, lead, and zinc in Pend Oreille and Stevens Counties, Washington, 1902–1956: U.S. Bur. Mines Inf. Circ. 7872, 51 p.
Gardner, E. D., 1934, Mining methods and costs at Herron and Laster lease, Superior, Arizona: U.S. Bur. Mines Inf. Circ. 6799, 9 p.
Gay, T. E., Jr., and Hoffman, S. R., 1954, Mines and mineral deposits of Los Angeles County, California: California Jour. Mines and Geology, v. 50, nos. 3–4, p. 467–709.
Gemmell, R. C., 1897, The Camp Floyd mining district and the Mercur mines, Utah: Eng. Mining Jour., v. 63, p. 403–404, 427–428.
George, R. D., and Crawford, R. D., 1909, The Hahns Peak region, Routt County, Colorado: Colorado Geol. Survey Rept. 1, 1908, p. 189–229.
Geyer, A. R., and others, 1958, Geology of the Lebanon quadrangle: Pennsylvania Geol. Survey, 4th Ser., Atlas 167C.
Gianella, V. P., 1936, Geology of the Silver City district and the southern portion of the Comstock Lode, Nevada: Nevada Univ. Bull., v. 30, no. 9, 105 p.
Gibson, Russell, 1948, Geology and ore deposits of the Libby quadrangle, Montana: U.S. Geol. Survey Bull. 956, 131 p.
Gilluly, James, 1932, Geology and ore deposits of the Stockton and Fairfield quadrangles, Utah: U.S. Geol. Survey Prof. Paper 173, 171 p.
——— 1937, Geology and mineral resources of the Baker quadrangle, Oregon: U.S. Geol. Survey Bull. 879, 119 p.
——— 1946, The Ajo mining district, Arizona: U.S. Geol. Survey Prof. Paper 209, 112 p [1947].
——— 1956, General geology of central Cochise County, Arizona: U.S. Geol. Survey Prof. Paper 281, 169 p.
Gilluly, James, Reed, J. C., and Park, C. F., Jr., 1933, Some mining districts of eastern Oregon: U.S. Geol. Survey Bull. 846–A, p. 1–140.
Glover, S. L., 1954, One hundred years of mining: Washington Div. Mines and Geology Bienn. Rept. 5, p. 9–20.
Goddard, E. N., 1936, The geology and ore deposits of the Tincup mining district, Gunnison County, Colorado: Colorado Sci. Soc. Proc., v. 13, no. 10, p. 551–595.
——— 1940, Preliminary report on the Gold Hill mining district, Boulder County, Colorado: Colorado Sci. Soc. Proc., v. 14, no. 4, p. 103–139.
Goodspeed, G. E., 1941, Geology of the gold-quartz veins of Cornucopia: Am. Inst. Mining Metall. Engineers Trans., v. 144, p. 172–189.
Goodwin, J. G., 1958, Mines and mineral resources of Tulare County, California: California Jour. Mines and Geology, v. 54, no. 3, p. 317–492.
Grant, U. S., and Higgins, D. F., 1910, Reconnaissance of the geology and mineral resources of Prince William Sound, Alaska: U.S. Geol. Survey Bull. 443, 89 p.
Graton, L. C., 1910, The occurrence of copper in Shasta County, California: U.S. Geol. Survey Bull. 430–B, p. 71–111.
Greenan, J. O., 1914, Geology of Fairview, Nevada: Eng. Mining Jour., v. 97, p. 791–793.
Hafer, Claude, 1914, The Iola mine, *in* Pratt, J. H., The mining industry in North Carolina during 1911 and 1912: North Carolina Geol. and Econ. Survey Econ. Paper 34, p. 26–29.
Hague, Arnold, 1892, Geology of the Eureka district, Nevada: U.S. Geol. Survey Mon. 20, 419 p.
Harley, G. T., 1934, The geology and ore deposits of Sierra County, New Mexico: New Mexico Bur. Mines and Mineral Resources Bull. 10, 220 p.
——— 1940, The geology and ore deposits of northeastern New Mexico: New Mexico Bur. Mines and Mineral Resources Bull. 15, 104 p.
Harrington, G. L., 1918, The Anvik-Andreafski region, Alaska: U.S. Geol. Survey Bull. 683, 70 p.
——— 1921, Mineral resources of the Goodnews Bay region [Alaska]: U.S. Geol. Survey Bull. 714–E, p. 207–228.
Harrison, J. E., and Wells, J. D., 1956, Geology and ore deposits of the Freeland-Lamartine district, Clear Creek County, Colorado: U.S. Geol. Survey Bull. 1032–B, p. 33–127.
Henderson, C. W., 1916, Gold, silver, and copper in Wyoming in 1914: U.S. Geol. Survey, Mineral Resources U.S., 1914, pt. 1, p. 247–254.
——— 1926, Mining in Colorado, a history of discovery, development, and production: U.S. Geol. Survey Prof. Paper 138, 263 p.
——— 1932, Gold, silver, copper, lead, and zinc in New Mexico: U.S. Bur. Mines, Mineral Resources U.S., 1929, pt. 1, p. 729–759.
Henshaw, P. C., 1942, Geology and mineral resources of the Cargo Muchacho Mountains, Imperial County, California: California Jour. Mines and Geology, v. 38, no. 2, p. 147–196.
Hess, F. L., 1910, Gold mining in the Randsburg quadrangle, California: U.S. Geol. Survey Bull. 430–A, p. 23–47.
Hewett, D. F., 1931, Geology and ore deposits of the Goodsprings quadrangle, Nevada: U.S. Geol. Survey Prof. Paper 162, 172 p.
Hewett, D. F., Callaghan, Eugene, Moore, B. N., Nolan, T. B., Rubey, W. W., and Schaller, W. T., 1936, Mineral resources of the region around Boulder Dam: U.S. Geol. Survey Bull. 871, 197 p.
Hickok, W. O., 4th, 1933, The iron ore deposits at Cornwall, Pa.: Econ. Geology, v. 28, no. 3, p. 193–255.

Hill, J. M., 1910a, Notes on the ecomonic geology of the Ramsey, Talapoosa, and White Horse mining districts in Lyon and Washoe Counties, Nevada: U.S. Geol. Survey Bull. 470, p. 99–108.

——— 1910b, Notes on the placer deposits of Greaterville, Arizona: U.S. Geol. Survey Bull. 430–A, p. 11–22.

——— 1912, The mining districts of Western United States: U.S. Geol. Survey Bull. 507, 309 p.

——— 1915, Some mining districts in northeastern California and northwestern Nevada: U.S. Geol. Survey Bull. 594, 200 p.

——— 1916, Notes on some mining districts in eastern Nevada: U.S. Geol. Survey Bull. 648, 214 p.

——— 1923, The Los Burros district, Monterey County, California: U.S. Geol. Survey Bull. 735–J, p. 323–329.

——— 1933, Lode deposits of the Fairbanks district, Alaska: U.S. Geol. Survey Bull. 849–B, p. 29–163.

Hodges, L. K., 1897, Mining in the Pacific Northwest: Seattle, Wash., The Post-Intelligencer, p. 85.

Hollister, O. J., 1867, The mines of Colorado: Springfield, Mass., S. Bowles and Co., 450 p.

Holt, S. P., Shepard, J. G., Thorne, R. L., Tolonen, A. W., and Fosse, E. L., 1948, Investigation of the Salt Chuck copper mine, Kasaan Peninsula, Prince of Wales Island, southeastern Alaska: U.S. Bur. Mines Rept. Inv. 4358, 16 p.

Hosterman, J. W., 1956, Geology of the Murray area, Shoshone County, Idaho: U.S. Geol. Survey Bull. 1027–P, p. 725–748.

Hotz, P. E., and Willden, Ronald, 1961, Preliminary geologic map and sections of the Osgood Mountains quadrangle, Humboldt County, Nevada: U.S. Geol. Survey Mineral Inv. Field Studies Map MF–161.

Howell, J. V., 1919, Twin Lakes district of Colorado [Lake and Pitkin Counties]: Colorado Geol. Survey Bull. 17, 108 p.

Hubbard, C. R., 1957, Mineral resources of Latah County: Idaho Bur. Mines and Geology County Rept. 2, 29 p.

Hughes, R. B., 1924, The story of the placers: Black Hills Engineer, v. 12, no. 1, p. 18–27.

Hummel, C. L., 1960, Structural geology and structural control of mineral deposits near Nome, Alaska, *in* Short papers in the geological sciences: U.S. Geol. Survey Prof. Paper 400–B, p. B33–B35.

Hundhausen, R. J., 1949, Investigation of Henderson Gulch tungsten deposit, Granite County, Montana: U.S. Bur. Mines Rept. Inv. 4513, 8 p.

Huntting, M. T., 1943, Inventory of mineral properties in Chelan County, Washington: Washington Div. Mines and Geology Rept. Inv. 9, 63 p.

——— 1955, Gold in Washington: Washington Div. Mines and Geology Bull. 42, 158 p.

Hutchinson, W. S., 1921, The Vulture mine: Eng. Mining Jour., v. 111, no. 7, p. 298–302.

International Geological Congress, 1935, Copper resources of the world: Internat. Geol. Cong., 16th, Washington, D.C., 1933, v. 1, 441 p.

Irving, J. D., and Bancroft, Howland, 1911, Geology and ore deposits near Lake City, Colorado: U.S. Geol. Survey Bull. 478, 128 p.

Irving, J. D., Emmons, S. F., and Jaggar, T. A., Jr., 1904, Economic resources of the northern Black Hills: U.S. Geol. Survey Prof. Paper 26, 222 p.

Johnson, B. L., 1914, The Port Wells gold-lode district [Alaska]: U.S. Geol. Survey Bull. 592–G, p. 195–236.

Johnston, W. D., Jr., 1940, The gold-quartz veins of Grass Valley, California: U.S. Geol. Survey Prof. Paper 194, 101 p.

Jones, E. L., Jr., 1916a, Gold deposits near Quartzite, Arizona: U.S. Geol. Survey Bull. 620–C, p. 45–57.

——— 1916b, A reconnaissance in the Kofa Mountains, Arizona: U.S. Geol. Survey Bull. 620–H, p. 151–164.

——— 1917, Lode mining in the Quartzburg and Grimes Pass porphyry belt, Boise Basin, Idaho: U.S. Geol. Survey Bull. 640–E, p. 83–111.

Jones, F. A., 1904, New Mexico mines and minerals [World's Fair ed.]: Santa Fe, The New Mexican Printing Co., 346 p.

Jones, S. P., 1909, Second report on the gold deposits of Georgia: Georgia Geol. Survey Bull. 19, 283 p.

Joralemon, Peter, 1951, The occurrence of gold at the Getchell mine, Nevada: Econ. Geology, v. 46, no. 3, p. 267–310.

Julihn, C. E., and Horton, F. W., 1938, Calaveras County, Part 1 *of* Mines of the southern Mother Lode region: U.S. Bur. Mines Bull. 413, 140 p.

——— 1940, Tuolumne and Mariposa Counties, Part 2 *of* Mines of the southern Mother Lode region: U.S. Bur. Mines Bull. 424, 179 p.

Karlstrom, T. N. V., 1948, Geology and ore deposits of the Hecla mining district, Beaverhead County, Montana: Montana Bur. Mines and Geology Mem. 25, 87 p.

Keith, Arthur, and Sterrett, D. B., 1931, Description of Gaffney and Kings Mountain quadrangles [South Carolina-North Carolina]: U.S. Geol. Survey Geol. Atlas, Folio 222.

King, Clarence, 1870, The Comstock Lode: U.S. Geol. Explor. 40th Parallel (King), v. 3, p. 11–96.

Kinkel, A. R., Jr., and Albers, J. P., 1951, Geology of the massive sulfide deposits at Iron Mountain, Shasta County, California: California Div. Mines Spec. Rept. 14, 19 p.

Kinkel, A. R., Jr., Hall, W. E., and Albers, J. P., 1956, Geology and base-metal deposits of West Shasta copper-zinc district, Shasta County, California: U.S. Geol. Survey Prof. Paper 285, 156 p. [1957].

Kirk, C. T., 1908, Montana: U.S. Geol. Survey, Mineral Resources U.S., 1907, pt. 1, p. 312–337.

Klepper, M. R., Weeks, R. A., and Ruppel, E. T., 1957, Geology of the southern Elkhorn Mountains, Jefferson and Broadwater Counties, Montana: U.S. Geol. Survey Prof. Paper 292, 82 p. [1958].

Knechtel, M. M., 1959, Stratigraphy of the Little Rocky Mountains and encircling foothills, Montana: U.S. Geol. Survey Bull. 1072–N, p. 723–752 [1960].

Knopf, Adolph, 1912, The Sitka mining district, Alaska: U.S. Geol. Survey Bull. 504, 32 p.

——— 1913, Ore deposits of the Helena mining region, Montana: U.S. Geol. Survey Bull. 527, 143 p.

——— 1918, A geologic reconnaissance of the Inyo Range and the eastern slope of the southern Sierra Nevada, California, with a section on the stratigraphy of the Inyo Range, by Edwin Kirk: U.S. Geol. Survey Prof. Paper 110, 130 p.

——— 1921a, Ore deposits of Cedar Mountain, Mineral County, Nevada: U.S. Geol. Survey Bull. 725–H, p. 361–382.

Knopf, Adolph, 1921b, The Divide silver district, Nevada: U.S. Geol. Survey Bull. 715–K, p. 147–170.

——— 1923, The Candelaria silver district, Nevada: U.S. Geol. Survey Bull. 735–A, p. 1–22.

——— 1924, Geology and ore deposits of the Rochester district, Nevada: U.S. Geol. Survey Bull. 762, 78 p.

——— 1929, The Mother Lode system of California: U.S. Geol. Survey Prof. Paper 157, 88 p.

Koch, G. S., Jr., 1959, Lode mines of the central part of the Granite mining district, Grant County, Oregon: Oregon Dept. Geology and Mineral Industries Bull. 49, 49 p.

Koschmann, A. H., 1949, Structural control of the gold deposits of the Cripple Creek district, Teller County, Colorado: U.S. Geol. Survey Bull. 955–B, p. 19–60.

Koschmann, A. H., and Wells, F. G., 1946, Preliminary report on the Kokomo mining district, Colorado: Colorado Sci. Soc. Proc., v. 15, no. 2, p. 51–112.

Kral, V. E., 1951, Mineral resources of Nye County, Nevada: Nevada Univ. Bull., v. 45, no. 3, Geology and Mining Ser. 50, 223 p.

Krieger, Philip, 1932, Geology of the zinc-lead deposit at Pecos, New Mexico: Econ. Geology, v. 27, nos. 4–5, p. 344–364, 450–470.

Laizure, C. M., 1929, Fresno County: California State Mineralogist Rept. 25, p. 301–336.

Landes, Henry, Thyng, W. S., Lyon, D. A., and Roberts, Milnor, 1902, The metalliferous resources of Washington, except iron: Washington Geol. Survey Ann. Rept. for 1901, v. 1, pt. 2, 119 p.

Laney, F. B., 1910, The Gold Hill mining district of North Carolina: North Carolina Geol. and Econ. Survey Bull. 21, 137 p.

Lasky, S. G., 1932, The ore deposits of Socorro County, New Mexico: New Mexico Bur. Mines and Mineral Resources Bull. 8, 139 p.

——— 1936, Geology and ore deposits of the Bayard area, Central mining district, New Mexico: U.S. Geol. Survey Bull. 870, 144 p.

——— 1938, Geology and ore deposits of the Lordsburg mining district, Hidalgo County, New Mexico: U.S. Geol. Survey Bull. 885, 62 p.

Lasky, S. G., and Wootton, T. P., 1933, The metal resources of New Mexico and their economic features: New Mexico Bur. Mines and Mineral Resources Bull. 7, 178 p.

Lausen, Carl, 1931, Geology and ore deposits of the Oatman and Katherine districts, Arizona: Arizona Bur. Mines Bull. 131, Geol. Ser. 6, 126 p.

Lee, W. T., 1916, The Aztec gold mine, Baldy, New Mexico: U.S. Geol. Survey Bull. 620–N, p. 325–330.

Lian, H. M., and Simonson, R. R., 1962, Cook Inlet basin—structure, stratigraphy, exploration techniques, logistics, discoveries [abs.]: Am. Assoc. Petroleum Geologists Bull., v. 46, no. 2, p. 271; Oil and Gas Jour., v. 60, no. 13, p. 111–112.

Lincoln, F. C., 1923, Mining districts and mineral resources of Nevada: Reno, Nevada Newsletter Pub. Co., 295 p.

——— 1937, Mining in South Dakota, Part 1 *of* Lincoln, F. C., and others, The mining industry of South Dakota: South Dakota School Mines Bull. 17, p. 9–42.

Lindgren, Waldemar, 1896, The gold-quartz veins of Nevada City and Grass Valley districts, California: U.S. Geol. Survey 17th Ann. Rept., pt. 2, p. 1–262.

Lindgren, Waldemar, 1898, The mining districts of the Idaho Basin and the Boise Ridge, Idaho: U.S. Geol. Survey 18th Ann. Rept., pt. 3, p. 617–744.

——— 1900, The gold and silver veins of Silver City, De Lamar, and other mining districts in Idaho: U.S. Geol. Survey 20th Ann. Rept., pt. 3, p. 67–255.

——— 1901, The gold belt of the Blue Mountains of Oregon: U.S. Geol. Survey 22nd Ann. Rept., pt. 2, p. 551–776.

——— 1904, A geological reconnaissance across the Bitterroot Range and Clearwater Mountains in Montana and Idaho: U.S. Geol. Survey Prof. Paper 27, 123 p.

——— 1905, The copper deposits of the Clifton-Morenci district, Arizona: U.S. Geol. Survey Prof. Paper 43, 375 p.

——— 1906a, The Annie Laurie mine, Piute County, Utah: U.S. Geol. Survey Bull. 285–A, p. 87–90.

——— 1906b, The gold deposits of Dahlonega, Georgia, *in* Graton, L. C., Gold and tin deposits of the southern Appalachians: U.S. Geol. Survey Bull. 293, p. 119–128.

——— 1911, The Tertiary gravels of the Sierra Nevada of California: U.S. Geol. Survey Prof. Paper 73, 226 p.

——— 1915, Geology and mineral deposits of the National mining district, Nevada: U.S. Geol. Survey Bull. 601, 58 p.

——— 1926, Ore deposits of the Jerome and Bradshaw Mountains quadrangles, Arizona: U.S. Geol. Survey Bull. 782, 192 p.

Lindgren, Waldemar, and Bancroft, Howland, 1914, The Republic mining district, *in* Bancroft, Howland, Ore deposits of northeastern Washington: U.S. Geol. Survey Bull. 550, p. 133–166.

Lindgren, Waldemar, Graton, L. C., and Gordon, C. H., 1910, The ore deposits of New Mexico: U.S. Geol. Survey Prof. Paper 68, 361 p.

Lindgren, Waldemar, and Loughlin, G. F., 1919, Geology and ore deposits of the Tintic mining district, Utah, with a historical review, by V. C. Heikes: U.S. Geol. Survey Prof. Paper 107, 282 p.

Lindgren, Waldemar, and Ransome, F. L., 1906, Geology and gold deposits of the Cripple Creek district, Colorado: U.S. Geol. Survey Prof. Paper 54, 516 p.

Lindgren, Waldemar, and Turner, H. W., 1895, Description of the Smartsville quadrangle [California]: U.S. Geol. Survey Geol. Atlas, Folio 18.

Lines, H. L., 1940, Mining and milling methods and costs at the Ash Peak mine of the Veta Mines, Inc., Duncan, Arizona: U.S. Bur. Mines Inf. Circ. 7119, 26 p.

Logan, C. A., 1926, Shasta County: California State Mineralogist Rept. 22, p. 121–216.

——— 1929, Sierra County: California State Mineralogist Rept. 25, p. 151–212.

——— 1936, Gold mines of Placer County: California Jour. Mines and Geology, v. 32, no. 1, p. 7–96.

——— 1941, Mineral resources of Nevada County: California Jour. Mines and Geology, v. 37, no. 3, p. 374–408.

——— 1950, Mines and mineral resources of Madera County, California: California Jour. Mines and Geology, v. 46, no. 4, p. 445–482.

Logan, C. A., Braun, L. T., and Vernon, J. W., 1951, Mines and mineral resources of Fresno County, California: California Jour. Mines and Geology, v. 47, no. 3, p. 485–552.

Lorain, S. H., 1938, Gold mining and milling in Idaho County, Idaho: U.S. Bur. Mines Inf. Circ. 7039, 90 p.

Lorain, S. H., and Metzger, O. H., 1938, Reconnaissance of placer mining districts in Idaho County, Idaho: U.S. Bur. Mines Inf. Circ. 7023, 93 p.

——— 1939, Reconnaissance of placer-mining districts in Lemhi County, Idaho: U.S. Bur. Mines Inf. Circ. 7082, 81 p.

Loughlin, G. F., Ferguson, H. G., and others, 1930, Gold reserves of the United States, *in* Gold resources of the world: Internat. Geol. Cong., 15th, Pretoria, 1929, p. 389–414.

Loughlin, G. F., and Koschmann, A. H., 1935, Geology and ore deposits of the Cripple Creek district, Colorado: Colorado Sci. Soc. Proc., v. 13, no. 6, p. 217–435.

Lovering, T. S., 1930, The New World or Cooke City mining district, Park County, Montana: U.S. Geol. Survey Bull. 811–A, p. 1–87.

——— 1934, Geology and ore deposits of the Breckenridge mining district, Colorado: U.S. Geol. Survey Prof. Paper 176, 64 p.

——— 1935, Geology and ore deposits of the Montezuma quadrangle, Colorado: U.S. Geol. Survey Prof. Paper 178, 119 p.

Lovering, T. S., and Goddard, E. N., 1950, Geology and ore deposits of the Front Range, Colorado: U.S. Geol. Survey Prof. Paper 223, 319 p.

Lovitt, E. H., and McDowell, Vere, 1954, The Gold King mine: Western Miner and Oil Rev., v. 27, no. 3, p. 37–39.

Luedke, R. G., and Burbank, W. S., 1962, Geology of the Ouray quadrangle, Colorado: U.S. Geol. Survey Geol. Quad. Map GQ–152.

Lyden, C. J., 1948, The gold placers of Montana: Montana Bur. Mines and Geology Mem. 26, 151 p.

MacDonald, D. F., 1910, The Weaverville-Trinity Center gold gravels, Trinity County, California: U.S. Geol. Survey Bull. 430–A, p. 48–58.

——— 1913, Notes on the gold lodes of the Carrville district, Trinity County, California: U.S. Geol. Survey Bull. 530–D, p. 9–41.

MacNeil, F. S., Wolfe, J. A., Miller, D. J., and Hopkins, D. M., 1961, Correlation of Tertiary formations of Alaska: Am. Assoc. Petroleum Geologists Bull., v. 45, no. 11, p. 1801–1809.

Maddren, A. G., 1911, Gold placer mining developments in the Innoko-Iditarod region [Alaska]: U.S. Geol. Survey Bull. 480–I, p. 236–270.

——— 1913a, The Koyukuk-Chandalar region, Alaska: U.S. Geol. Survey Bull. 532, 119 p.

——— 1913b, Mineral deposits of the Yakataga district [Alaska]: U.S. Geol. Survey Bull. 592–E, p. 119–153.

——— 1915, Gold placers of the lower Kuskokwim, with a note on copper in the Russian Mountains [Alaska]: U.S. Geol. Survey Bull. 622–H, p. 292–360.

Mansfield, G. R., 1927, Geography, geology and mineral resources of part of southeastern Idaho, with descriptions of Carboniferous and Triassic fossils, by G. H. Girty: U.S. Geol. Survey Prof. Paper 152, 453 p.

Marsell, R. E., ed., 1952, Geology of the central Wasatch Mountains, Utah: Utah Geol. Soc. Guidebook to the geology of Utah, no. 8, 71 p.

Martin, A. J., 1953, The mineral industry of New Mexico: U.S. Bur. Mines Minerals Yearbook, 1952, v. 3, p. 628–652.

Martin, A. J., 1954, Wyoming; gold, silver, copper, and lead: U.S. Bur. Mines Minerals Yearbook, 1951, p. 1617–1618.

Martin, G. C., 1905, Gold deposits of the Shumagin Islands, *in* Brooks, A. H., and others, Mineral resources of Alaska in 1904: U.S. Geol. Survey Bull. 259, p. 100–101.

——— 1922, Gold lodes in the upper Kuskokwim region [Alaska]: U.S. Geol. Survey Bull. 722–E, p. 149–161.

Martin, G. C., Johnson, B. L., and Grant, U. S., 1915, Geology and mineral resources of Kenai Peninsula, Alaska: U.S. Geol. Survey Bull. 587, 243 p.

Mendenhall, W. C., 1905, Geology of the central Copper River region, Alaska: U.S. Geol. Survey Prof. Paper 41, 133 p.

Mertie, J. B., Jr., 1918, The gold placers of the Tolovana district [Alaska]: U.S. Geol. Survey Bull. 662–D, p. 221–277.

——— 1921, Lode mining in the Juneau and Ketchikan districts [Alaska]: U.S. Geol. Survey Bull. 714–B, p. 105–128.

——— 1925, Geology and gold placers of the Chandalar district, Alaska: U.S. Geol. Survey Bull. 773–E, p. 215–263.

——— 1930, Geology of the Eagle-Circle district, Alaska: U.S. Geol. Survey Bull. 816, 168 p.

——— 1932, Mining in the Circle district, Alaska: U.S. Geol. Survey Bull. 824–D, p. 155–172.

——— 1934, Mineral deposits of the Rampart and Hot Springs district, Alaska: U.S. Geol. Survey Bull. 844–D, p. 163–226.

——— 1936, Mineral deposits of the Ruby-Kuskokwim region [Alaska]: U.S. Geol. Survey Bull. 864–C, p. 115–245.

——— 1937, The Yukon-Tanana region, Alaska: U.S. Geol. Survey Bull. 872, 276 p.

——— 1938, Gold placers of the Fortymile, Eagle, and Circle districts, Alaska: U.S. Geol. Survey Bull. 897–C, p. 133–261.

Mertie, J. B., Jr., and Harrington, G. L., 1924, The Ruby-Kuskokwim region, Alaska: U.S. Geol. Survey Bull. 754, 129 p.

Miller, W. J., and Webb, R. W., 1940, Descriptive geology of the Kernville quadrangle, California: California Jour. Mines and Geology, v. 36, no. 4, p. 343–378 [1941].

Milton, M. C., 1913, The Oro Blanco district of Arizona: Eng. Mining Jour., v. 96, no. 22, p. 1005–1007.

Mining World, 1961, Alaska, *in* What's going on in mining: Mining World, v. 23, no. 4, p. 32.

Moench, R. H., Harrison, J. E., and Sims, P. K., 1962, Precambrian folding in the Idaho Springs-Central City area, Front Range, Colorado: Geol. Soc. America Bull., v. 73, no. 1, p. 35–58.

Moffit, F. H., 1905, The Fairhaven gold placers, Seward Peninsula, Alaska: U.S. Geol. Survey Bull. 247, 85 p.

——— 1913, Geology of the Nome and Grand Central quadrangles, Alaska: U.S. Geol. Survey Bull. 533, 140 p.

——— 1938, Geology of the Chitina Valley and adjacent area, Alaska: U.S. Geol. Survey Bull. 894, 137 p. [1939].

——— 1944, Mining in the northern Copper River region, Alaska: U.S. Geol. Survey Bull. 943–B, p. 25–47.

——— 1946, Introduction, *in* Miller, D. J., Copper deposits of the Nizina district, Alaska: U.S. Geol. Survey Bull. 947–F, p. 93–94.

Moffit, F. H., 1954, Geology of the Prince William Sound region, Alaska: U.S. Geol. Survey Bull. 989–E, p. 225–310.

Moffit, F. H., and Capps, S. R., 1911, Geology and mineral resources of the Nizina district, Alaska: U.S. Geol. Survey Bull. 448, 111 p.

Montana Bureau Agriculture, Labor, and Industry, 1900, 7th Annual Report.

Moore, F. B., Cavender, W. S., and Kaiser, E. P., 1957, Geology and uranium deposits of the Caribou area, Boulder County, Colorado: U.S. Geol. Survey Bull. 1030–N, p. 517–552 [1958].

Muessig, S. J., and Quinlan, J. J., 1959, Geologic map of the Republic and part of the Wauconda quadrangles, Washington: U.S. Geol. Survey open-file rept.

Nevius, J. N., 1921, Resuscitation of the Octave gold mine: Mining Sci. Press, v. 123, p. 122–124.

Newhouse, W. H., ed., 1942, Ore deposits as related to structural features: Princeton, N.J., Princeton Univ. Press, 280 p.

Newton, Edmund, Gregg, D. B., and Mosier, McHenry, 1940, Operations at the Haile gold mine, Kershaw, S.C.: U.S. Bur. Mines Inf. Circ. 7111, 42 p.

Newton, Henry, and Jenney, W. P., 1880, Report on the geology and resources of the Black Hills of Dakota: U.S. Geog. and Geol. Survey of the Rocky Mountain Region (Powell), 566 p.

Nitze, H. B. C., and Hanna, G. B., 1896, Gold deposits of North Carolina: North Carolina Geol. Survey Bull. 3, 200 p.

Noble, J. A., 1950, Ore mineralization in the Homestake gold mine, Lead, South Dakota: Geol. Soc. America Bull., v. 61, no. 3, p. 221–252.

——— 1952, Structural features of the Black Hills and adjacent areas developed since pre-Cambrian time, *in* Billings Geological Society Guidebook, 3d Annual Field Conference, Black Hills-Williston Basin, 1952: p. 31–37.

Noble, J. A., and Harder, J. O., 1948, Stratigraphy and metamorphism in a part of the northern Black Hills and the Homestake mine, Lead, South Dakota: Geol. Soc. America Bull., v. 59, no. 9, p. 941–975.

Nolan, T. B., 1933, Epithermal precious-metal deposits, *in* Ore deposits of the Western States [Lindgren volume]: New York, Am. Inst. Mining Metall. Engineers, p, 623–640.

——— 1935a, The Gold Hill mining district, Utah: U.S. Geol. Survey Prof. Paper 177, 172 p.

——— 1935b, The underground geology of the Tonopah mining district, Nevada: Nevada Univ. Bull., v. 29, no. 5, 49 p.

——— 1936a, The Tuscarora mining district, Elko County, Nevada: Nevada Univ. Bull., v. 30, no. 1, 38 p.

——— 1936b, Nonferrous-metal deposits, *in* Hewett, D. F., and others, Mineral resources of the region around Boulder Dam: U.S. Geol. Survey Bull. 871, p. 5–77.

——— 1962, The Eureka mining district, Nevada: U.S. Geol. Survey Prof. Paper 406, 78 p.

Norman, L. A., Jr., and Stewart, R. M., 1951, Mines and mineral resources of Inyo County: California Jour. Mines and Geology, v. 47, no. 1, p. 17–223.

O'Brien, J. C., 1947, Mines and mineral resources of Siskiyou County [California]: California Jour. Mines and Geology, v. 43, no. 4, p. 413–462.

O'Brien, J. C., 1949, Mines and mineral resources of Butte County, California: California Jour. Mines and Geology, v. 45, no. 3, p. 417–454.

——— 1952a, Mines and mineral resources of Yuba County [California]: California Jour. Mines and Geology, v. 48, no. 2, p. 143–179.

——— 1952b, Mines and mineral resources of Del Norte County, California: California Jour. Mines and Geology, v. 48, no. 4, p. 261–309.

O'Harra, C. C., and Todd, J. E., 1902, Mineral resources of South Dakota: South Dakota Geol. Survey Bull. 3, 136 p.

Oregon Department of Geology and Mineral Industries, 1939, Oregon metal mines handbook; Northeastern Oregon, east half: Oregon Dept. Geology and Mineral Resources Bull. 14–A, 125 p.

——— 1940, Oregon metal mines handbook; Coos, Curry, and Douglas Counties: Oregon Dept. Geology and Mineral Industries Bull. 14–C, v. 1, 133 p.

———1941, Oregon metal mines handbook; Grant, Morrow, and Umatilla Counties: Oregon Dept. Geology and Mineral Industries Bull. 14–B, 157 p.

——— 1942, Oregon metal mines handbook; Josephine County: Oregon Dept. Geology and Mineral Industries Bull. 14–C, v. 2, sec. 1, 229 p.

——— 1943, Oregon metal mines handbook; Jackson County: Oregon Dept. Geology and Mineral Industries Bull. 14–C, v. 2, sec. 2, 208 p.

Osterwald, F. W., and Osterwald, D. B., 1952, Wyoming mineral resources: Wyoming Geol. Survey Bull. 45, 215 p.

Overton, T. D., 1947, Mineral resources of Douglas, Ormsby, and Washoe Counties: Nevada Univ. Bull., v. 41, no. 9, Geology and Mining Ser. 46, 91 p.

Page, B. M., 1959, Geology of the Candelaria mining district, Mineral County, Nevada: Nevada Bur. Mines Bull. 56, 67 p.

Paige, Sidney, 1911, The ore deposits near Pinos Altos, New Mexico: U.S. Geol. Survey Bull. 470–A, p. 109–125.

Pardee, J. T., 1918, Ore deposits of the northwestern part of the Garnet Range, Montana: U.S. Geol. Survey Bull. 660–F, p. 159–239.

——— 1934, Beach placers of the Oregon coast: U.S. Geol. Survey Circ. 8, 41 p.

——— 1951, Gold placer deposits of the Pioneer district, Montana: U.S. Geol. Survey Bull. 978–C, p. 69–99 [1952].

Pardee, J. T., and Hewett, D. F., 1914, Geology and mineral resources of the Sumpter quadrangle: Oregon Bur. Mines and Geology, Mineral Resources of Oregon, v. 1, no. 6, p. 3–128.

Pardee, J. T., and Park, C. F., Jr., 1948, Gold deposits of the southern Piedmont: U.S. Geol. Survey Prof. Paper 213, 156 p.

Pardee, J. T., and Schrader, F. C., 1933, Metalliferous deposits of the greater Helena mining region, Montana: U.S. Geol. Survey Bull. 842, 318 p.

Park, C. F., Jr., 1933, The Girdwood district, Alaska: U.S. Geol. Survey Bull. 849–G, p. 381–424 [1934].

——— 1935, Hog Mountain gold district, Alabama: Am. Inst. Mining Metall. Engineers Tech. Pub. 598, 19 p.

Parks, H. M., and Swartley, A. M., 1916, Handbook of the mining industry of Oregon: Oregon Bur. Mines and Geology, Mineral resources of Oregon, v. 2, no. 4, 306 p.

Patton, H. B., 1915, Geology and ore deposits of the Bonanza district, Saguache County, Colorado: Colorado Geol. Survey Bull. 9, 136 p. [1916].

Patty, E. N., 1921, The metal mines of Washington: Washington Geol. Survey Bull. 23, 366 p.

Peterson, N. P., 1938, Geology and ore deposits of the Mammoth mining camp area, Pinal County, Arizona: Arizona Bur. Mines Bull. 144, Geol. Ser. 11, 63 p.

——— 1962, Geology and ore deposits of the Globe-Miami district, Arizona: U.S. Geol. Survey Prof. Paper 342, 151 p.

Piper, A. M., and Laney, F. B., 1926, Geology and metalliferous resources of the region about Silver City, Idaho: Idaho Bur. Mines and Geology Bull. 11, 165 p.

Pogue, J. E., Jr., 1910, Cid mining district of Davidson County, North Carolina: North Carolina Geol. and Econ. Survey Bull. 22, 144 p.

Prindle, L. M., 1904, Gold placers of the Fairbanks district, Alaska: U.S. Geol. Survey Bull. 225, p. 64–73.

——— 1906, The Yukon-Tanana region, Alaska—description of Circle quadrangle: U.S. Geol. Survey Bull. 295, 27 p.

——— 1907, The Bonnifield and Kantishna region, Alaska: U.S. Geol. Survey Bull. 314–L, p. 205–226.

——— 1913, A geologic reconnaissance of the Fairbanks quadrangle, Alaska, with a detailed description of the Fairbanks district, by L. M. Prindle and F. J. Katz, and an account of lode mining near Fairbanks, by P. S. Smith: U.S. Geol. Survey Bull. 525, 220 p.

Prindle, L. M., and Hess, F. L., 1906, The Rampart gold placer region, Alaska: U.S. Geol. Survey Bull. 280, 54 p.

Prout, J. W., Jr., 1940, Geology of the Big Blue group of mines, Kernville, California: California Jour. Mines and Geology, v. 36, no. 4, p. 379–421 [1941].

Purington, C. W., 1898, Preliminary report on the mining industries of the Telluride quadrangle, Colorado: U.S. Geol. Survey 18th Ann. Rept., pt. 3, p. 745–850.

Rand, H. B., 1959, Gold and Oregon's settlement: The Ore-Bin (Oregon Dept. Geology and Mineral Industries), v. 21, no. 5, p. 41–47.

Ransome, F. L., 1901a, The ore deposits of the Rico Mountains, Colorado: U.S. Geol. Survey 22d Ann. Rept., pt. 2, p. 229–398.

——— 1901b, A report on the economic geology of the Silverton quadrangle, Colorado: U.S. Geol. Survey Bull. 182, 265 p.

——— 1903, Geology of the Globe copper district, Arizona: U.S. Geol. Survey Prof. Paper 12, 168 p.

——— 1904, The geology and ore deposits of the Bisbee quadrangle, Arizona: U.S. Geol. Survey Prof. Paper 21, 168 p.

——— 1907, Preliminary account of Goldfield, Bullfrog, and other mining districts in southern Nevada, with notes on the Manhattan district, by G. H. Garrey and W. H. Emmons: U.S. Geol. Survey Bull. 303, 98 p.

——— 1909a, Geology and ore deposits of Goldfield, Nevada: U.S. Geol. Survey Prof. Paper 66, 258 p.

——— 1909b, The Hornsilver district, Nevada: U.S. Geol. Survey Bull. 380–A, p. 41–43.

——— 1911, Geology and ore deposits of the Breckenridge district, Colorado: U.S. Geol. Survey Prof. Paper 75, 187 p.

——— 1913, The Turquoise copper-mining district, Arizona: U.S. Geol. Survey Bull. 530–C, p. 125–134.

Ransome, F. L., 1919, The copper deposits of Ray and Miami, Arizona: U.S. Geol. Survey Prof. Paper 115, 192 p.

——— 1923, Geology of the Oatman gold district, Arizona: U.S. Geol. Survey Bull. 743, 71 p.

Ransome, F. L., and Calkins, F. C., 1908, The geology and ore deposits of the Coeur d'Alene district, Idaho: U.S. Geol. Survey Prof. Paper 62, 203 p.

Ransome, F. L., Emmons, W. H., and Garrey, G. H., 1910, Geology and ore deposits of the Bullfrog district, Nevada: U.S. Geol. Survey Bull. 407, 130 p.

Ransome, F. L., Paige, Sidney, and Tenney, J. B., 1932, Ore deposits of the Southwest: Internat. Geol. Cong., 16th, Washington, D. C., 1933, Guidebook 14, Excursion C–1, 67 p.

Ray, R. G., 1954, Geology and ore deposits of the Willow Creek mining district, Alaska: U.S. Geol. Survey Bull. 1004, 86 p.

Raymond, R. W., 1870, Statistics of mines and mining in the states and territories west of the Rocky Mountains [2d report]: U.S. 41st Cong., 2d sess., H.R. 207, 805 p.

——— 1873, Statistics of mines and mining in the states and territories west of the Rocky Mountains [4th annual report]: Washington, D.C., U.S. Treasury Dept., 566 p.

Reed, G. C., 1950, Mines and mineral deposits (except fuels), Park County, Montana: U.S. Bur. Mines Inf. Circ. 7546, 64 p.

Reed, J. C., 1934, Gold-bearing gravel of the Nezperce National Forest, Idaho County, Idaho: Idaho Bur. Mines and Geology Pamph. 40, 26 p.

——— 1937, Geology and ore deposits of the Warren mining district, Idaho County, Idaho: Idaho Bur. Mines and Geology Pamph. 45, 65 p.

Reed, J. C., and Coats, R. R., 1941, Geology and ore deposits of the Chichagof mining district, Alaska: U.S. Geol. Survey Bull. 929, 148 p.

Reed, J. C., Jr., 1961, Geology of the Mount McKinley quadrangle, Alaska: U.S. Geol. Survey Bull. 1108–A, p. 1–36.

Richthofen, F. B. von, 1866, The Comstock Lode, its character and probable mode of continuance in depth: Published by Sutro Tunnel Co.; Towne and Bacon, printers.

Rinehart, C. D., and Ross, D. C., 1956, Economic geology of the Casa Diablo Mountain quadrangle, California: California Div. Mines Spec. Rept. 48, 17 p.

Robertson, A. F., 1950, Mines and mineral deposits (except fuels), Fergus County, Montana: U.S. Bur. Mines Inf. Circ. 7544, 76 p.

——— 1951, Mines and mineral deposits (except fuels), Cascade County, Montana: U.S. Bur. Mines Inf. Circ. 7589, 81 p.

Robertson, Forbes, 1953, Geology and mineral deposits of the Zosell (Emery) mining district, Powell County, Montana: Montana Bur. Mines and Geology Mem. 34, 29 p.

Roby, R. N., Ackerman, W. C., Fulkerson, F. B., and Crowley, F. A., 1960, Mines and mineral deposits (except fuels), Jefferson County, Montana: Montana Bur. Mines and Geology Bull. 16, 122 p.

Ross, C. P., 1925, Ore deposits of the Saddle Mountain and Banner mining districts, Arizona: U.S. Geol. Survey Bull. 771, 72 p.

——— 1927, Ore deposits in Tertiary lava in the Salmon River Mountains, Idaho: Idaho Bur. Mines and Geology Pamph. 25, 21 p.

Ross, C. P., 1930a, Geology and ore deposits of the Seafoam, Alder Creek, Little Smokey and Willow Creek mining districts, Custer and Camas Counties, Idaho: Idaho Bur. Mines and Geology Pamph. 33, 26 p.

——— 1930b, A graphic history of metal mining in Idaho: U.S. Geol. Survey Bull. 821–A, p. 1–9.

——— 1933a, The lode deposits in the Boise Basin, Idaho: Econ. Geology, v. 28, no. 4, p. 329–343.

——— 1933b, The Valdez Creek mining district, Alaska: U.S. Geol. Survey Bull. 849–H, p. 425–468.

——— 1934, Geology and ore deposits of the Casto quadrangle, Idaho: U.S. Geol. Survey Bull. 854, 135 p. [1935].

——— 1937, Geology and ore deposits of the Bayhorse region, Custer County, Idaho: U.S. Geol. Survey Bull. 877, 161 p.

——— 1938, The geology of part of the Wallowa Mountains: Oregon Dept. Geology and Mineral Industries Bull. 3, 74 p.

——— 1941, The metal and coal mining districts of Idaho, with notes on the non-metallic mineral resources of the State: Idaho Bur. Mines and Geology Pamph. 57, pt. 1, 110 p.

——— 1953, The geology and ore deposits of the Reese River district, Lander County, Nevada: U.S. Geol. Survey Bull. 997, 132 p. [1954].

Ross, C. S., 1935, Origin of the copper deposits of the Ducktown type in the southern Appalachian region: U.S. Geol. Survey Prof. Paper 179, 165 p.

Ross, D. C., 1961, Geology and mineral deposits of Mineral County, Nevada: Nevada Bur. Mines Bull. 58, 98 p.

Rott, E. H., Jr., 1931, Ore deposits of the Gold Circle mining district, Elko County, Nevada: Nevada Univ. Bull., v. 25, no. 5, 30 p.

Russell, I. C., 1900, A preliminary paper on the geology of the Cascade Mountains in northern Washington: U.S. Geol. Survey 20th Ann. Rept., pt. 2, p. 83–210.

Sahinen, U. M., 1939, Geology and ore deposits of the Rochester and adjacent mining districts, Madison County, Montana: Montana Bur. Mines and Geology Mem. 19, 53 p.

Sales, R. H., 1914, Ore deposits at Butte, Montana: Am. Inst. Mining Engineers Trans., v. 46, p. 3–109.

Sales, R. H., and Meyer, Charles, 1948, Wall rock alteration at Butte, Montana: Am. Inst. Mining Metall. Engineers Tech. Pub. 2400, 25 p.

Sampson, R. J., and Tucker, W. B., 1940, Mineral resources of Mono County, California: California Jour. Mines and Geology, v. 36, no. 2, p. 117–156.

——— 1942, Mineral resources of Imperial County, California: California Jour. Mines and Geology, v. 38, no. 2, p. 105–145.

Schafer, P. A., 1935, Geology and ore deposits of the Neihart mining district, Cascade County, Montana: Montana Bur. Mines and Geology Mem. 13, 62 p.

Schrader, F. C., 1900, A reconnaissance of a part of Prince William Sound and the Copper River district, Alaska, in 1898: U.S. Geol. Survey 20th Ann. Rept., pt. 7, p. 341–423.

——— 1909, Mineral deposits of the Cerbat Range, Black Mountains, and Grand Wash Cliffs, Mohave County, Arizona: U.S. Geol. Survey Bull. 397, 226 p.

——— 1912, A reconnaissance of the Jarbidge, Contact, and Elk Mountain mining districts, Elko County, Nevada: U.S. Geol. Survey Bull. 497, 162 p.

Schrader, F. C., 1915, Mineral deposits of the Santa Rita and Patagonia Mountains, Arizona: U.S. Geol. Survey Bull. 582, 373 p.

——— 1921, Pyrite at the Haile mine, Kershaw, South Carolina, with a note on the pyritization at the Brewer mine near Jefferson: U.S. Geol. Survey Bull. 725–F, p. 331–345.

——— 1923, The Jarbidge mining district, Nevada, with a note on the Charleston district: U.S. Geol. Survey Bull. 741, 86 p.

——— 1931, Cherry Creek (Egan Canyon) district, White Pine County: Nevada Univ. Bull., v. 25, no. 7, p. 25–39.

Schwartz, G. M., 1953, Geology of the San Manuel copper deposit, Arizona: U.S. Geol. Survey Prof. Paper 256, 65 p.

Seager, G. F., 1944, Gold, arsenic, and tungsten deposits of the Jardine-Crevasse Mountain district, Park County, Montana: Montana Bur. Mines and Geology Mem. 23, 111 p.

Searls, Fred, Jr., 1948, A contribution to the published information on the geology and ore deposits of Goldfield, Nevada: Nevada Univ. Bull., v. 42, no. 5, Geology and Mining Ser. 48, 24 p.

Shenon, P. J., 1931, Geology and ore deposits of Bannack and Argenta, Montana: Montana Bur. Mines and Geology Bull. 6, 80 p.

——— 1933a, Geology of the Robertson, Humdinger, and Robert E. gold mines, southwestern Oregon: U.S. Geol. Survey Bull. 830–B, p. 33–55.

——— 1933b, Geology and ore deposits of the Takilma-Waldo district, Oregon, including the Blue Creek district: U.S. Geol. Survey Bull. 846–B, p. 141–194.

——— 1933c, Copper deposits in the Squaw Creek and Silver Peak districts and at the Almeda mine, southwestern Oregon, with notes on the Pennell and Farmer and Banfield prospects: U.S. Geol. Survey Circ. 2, 35 p.

——— 1938, Geology and ore deposits near Murray, Idaho: Idaho Bur. Mines and Geology Pamph. 47, 44 p.

——— 1961, The Coeur d'Alene mining district, *in* Campbell, A. B., and others, Guidebook to the geology of the Coeur d'Alene mining district: Idaho Bur. Mines and Geology, Bull. 16, p. 1–2.

Shenon, P. J., and Reed, J. C., 1934, Geology and ore deposits of the Elk City, Orogrande, Buffalo Hump, and Tenmile districts, Idaho County, Idaho: U.S. Geol. Survey Circ. 9, 89 p.

Shenon, P. J., and Ross, C. P., 1936, Geology and ore deposits near Edwardsburg and Thunder Mountain, Idaho: Idaho Bur. Mines and Geology Pamph. 44, 45 p.

Shockey, P. N., 1957, Reconnaissance geology of the Leesburg quadrangle, Lemhi County, Idaho: Idaho Bur. Mines and Geology Pamph. 113, 42 p.

Short, M. N., and others, 1943, Geology and ore deposits of the Superior mining area, Arizona: Arizona Bur. Mines Bull. 151, Geol. Ser. 16, 159 p.

Silliman, Benjamin, 1837, Remarks on some of the gold mines, and on parts of the gold region of Virginia, founded on personal observations, made in the months of August and September, 1836: Am. Jour. Sci., v. 32, p. 98–130.

Simmons, W. W., 1950, Recent geological investigations in the Ducktown mining district, Tennessee, *in* Snyder, F. G., ed., Symposium on mineral resources of the southeastern United States: Knoxville, Univ. Tennessee Press, p. 67–71.

Sims, P. K., 1956, Paragenesis and structure of pitchblende-bearing veins, Central City district, Gilpin County, Colorado: Econ. Geology, v. 51, no. 8, p. 739–756.

Singewald, J. T., Jr., 1933, Magmatic segregations, *in* Ore deposits of the Western States [Lindgren volume]: Am. Inst. Mining Metall. Engineers, p. 504–524.

Singewald, Q. D., 1950, Gold placers and their geologic environment in northwestern Park County, Colorado: U.S. Geol. Survey Bull. 955–D, p. 103–172 [1951].

Singewald, Q. D., and Butler, B. S., 1941, Ore deposits in the vicinity of the London fault, Colorado: U.S. Geol. Survey Bull. 911, 74 p.

Sloan, B. E., 1908, Catalogue of the mineral localities of South Carolina: South Carolina Geol. Survey, Ser. 4, Bull. 2, 504 p.

Smith, G. H., 1943, The history of the Comstock Lode, 1850–1920: Nevada Univ. Bull., v. 37, no. 3, Geology and Mining Ser. 37, 297 p.

Smith, G. O., 1903, Gold mining in central Washington: U.S. Geol. Survey Bull. 213, p. 76–80.

Smith, P.S., 1910, Geology and mineral resources of the Solomon and Casadepaga quadrangles, Seward Peninsula, Alaska: U.S. Geol. Survey Bull. 433, 234 p.

——— 1933, Past placer gold production from Alaska: U.S. Geol. Survey Bull. 857–B, p. 93–98.

——— 1939, Areal geology of Alaska: U.S. Geol. Survey Prof. Paper 192, 100 p.

——— 1941, Past lode-gold production from Alaska: U.S. Geol. Survey Bull. 917–C, p. 159–209.

——— 1942, Mineral industry of Alaska in 1940: U.S. Geol. Survey Bull. 933–A, p. 1–102.

——— 1944, Mineral industry of Alaska in 1941 and 1942: U.S. Geol. Survey Bull. 943–A, p. 1–23.

Smith, P. S., and Eakin, H. M., 1910, Mineral resources of the Nulato-Council region [Alaska]: U.S. Geol. Survey Bull. 442–H, p. 316–352.

——— 1911, The Shungnak region, Kobuk Valley [Alaska]: U.S. Geol. Survey Bull. 480–J, p. 271–305.

Smith, P. S., and Mertie, J. B., Jr., 1930, Geology and mineral resources of northwestern Alaska: U.S. Geol. Survey Bull. 815, 351 p.

Smith, W. C., 1938, Geology of the Caribou stock in the Front Range, Colorado: Am. Jour. Sci., 5th ser., v. 36, no. 213, p. 161–196.

Smith, W. D., and Ruff, L. L., 1938, The geology and mineral resources of Lane County, Oregon: Oregon Dept. Geology and Mineral Industries Bull. 11, 65 p.

Spencer, A. C., 1906, The Juneau gold belt, Alaska: U.S. Geol. Survey Bull. 287, 161 p.

——— 1916, The Atlantic gold district and the North Laramie Mountains, Fremont, Converse, and Albany Counties, Wyoming: U.S. Geol. Survey Bull. 626, 85 p.

——— 1917, The geology and ore deposits of Ely, Nevada: U.S. Geol. Survey Prof. Paper 96, 189 p.

Spencer, A. C., and Paige, Sidney, 1935, Geology of the Santa Rita mining area, New Mexico: U.S. Geol. Survey Bull. 859, 78 p.

Spurr, J. E., 1900, A reconnaissance in southwestern Alaska in 1898: U.S. Geol. Survey 20th Ann. Rept., pt. 7, p. 31–264.

——— 1901, The ore deposits of Monte Cristo, Washington: U.S. Geol. Survey 22d Ann. Rept., pt. 2, p. 777–865.

——— 1906, Ore deposits of the Silver Peak quadrangle, Nevada: U.S. Geol. Survey Prof. Paper 55, 174 p.

Spurr, J. E., Garrey, G. H., and Ball, S. H., 1908, Economic geology of the Georgetown quadrangle (together with the Empire district), Colorado: U.S. Geol. Survey Prof. Paper 63, 422 p.

Spurr, J. E., and Goodrich, H. B., 1898, Geology of the Yukon gold district, Alaska: U.S. Geol. Survey 18th Ann. Rept., pt. 3, p. 87–392.

Staatz, M. H., 1960, The Republic graben, a major structure in northeastern Washington: U.S. Geol. Survey Prof. Paper 400–B, p. B304–B306.

Staley, W. W., 1946, Gold in Idaho: Idaho Bur. Mines and Geology Pamph. 68, 32 p.

Staunton, W. F., 1926, Ore possibilities at the Congress mine: Eng. Mining Jour., v. 122, no. 20, p. 769–771.

Steven, T. A., and Ratté, J. C., 1960a, Relation of mineralization to caldera subsidence in the Creede district, San Juan Mountains, Colorado: U.S. Geol. Survey Prof. Paper 400–B, p. B14–B17.

——— 1960b, Geology and ore deposits of the Summitville district, San Juan Mountains, Colorado: U.S. Geol. Survey Prof. Paper 343, 70 p.

Stinson, M. C., 1957, Geology of the Island Mountain copper mine, Trinity County, California: California Jour. Mines and Geology, v. 53, nos. 1–2, p. 9–33.

Stoddard, Carl, and Carpenter, J. A., 1950, Mineral resources of Storey and Lyon Counties, Nevada: Nevada Univ. Bull., v. 44, no. 1, Geology and Mining Ser. 49, 115 p.

Stone, R. W., 1911, Geologic relation of ore deposits in the Elkhorn Mountains, Montana: U.S. Geol. Survey Bull. 470, p. 75–98.

Stuckey, J. L., 1958, Geologic map of North Carolina: North Carolina Div. Mineral Resources, scale 1:500,000.

Stuckey, J. L., and Conrad, S. G., 1958, Explanatory text for geologic map of North Carolina: North Carolina Div. Mineral Resources Bull. 71, 51 p.

Swartley, A. M., 1914, Ore deposits of northeastern Oregon: Oregon Bur. Mines and Geology, Mineral Resources of Oregon, v. 1, no. 8, 306 p.

Taber, Stephen, 1913, Geology of the gold belt in the James River basin, Virginia: Virginia Geol. Survey Bull. 7, 271 p.

Tansley, Wilfred, Schafer, P. A., and Hart, L. H., 1933, A geological reconnaissance of the Tobacco Root Mountains, Madison County, Montana: Montana Bur. Mines and Geology Mem. 9, 57 p.

Tenney, J. B., 1934, History of Arizona gold mining, *in* Wilson, E. D., Cunningham, J. B., and Butler, G. M., Arizona lode gold mines and gold mining: Arizona Bur. Mines Bull. 137, Mineral Tech. Ser. 37, p. 16–18.

Thayer, T. P., 1940, Chromite deposits of Grant County, Oregon: U.S. Geol. Survey Bull. 922–D, p. 75–113.

Thomson, F. A., and Ballard, S. M., 1924, Geology and gold resources of north central Idaho: Idaho Bur. Mines and Geology Bull. 7, 127 p.

Trumbull, L. W., 1914, Atlantic City gold mining district, Fremont County, Wyoming: Wyoming Geologist's Office, Ser. B, Bull. 7, p. 69–97.

Tuck, Ralph, 1933, The Moose Pass-Hope district, Kenai Peninsula, Alaska: U.S. Geol. Survey Bull. 849–I, p. 469–527.

——— 1938, The Valdez Creek mining district [Alaska] in 1936: U.S. Geol. Survey Bull. 897–B, p. 109–131.

Tucker, W. B., 1925a, Ventura County [California]: California State Mineralogist Rept. 21, p. 223–245.
——— 1925b, Santa Barbara County [California]: California State Mineralogist Rept. 21, p. 539–562.
Tucker, W. B., and Reed, C. H., 1939, Mineral resources of San Diego County [California]: California Jour. Mines and Geology, v. 35, no. 1, p. 8–55.
Tucker, W. B., and Sampson, R. J., 1933, Gold resources of Kern County [California]: California Jour. Mines and Geology, v. 29, nos. 3–4, p. 271–339 [1934].
——— 1945, Mineral resources of Riverside County [California]: California Jour. Mines and Geology, v. 41, no. 3, p. 121–182.
Tucker, W. B., Sampson, R. J., and Oakeshott, G. B., 1949, Mineral resources of Kern County [California]: California Jour. Mines and Geology, v. 45, no. 2, p. 203–297.
Tweto, Ogden, 1960, Pre-ore age of faults at Leadville, Colorado: U.S. Geol. Survey Prof. Paper 400–B, p. B10–B11.
Tweto, Ogden, and Sims, P. K., 1960, Relation of the Colorado mineral belt to Precambrian structure: U.S. Geol. Survey Prof. Paper 400–B, p. B8–B10.
Umpleby, J. B., 1910, Geology and ore deposits of Republic mining district: Washington Geol. Survey Bull. 1, 67 p.
——— 1911a, Geology and ore deposits of the Myers Creek mining district: Washington Geol. Survey Bull. 5, pt. 1, p. 9–52.
——— 1911b, Geology and ore deposits of the Oroville-Nighthawk mining district: Washington Geol. Survey Bull. 5, pt. 2, p. 53–107.
——— 1913a, Some ore deposits in northwestern Custer County, Idaho: U.S. Geol. Survey Bull. 539, 104 p.
——— 1913b, Geology and ore deposits of Lemhi County, Idaho: U.S. Geol. Survey Bull. 528, 182 p.
——— 1915, Ore deposits in the Sawtooth quadrangle, Blaine and Custer Counties, Idaho: U.S. Geol. Survey Bull. 580–K, p. 221–249.
——— 1917, Geology and ore deposits of the Mackay region, Idaho: U.S. Geol. Survey Prof. Paper 97, 129 p.
Umpleby, J. B., Westgate, L. G., and Ross, C. P., 1930, Geology and ore deposits of the Wood River region, Idaho, with a description of the Minnie Moore and nearby mines, by D. F. Hewett: U.S. Geol. Survey Bull. 814, 250 p.
U.S. Bureau of Mines, 1925–34, Mineral resources of the United States [annual volumes, 1924–31]: Washington, U.S. Govt. Printing Office.
——— 1933–66, Minerals yearbook [annual volumes, 1932–65]: Washington, U.S. Govt. Printing Office.
U.S. Geological Survey, 1896–1900, Annual reports [17th through 21st, 1895–1900]: Washington, U.S. Govt. Printing Office.
———1883–1924, Mineral resources of the United States [annual volumes, 1882–1923]: Washington, U.S. Govt. Printing Office.
Vanderburg, W. O., 1936a, Placer mining in Nevada: Nevada Univ. Bull., v. 30, no. 4, 180 p.
——— 1936b, Reconnaissance of mining districts in Pershing County, Nevada: U.S. Bur. Mines Inf. Circ. 6902, 57 p.
——— 1937a, Reconnaissance of mining districts in Clark County, Nevada: U.S. Bur. Mines Inf. Circ. 6964, 81 p.
——— 1937b, Reconnaissance of mining districts in Mineral County, Nevada: U.S. Bur. Mines Inf. Circ. 6941, 79 p.
Vanderburg, W. O., 1938a, Reconnaissance of mining districts in Eureka County, Nevada: U.S. Bur. Mines Inf. Circ. 7022, 66 p.
——— 1938b, Reconnaissance of mining districts in Humboldt County, Nevada: U.S. Bur. Mines Inf. Circ. 6995, 54 p.
——— 1939, Reconnaissance of mining districts in Lander County, Nevada: U.S. Bur. Mines Inf. Circ. 7043, 83 p.
——— 1940, Reconnaissance of mining districts in Churchill County, Nevada: U.S. Bur. Mines Inf. Circ. 7093, 57 p.
Vanderwilt, J. W., and Koschmann, A. H., 1932, Geology of the Independence district, Colorado: U.S. Geol. Survey press release 67484.
Vanderwilt, J. W., and others, 1947, Mineral resources of Colorado: Denver, Colorado Mineral Resources Board, 547 p.
Varnes, D. J., 1963, Geology and ore deposits of the South Silverton mining area, San Juan County, Colorado: U.S. Geol. Survey Prof. Paper 378–A, p. A1–A56.
Vaughan, F. E., 1922, Geology of the San Bernardino Mountains north of San Gorgonio Pass: California Univ. Pubs. Dept. Geol. Sci. Bull., v. 13, no. 9, p. 319–411.
Vhay, J. S., 1948, Cobalt-copper deposits of the Blackbird district, Lemhi County, Idaho: U.S. Geol. Survey Strategic Mineral Inv. Prelim. Rept. 3–219, 26 p.
Wagner, N. S., 1959, Mining in Baker County, 1861 to 1959: The Ore-Bin (Oregon Dept. Geology and Mineral Industries), v. 21, no. 3, p. 21–27.
Wallace, R. E., and Hosterman, J. W., 1956, Reconnaissance geology of western Mineral County, Montana: U.S. Geol. Survey Bull. 1027–M, p. 575–612.
Warner, L. A., Goddard, E. N., and others, 1961, Iron and copper deposits of Kasaan Peninsula, Prince of Wales Island, southeastern Alaska: U.S. Geol. Survey Bull. 1090, 136 p.
Washington State Planning Council, 1940, Cascade Mountains study, State of Washington: Olympia, Washington State Planning Council, 56 p.
Waters, A. C., 1932, A petrologic and structural study of the Swakane gneiss, Entiat Mountains, Washington: Jour. Geology, v. 40, no. 6, p. 604–633.
Watson, T. L., 1907, Mineral resources of Virginia: Lynchburg, Virginia Jamestown Exposition Comm., 618 p.
Wayland, R. G., 1943, Gold deposits near Nabesna [Alaska]: U.S. Geol. Survey Bull. 933–B, p. 175–199.
Weaver, C. E., 1911, Geology and ore deposits of the Blewett mining district: Washington Geol. Survey Bull. 6, 104 p.
——— 1920, The mineral resources of Stevens County: Washington Geol. Survey Bull. 20, 350 p.
——— 1949, Geology and mineral deposits of an area north of San Francisco Bay, California: California Div. Mines Bull. 149, 135 p.
Weed, W. H., 1900, Geology of the Little Belt Mountains, Montana: U.S. Geol. Survey 20th Ann. Rept., pt. 3, p. 257–461.
——— 1903, Gold mines of the Marysville district, Montana: U.S. Geol. Survey Bull. 213, p. 88–89.
——— 1912, Geology and ore deposits of the Butte district, Montana: U.S. Geol. Survey Prof. Paper 74, 262 p.
Weed, W. H., and Pirsson, L. V., 1896, The geology of the Little Rocky Mountains: Jour. Geology, v. 4, no. 4, p. 399–428.
——— 1898, Geology and mineral resources of the Judith Mountains of Montana: U.S. Geol. Survey 18th Ann. Rept., pt. 3, p. 437–616.

Weeks, F. B., 1908, Geology and mineral resources of the Osceola mining district, White Pine County, Nevada: U.S. Geol. Survey Bull. 340–A, p. 117–133.

Wells, E. H., and Wootton, T. P., 1940, Gold mining and gold deposits in New Mexico [revised ed.]: New Mexico Bur. Mines and Mineral Resources Circ. 5, 24 p.

Wells, F. G., 1933a, Lode deposits of Eureka and vicinity, Kantishna district, Alaska: U.S. Geol. Survey Bull. 849–F, p. 335–378.

——— 1933b, Notes on the Chieftain and Continental mines, Douglas County, Oregon: U.S. Geol. Survey Bull. 830–B, p. 57–62.

——— 1956, Geology of the Medford quadrangle, Oregon-California: U.S. Geol. Survey Geol. Quad. Map GQ–89.

Wells, F. G., Hotz, P. E., and Cater, F. W., Jr., 1949, Preliminary description of the geology of the Kerby quadrangle, Oregon: Oregon Dept. Geology and Mineral Industries Bull. 40, 23 p.

Wells, F. G., and Walker, G. W., 1953, Geology of the Galice quadrangle, Oregon: U.S. Geol. Survey Geol. Quad. Map GQ–25.

Wells, F. G., and others, 1940, Preliminary geologic map of the Grants Pass quadrangle, Oregon: Oregon Dept. Geology and Mineral Industries.

Wells, J. D., 1960, Petrography of radioactive Tertiary igneous rocks, Front Range mineral belt, Colorado: U.S. Geol. Survey Bull. 1032–E, p. 223–272 [1961].

Westgate, L. G., and Knopf, Adolph, 1932, Geology and ore deposits of the Pioche district, Nevada: U.S. Geol. Survey Prof. Paper 171, 79 p.

Wiese, J. H., 1950, Geology and mineral resources of the Neenach quadrangle, California: California Div. Mines Bull. 153, 53 p.

Wilkerson, A. S., 1939, Geology and ore deposits of the Magnolia mining district and adjacent area, Boulder County, Colorado: Colorado Sci. Soc. Proc., v. 14, no. 3, p. 81–101.

Willden, C. R., and Hotz, P. E., 1955, A gold-scheelite-cinnabar placer in Humboldt County, Nevada: Econ. Geology, v. 50, no. 7, p. 661–668.

Williams, N. C., ed., 1959, Guidebook to the geology of the Wasatch and Uinta Mountains transition area [Utah-Wyoming]: Salt Lake City, Intermountain Assoc. Petroleum Geologists 10th Ann. Field Conf., 235 p.

Wilson, E. D., 1927, Geology and ore deposits of the Courtland-Gleeson region, Arizona: Arizona Bur. Mines Bull. 123, Geol. Ser. 5, 79 p.

——— 1933, Geology and mineral deposits of southern Yuma County, Arizona: Arizona Bur. Mines Bull. 134, Geol. Ser. 7, 236 p.

Wilson, E. D., 1952, Arizona gold placers, Part 1 *of* Arizona gold placers and placering [5th ed., revised]: Arizona Bur. Mines Bull. 160, Mineral Tech. Ser. 45, p. 11–86.

——— 1962, A résumé of the geology of Arizona: Arizona Bur. Mines Bull. 171, 140 p.

Wilson, E. D., Cunningham, J. B., and Butler, G. M., 1934, Arizona lode-gold mines and gold mining: Arizona Bur. Mines Bull. 137, Mineral Tech. Ser. 37, 261 p.

Winchell, A. N., 1914a, The mining districts of the Dillon quadrangle, Montana, and adjacent areas: U.S. Geol. Survey Bull. 574, 191 p.

——— 1914b, Petrology and mineral resources of Jackson and Josephine Counties, Oregon: Oregon Bur. Mines and Geology, Mineral Resources of Oregon, v. 1, no. 5, 265 p.

Wisker, A. L., 1936, The gold-bearing veins of Meadow Lake district, Nevada County: California Jour. Mines and Geology, v. 32, no. 2, p. 189–204.

Woodward, G. E., and Luff, Paul, 1943, Gold, silver, copper, lead, and zinc in Arizona: U.S. Bur. Mines Minerals Yearbook 1942, p. 231–259.

Worcester, P. G., 1920, The geology of the Ward region, Boulder County, Colorado: Colorado Geol. Survey Bull. 21, 74 p. [1921].

Wright, C. W., 1904, The Porcupine placer district, Alaska: U.S. Geol. Survey Bull. 236, 35 p.

——— 1906, A reconnaissance of Admiralty Island, Alaska, *in* Spencer, A. C., The Juneau gold belt, Alaska: U.S. Geol. Survey Bull. 287, p. 138–161.

Wright, F. E., and Wright, C. W., 1908, The Ketchikan and Wrangell mining districts, Alaska: U.S. Geol. Survey Bull. 347, 210 p.

Wright, L. A., Stewart, R. M., Gay, T. E., and Hazenbush, G. C., 1953, Mines and mineral deposits of San Bernardino County, California: California Jour. Mines and Geology, v. 49, nos. 1–2, p. 49–192.

Yeates, W. S., McCallie, S. W., and King, F. P., 1896, A preliminary report on a part of the gold deposits of Georgia: Georgia Geol. Survey Bull. 4–A, 542 p.

Young, E. B., 1950, The Pioche district, *in* Dunham, K. C., ed., Symposium on geology, paragenesis, and reserves of the ores of lead and zinc: Internat. Geol. Cong., 18th, London 1948, Rept., pt. 7, p. 111–120.

Youngberg, E. A., 1947, Mines and prospects of the Mount Reuben mining district, Josephine County, Oregon: Oregon Dept. Geology and Mineral Industries Bull. 34, 35 p.

INDEX OF LOCALITIES

[Italic page numbers indicate major references]

A — Page

Acton district, California ---- 57, *67*
A. D. and M. mine, Idaho ---- 135
Adelaide district, Nevada ---- *181*
Adelaide mine, Nevada ---- 181
Agua Fria district, Arizona ---- 33, 35, *46*
Ajo district, Arizona ---- 33, 35, *42*
Ajo mine, Arizona ---- 42
Alaska Juneau mine, Alaska ---- 9, 19, 20, 21
Albemarle mine, New Mexico ---- 208
Alder Creek district, Idaho ---- 123, *127*
Alder Gulch placers
Montana ---- 143, 146, 160, 163
Algonquin mine, Montana ---- 151
Alice district, Colorado ---- 85, *93*, 94
Alice mine, Colorado ---- 93
Alleghany district, California ---- 5, 54, 57, *79*
Alma district, Colorado ---- 85, *109*
Alma placers, Colorado ---- 109
Almeda mine, Oregon ---- 227
Alta mine, Colorado ---- 115
Alta mine, Montana ---- 154
Alvarado mine, Utah ---- 251
Amalie district, California ---- 57, *64*
Amalie mine, California ---- 64
American Fork district, Utah ---- 241, 248, *252*
American Lode mine, New Mexico ---- 207
American Nettie mine, Colorado ---- 108
American River placers,
California ---- 53, 55, 61, 72, 73, 75
Ames mining area, Colorado ---- 115
Amethyst mine, Colorado ---- 106
Angels Camp, California ---- 60
Animas district, Colorado ---- 85, *113*
Annie Laurie mine, Utah ---- 245
Antelope Valley district, California ---- 57, *67*
Apollo Consolidated mine, Alaska ---- 23
App-Heslep mine, California ---- 83
Arbacoochee district, Alabama ---- 6, *7*
Argenta district, Montana ---- 142, *144*
Argentine district, Colorado ---- 85, 93, *94*
Argentum mine, Nevada ---- 189
Argonaut mine, California ---- 58
Arizona mine, Arizona ---- 44
Arkansas River valley placers,
Colorado ---- 85, *104*
Arondo mine, California ---- 63
Ashdown mine, Nevada ---- 182
Ashland district, Oregon ---- 217, *224*
Ashland mine, Oregon ---- 224
Ash Peak district, Arizona ---- 35, *39*
Aspen district, Colorado ---- 86, 110
Atlanta district, Idaho ---- 123, 124, *129*
Atlantic City-South Pass district,
Wyoming ---- 262, 263
Auburn mine, Nevada ---- 196
August mine, Montana ---- 167
Auld Lang Syne mine, Nevada ---- 196
Aurora district, Nevada ---- 171, 173, *188*
Avon district, Montana ---- *168*
Awakening district, Nevada ---- 173, 180, *181*
Aztec mine, New Mexico ---- 204

B — Page

Baby mine, Oregon ---- 227
Backer district, Montana ---- *146*
Badger mine, Oregon ---- 224
Bagdad-Chase mine, California ---- 76
Bagdad district, Arizona ---- *47*
Bagdad mine, Arizona ---- 47
Baisley-Elkhorn mine, Oregon ---- 220
Baker district, Oregon ---- 216, *217*
Baker mine, Colorado ---- 94
Balaklala mine, California ---- 78
Bald Mountain district,
South Dakota ---- 233, *235*, 238
Ballarat district, California ---- 57, 62, *63*
Bannack district, Montana ---- 142, 144, *145*
Banner district, Arizona ---- 33, 35, *37*
Barnes-King mine, Montana ---- 149
Barnhardt mine, North Carolina ---- 215
Basin and Boulder district, Montana ---- 142, *152*
Bass mine, Nevada ---- 175
Bassick mine, Colorado ---- 97
Battle Mountain district, Colorado ---- *99*
Battle Mountain district, Nevada ---- 173, *183*
Bayhorse district, Idaho ---- 127
Beaver Creek district, Colorado ---- *110*
Beaver Creek district, Montana ---- 147
Beaver district, Idaho ---- 139
Beaver Lake district, Utah ---- 242
Bell district, Nevada ---- 173, *188*
Bellevue mine, California ---- 73
Bellota district, California ---- 57, *77*
Belmont mine, Colorado ---- 94
Belshazzar mine, Idaho ---- 125
Bendigo district, California ---- 74
Benton mine, Oregon ---- 227
Betty O'Neal mine, Nevada ---- 184
Bibliography ---- 263
Big and Little Smoky-Rosetta district,
Idaho ---- 123, 126
Big Blue mine, California ---- 65
Big Buffalo mine, Idaho ---- 131
Big Bug district, Arizona ---- 33, 35, 45, *46*
Big Bug Mine, Arizona ---- 46
Big Canyon mine, California ---- 61
Big Cottonwood camp, Utah ---- 246, 248
Big Eye mine, Arizona ---- 51
Big Gun mine, California ---- 72
Big Hurrah mine, Alaska ---- 16, 19
Bimetallic mine, Montana ---- 151
Bingham district,
Utah ---- 3, 5, 6, 240, 241, 242, *246*, 251
Bisbee district, Arizona ---- 5, 33, *35*
Black Bear mine, California ---- 81
Black Bear mine, Oregon ---- 227
Blackbird district, Idaho ---- 123, *134*
Black Canyon district, Arizona ---- 35, *46*
Black Hornet district, Idaho ---- *120*, 123
Black Jack mine, Idaho ---- 138
Black Rock district, Arizona ---- 35, *47*
Blanchard district, California ---- 67, 69
Blewett district, Washington ---- 255, *256*
Blue Ledge district, Utah ---- 249

Page

Blue River district, Colorado ---- *116*
Blue River district, Oregon ---- 217, 229, *230*
Blue Tent placers, California ---- 70, 72
Blue Wing district, Montana ---- 144
Bluff camp, Alaska ---- 19
Bodie district, California ---- 57, 69, *70*
Bodie mine, Washington ---- 259
Bohemia district, Oregon ---- 217, 229, *230*
Boise Basin district, Idaho ---- 5, 123, *124*
Bolinger mine, Washington ---- 259
Bonanza district, Colorado ---- 85, *112*
Bonanza King mine, Nevada ---- 197
Bonanza mine, Arizona ---- 52
Bonanza mine, California ---- 84
Bonanza mine, Oregon ---- 219
Bonnifield district, Alaska ---- 10, *24*
Boss Tweed mine, Montana ---- 161
Boulder Creek district, Montana ---- 142, *150*
Boundary-Red Mountain mine,
Washington ---- 262
Bouquet placer district, California ---- 67
Braden mine, Oregon ---- 225
Brazos mine, Oregon ---- 221
Breckenridge district, Colorado ---- 85, 86, *116*
Brewer mine, South Carolina ---- 231
Bright Star mine, California ---- 65
Brindletown placers, North Carolina ---- 211
Broadway mine, Montana ---- 162
Brooklyn mine, California ---- 76
Brown Monster mine, California ---- 63
Browns Valley-Smartville district,
California ---- 57, *84*
Brownsville-Challenge-Dobbins district,
California ---- 57, *84*
Bruner district, Nevada ---- 173, *191*
Bryant district, Montana ---- 142, 144, *145*
Buckhorn district, Nevada ---- 173, *179*
Buckhorn mine, Nevada ---- 179
Buena Vista district, Nevada ---- 195
Buffalo Hump district,
Idaho ---- 123, 130, *131*, *133*
Bullfrog district, Nevada ---- 173, *191*
Bullion district, Nevada ---- 173, 183, *184*
Bull Run mine, Nevada ---- 176
Bunker Hill and Sullivan mine, Idaho ---- 139
Burke district, Idaho ---- 139
Busby mine, Virginia ---- 253
Buster mine, Idaho ---- 132
Butte district, Montana ---- 5, 142, 143, 144, *169*

C

Cable mine, Montana ---- 148
Cable placer, Montana ---- 148
Cactus mine, Utah ---- 243
Calaveras River placers,
California ---- 55, 59, 60, 77
Calera cobalt-copper mine, Idaho ---- 135
Calistoga district, California ---- 57, 70
Callahan mine, Montana ---- 153
Camanche district, California ---- 57, *59*

Page

Camas district, Idaho ---------------*121*, 123
Camas 2 mine, Idaho ---------------121
Cambridge district, Nevada ---------------*187*
Camp Bird mine, Colorado ---------------107
Camp Douglas district, Nevada ---------------*190*
Camp Floyd district, Utah ---240, 241, *250*, 251
Campo Seco district, California ---------57, *59*
Canada Hill district, California ---------------72
Canada Hill mine, California ---------------71
Candelaria district, Nevada ----------173, *189*
Cane Springs mine, Utah ---------------251
Canyon Creek district,
Oregon ---------216, 217, 218, *222*
Cardinal mine, California ---------------64
Cardwell district, Montana ---------------*154*
Cargo Muchacho district, California ----57, *62*
Carlin mine, Nevada ------------171, 174, 180
Carlisle mine, New Mexico ---------------206
Carmen Creek camp, Idaho ---------------135
Carmen Creek-Eldorado-Pratt
Creek-Sandy Creek district,
Idaho ---------------123, *135*
Carrville district, California ------------57, *81*
Cascade Creek camp, Colorado ---------------96
Cascade district, Washington ---------256, *259*
Castle Dome district, Arizona ----------35, *51*
Cataract channel placer deposits,
California ---------------59, 60
Cave Creek district, Arizona ---------------35, *40*
Cedar and Mount Gleason district,
California ---------------*67*
Cedar Creek-Trout Creek district,
Montana ---------------142, *164*
Cedar Mountain district, Nevada ---------*188*
Cedar Plains district, Montana ---------------*146*
Centennial Eureka mine, Utah ---------------244
Center Reef mine, Montana ---------------153
Centerville district, Idaho ---------------*124*
Central City district,
Colorado -----5, 85, 94, 96, 97, *100*
Central district, Colorado ---------------88, *89*
Central district, New Mexico ----201, 203, *205*
Central Eureka mine, California ----------58
Cerbat camp, Arizona ---------------41
Cerrillos district, New Mexico ---------------*210*
Chafey district, Nevada ---------------*196*
Chalk Creek district, Colorado----85, 86, 91, *92*
Champion mine, California ---------------71
Chandalar district, Alaska ---------------10, *25*
Chelan Lake district, Washington--255, 256, *257*
Cherry Creek district, Nevada ---------173, *199*
Cherry Creek mine, Nevada ---------------199
Chewelah district, Washington ---------------261
Chewsaw district, Washington ---------------*260*
Chicago Creek camp, Colorado ---------------96
Chichagof district, Alaska ----------10, 19, *20*
Chichagof mine, Alaska ---------------20
Chief mine, Utah ---------------244
Chief 1 mine, Utah ---------------244
Chisana district, Alaska ---------------10, *25*
Chistochina district, Alaska ---------10, 13, *14*
Chitina district, Alaska ---------------13
Chloride Cliff district, California ----57, 62, *63*
Chloride camp, Arizona ---------------41
Christmas district, Arizona ---------------*37*
Christmas mine, Arizona ---------------37, 38
Chocolate Mountains district, California ----62
Church mine, California ---------------61
Cid district, North Carolina ---------------212
Cid mine, North Carolina ---------------213
Cienega district, Arizona ---------------35, *51*
Circle district, Alaska -----------10, 23, *25*, 26
Clancy district, Montana ---------142, 152, *153*
Clay Peters mine, Nevada ---------------189
Clear Creek placers, Colorado ------85, 87, 103
Clementine mine, Nevada ---------------175
Clements district, California -----------57, *77*
Cliff mine, Alaska ---------------31
Clifton district, Utah ------------241, 250, *251*
Clifton-Morenci district, Arizona ----33, 35, *39*

Climax district, Colorado ---------------103
Clipper mine, Montana ---------------161
Cloverleaf mine, South Dakota ---------------236
Cochiti district, New Mexico ---------203, *208*
Coeur d'Alene region, Idaho ----------123, *139*
Cold Spring mine, Colorado ---------------88
Colorado district, Montana ---------------*154*
Colorado mineral belt,
Colorado ----84, 86, 90, 95, 98, 105
Columbia Basin-Jamestown-Sonora
district, California ------5, 57, *82*
Columbia mine, Colorado ---------------90
Columbia River placers, Washington ------258
Columbia district, Colorado ---------------*112*
Colville district, Washington ---------------255
Comet mine, Jefferson County, Mont ------154
Comet mine, Missoula County, Mont-------164
Como district, Nevada ---------------173, *187*
Comstock Lode district,
Nevada ---5, 171, 173, 174, 187, *197*
Comstock Lode,
Nevada --5, 171, 186, 187, 197, *198*
Confederate Gulch district,
Montana ------------142, *146*, 147
Congress mine, Arizona ---------------49
Connor Creek district, Oregon ---------217, *218*
Connor Creek mine, Oregon ---------------218
Conrad Hill mine, North Carolina ----211, 213
Consolidated Virginia mine, Nevada ------198
Cooke City district, Montana ----142, 165, *166*
Cooney district, New Mexico ---------------*202*
Copper Contact mine, Nevada ---------------189
Copper Queen mine, Arizona ---------------35
Copper Rock camp, Colorado ---------------90
Cornwall iron mine, Pennsylvania ---------231
Cornucopia district, Oregon --216, 217, 218, *219*
Cortez district, Nevada ---------------173, *179*
Cosumnes River placers,
California -----------57, *58*, 61, 75
Cottonwood district,
Utah -------241, 246, *248*, 252, 253
Cottonwood-Fort Jones-Yreka district,
California ---------------57, *80*
Council district, Alaska ----------8, 10, 16, *17*
Courtland district, Arizona ---------------35, *37*
Cove district, California ------------57, 64, *65*
Cowles mine, New Mexico ---------------209
Cracker Creek district, Oregon ---216, 217, *219*
Crater mine, California ---------------73
Creede district, Colorado ----------85, 86, *106*
Creighton mine, Georgia ---------------118, 119
Crescent Mills district, California ------57, *73*
Cresson mine, Colorado ---------------118
Cripple Creek district,
Colorado ----------3, 5, 84, 85, 86,
87, 106, *117*
Crow Creek district, Montana ---------------*146*
Crown King district, Arizona ---------------*50*
Crown King mine, Arizona ---------------50
Crown Point mine, Washington ---------------257
Crown Queen mine, Nevada ---------------174
Crowning Glory mine, Nevada ---------------178
Curry mine, Nevada ---------------197

D

Dahlonega district, Georgia ---------------119
Daisy mine, Oregon ---------------227
Daisy mine, Utah ---------------250
Dale district, California ------------57, 75, *76*
Dan Tucker mine, Nevada ---------------173
Danville district, Washington ---------------258
Deadwood Creek camp, South Dakota ------235
Deadwood-French Gulch district,
California ---------------57, 77, *78*
Deadwood Gulch placers,
South Dakota -----------234, 235
Deadwood-Two Bit district,
South Dakota -----------233, *235*
Deep Gravel placer mine, Oregon ---------229

Deer Trail district, Washington ---------------261
Deertrail mine, Utah ---------------246
Delamar district, Nevada --------171, 173, *185*
De Lamar mine, Idaho ---------------138
Delamar mine, Nevada ---------------185
Delamar mine, Utah ---------------250
Denn mine, Arizona ---------------35
De Soto mine, Arizona ---------------50
Dewey mine, Idaho ---------------140
Dexter mine, Nevada ---------------177
Diamond district, Nevada ---------------179
Diamond mine, Nevada ---------------179
Diamond Mountain district, California --57, *66*
Dirt mine, Colorado ---------------100
Divide district, Nevada ---------------173, *177*
Divide Extension mine, Nevada ---------------177
Dixie Creek district, Oregon ---------------*220*
Dixie district, Idaho ---------------123, 130, *131*
Dolcoath mine, Montana ---------------153
Dolores district, New Mexico ---------------*210*
Dome district, Arizona ---------------32, 35, *52*
Dorn mine, South Carolina ------------231, 232
Dorothea mine, Oregon ---------------228
Dos Cabezas district, Arizona -------33, 35, *36*
Douglas Creek district, Wyoming ---------262
Downieville district, California ---5, 54, 57, *79*
Drinkwater mine, Nevada ---------------178
Drumlummon mine, Montana ---------------156
Dry Gulch district, Montana ---------------155
Ducktown district, Tennessee ---------------240
Dun Glen district, Nevada ---------------*196*
Duplex mine, Nevada ---------------175
Dutch-App mine, California ---------------83
Dutch mine, California ---------------83
Dutch Flat-Gold Run district,
California ---------------57, *72*
Dutch Flat placer district, Nevada ----173, *181*

E

Eagle Creek district, Oregon -----216, 217, *219*
Eagle district, Alaska ---------------10, *26*
Eagle district, Idaho ---------------139
Eagle-Shawmut mine, California ---------------83
East Belt districts,
California --5, 57, 59, *60*, *61*, *68*, *83*
East Belt gold deposits,
California -------54, 57, 59, 60, 61,
68, 82, 83
East Tintic district, Utah ---------------244, 252
Ebner mine, Alaska ---------------20
Echo district, Nevada ---------------*196*
Edgemont district, Nevada --------173, 175, *176*
Egan Canyon district, Nevada ---------------*199*
Eldorado camp, Idaho ---------------135
Eldorado district, Nevada ---------------173, *174*
Eldorado (Humboldt) district, Nevada ----195
Eldorado mine, Arizona ---------------40
Eldorado Rand mine, Nevada ---------------174
Elizabethtown-Baldy district,
New Mexico ---------------203, *204*
Elk City district, Idaho --123, 130, 131, *132*, 133
Elk Creek camp, South Dakota ---------------235
Elk Creek-Coloma district, Montana --142, *164*
Elkhorn district, Montana -------142, 152, *153*
Elkhorn mine, Montana ---------------153
Elkhorn Queen mine, Montana ---------------153
Elko Prince mine, Nevada ---------------176
Ellamar copper ores ---------------32
Ellamar district, Alaska ---------------31
Ellendale district, Nevada ---------------173, *192*
Ellendale mine, Nevada ---------------192
Ellsworth district, Arizona ---------------35, *52*
Elmore mine, Idaho ---------------130
Ely district, Nevada ---------------171, 173, *199*
Emery district, Montana ---------------*169*
Emery mine, Montana ---------------169
Emigrant Creek district, Montana ----142, *165*
Emma mine, Utah ---------------248
Emmons mine, North Carolina ---------------213

Page

Empire district, Colorado ---- 85, 93, *94*
Empire district, Nevada ---- *194*
Empire mine, California ---- 70, 71
Empire mine, Idaho ---- 127
Entiat district, Washington ---- 256, *257*
Ermont mine, Montana ---- 144
Ester Dome mine, Alaska ---- 26, 27
Etta spodumene mine, South Dakota ---- 238
Eureka Consolidated mine, Nevada ---- 179
Eureka district, Arizona ---- 35, *47*
Eureka district, Colorado ---- 85, 113, *114*
Eureka district, Nevada ---- 171, 173, *179*
Eureka district, Washington ---- *258*
Eureka Hill mine, Utah ---- 244
Eureka Lilly mine, Utah ---- 244
Eureka mine, Washington ---- 262
Evolution district, Idaho ---- 139
Exchequer mine, Nevada ---- 199

F

Fairbanks district, Alaska ---- 5, 8, 9, 10, 23, 24, *26*, 31
Fairfield Valley placers, North Carolina ---- 212, *215*
Fairhaven district, Alaska ---- 8, 10, 16, *17*
Fairplay district, Colorado ---- 85, 109, *110*
Fairplay placers, Colorado ---- 110
Fairview district, Nevada ---- *172*, 173
Feather River gravels, California ---- 55, 59
Featherville district, Idaho ---- 123, *129*
Fern mine, Idaho ---- 141
Fiddletown district, California ---- 57, *58*
Finn district, Montana ---- 142, *167*
First Chance district, Montana ---- 142, 150, *151*, 164
First Thought mine, Washington ---- 261
Flagstaff mine, Nevada ---- 174
Flagstaff mine, Oregon ---- 221
Flint camp, Idaho ---- 138
Flint Creek district, Montana ---- 142, 150, *151*
Florida Mountain-War Eagle Mountain camp, Idaho ---- 138
Flowery district, Nevada ---- 197
Folsom district, California ---- 5, 57, *75*
Foresthill district, California ---- 57, *72*
Fortuna district, Arizona ---- 35, *52*
Fortuna mine, Arizona ---- 52
Fortymile district, Alaska ---- 10, 23, 26, *27*
Forty-nine Diggings placer mine, Oregon ---- 224
Franklin mine, Georgia ---- 119
Franklin mine, Idaho ---- 129
Franklin mine, Montana ---- 158
Franklin mine, Virginia ---- 253
Freeland-Lamartine district, Colorado ---- 85, 93, *95*
Freeland mine, Colorado ---- 95
French Creek district, Montana ---- 142, *148*
French Creek-Florence district, Idaho ---- 123, *132*
French Diggings placer mine, Oregon ---- 223
Friant district, California ---- 57, 62
Friday mine, Washington ---- 259
Frisco camp, Colorado ---- 117

G

Galena district, Nevada ---- 199
Galice district, Oregon ---- 217, 218, 226, *227*
Gambrinus district, Idaho ---- *124*
Garden district, South Dakota ---- 233, 235, *236*, 238
Gardner Hill mine, North Carolina ---- 212, 213
Garfield district, Nevada ---- 173, *189*
Garfield mine, Nevada ---- 189
Garnet district, Montana ---- *151*
Garrison mine, Nevada ---- 179
Gemini mine, Utah ---- 244

Page

General Custer mine, Idaho ---- 128
Georgetown district, Alaska ---- 10, 14, *15*
Georgetown district, Montana ---- 142, *148*
Georgetown placers, Montana ---- 149
Georgetown-Silver Plume district, Colorado ---- 85, 93, 94, *95*
Georgia Gulch placers, Colorado ---- 116
Georgia Slide district, California ---- 57, *61*
Getchell mine, Nevada ---- 171, 180, 182
Geyser-Marion mine, Utah ---- 250
Gibbonsville district, Idaho ---- 123, *135*
Gila City district, Arizona ---- 32, 33, *52*
Gilman district, Colorado ---- 85, 98, *99*
Girdwood district, Alaska ---- 11
Gleason mine, Oregon ---- 220
Gleeson district, Arizona ---- 35, *37*
Globe-Miami district, Arizona ---- 33, 35, 37, *38*, 44
Globe mine, Arizona ---- 38
Gnome mine, Idaho ---- 132
Gold Acres camp, Nevada ---- 184
Gold Bar mine, Arizona ---- 47
Gold Basin district, Arizona ---- 35, *40*
Gold Brick-Quartz Creek district, Colorado ---- 85, *101*
Gold Bug camp, Arizona ---- 41
Gold Bug mine, Oregon ---- 227
Gold Canyon district, Nevada ---- *199*
Gold Circle district, Nevada ---- 173, *176*
Gold Cliff mine, California ---- 60
Gold Creek placers, Montana ---- 143, 167, 168
Gold Hill camp, Colorado ---- 88, 90
Gold Hill district, Idaho ---- 124, *125*
Gold Hill district, Nevada ---- 173, *192*
Gold Hill district, North Carolina ---- 212, *214*
Gold Hill district, Oregon ---- 217, 224, *225*
Gold Hill district, Utah ---- *251*
Gold Hill mine, Idaho ---- 125
Gold Hill mine, North Carolina ---- 211
Gold Hill mine, Utah ---- 251
Gold Hill-Sugarloaf district, Colorado ---- 85, *88*, 89, 90
Gold King mine, Colorado ---- 114
Gold King mine, Washington ---- 254, 258
Gold Mountain district, Nevada ---- *177*
Gold Mountain district, Utah ---- 241, *245*, 246
Gold Park district, Nevada ---- *192*
Gold Range district, Nevada ---- 173, *190*
Gold Ridge mine, Oregon ---- 220
Gold Ridge mine, Washington ---- 262
Gold Run district, Nevada ---- 173, *181*
Gold Springs district, Utah ---- *243*
Golden Age mine, Idaho ---- 125
Golden Curry mine, Montana ---- 153
Golden Cycle mine, Colorado ---- 118
Golden Eagle mine, Arizona ---- 52
Golden Eagle mine, California ---- 80
Golden Gate mine, Nevada ---- 190
Golden Messenger mine, Montana ---- 157
Golden Mile mine, Nevada ---- 189
Golden Rule mine, California ---- 83
Golden Sunlight mine, Montana ---- 154
Goldfield district, Nevada ---- 5, 171, 173, 174, *177*
Goldstone mine, Idaho ---- 135
Goldville mine, Alabama ---- 6
Good Hope mine, California ---- 74
Goodnews Bay district, Alaska ---- 10, 14, *15*
Goodsprings district, Nevada ---- 173, *174*
Gould district, Montana ---- *158*
Gould mine, Nevada ---- 197
Governor mine, California ---- 67
Grand Island-Caribou district, Colorado ---- 85, 88, *89*
Grand Prize mine, Nevada ---- 176
Granite-Bimetallic mine, Montana ---- 151
Granite district, Idaho ---- 124, *125*
Granite district, Nevada ---- *193*
Granite district, Oregon ---- 217, *222*
Granite Hill mine, Oregon ---- 227
Granite mine, Colorado ---- 118

Page

Granite mine, Idaho ---- 139
Granite Mountain mine, Montana ---- 150, 151
Grants Pass district, Oregon ---- 217, 226, *227*, 228
Grass Valley camp, California ---- 71
Grass Valley-Nevada City district, California ---- 3, 5, 54, 57, *70*
Greaterville district, Arizona ---- 35, 42, *43*
Greenback district, Oregon ---- 217, 226, *228*
Greenback mine, Oregon ---- 228
Green Campbell mine, Montana ---- 162
Green Emigrant mine, California ---- 73
Greenhorn district, Oregon ---- 217, *219*, 222, *223*
Green Mountain district, California ---- 57, 64, *65*
Green Mountain mine, California ---- 73
Gregory diggings, Colorado ---- 99, 100
Gregory mine, Montana ---- 154
Griffith district, Colorado ---- *95*
Grimes Pass district, Idaho ---- 124, *125*
Groveland-Moccasin-Jacksonville area, California ---- 57, *83*
Grunter mine, Idaho ---- 136

H

Hahns Peak district, Colorado ---- 85, *112*
Haile mine, South Carolina ---- 7, 231, 232
Hailey district, Idaho ---- *121*
Hamilton mine, New Mexico ---- 209
Hammersley mine, Oregon ---- 227
Hammonton district, California ---- 5, 57, *84*
Hardscrabble district, Idaho ---- *129*
Harquahala district, Arizona ---- 33, *52*
Harrison Gulch district, California ---- 57, 77, *78*
Harvard mine, California ---- 83
Hassayampa-Groom Creek district, Arizona ---- 32, 35, 45, *48*
Hassel district, Montana ---- *146*
Hattie mine, Idaho ---- 121
Hawthorne district, Nevada ---- 173, *190*
Hayden Hill district, California ---- 57, *66*
Hearst mine, California ---- 59
Hecla district, Montana ---- 144, *145*
Helena-Last Chance district, Montana ---- 142, 143, 154, *155*
Henderson placers, Montana ---- 142, *152*
Hermes mine, Idaho ---- 141
Hidden Treasure mine, California ---- 72
Hidden Treasure mine, Oregon ---- 221
Hidden Treasure mine, South Dakota ---- 236
Hidden Treasure mine, Washington ---- 259
High Grade district, California ---- 57, 69
Highland Boy mine, Utah ---- 247
Highland district, Montana ---- 142, 169, *170*
Highland Light mine, Washington ---- 259
Hillabee mine, Alabama ---- 8
Hill City district, South Dakota ---- 233, *239*
Hillsboro district, New Mexico ---- 203, *210*
Hillside mine, Arizona ---- 47
Hilltop district, Nevada ---- 173, *184*
Hilltop mine, Nevada ---- 184
Hirshey mine, Alaska ---- 11
Hirst-Chichagof mine, Alaska ---- 20
Hite mine, California ---- 69
Hoge mine, California ---- 71
Hog Mountain district, Alabama ---- 6, 7, *8*
Hog Mountain mine, Alabama ---- 8
Holcomb district, California ---- 57, 75, *76*
Holcomb Valley placers, California ---- 76
Holden district, Washington ---- *257*
Holden mine, Washington ---- 255, 257, 258
Homestake mine, New Mexico ---- 208
Homestake mine, South Dakota ---- 5, 166, 235, 237
Honeycutt mine, North Carolina ---- 215
Hoodoo district, Idaho ---- 123, *134*
Hoover Hill mine, North Carolina ---- 212, 214
Hope mine, Montana ---- 150, 151
Hornitos district, California ---- 57, 67, *68*, 69
Horn Silver mine, Utah ---- 242

Page

Hornsilver district, Nevada --173, *178*
Horseshoe mine, Idaho --127
Horseshoe placers, Colorado --109
Hot Creek district, Nevada --*194*
Hot Springs district, Alaska --10, 23, *27*, 30
Howie mine, North Carolina --212, *215*
Hughes Creek district, Montana --142, 169
Hughes Creek placers, Montana --169
Hully and Logan mine, Nevada --187
Humboldt district, Nevada --173, *195*
Humbug district, California --57, *80*
Humdinger mine, Oregon --229
Hunter district, Idaho --139

I

Idaho City district, Idaho --*124*
Idaho-Maryland mine, California --71
Idaho Springs district, Colorado --85, 93, *96*
Iditarod district, Alaska --10, 24, *28*
Igo district, California --57, 77, *78*
Illinois mine, Nevada --193
Illinois River district, Oregon --217, *228*
Imlay district, Nevada --*195*
Imlay mine, Nevada --195
Independence mine, Colorado --118
Independence mine, Placer County, Calif --72
Independence mine, Siskiyou County, Calif --81
Independence Pass district, Colorado --85, *110*
Index district, Washington --260
Indian Creek district, Montana --*146*
Indian Queen mine, Nevada --190
Indian Springs district, Nevada --*187*
Innoko district, Alaska --10, 24, *28*
Inyo Range district, California --*63*
Iola mine, North Carolina --212, 214
Iowa Hill district, California --57, *72*
Iron Blossom mine, Utah --244
Iron King mine, Arizona --46
Iron Mountain mine, California --78
Iron Rod mine, Montana --162
Iron Springs district, Utah --243
Iron Springs mining area, Colorado --115
Isabella mine, Colorado --118

J

Jacks Hill mine, North Carolina --212, 213
Jackson district, Nevada --173, *192*
Jacksonville district, Oregon --217, 224, *225*
Jamestown district, Colorado --85, 88, *89*
Jarbridge district, Nevada --171, 173, 175, *176*
Jardine district, Montana --142, *165*
Jarilla district, New Mexico --203, *208*
Jay Gould mine, Montana --158
Jefferson Canyon district, Nevada --173, *192*
Jefferson mine, Nevada --192
Jenny Lind district, California --57, *60*, 77
Jenny Lind mine, California --72
Jerome district, Arizona --35, 45, *48*
Joe Walker mine, California --57, 66
Johnnie district, Nevada --173, *192*
Johnnie mine, Nevada --192
Johnsville district, California --57, 73, *74*
Jordon Creek placers, Idaho --138
Josephine mine, California --69
Julian district, California --57, 77
Jumbo district, Nevada --199
Jumbo mine, Humboldt County, Nev --180, 181
Jumbo mine, Lincoln County, Nev --185
Jumpoff Joe Creek camp, Oregon --227
Juneau district, Alaska --5, 9, 10, 19, *20*

K

Kantishna district, Alaska --10, 24, *28*
Katherine camp, Arizona --40
Keane Wonder mine, California --63
Kearsarge mine, Montana --163
Kenai Peninsula district, Alaska --8, 10, *11*
Kendall district, Montana --*149*
Kennedy mine, California --58
Kentuck mine, Idaho --136
Kerber Creek district, Colorado --*112*
Ketchikan-Hyder district, Alaska --10, 19, 20, *21*
Keyes district, California --57, 64, *65*
Keyes mine, California --64
Keystone district, Nevada --*194*
Keystone district, South Dakota --233, 238, *239*
Keystone-Holy Terror mine, South Dakota --239
Keystone mine, California --58
Keystone mine, Nevada --175
Keystone mine, Wyoming --263
Kimberly district, Utah --*245*
King of Arizona mine, Arizona --52
Kings Mountain mine, North Carolina --211, 212, 213
Kirtley Creek district, Idaho --123, *135*
Kittie Burton mine, Idaho --136
Klamath River district, California --57, *81*
Klamath River placers, California --57, 62, 80, 81
Knob Hill mine, Washington --254, 258
Kofa district, Arizona --33, 35, *52*
Kokomo district, Colorado --86, 117
Kougarok district, Alaska --10, 16, *17*
Kougarok placers, Alaska --18
Koyuk district, Alaska --10, 16, 17, *18*
Koyukuk district, Alaska --10, *29*

L

La Belleview mine, Oregon --222
La Cigale mine, Utah --250
La Grange mine, California --82
La Grange-Waterford district, California --57, 81
Laguna district, Arizona --35, *52*
Lake City district, Colorado --85, 86, *103*
Lake Superior mine, Arizona --44
Lamartine mine, Colorado --95
Landon-Arizona mine, Arizona --38
LaPanta mine, Nevada --190
La Paz district, Arizona --32, 35, *53*
La Plata district, Colorado --85, *105*
La Porte district, California --5, 57, 73, *74*
Las Animas district, New Mexico --*210*
Last Chance mine, Colorado --106
Last Chance Gulch placers, Montana --143, 146, 154, 155
La Touche Island copper ores, Alaska --32
Layton placer mine, Oregon --226
Lead district, South Dakota --3, 5, 6, 233, 234, 235, *237*
Leadville district, Colorado --5, 85, 86, 98, 103, *104*, 109, *117*
Leadville district, Nevada --199
Leesburg district, Idaho --*136*
Lelande district, Idaho --139
Lewis district, Nevada --173, 183, *184*
Libby district, Montana --142, *159*
Liberty Bell mine, Colorado --115
Lincoln district, Montana --142, *155*
Lincoln district, Utah --242
Lindsay mine, North Carolina --212, 213
Little Annie mine, Colorado --111
Little Bonanza mine, Oregon --220
Little Cottonwood camp, Utah --246, 248, 249
Little Hill mine, Oregon --220
Little Rocky Mountains district, Montana --142, *167*
Livingston mine, Oregon --228
Llano de Oro placer mine, Oregon --229
Lodi district, Nevada --173, *193*
London mine, Colorado --109
Lone Jack mine, Washington --262
Lone Mountain district, Nevada --173, *178*
Lone Pine mine, Washington --258
Longfellow mine, California --83
Loon Creek district, Idaho --123, 127, *128*
Lordsburg district, New Mexico --201, 203, *207*
Lost Horse mine, California --75
Lost Packer mine, Idaho --128
Low Divide district, California --60
Lower Applegate district, Oregon --217, *228*
Lower Burnt River valley district, Oregon --217, *220*
Lucky Boy mine, Idaho --128
Lucky Boy mine, Nevada --190
Lucky Boy mine, Oregon --230
Lucky Girl mine, Nevada --176
Luxemburg placers, New Mexico --210
Lynn district, Nevada --171, 173, *180*
Lynx Creek-Walker district, Arizona --32, 35, 45, *49*

M

Mabel mine, Nevada --189
McCabe-Gladstone mine, Arizona --46
McClellan district, Montana --142, *156*
McKeen mine, California --81
Mackinaw district, Idaho --123, *136*
McKinley district, Alaska --10, 14, *15*
Mad Mule mine, California --79
Madonna mine, Colorado --92
Magalia district, California --57, 58, *59*
Magdalena district, New Mexico --210
Magma mine, Arizona --44
Magnolia district, Colorado --85, 88, *90*
Magnolia mine, Nevada --185
Maiden-Gilt Edge district, Montana --*150*
Maitland district, South Dakota --*236*
Maitland mine, South Dakota --237
Malachite mine, Colorado --103
Malheur district, Oregon --217, *220*, *230*
Mammoth district, Arizona --35, *43*
Mammoth mine, Arizona --43
Mammoth mine, Idaho --139
Mammoth mine, Kern County, Calif --64
Mammoth mine, Montana --164
Mammoth mine, Shasta County, Calif --78
Mammoth mine, Utah --244
Mammoth mine, Washington --262
Manhattan district, Nevada --171, 173, 191, *193*
Marble district, Nevada --*193*
Maricopa mine, Arizona --40
Marietta mine, Montana --146
Mariposa mine, California --68, 69
Marshall district, Alaska --10, *29*
Martinez district, Arizona --35, *49*
Mary Ann Creek district, Washington --*260*
Mary Murphy mine, Colorado --92
Marysville-Silver Creek district, Montana --142, 143, *154*, 155, *156*
Mascot mine, South Dakota --236
Masonic district, California --57, 69, *70*
Mayflower mine, Montana --161
Mayflower mine, Nevada --196
Mazuma Hills mine, Nevada --196
Meadow Creek mine, Idaho --141
Meadow Lake district, California --57, *71*
Merced River placers, California --55, 67, *68*, 69
Mercur district, Utah --*250*
Mercur mine, Utah --250
Merlin camp, Oregon --227
Methow district, Washington --256, *259*
Mexican mine, Alaska --20
Mexican mine, Nevada --198
Michigan Bluff district, California --57, *72*
Michigan Bluff placers, California --72
Midas mine, California --78
Middle Boise district, Idaho --*129*
Miller mine, Utah --252
Mills mine, North Carolina --211, 212
Minah mine, Montana --154
Mineral Creek district, Arizona --*43*

Page

Mineral Hill and Indian Creek district, Idaho ____123, *136*
Mineral Hill district, Idaho ____*121*
Mineral Park camp, Arizona ____41
Mineral Ridge district, Nevada ____*178*
Minnesota mine, Colorado ____94
Missouri River-York district, Montana ____142, *156*
Mocking Bird mine, Nevada ____174
Mockingbird camp, Arizona ____41
Mogollon district, New Mexico ____201, *202*, 203, 210
Mokelumne River placers, California ____55, 58, 59, 77
Monarch district, Colorado ____85, 86, 91, *92*
Montana district, Montana ____142, *148*
Monte Cristo district, Washington__255, 256, *260*
Montezuma district, Colorado ____94
Montgomery placers, Colorado ____109
Montgomery-Shoshone mine, Nevada ____191
Monumental mine, Oregon ____222
Moore Creek district, Idaho ____*124*
Moose Pass-Hope district, Alaska ____11
Mormon Bar district, California ____57, *68*
Mormon Basin district, Oregon ____216, 217, 218, *220*, *230*
Morning mine, Idaho ____139
Morning Star mine, California ____72
Morning Star mine, Nevada ____184
Mosquito-Buckskin placers, Colorado ____109
Moss mine, Virginia ____253
Mother Lode counties, California ____55, 58, 67, 82
Mother Lode districts, California ____5, 57, *58*, 59, *60*, *61*, *68*, *83*
Mother Lode gold deposits, California __5, 54, 55, 57, 58, 59, 60, 61, 67, 68, 82, 83, 183
Mount Baker district, Washington__255, 256, *262*
Mount Baldy district, Utah ____241, 245, *246*
Mount Diable mine, Nevada ____189
Mount Gleason and Cedar district, California ____*67*
Mount Montgomery district, Nevada __173, *190*
Mount Ophir mine, California ____69
Mount Pisgah district, Idaho ____123, *126*
Mount Pleasant mine, California ____61
Mount Reuben district, Oregon ____227
Mount Wilson district, Colorado ____85, *114*
Mountain Chief mine, Idaho ____125
Mullan district, Idaho ____139
Munroe mine, Nevada ____196
Murray district, Idaho ____139
Murray placers, Idaho ____139
Myers Creek district, Washington ____256, 259, *260*

N

Nabesna district ____10, 24, *30*
Nabesna mine, Alaska ____30
Nacoochee district, Georgia ____119, 120
Napoleon mine, Washington ____261
National district, Nevada ____171, 173, 180, *181*
National mine, Nevada ____181
Neal district, Idaho ____123, *129*
Neenach district, California ____67
Neihart district, Montana ____*148*
Nelchina placers, Alaska ____18
Nevada City camp, California ____71
Nevada City mine, California ____71
Nevada Hills mine, Nevada ____172
Nevada Wonder mine, Nevada ____173
New Cornelia mine, Arizona ____42
New Eldorado mine, California ____75
New Jersey mine, California ____72
New Park mine, Utah ____250
New Pass district, Nevada ____173, *185*
New Placer district, New Mexico ____203, *209*
New World district, Montana ____*166*
New York mine, Colorado ____106
Nightingale mine, California ____76
Ninemile Creek district, Montana ____142, 164, *165*
Nixon Fork mine, Alaska ____15
Niwot mine, Colorado ____90
Nizina district, Alaska ____10, 13, *14*
Nogal district, New Mexico ____203, *207*
Nome district, Alaska ____5, 8, 9, 10, 16, 17, *18*
Nome placers, Alaska ____8, 9, 18
Norris district, Montana ____142, *160*
North Columbia placers, California ____70, 72
North Fork district, Oregon ____217, 222, *223*
North Fork placer mine, Oregon ____223
North Lilly mine, Utah ____244
North Moccasin district, Montana ____142, *149*
North Moccasin mine, Montana ____149
North Star-Mann mine, Colorado ____93
North Star mine, Arizona ____52
North Star mine, California ____71
North States mine, North Carolina ____212, 213
North Union district, Nevada ____192
Northern Belle mine, Nevada ____189
Northern Gilpin district, Colorado ____85, *100*
Northumberland district, Nevada ____173, *193*

O

Oakdale-Knights Ferry district, California ____57, 81
Oatman camp, Arizona ____33, 40
O'Brien mine, Arizona ____47
Octave mine, Arizona ____50
Ohio district, Utah ____*246*
Old Abe mine, New Mexico ____208
Old Amber mine, Montana ____157
Old Channel placer mine, Oregon ____227
Old Diggings district, California ____77
Old Emma mine, Utah ____249
Old Eureka mine, California ____58
Old Field mine, North Carolina ____215
Old Hat district, Arizona ____*43*
Old Placer district, New Mexico __203, 209, *210*
Old Sturgis placer mine, Oregon ____226
Olinghouse district, Nevada ____173, *199*
Olympic mine, Nevada ____189
Omco mine, Nevada ____189
Oneota district, Nevada ____173, *190*
Ophir district, California ____57, 72, *73*
Ophir district, Colorado ____85, 114, *115*
Ophir district, Montana ____142, 167, *168*
Ophir mine, Nevada ____197, 198
Ophir-Rush Valley district, Utah__241, 250, *251*
Opp mine, Oregon ____225
Oregon Bonanza mine, Oregon ____229
Ore Knob mine, North Carolina ____211
Organ district, New Mexico ____203, *204*
Orient district, Washington ____256, *261*
Original and Ferguson mine, California ____69
Oriole mine, Oregon ____227
Oro Blanco district, Arizona ____35, *45*
Oro Cache mine, Montana ____163
Oro Fina mine, California ____73
Oro Fino mine, South Dakota ____236
Orogrande district, Idaho ____123, 130, *132*
Orogrande district, New Mexico ____*208*
Orogrande-Frisco mine, Idaho ____132
Oroville district, California ____57, 58, *59*
Oroville-Nighthawk district, Washington ____255, 256, 259, *260*
Ortiz district, New Mexico ____*210*
Osceola district, Nevada ____173, 199, *200*
Ottawa district, Montana ____*156*
Overland mine, Utah ____250
Ozier mine, California ____76

P

Palmer Mountain district, Washington ____*260*
Palmyra district, Nevada ____*187*
Pamlico mine, Nevada ____190
Pansy Lee mine, Nevada ____183
Paradise Valley district, Nevada ____173, *182*
Park City district, Utah ____240, 241, 242, 248, *249*
Park district, Montana ____142, *146*
Parker mine, North Carolina ____212, *215*
Paymaster district, California ____62
Paymaster mine, Nevada ____191
Pearce placer mine, Oregon ____226
Pearl-Horseshoe Bend district, Idaho ____*130*
Peavine district, Nevada ____199
Peck district, Arizona ____35, *49*
Peck mine, Arizona ____49
Pecos district, New Mexico ____*209*
Pecos mine, New Mexico ____209
Pedro Dome mine, Alaska ____26, 27
Penelas mine, Nevada ____*191*
Perigo mine, Colorado ____100
Pern mine, California ____59
Perschbaker mine, California ____59
Peshastin district, Washington ____*256*, 259
Philipsburg district, Montana ____*151*
Phoenix mine, Arizona ____40
Phoenix mine, North Carolina ____211, *212*
Phomolite district, Nevada ____*191*
Picacho district, California ____62
Pierce district, Idaho ____123, *126*
Pierre Lake district, Washington ____*261*
Pilgrim camp, Arizona ____41
Pinacate district, California ____57, *74*
Pine Creek mine, California ____64
Pine Grove camp, Arizona ____50
Pine Grove district, Idaho ____123, *129*
Pine Grove district, Nevada ____*187*
Pine Grove-Tiger district, Arizona ____35, *50*
Pine Tree mine, Kern County, Calif ____57, 66
Pine Tree mine, Mariposa County, Calif ____69
Pinon-Dale district, California ____57, *74*
Pinos Altos district, New Mexico ____203, 205, *206*
Pioche district, Nevada ____171, 173, 185, *186*
Pioneer district, Arizona ____*44*
Pioneer district, California ____66
Pioneer district, Colorado ____*98*
Pioneer district, Montana ____142, 167, *168*
Pioneer mine, California ____72
Pioneerville district, Idaho ____123, 124, *125*
Pittsburg-Idaho mine, Idaho ____137
Pittsburg-Liberty mine, California ____70
Pittsburg mine, Idaho ____130
Pittsburg mine, Nevada ____184
Pittsburg Red Top mine, Nevada ____184
Placer Center district, Idaho ____139
Placers in Tertiary gravels in Calaveras County, Calif__54, 57, *60*
Placers in Tertiary gravels in El Dorado County, Calif ____54, 57, *61*
Placers in Tertiary gravels in Mariposa County, Calif__54, 57, *69*
Placerville district, Idaho ____124, *125*
Platerica placer mine, Oregon ____229
Plomosa district, Arizona ____35, *53*
Plumas Eureka mine, California ____74
Pocket Belt district, California ____57, *84*
Pocket Belt gold deposits, California ____82
Pony district, Montana ____142, *160*
Poorman mine, Idaho ____139
Poorman mine, Nevada ____*190*
Porcupine district, Alaska ____10, 19, *22*
Porcupine mine, Oregon ____229
Port Clarence district, Alaska ____10, 16, 17, *19*
Port Valdez district, Alaska ____31, 32
Port Wells district, Alaska ____31, 32
Portis placers, North Carolina ____212, 213
Portland mine, Colorado ____118
Potosi district, Nevada ____171, 173, 180, *182*
Potosi mine, Nevada ____174, 175
Pratt Creek camp, Idaho ____135
Pride of the Mountain mine, Nevada ____183

Page

Princeton mine, California -- 69
Providence mine, California -- 71
Prussian mine, Nevada -- 192
Pyramid camp, Arizona -- 41
Pyramid camp, New Mexico -- 207
Pyramid district, Nevada -- 199
Pyramid mine, California -- 61

Q

Quaker Hill placers, California -- 70, 72
Quartette mine, Nevada -- 175
Quartz Mountains district, Nevada -- *193*
Quartzburg district, Idaho -- 123, 124, *125*
Quartzburg district, Oregon -- 217, 222, *223*
Queen of Bronze copper mine, Oregon -- 229

R

Radersburg district, Montana -- 142, *146*
Railroad Creek district, Washington -- *257*
Rainbow mine, Oregon -- 220
Rambler mine, Nevada -- 174
Rampart district, Alaska -- 10, 23, 26, 27, *30*
Rand district, California -- 57, 64, *65*, 75
Randolph mine, North Carolina -- 215
Ratcliffe mine, California -- 63
Rawhide district, Nevada -- 171, 173, *191*
Rawhide mine, Placer County, Calif -- 72
Rawhide mine, Tuolumne County, Calif -- 83
Ray district, Arizona -- 33, 35, *43*
Ready Bullion mine, Alaska -- 20
Red Cliff district, Colorado -- *99*
Red Cloud mine, Colorado -- 88
Red Dog-You Bet placers, California -- 70, 72
Red Lion camp, Montana -- 151
Red Mountain camp, Colorado -- 107
Red Shirt mine, Washington -- 259
Reed mine, North Carolina -- 211, *212*
Reese River district, Nevada -- 171, 173, 183, *185*
Regent district, Nevada -- *191*
Reid mine, North Carolina -- *212*
Renova district, Montana -- 142, 160, *161*
Republic district, Washington -- 254, 255, 256, *258*
Republic mine, Montana -- 166
Republic mine, Washington -- 258
Resort district, Idaho -- *133*
Resting Springs district, California -- 57, 62, *63*
Reward mine, California -- 63
Rex mine, Washington -- 257
Richardson district, Alaska -- 10, *31*
Richmond mine, Nevada -- 179
Rico district, Colorado -- 85, *98*
Riley mine, Nevada -- 182
Rimini-Tenmile district, Montana -- 142, 155, *157*
Rising Sun mine, California -- 57, *73*
Robertson mine, Oregon -- 227
Robinson camp, Colorado -- 117
Robinson district, Nevada -- *199*
Rochester district, Nevada -- 173, *196*
Rock Creek district, Oregon -- 217, *220*
Rockland district, Nevada -- *187*
Rockland mine, Nevada -- 188
Rocky Bar district, Idaho -- 123, 129, *130*
Rogers mine, Washington -- 257
Rogue River camp, Oregon -- 227
Rollins mine, Utah -- 240, 242
Ropes mine, Michigan -- 141
Rosamond-Mojave district, California -- 57, 64, *66*
Rosedale district, New Mexico -- 203, 210, *211*
Rosedale mine, New Mexico -- 211
Rosita Hills district, Colorado -- 85, 86, *97*
Round Mountain district, Nevada -- 171, 173, 184, 191, *193*
Rover mine, Nevada -- 174
Rowena camp, Colorado -- 88

Page

Royal mine, California -- 60
Royal mine, Montana -- 150
Ruby district, Alaska -- 10, 24, *30*
Ruby Gulch mine, Montana -- 167
Rudisil mine, North Carolina -- 211, 212, 213
Russ district, California -- 62
Russell mine, North Carolina -- 212, *214*
Ruth mine, California -- 63
Rye Patch district, Nevada -- 173, *196*
Rye Patch mine, Nevada -- 196
Rye Valley district, Oregon -- *220*

S

Sacramento mine, Utah -- 250
Sailor Flat placers, California -- 70, 72
St. Catherine mine, North Carolina -- 212, 213
St. John mine, California -- 57, 66
Salina camp, Colorado -- 88
Salmon River district, California -- 57, *81*
Salmon River placers, California -- 80, 81
Salt Chuck mine, Alaska -- 22
Salt Springs district, Arizona -- *40*
San Francisco district, Arizona -- 33, 35, *40*
San Francisco district, Utah -- 241, *242*
San Gabriel district, California -- 57, *67*
San Juan Ridge placers, California -- 70, 72
San Manuel mine, Arizona -- 33, 43
San Pedro district, New Mexico -- *209*
San Rafael mine, Nevada -- 193
Sand Springs district, Nevada -- *173*
Sandy Creek camp, Idaho -- 135
Sanger mine, Oregon -- 219
Scott River district, California -- 57, *81*
Scott River placers, California -- 80, 81
Scotts Flat placers, California -- 70, 72
Scratchgravel mine, Montana -- 158
Searchlight district, Nevada -- 173, 174, *175*
Sells mine, Utah -- 249
700 Foot mine, Alaska -- 20
Seven Troughs district, Nevada -- 173, *196*
Sevenmile-Scratchgravel district, Montana -- 142, 155, *158*
Sevier mine, Utah -- 245
Shakespear camp, New Mexico -- 207
Sheepeater district, Montana -- *165*
Sheepranch mine, California -- 60
Sheridan district, Montana -- 142, 144, 160, *161*
Sherman district, California -- 57, 62, *63*
Shoshone mines, California -- 63
Shungnak district, Alaska -- 10, *16*
Sierra Buttes district, California -- 57, 79, *80*
Sierra Buttes mine, California -- 80
Sierra district, Nevada -- 173, *196*
Silver City district, Idaho -- 123, 124, *138*
Silver City district, Nevada -- 173, 186, *187*
Silver Creek district, Washington -- 260
Silver Hill mine, North Carolina -- 213
Silver Lake mine, Colorado -- 113
Silver Peak district, Nevada -- 171, 173, *178*
Silver Pick mine, Colorado -- 114
Silver Queen mine, Arizona -- 44
Silver Star district, Nevada -- *190*
Silver Star-Rochester district, Montana -- 142, 144, 160, *162*
Silverton district, Colorado -- *113*
Silverton district, Washington -- 256, 260, *261*
Simon mine, Nevada -- 189
Simpson-Camp Howard-Riggins placer district, Idaho -- 123, 130, *132*
Sixteen to One mine, California -- 79
Skidoo mine, California -- 64
Skyline mine, Montana -- 153
Slate Creek district, Washington -- 255, 256, *262*
Sliger mine, California -- 61
Sloughhouse district, California -- 57, *75*
Smith River placers, California -- 57, 60
Smuggler-Union mine, Colorado -- 108, 116
Smuggler vein, Colorado -- 114, 115
Snake Creek district, Utah -- 249

Page

Snake River placers, Idaho -- 121, 123, 126, 138, 139
Sneffels camp, Colorado -- 107
Sneffels-Red Mountain district, Colorado -- 85, *107*, 113, 114, 115
Snowshoe district, Montana -- *159*
Snowstorm placers, Colorado -- 110
Solomon-Bluff district, Alaska -- 10, 16, 17, *19*
Soulsby mine, California -- 83
South Boulder camp, Montana -- 161
South Park district, California -- *63*
South Telluride mining area, Colorado -- 115
Southern Cross mine, Montana -- 149
Spar City district, Colorado -- 106
Sparta district, Oregon -- 217, *221*
Spaulding placer mine, Oregon -- 226
Spring Valley district, Nevada -- 173, *197*
Squaw Creek district, South Dakota -- 233, 235, *238*
Squaw Creek district, Washington -- *259*
Star district, Nevada -- 195
Star district, Utah -- 242
Star mine, Nevada -- 199
Star of the West mine, Nevada -- 187
Star Peak mine, Nevada -- 195
Stateline district, Utah -- 241, *243*
Steamboat mine, Oregon -- 226
Stedman district, California -- 57, 75, *76*
Steel mine, North Carolina -- 212, *214*
Steeple Rock district, New Mexico -- 203, 205, *206*
Stemple-Virginia Creek district, Montana -- 142, 155, *158*
Sterling, placer mine, Oregon -- 226
Stockton camp, Arizona -- 41
Stockton district, Utah -- *251*
Stoddard mine, Arizona -- 46
Strawberry Creek camp, South Dakota -- 235
Strong mine, Colorado -- 118
Sugarloaf camp, Colorado -- 88
Sultan district, Washington -- 260
Sumdum mine, Alaska -- 20
Summit camp, Montana -- 163
Summit district, Idaho -- 139
Summit Flat district, Idaho -- 124, *125*
Summit Valley district, Montana -- *169*
Summitville district, Colorado -- 85, *111*
Sumpter district, Oregon -- 216, 217, 218, *221*
Sunnyside mine, Colorado -- 113, 114
Sunnyside mine, Idaho -- 140
Sunset camp, Colorado -- 90
Sunshine camp, Colorado -- 88
Sunshine mine, Utah -- 250
Superior district, Arizona -- 33, 35, 43, *44*
Supply mine, California -- 76
Susanville district, Oregon -- 217, 222, *224*
Swauk district, Washington -- 256, *259*
Sweeney mine, California -- 83
Swissmont mine, Montana -- 153
Sylvanite district, Montana -- 142, 159, *160*
Sylvanite mine, Oregon -- 225

T

Table Mountain channel placer deposits, California -- 59, 60
Tallulah mine, Nevada -- 196
Tarryall district, Colorado -- 85, 109, *110*
Tarryall placers, Colorado -- 110
Taylor district, Nevada -- 199
Taylor mine, California -- 61
Teacup mine, Nevada -- 199
Techatticup mine, Nevada -- 174
Telluride district, Colorado -- 5, 85, 86, 107, 108, 114, *115*
Tellurium mine, Virginia -- 253
Tenabo camp, Nevada -- 184
Tenderfoot district, Alaska -- *31*
Tenmile district, Colorado -- 85, 116, *117*

Page

Tenmile district, Idaho ____ 123, 130, *133*
Tertiary placer districts in Nevada County, California ____ 5, 57, *72*
Teviston placers, Arizona ____ 36
Texas Canyon placer district, California ____ 67
Texas district, Idaho ____ 123, *137*
Three Stars mine, California ____ 73
Thunder Mountain district, Idaho ____ 123, *140*, 141
Tidal Wave district, Montana ____ 142, 160, *162*
Tiger camp, Arizona ____ 50
Tiger mine, Idaho ____ 139
Tijeras Canyon district, New Mexico ____ *202*, 203
Tincup district, Colorado ____ 85, 101, *102*
Tintic district, Utah ____ 5, 240, 241, 242, 243, *244*, 252
Tintic Standard mine, Utah ____ 244
Tiptop district, Arizona ____ 35, *50*
Tiptop mine, Arizona ____ 50
Tip Top mine, Nevada ____ 190
Tizer district, Montana ____ 142, *153*
Tolavana district, Alaska ____ 10, 24, *31*
Tomboy mine, Colorado ____ 115
Tombstone district, Arizona ____ 33, 35, *36*
Tonopah district, Nevada ____ 5, 171, 173, 174, 191, *194*
Tonopah Divide mine, Nevada ____ 177
Tonopah Hasbrouck mine, Nevada ____ 177
Town mine, Oregon ____ 225
Trail district, Colorado ____ *95*
Treadwell mine, Alaska ____ 20
Trinity River basin, California ____ 57, 81, *82*
Trinity River placers, California ____ 62, 81, 82
Triumph mine, Idaho ____ 123
Tropico mines, California ____ 66
Troutman mine, North Carolina ____ 215
Tuluksak-Aniak district, Alaska ____ 10, 14, *16*
Tumco district, California ____ 62
Tuolumne River placers, California ____ 55, 81
Turnagain Arm district, Alaska ____ 11
Turquoise district, Arizona ____ 33, 35, *37*
Tuscarora district, Nevada ____ 173, 175, *176*
Twin Bridges district, Montana ____ *162*
Twin Lakes district, Colorado ____ 111
Two Bit Creek camp, South Dakota ____ 235
Tybo district, Nevada ____ 173, 191, *194*
Tybo mine, Nevada ____ 195

U

Uinta district, Utah ____ 249
Ulysses mine, Idaho ____ 136
Uncompahgre district, Colorado ____ 85, 107, *108*
Unga district, Alaska ____ 10, *23*
Union Copper mine, North Carolina ____ 215
Union district, California ____ 57, *63*
Union district, Nevada ____ 173, *195*
Union mine, California ____ 61
United Verde Extension mine, Arizona ____ 48
United Verde mine, Arizona ____ 48
Upper Applegate district, Oregon ____ 217, 224, *226*

Page

Upper Burnt River district, Oregon ____ 217, *221*
Upper San Miguel district, Colorado ____ *115*
Utah Copper mine, Utah ____ 247
Ute Creek camp, Colorado ____ 96
Utica mine, California ____ 60
Uwarra mine, North Carolina ____ 212, 214

V

Valdez Creek district, Alaska ____ 10, 11, *12*
Vaucluse mine, Virginia ____ 254
Vaughn district, Montana ____ *157*
Verde district, Arizona ____ 45, *48*
Victor mine, Colorado ____ 118
Vindicator mine, Colorado ____ 118
Virgilina district, Virginia ____ 253
Virginia camp, Arizona ____ 41
Virginia camp, New Mexico ____ 207
Virginia City-Alder Gulch district, Montana ____ 5, 142, 143, 160, *163*
Virtue district, Oregon ____ 217, *221*
Virtue mine, Oregon ____ 221
Vulture district, Arizona ____ 33, 35, *40*
Vulture mine, Arizona ____ 40
Volcano district, California ____ 57, *58*

W

Wagon Wheel Gap fluorspar district, Colorado ____ 106
Waldo district, Oregon ____ 217, 218, 226, *229*
Walker camp, Arizona ____ 49
Wallace district, Idaho ____ 139
Wallapai district, Arizona ____ 33, 35, 40, *41*
Wall Street mine, Nevada ____ 174
Ward district, Colorado ____ 85, 88, 89, *90*
Ward district, Nevada ____ 199
Warm Springs district, Idaho ____ *121*, 123
Warm Springs district, Montana ____ 142, 149, *150*
Warm Springs district, Nevada ____ 173, *182*
Warren district, Arizona ____ *35*
Warren-Marshall district, Idaho ____ 123, 124, 130, 131, *133*
Washington mine, California ____ 78
Washington mine, Colorado ____ 118
Watseca mine, Montana ____ 162
Wauconda district, Washington ____ *259*
Wauconda mine, Washington ____ 259
Weaver district, Arizona ____ 33, 35, 40, *41*
Weaver (La Paz) district, Arizona ____ *53*
Weaver-Rich Hill district, Arizona ____ 32, 35, 45, *50*
Wedekind district, Nevada ____ 199
Wellington mine, Colorado ____ 116
Wenatchee district, Washington ____ 254, 255, 256, *258*
West Belt districts, California ____ 5, 57, 59, *60*, *61*, *69*
West Belt gold deposits, California ____ 54, 57, 59, 60, 61, 67, 68

Page

West Jordan mine, Utah ____ 247
West Mountain district, Utah ____ 240, *246*
West Shasta copper-zinc district, California ____ 57, 77, *78*
Westview district, Idaho ____ 123, *130*
Wheeler mine, Nevada ____ 188
Whiskeytown district, California ____ 55, 77, *79*
White Creek district, Montana ____ 142, *147*
White Horse district, Nevada ____ *199*
White House mine, Idaho ____ 136
White Oaks district, New Mexico ____ 203, 207, *208*
White River district, California ____ 57, 82
White Swan mine, Oregon ____ 221
Whitehall district, Montana ____ 142, 152, *154*
Whitehall mine, Virginia ____ 254
Whitlatch-Union mine, Montana ____ 143, 155
Whitney mine, North Carolina ____ 215
Whitney mine, Oregon ____ 225
Wickes district, Montana ____ 142, *154*
Wild Rose district, California ____ 57, 62, *64*
Wild Rose mine, Idaho ____ 127
Willow Creek district, Alaska ____ 10, 11, *12*
Willow Creek district, New Mexico ____ 201, 203, *209*
Willow Springs district, Utah ____ 241, 250, *252*
Willshire-Bishop Creek district, California ____ 57, 63, *64*
Wilson Creek district, Montana ____ *153*
Wilson district, Nevada ____ 171, 173, *187*
Wilson mine, Nevada ____ 188
Windfall mine, Nevada ____ 180
Winnemucca district, Nevada ____ 173, *183*
Winona camp, Oregon ____ 227
Winston district, Montana ____ 142, *147*
Wonder district, Nevada ____ *173*

Y

Yaak district, Montana ____ *160*
Yakataga district, Alaska ____ 10, 19, *22*
Yankee Fork district, Idaho ____ 123, 127, *128*
Yankee Hill district, California ____ 57, 58, *59*
Yankee Jim district, California ____ 72
Yellow Aster mine, California ____ 65
Yellow Jacket district, Idaho ____ 123, *137*
Yellow Jacket mine, Idaho ____ 137
Yellow Jacket mine, Nevada ____ 198
Yellow Pine district, Idaho ____ 123, 124, 140, *141*
Yellow Pine district, Nevada ____ 171, *174*
Yellow Pine mine, Idaho ____ 141
Yentna-Cache Creek district, Alaska ____ 10, 11, *13*
Yreka district, Idaho ____ 139
Yuba district, Idaho ____ 129
Yuba River placers, California ____ 55, 74, 84

Z

Zantgraf mine, California ____ 61
Zortman-Landusky district, Montana ____ *167*
Zosell district, Montana ____ 142, 167, *169*

U.S. GOVERNMENT PRINTING OFFICE: 576-034—1982